Essentials of
Nuclear Chemistry

HARI JEEVAN ARNIKAR

Professor Emeritus,
Formerly Senior Professor of Chemistry,
University of Poona,
Pune

WILEY EASTERN LIMITED
New Delhi   Bangalore   Bombay   Calcutta

Copyright © 1982, Wiley Eastern Limited

WILEY EASTERN LIMITED

4835/24 Ansari Road, Daryaganj, New Delhi 110 002
4654/21 Daryaganj, New Delhi 110 002
6 Shri B.P. Wadia Road, Basavangudi, Bangalore 560 004
Abid House, Dr Bhadkamkar Marg, Bombay 400 007
40/8 Ballygunge, Circular Road, Calcutta 700 019

ISBN 0 85226 033 4

Published by Mohinder Singh Sejwal for Wiley Eastern Limited,
4835/24 Ansari Road, Daryaganj, New Delhi 110 002 and printed by
Abhay Rastogi at Prabhat Press, 20/1 Nauchandi Grounds,
Meerut 250 002.   Printed in India.

To Professors

Frédéric Joliot-Curie, N.L.,
Shridhar Sarvottam Joshi,
Marius Chemla.

Foreword

We live in a world where nothing is more essential for the survival of mankind than to insure that nuclear energy will never be used in warfare. Such use would mean the end of civilization as we know it. If we can avoid this catastrophy, the opportunities for using nuclear processes for the benefit of mankind are very great—as a nearly limitless source of energy, and as an aid to research in the medical sciences and many other fields. It is to be hoped that this book on the *Essentials of Nuclear Chemistry* by Professor Arnikar will provide large number of students an added understanding of nuclear science which will catalyze in them the wisdom and initiative to help the world avoid the fate of nuclear conflict on the one hand, and to safely exploit the peaceful benefits of nuclear processes on the other.

University of Wisconsin   J.E. WILLARD
Madison, Wis.
June 1981

Preface

While several excellent books on Nuclear and Radiation Chemistry are available, the experience of teaching the subject over the years has revealed the need for a book at the Honours and post-Graduate levels which emphasizes the basic physical concepts and which serves as an introduction to advanced books. The *Essentials of Nuclear Chemistry* is an effort to meet the above requirement. An attempt has been made to present abstract concepts lucidly adopting a non-mathematical approach. The importance of understanding the basic concepts is stressed, even at the risk of redundance of words at places.

The book covers theories of nuclear structure and stability; different types of radioactivity; nuclear reactions including fission and fusion, spallation and heavy ion induced reactions; principles of the nuclear reactor; elements of Radiation Chemistry and typical applications of nuclear radiations and isotopes in research, medicine, agriculture and industry. Some essential concepts of nuclear physics, usually left out in books on nuclear chemistry, are included in a simplified form to rouse the curiosity of the brighter student.

SI units have been used in the main, often with their cgs equivalents. Though the bequerel, gray and sievert are mentioned, the more familiar curie, rad and rem are retained. The understanding of a concept is not complete unless some problems bearing on its applications are solved. With this view, problems with answers are appended to each chapter. The chapter-wise references and a comprehensive bibliography provided at the end would, it is hoped, serve the needs of those interested in studying the subject in greater depth. The purpose in including the results of some experiments of the author is to encourage work in this area even under conditions of limited facilities.

A book whose scope extends from nuclear theories to applications in industry cannot be written without drawing liberally from standard books and published literature. I take this opportunity to express my grateful thanks to several of the well-known publishers who have graciously accorded me permission to use some figures and data from their publications which are acknowledged in the text. I am also indebted to heads of several institutions for allowing me to use some of the results of investigations carried out in their laboratories, some of whose authors could not be located despite all effort. I also received warm encouragement from J.M. Alexander, K.S. Bhatki, H.M. Foley, M.S. Freedman, E.G. Fuller, S.N. Ghoshal, I. Halpern, G.R. Keepin, P.F.A. Klinkenberg, F.P. Mooring, G.W.A. Newton, B.W. Sargent, G.T. Seaborg, A.H. Snell, W.E. Stein, and H.E. White: by letting me draw materials from some of their well-known contributions, referred to in the text.

I am deeply grateful to Professor John E. Willard for writing the Foreword. I am also thankful to the manuscript reviewers for their helpful comments. Lastly, I acknowledge with pleasure my indebtedness to Dr. A.K. Ganguly of the Bhabha Atomic Research Centre and to my colleagues, Drs. S.F. Patil, B.S. Madhava Rao, P.N. Joshi, S.V. Amarapurkar and V.N. Bhoraskar for their valuable suggestions. I am also much obliged to Prof. V.K. Phansalkar, Head of the Department of Chemistry, for his continued interest in the book. My special thanks are due to Dr. N.G. Adhyapak for her help in correcting the proofs with patience and meticulous care. I am equally thankful to Mr. K.S. Bapat, Miss L.N. Pavangadkar, Mrs. M.M. Puranik, Mr. B.B. Pawar, and Mr. N.K. Divate for their assistance in preparing the manuscript. In the end, I would like to place on record my sincere thanks to the Wiley Eastern Ltd. for their cooperation in bringing out the book so well.

It is hoped that students and teachers would find the book a useful companion. It is my earnest request to all the readers that they may bring to my notice errors that have missed my attention.

University of Poona
April 1982

H.J. ARNIKAR

Contents

211p

Chapter 1

The Atomic Nucleus

1.1 The Atom

The present concept of the atom, gained after innumerable scientific investigations over many decades, is that it is composite, hence divisible and synthesizable with effort. It is now universally accepted that the atom consists of two distinct regions: the tiny central core, called the *nucleus* having a radius of the order of a few fermis ($\sim 10^{-15}$ m), and the relatively extensive surrounding space referred to as the *outer sphere* which has a radius of the order of 10^{-10} m.

The millions of forms of matter found in the universe are a result of the endless ways in which atoms combine. Every atom in turn is made up of three different elementary particles, the *electrons, protons* and *neutrons.* The single exception to this is the atom of ordinary hydrogen which contains only an electron and a proton but no neutron. It is further well established that while the electrons occupy the outer sphere, the protons and neutrons are inside the nucleus. The essential characteristics of these subatomic particles are listed in Table 1.1. The table also lists the other relevant fundamental particles which are either extremely short-lived transients, such as mesons, or are stable but released only during nuclear transformation, such as photons and neutrinos.

1.2 Units used in Nuclear Chemistry

We shall now consider the units of some of the quantities commonly used in nuclear chemistry, and their equivalents in *SI* and *cgs* units*. These are listed below:

*The *cgs*, or the centimetre-gram-second, are the basic classical metric units, which are still in partial use. The *mks* or the metre-kilogram-second are an advance over the cgs units, while the *SI* units (*système internationale d' unités*) based on the *mks* units are being increasingly used by the scientific community the world over. The great advantage of the *SI* units is that they are *coherent, i e.* any derived unit may be obtained by merely multiplying or dividing by the relevant basic units without involving any numerical factor, not even powers of ten.[1,2,3]

TABLE 1.1: Characteristics of relevant fundamental particles

(i) Stable subatomic particles

Particle	Electron	Proton	Neutron
Symbol	e	p	n
Location	outer sphere	nucleus	nucleus
Charge/e	-1	$+1$	0
Mass/u	0.000 55	1.007 277	1.008 665
Rest mass energy/MeV	0.511	938.259	939.552
Spin/$\hbar$	1/2	1/2	1/2
Mean life/s	stable	stable	932
Decay products	—	—	$p+e^-+\bar{\nu}$
Antiparticle*	positron (e^+)	antiproton (p^-)	antineutron ($\bar{n}$)

(ii) Stable but appear only in some nuclear reactions

Particle	Neutrino	Photon
Symbol	ν	γ
Charge/e	0	0
Mass	0	0
Spin/$\hbar$	1/2	1
Antiparticle*	antineutrino ($\bar{\nu}$)	self**

(iii) Unstable mesons

Particle	Pion charged	Pion neutral	Muon
Symbol	$\pi^\pm$	π°	$\mu^\pm$
Charge	±1	0	±1
Mass/m_e	273	264	207
Rest mass energy/MeV	139.5	135	105.8
Spin/$\hbar$	0	0	1/2
Mean life/s	2.6×10^{-8}	0.76×10^{-16}	2.2×10^{-6}
Decay products	$\mu^\pm+\nu$	2γ	$e^\pm+\nu+\bar{\nu}$
Antiparticle*	$\pi^\mp$	self**	$\mu^\mp$

*An antiparticle differs from corresponding particle only in charge or spin orientation.
**Where a particle and its antiparticle cannot be distinguished.

The unified atomic mass unit $u = 1.661 \times 10^{-27}$ kg (on ^{12}C scale)

The unit of charge $\qquad\qquad e = 4.8 \times 10^{-10}$ esu
$\qquad\qquad\qquad\qquad\qquad = 1.602 \times 10^{-20}$ emu
$\qquad\qquad\qquad\qquad\qquad = 1.602 \times 10^{-19}$ coulomb

The unit of action $\qquad\quad h = 6.626\ 2 \times 10^{-34}$ J-s
(Planck's constant)

The unit of angular momentum $\hbar = h/2\pi = 1.054\ 6 \times 10^{-34}$ J-s
The unit of length F (fermi) $\qquad = 10^{-15}$ m
The unit of energy $\qquad\qquad$ eV $= 1.602 \times 10^{-19}$ J
(electron volt)

The higher units of energy are $1 \text{ keV} = 10^3 \text{ eV}$

$$1 \text{ MeV} = 10^6 \text{ eV}$$

$$1 \text{ GeV} = 10^9 \text{ eV}$$

The unit of *amount* of substance for a chemist is neither an individual particle nor a gram (or kg), but is a *mole* of the substance. *A mole* of a given species of particles (electrons, protons, or atoms, or molecules, or ions or photons, etc.) is defined as *that much amount which contains the Avogadro number*[*] ($L = 6.022\ 17 \times 10^{23}$) *of the given particle species.* The amounts of reactants participating, or products formed in a reaction, are always expressed in moles, or its submultiples, such as milli (10^{-3}) or micro (10^{-6}) mole. Hence, from a practical standpoint, the energy in eV per particle is to be correlated to the value per mole. Obviously, the latter is just L times greater.

Thus, an energy of 1 eV per particle $= 6.022 \times 10^{23}$ eV per mole, or 96.472 kJ/mol.

Similarly 1 MeV/particle $= 96.472 \times 10^6$ kJ/mol.

Let us note in passing that in chemical reactions of even the most violently explosive type the energy liberated rarely exceeds 20 eV as evidenced by the following reactions where the energy liberated is given both in kJ per mole and in eV per molecule of the product.

	kJ/mol	eV/molecule
$H_2 + 0.5 O_2 \rightarrow H_2O$ (g)	241.8	2.5
$C + O_2 \rightarrow CO_2$	393.5	4.1
$0.5 H_2 + 0.5 F_2 \rightarrow HF$	271.1	2.8
$2Al + 1.5 O_2 \rightarrow Al_2O_3$	1675.7	17.4
$C_7H_5(NO_2)_3$ (TNT) $\rightarrow$ explosion products	887.2[4]	9.2

In contrast to these, the nuclear reactions are characterized by energies of the order of several MeV, *i.e.* 10^6 times larger, *e.g.*

$$^{60}\text{Co} \rightarrow {}^{60}\text{Ni} + \beta^- + 2.5\ \bar{\nu} + \text{MeV (energy)}$$

$$^{235}\text{U} + n \rightarrow \text{fission products} + 200 \text{ MeV (energy)}.$$

Other relevant units will be described as and when they occur in the text.

1.3 The Nucleus and the Outer Sphere

As indicated in Table 1.1, the nucleus of an atom contains all the protons and neutrons while the electrons are all in the outer sphere.

---

[*]L is the symbol recently proposed for the Avogadro number. It was formerly represented by N.

Conventionally, the number of protons and neutrons in the nucleus, which must obviously be whole numbers, are represented by the symbols Z and N respectively. It follows that the charge on the nucleus is $+Ze$ and that of the outer sphere is $-Ze$, as the number of electrons must equal that of the protons, to make the atom neutral as a whole. It further follows that the entire mass of the atom is in the nucleus, as the mass of an electron is negligible in comparison to that of the *nucleon* (the common name for protons and neutrons). As a result of this, the density of the nucleus, or the pure nuclear matter, comes out to be of the unimaginably high value some 10^{15} times the density of ordinary matter (being the ratio of the total volume of the atom to that of the nucleus).

The structure of the outer sphere of the atom, its division into different orbitals or volume elements, their shapes and sizes, the rules governing the distribution of the Z electrons into these orbitals, and the changes therein is the subject matter of atomic and molecular chemistry. We shall concern ourselves here only with the nucleus, its structure, the arrangement of the Z protons and the N neutrons in it and the effects arising out of the changes spontaneously occurring (radioactivity), or effected otherwise, in the normal arrangement leading to nuclear reactions. An atomic nucleus, considered without relation to the outer sphere, is often referred to as a *nuclide* and is symbolized by ${}_Z^A X$ where X is the symbol of the chemical element with Z protons, and A is the total number of protons and neutrons in the nucleus, *i.e.* $A = Z + N$, also known as the *mass number*.* Thus ${}_{15}^{31}P$ and ${}_{15}^{32}P$, stand for the two nuclides of phosphorus having 15 protons each and 16 and 17 neutrons respectively. As each chemical element is characterized by a particular Z value ($Z = 15$ for P, 50 for Sn, *etc*.), it is not necessary to write the Z value. Nuclides may thus be more simply characterized by the chemical symbol and the mass number only, such as ${}^{31}P$, ${}^{32}P$, ${}^{32}S$, *etc*.

1.4   Classification of Nuclides

Nuclides can be grouped together in more than one way. We present here two such ways.

1.4.1   ON THE BASIS OF THEIR Z AND N VALUES

This results in the following groups of nuclei.

(a) *Isotopes:* These are nuclei of the same chemical element and hence have the *same proton number* Z. They differ in the neutron number N and hence in A ($= Z + N$).

---

*The mass number A is invariably a whole number, being equal to $N + Z$. *A is not atomic weight*, as sometimes it is so described carelessly and wrongly. Atomic mass is always a fraction, running into 10^{-6} u, or beyond, being the ratio of the mass of the atom to that of a ${}^{12}C$ atom. Thus, for instance, the atomic mass of ${}^{32}P = 31.973\,908$ u, and that of ${}^{32}S = 31.972\,074$ u.

Examples   Isotopes of hydrogen $(Z = 1)$: ^1H, ^2H, ^3H,

Isotopes of sodium $(Z = 11)$: ^{22}Na, ^{23}Na, ^{24}Na,

Isotopes of chlorine $(Z = 17)$: ^{34}Cl, ^{35}Cl, ^{36}Cl, ^{37}Cl, ^{38}Cl,

Isotopes of uranium $(Z = 92)$: ^{233}U, ^{235}U, ^{238}U.

In the Periodic Table of elements, the isotopes of the same element (*i.e.* constant Z) naturally occupy the same place. Hence, in the symbols for isotopes, the Z value need not be mentioned.

All isotopes of the same element have very nearly similar chemical properties, as these depend only on Z. Hence, a separation of isotopes is extremely difficult and very special methods have to be used for effecting even a partial separation or enrichment. All these methods depend on slight differences in their physical or thermodynamic properties due to the small relative difference in their atomic masses.

(b) *Isobars:* These are nuclei of different neighbouring chemical elements having *the same* $A (= Z + N)$, but differing Z and N values. If necessary, the N value is shown as a subscript on the right.

Examples: Isobars of $A = 3$: $^3_1H_2$, $^3_2He_1$,

Isobars of $A = 14$: $^{14}_6C_8$, $^{14}_7N_7$,

Isobars of $A = 24$: $^{24}_{11}Na_{13}$, $^{24}_{12}Mg_{12}$,

Isobars of $A = 64$: $^{64}_{27}Co_{37}$, $^{64}_{28}Ni_{36}$, $^{64}_{29}Cu_{35}$, $^{64}_{30}Zn_{34}$.

Mirror nuclei are pairs of isobars in which the Z and N values, differing by one, are interchanged.

Examples: $^{13}_6C_7 - ^{13}_7N_6^-$; $^{15}_7N_8 - ^{15}_8O_7$; $^{23}_{11}Na_{12} - ^{23}_{12}Mg_{11}$; $^{39}_{19}K_{20} - ^{39}_{20}Ca_{19}$.

The properties of mirror nuclei provide valuable information in understanding nuclear structure, (see Sec. 3.3.5).

(c) *Isotones:* These are nuclei having the same neutron number N and hence different Z and A values.

Examples: $^3_1H_2 - ^4_2He_2$; $^{13}_6C_7 - ^{14}_7N_7$; $^{23}_{11}Na_{12} - ^{24}_{12}Mg_{12}$.

(d) *Isomers:* Two nuclides having the same Z, N (and hence A) values, but differing in energy states, constitute nuclear isomers. There is a large difference in their spins. The isomer of the higher energy is in a *metastable state* and is indicated by writing m after the mass number. *Examples* are ^{60m}Co and ^{60}Co; ^{80m}Br and ^{80}Br. The metastable isomer is radioactive and decays by γ emission into the ground state isomer, which may also be radioactive (see Sec. 4.8.3).

1.4.2 ON THE BASIS OF NUCLEAR STABILITY

This is obviously a clear way of classifying into (a) *stable* and (b) *unstable* or *radioactive* nuclides.

(a) *Stable nuclides* are those which are permanent (or eternally stable?). Their proton and neutron contents remain unchanged for ever, no matter how the electrons in the outer sphere may change in location or even in their number (via chemical reactions). The nucleus of a stable nuclide can be changed only under severe conditions of bombardment by external radiation or particles of very high energy ($\sim$ 1-10 MeV or higher). About 274 naturally occurring nuclides are considered stable.*

Example: ^1H**, ^2H; ^{16}O, ^{17}O, ^{18}O; ^{19}F; ^{23}Na; ^{27}Al; ^{31}P; ^{35}Cl, ^{37}Cl; ^{63}Cu, ^{65}Cu, *etc.*

(b) *Radioactive nuclides* are intrinsically unstable and undergo spontaneous change with time forming new nuclides by one or the other way of rearranging or losing some of their protons and neutrons. About 700–800 nuclides including a very large number of man made ones are known to be radioactive of one type or other. In Chapter 4 are considered the phenomenon of radioactivity, its types and characteristics.

1.5 Nuclear Stability

The question naturally arises why some nuclides are stable while others are radioactive: in other words, what are the factors leading to nuclear stability? A study of the characteristics of a large number of stable and radioactive nuclides show the following to be some of the important factors involved.

1.5.1 EVEN-ODD NATURE OF THE NUMBER OF PROTONS AND NEUTRONS

Table 1.2 gives the frequency distribution of stable nuclides in terms of the evenness or oddness of the number of protons (Z) and of neutrons (N) making up the nucleus.

Some conclusions from the observed frequency distribution of stable nuclides are:

(i) The number of stable nuclides is a maximum when both Z and N are even numbers suggesting a tendency to form p-p and n-n pairs as conducive to stability. This is reminiscent of extra stability of molecules which have electron pairs. This is well brought out by the composition of the earth's crust about 85% of which consists of even-Z, even-N nuclides as, (with the percentage abundance in parentheses),

*A nuclide is considered stable if it remains unchanged up to about 10^{21} years. However, this limit is being ever pushed upwards as more advanced techniques of detecting slow rates of decay are becoming available. For instance, ^{130}Te long considered to be stable, is now considered radioactive with a decay period of $\sim 10^{21}$ years.

**Recent experiments (April 1981) by Indian and Japanese physicists in the depths of the Kolar gold mines, seem to suggest that the protons, hitherto believed to be stable are, in fact, decaying imperceptibly slowly, at a rate of about one proton out of some 10^{30} per month! The proton decay had been predicted earlier by Nobel Laureate Andrei Sakharov. If this result gets confirmed, the material Universe would seem to have a limited life, as all the matter of the Universe would have decayed into radiation in some remote future.

TABLE 1.2: Frequency distribution of stable nuclides

Z	N	A $(=Z+N)$	No. of stable nuclides	Examples
Even	Even	Even	165	$^4_2$He, $^{24}_{12}$Mg, $^{208}_{82}$Pb
Even	Odd	Odd	55	$^{17}_8$O, $^{25}_{12}$Mg, $^{57}_{26}$Fe
Odd	Even	Odd	50	$^7_3$Li, $^{19}_9$F, $^{63}_{29}$Cu
Odd	Odd	Even	4	$^2_1$H, $^6_3$Li, $^{10}_5$B, $^{14}_7$N only*

*$^{180}_{73}$Ta$_{107}$ is now known to be another odd-Z, odd-N stable isotope. It has an 8.1h metastable isomer (Sec. 4.8.3).

$^{16}_8$O (48), $^{28}_{14}$Si (26), $^{56}_{26}$Fe (5), $^{40}_{20}$Ca (3.5), $^{24}_{12}$Mg (2) and about 13% of odd-Z, even-N nuclides as $^{27}_{13}$Al (8.5), $^{23}_{11}$Na (2.8) and $^{39}_{19}$K (2.5).[5,6]

(ii) The number of stable nuclides in which either the Z or N is odd is about a third of those where both are even. Further, the number of stable nuclides of odd A is about the same whether the odd number is of protons or of neutrons. This suggests the possibility of the neutrons and protons behaving similarly, or the charge independent nature of the nucleons in respect of stability. This is remarkable despite the fact that a proton does not generally tend to pair with a neutron.

The tendency for a proton to pair with a proton and of a neutron with a neutron is well brought out in the distribution of stable nuclides amongst light elements from oxygen to about chlorine. The rule for forming *stable nuclides over this range* is the successive addition, *strictly*, of two neutrons, one at a time, followed by the addition of two protons, one at a time, and then it is again the turn of neutrons, and so on. This results in the formation of 3 isotopes of elements of even Z as A, $(A + 1)$ and $(A + 2)$, but only one isotope of elements of odd Z. This is illustrated in Fig. 1.1 for the progressive formation of stable nuclides from ^{16}O to ^{35}Cl, the horizontal arrow indicates the addition of a neutron yielding an isotope and the vertical arrow indicates the addition of a proton yielding a new element.

It may be noted that a violation of the above rule of adding in the sequence of $n + n$; $p + p$; $n + n$; ..., results in the formation of a radioactive nuclide, a few examples of which are shown in Fig. 1.1 with a crossed arrow and an asterisk. Beyond ^{35}Cl, however, the rule of nucleon addition becomes more complicated; often, *but not always*, two neutrons are added together to an odd Z nuclide to form a pair of stable isotopes of mass numbers A and $A + 2$, as

^{35}Cl — ^{37}Cl; ^{39}K — ^{41}K; ^{63}Cu — ^{65}Cu; ^{79}Br — ^{81}Br; ^{85}Rb — ^{87}Rb; ^{107}Ag — ^{109}Ag.

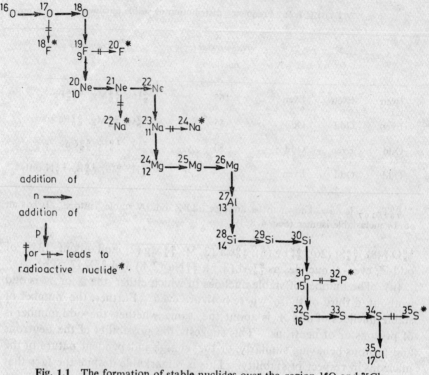

Fig. 1.1 The formation of stable nuclides over the region ^{16}O and ^{35}Cl: the $(n + n)$; $(p + p)$; $(n + n)$; ..., rule. Deviation from the rule results in a radioactive nuclide.

It may further be noted that of the 20 stable elements which occur in nature as monoisotopic nuclides, 19 are of odd Z, the sole exception being ^9_4Be. These odd Z monoisotopic nuclides are listed below.

$^{19}_9F$, $^{23}_{11}Na$, $^{27}_{13}Al$, $^{31}_{15}P$, $^{45}_{21}Sc$, $^{55}_{25}Mn$, $^{59}_{27}Co$, $^{75}_{33}As$, $^{89}_{39}Y$, $^{93}_{41}Nb$,

$^{103}_{45}Rh$, $^{127}_{53}I$, $^{133}_{55}Cs$, $^{141}_{59}Pr$, $^{159}_{65}Tb$, $^{165}_{47}Ho$, $^{169}_{69}Tm$, $^{197}_{79}Au$ and $^{209}_{83}Bi$.

The elements having no stable isotope are also of odd Z, these being $_{43}Tc$, $_{61}Pm$ and elements beyond $_{83}Bi$.

1.5.2 The Neutron to Proton Ratio N/Z

Except in the case of light or ordinary hydrogen (^1H), all other nuclides contain both neutrons and protons. A look at the stable nuclides shows that the ratio N/Z in them is $\geqslant 1$. The ratio is $\simeq 1$ in all the light stable nuclides up to $^{40}_{20}Ca_{20}$ and thereafter the ratio is > 1 for heavy nuclei, as may be seen from Table 1.3.

The variation of N vs. Z as a function of Z for stable nuclides is shown in Fig. 1.2[7], known also as the Segrè chart.[8] Since a large number of elements have several stable isotopes, the curve is in the nature of a strip or zone which widens out at higher Z values. All stable nuclides fall

TABLE 1.3: Neutron/proton ratio in some stable nuclides

$_AX$	^2H	^{20}Ne	^{40}Ca	^{64}Zn	^{90}Zr	^{120}Sn	^{150}Nd	^{202}Hg
Z	1	10	20	30	40	50	60	80
N	1	10	20	34	50	70	90	122
N/Z	1.00	1.00	1.00	1.13	1.25	1.40	1.50	1.53

within this zone and it is significant that nuclides falling outside the zone are invariably radioactive. Those lying above the zone are richer in neutrons than required for stability and they display a tendency to have one neutron transformed into a proton (β^- radioactivity) and thus approach the zone of stability. The reverse holds good for nuclides lying below the zone which are deficient in neutrons and they exhibit β^+ or EC radioactivity by which a proton is converted into a neutron (see Chapter 4).

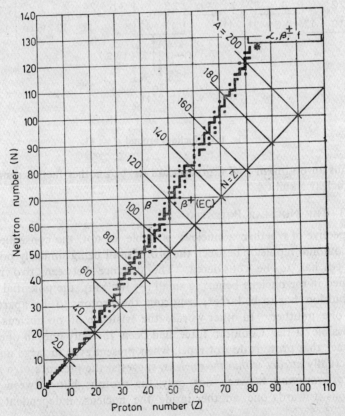

Fig. 1.2 The neutron number N *vs* the proton number Z in stable nuclides: the Segrè chart. Nuclides above the stability zone are β^- active and those below are β^+ and/or EC active. $^{208}_{82}Pb_{126}$ and $^{209}_{83}Bi$ are the heaviest stable nuclides: others with higher Z or N decay by α, or $\beta\pm$, or by fission process.

Consider the nuclides with $Z = 11$ (sodium). The only stable nuclide is $^{23}_{11}Na_{12}$. Replacing a proton by a neutron results in $^{23}_{10}Ne_{13}$ which is radioactive (β^-, 38s). Similarly, replacing a neutron by a proton results in $^{23}_{12}Mg_{11}$ which is also radioactive (β^+, 12s). Again, keeping Z constant, the removal of a neutron from, or its addition to $^{23}_{11}Na_{12}$ results respectively in 2.6y β^+ active $^{22}_{11}Na_{11}$, or 15h β^- active $^{24}_{11}Na_{13}$ (Fig. 1.3).

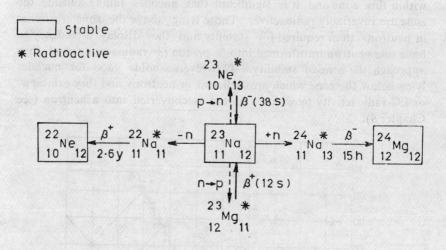

Fig. 1.3 Nuclides around $Z = 11$.

Thus an optimum N/Z ratio appears to be another factor responsible for nuclear stability.

1.5.3 THE NUCLEAR POTENTIAL

Irrespective of whether a nucleus is stable or not, the consequence of the Coulomb repulsion between the protons, all being similarly positively charged, has to be considered. The distance between two protons confined in the nucleus being so small ($\sim 10^{-15}$ m), the potential energy of repulsion has to be large*, requiring the protons to fly apart away from one another. In other words, the existence of no nucleus would be possible if the Coulomb force had been the only one in operation. The fact that protons do not repel, when present even in large numbers, but actually *attract within the nucleus*, suggests the presence of a *nuclear force of attraction* between not only the protons but between all the nucleons towards one another inside the nucleus, independent of the

*The Coulomb force of repulsion between two like charges q_1 and q_2 separated by a distance r is proportional to q_1q_2/r^2 and the corresponding Coulomb potential energy is equal to q_1q_2/r (in *cgs* units). To get the value in SI units, one has to divide by $4\pi\in_0$ the corresponding values for the same being $q_1q_2/(4\pi\in_0)$ r^2 and $q_1q_2/4\pi\in_0 r$ where $\in_0$ is the permittivity of free space or vacuum and is equal to 8.85419×10^{-12} J^{-1} c^{2}m^{-1}.

charge they bear.   This is a short-range nuclear attractive force operative only in the nucleus.   It has to be postulated to vanish to zero abruptly on crossing the nuclear border outside which is the normal Coulomb regime.   The simplest approach to such a postulate regarding the nuclear potential is what is termed the *square-well potential*.   The nuclear potential $V_{(r)}$ according to this is given by

$$V_r = 0 \text{ for } r \geqslant R$$
$$V_r = -V_0 \text{ for } r \leqslant R \tag{1.1}$$

where R is the radius of the nucleus.   Usually V_0 is around 30 MeV, the negative sign signifying the force of attraction.   The square-well potential is shown graphically in Fig. 1.4.   The nature of the nuclear potential is considered in detail in Sec. 3.2.2.

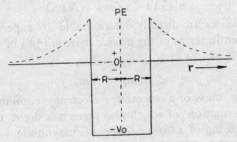

Fig. 1.4   The square- or rectangular-well potential—
The Coulomb potential. . . .
$R = $ Nuclear radius
P.E. = Potential energy
$V_0 \simeq -30$ MeV

1.5.4   THE BINDING ENERGY

The *binding energy* is another important characteristic of each nuclide, whether stable or not, by virtue of which it holds the nucleons together in the nucleus.   The origin of the binding energy is in the annihilation of a part of the mass when the nucleons come within the range of the nuclear force to form the nucleus.   Such a mass loss occurs without exception in the formation of all nuclei.

This conversion constitutes a direct illustration of Einstein's theory of matter $\leftrightarrow$ energy interconversion, proposed as long back as 1905 in the form of his famous equation $E = mc^2$ where E and m are the energy and mass interconverted and c is the velocity of light.   Thus the energy released in the destruction of mass equal to one atomic mass unit is given by

$$E = uc^2 = 1.661 \times 10^{-27} \times (3 \times 10^8)^2 \text{ J}$$
$$= 14.95 \times 10^{-11} \text{ J}$$
$$= 931 \text{ MeV} \quad (\because \ 1.6 \times 10^{-13} \text{ J} = 1 \text{ MeV})$$

Today we know that the energy from the sun and the stars is due to the conversion of matter into energy, mainly through the thermonuclear reaction

$$4 \, {}^1\text{H} \;\rightarrow\; {}^4\text{He} + 2\beta^+ + 2\nu; \quad \Delta m = -0.02871 \; u = 26.07 \text{ MeV.}$$

The sun is losing 4.2 million tonnes of mass every second and its equivalent of 10^{20} MJ energy is being radiated into space per second (see Sec. 5.10.1).

It is observed that the actual mass of every nucleus is distinctly less than the sum of the masses of the protons and neutrons constituting it. Consider a general case of a nuclide like ${}_Z^A X$ containing Z protons, each of mass 1.007 277 u and $N \, (= A - Z)$ neutrons each of mass 1.008 665 u. One would expect the mass of the nuclide $m' \, ({}_Z^A X)$ to be just the sum of $(1.0073 \, Z + 1.0087 \, N) \, u$, but in reality

$$m' \, ({}_Z^A X) < (Z \, m_p + N \, m_n). \tag{1.2a}$$

Since atomic masses are directly determinable by experiment, the above may be rewritten in terms of the *atomic mass m* $({}_Z^A X)$ of the atom.

$$m \, ({}_Z^A X) \ll (Z \, m_p + Z \, m_e + N \, m_n)$$
$$< (Z \, m_H + N \, m_n) \tag{1.2b}$$

where m_H is the mass of a (proton + electron) combination, or an H atom, in the formation of which also there is a slight mass loss. This last, however, being of a lower order of magnitude ($\sim 1.7 \times 10^{-8} \, u$) will be neglected*.[9] The mass loss Δm in the synthesis of an atom ${}_Z^A X$ is given in units of u, by,

$$\Delta m = Z \, m_H + N \, m_n - m \, ({}_Z^A X) \tag{1.3}$$

The energy equivalence of this mass loss, which is the *binding energy B*, is given by

$$B = \Delta m \times 931 \text{ MeV} \tag{1.4}$$

The magnitude of this binding energy is appreciable as may be seen from the following examples using known values of $m_H = 1.007 \, 825 \, u$ and $m_n = 1.008 \, 665 \, u$ and the actual value of $m \, ({}_Z^A X)$ from Tables.[10]

(i) *Heavy Hydrogen Atom* ${}_1^2 \text{H}$; $m({}^2\text{H}) = 2.014 \, 102$ u

$\Delta m = (1.007 \, 825 + 1.008 \, 665 - 2.014 \, 102) \, \text{u}$

   $= 0.002 \, 388$ u

$B = 2.22$ MeV

This is the total binding energy holding $A \, (= 2)$ nucleons in this case. Hence, the mean binding energy $\bar{B} = B/A$ comes to be equal to 1.11 MeV per nucleon.

*The binding energy $B \, (Z)$ of Z electrons with as many protons in an atom of atomic number Z is given by

$$B \, (Z) = 15.73 \, Z^{7/3} \text{ eV} \; [9]$$

This in the heaviest elements approaches 1 MeV whereas the *total* binding energy in heavy elements is above 1600 MeV.

(ii) *Iron Atom* $_{26}^{56}$Fe; $m\left(_{26}^{56}\text{Fe}\right) = 55.934\,932$ u

$\Delta m = [(26 \times 1.007\,825) + (30 \times 1.008\,665) - (55.934\,932)]$ u

$\quad = 0.528\,068$ u

$B = 491.63$ MeV

$\bar{B} = 8.78$ MeV.

In the same way the mean binding energy of all stable nuclides have been calculated and the curve of $\bar{B}$ *vs.* A is shown in Fig. 1.5. The fact that the binding energy is positive for *all* nuclides, stable or not, means that any combination of protons and neutrons when brought together within a nuclear distance is *relatively* more stable than the assembly of nucleons outside this distance. In other words, protons and neutrons *attract* one another when brought to within a nuclear distance, proving the existence of a nuclear force of attraction.

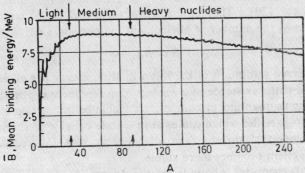

Fig. 1.5 The mean binding energy per nucleon $\bar{B}$ as a function of atomic mass number A for stable nuclides[11] (from *Introduction to Atomic and Nuclear Physics* by H.E. White, Van Nostrand Rhinehold Co., 1964, with author's permission).

A study of the variation of the mean binding energy as a function of the atomic mass number (Fig. 1.5) reveals the following features for the light, medium and heavy nuclides.

(i) *Light Nuclides:* $A < 30$

There is a periodic recurrence of maxima or peaks for values of A which are multiples of four (*e.g.* $_2^4$He, $_6^{12}$C, $_8^{16}$O, $_{10}^{20}$Ne, $_{12}^{24}$Mg and $_{14}^{28}$Si). These represent the most tightly bound nuclei relative to their neighbours on either side. However, $_4^8$Be is an exception having no ground state: it splits instantly into two alpha particles ($_4^8$Be $\to 2\,_2^4$He).

(ii) *Medium Nuclides:* $30 < A < 90$

A rise occurs in the mean binding energy $\bar{B}$ from 8.0 MeV for $A = 16$ (oxygen) to about 8.3 MeV for A between 28–32 (silicon–sulphur). This is followed by a plateau, the $\bar{B}$ varying between 8.3 and 8.7 MeV, the broad maximum being around $A = 60$ or the region of iron, cobalt and nickel.

(iii)   *Heavy Nuclides:* $A > 90$

For nuclides $A > 90$ (beyond zirconium), the mean binding energy decreases monotonically from the maximum of 8.7 to 7.7 MeV for $A \simeq 210$. In fact $^{209}_{83}$Bi is the heaviest stable nuclide. Beyond this the nuclides are all radioactive, mainly α emitters, with $\bar{B}$ around 7.3 MeV, the value for ^{238}U.

1.5.5 EXCHANGE FORCE ⟶ *for more stability*

If only the short range charge independent attractive force were to operate between the nucleons, the attractive force would grow limitlessly till the nucleus collapsed ultimately. There is need, therefore, for some *repulsive* forces to lead to the saturation of the attractive force. That the attractive forces saturate is revealed through the fact that the *mean binding energy* per nucleon (B/A) is nearly constant, around 8.5 MeV for all nuclides of maximum stability of the plateau region of Fig. 1.5 (for $30 < A < 120$). The *total binding energy* B is, of course, proportional to A, the number of nucleons in the nucleus, i.e.

$$B = \bar{B}A \tag{1.5}$$

The observed saturation of the mean binding energy per nucleon finds explanation if the existence of a *nuclear exchange force* is postulated.

According to quantum mechanics, an exchange interaction is possible between two particles which can exist in a state capable of sharing some common property: thereby, the total energy gets lowered; in other words the system becomes more stable.

Structural chemistry abounds in the examples of molecules which permit two or more electron rearrangements by the exchange of an electron between neighbour atoms, as in the case of the hydrogen molecule ion H_2^+, or the benzene molecule. Such molecules acquire additional stability due to resonance between the alternative structures. A similar situation is envisaged for the atomic nucleus by assuming a ceaseless exchange of *a common property* between neighbour nucleons in the same state of motion. The common property for exchange may be the charge, spin, or position and known by the names shown below.

(i)   *Heisenberg's Charge Exchange Force*

Heisenberg first believed the common property under exchange was the electron charge as in the case of the H_2^+ ion molecule. Later, he extended the concept to include positrons and neutrinos:

$$n \rightleftharpoons p + e^- + \bar{\nu}$$

and

$$p \rightleftharpoons n + e^+ + \nu$$

This concept had to be abandoned as it was soon realized that such interactions are very much weaker by a factor of 10^{-14} than what is required on the square well potential for the nucleus with a diameter of the order of a few fermis.

This was about the time of Yukawa's prediction of the existence of mesons* (1935) and very soon the π meson (or pion) ($m_\pi = 273\,m_e$) was experimentally observed. Immediately, the particles of Heisenberg exchange were recognized to be the pions (π^+, π^-, or π°) (Figs. 1.6a, b, c and 2.6).

$$n \rightleftharpoons p + \pi^-$$
$$p \rightleftharpoons n + \pi^+$$
$$p \rightleftharpoons p + \pi^\circ$$
$$n \rightleftharpoons n + \pi^\circ$$

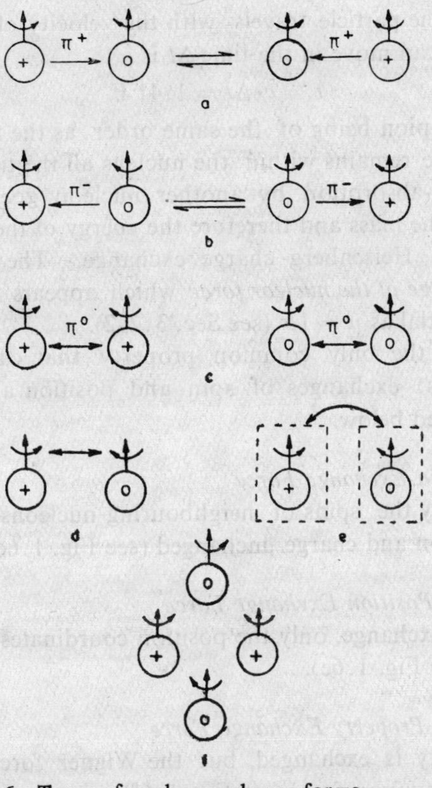

Fig. 1.6   Types of nuclear exchange forces

⊕ proton,   ⊙ neutron,   ↯ ↯   spin orientations

(a), (b), (c)   Heisenberg charge exchange,
        (d)   Bartlett spin exchange,
        (e)   Majorana position exchange,
        (f)   Wigner's no property (or ordinary) exchange.

This, however, created a new difficulty, *viz.* the violation of the conservation of mass (and hence of energy) associated with the creation of

*Mesons are particles of mass intermediate between an electron and a nucleon (see Table 1.1).

a pion, *viz.* $m_\pi c^2$. Classically, the above pion emission cannot occur. A brilliant suggestion due to Wick[12] however saved the situation. He showed that the difficulty is only an apparent one. He argued on the basis of Heisenberg's own *Principle of Uncertainty* that the emission is only *virtual*, as the pion is very soon recaptured within a time Δt before it can get out of the nucleus, the energy ΔE and the free life time Δt of the pion being related through the uncertainty principle:

$$\Delta E \cdot \Delta t = \hbar \qquad (1.6)$$

Hence, $\Delta t = \hbar/\Delta E = \hbar/m_\pi c^2 = 4.72 \times 10^{-24}$ s

Even assuming the particle travels with the velocity of light, the maximum distance it can move in the time Δt is

$$r = c \cdot \Delta t = 1.41 \text{ F} \qquad (1.7)$$

The range of the pion being of the same order as the nuclear radius, it means the particle remains within the nucleus all the time; emission by a nucleon and re-absorption by another nucleon goes on incessantly. In other words, the mass and therefore the energy of the nucleus remains unaltered in the Heisenberg charge exchange. The distance r also represents the *range of the nuclear force* which appears in some forms of the nuclear potential as $\mu = 1/r$ (see Sec. 3.2.2).

Charge is not the only common property that can be exchanged between nucleons; exchanges of spin and position are also possible. These are described below.

(ii)   Bartlett's Spin Exchange Force

In this type only the spins of neighbouring nucleons are exchanged, leaving the position and charge unchanged (see Fig. 1.6d).

(iii)   Majorana's Position Exchange Force

In this type of exchange, only the position coordinates of two nucleons are exchanged (see Fig. 1.6e).

(iv)   Wigner's No Property Exchange Force

Here no property is exchanged, but the Wigner force represents the ordinary nucleon-nucleon force (see Fig. 1.6f).

The four exchange forces, illustrated in Fig. 1.6 may give rise to the impression that the spins of a neutron and the neighbour proton should be antiparallel for stability. This is not necessarily correct. Neutrons and protons can have an attractive interaction, as in the ^2H nucleus, where the ground state is a triplet, *i.e.* with the neutron and proton having parallel spins.

1.6   Atomic Energy

It is by now clear how every atomic nucleus, *without exception*, is a storehouse of a vast amount of energy, some of which may be released through appropriate nuclear reactions. The amount of energy thus released is the equivalent of the mass annihilated in the reaction. A careful study of the factors conducive to nuclear stability, especially the nature of the variation of the mean binding energy $\bar{B}$ with the atomic mass number A (Fig. 1.5) reveals the secret of releasing some of this atomic energy. The medium mass elements being the stablest with maximum $\bar{B}$, any attempt to transform them into lighter or heavier elements would need the *putting in* of a vast amount of energy from outside, as in such a process additional mass has to be created. The medium mass elements being thus unavailable for tapping atomic energy, one has to look to the extreme ends, *i.e.* either,

(a) very light elements of low $\bar{B}$, or,

(b) very heavy elements also of low $\bar{B}$. *How to get E out of atoms.*

The following two pathways are thus available for generating atomic energy.

(a) *Via nuclear fusion:* When two or more light nuclei of low $\bar{B}$ fuse to form a larger nucleus of higher $\bar{B}$, the process involves the annihilation of mass which is released as energy, *e.g.*

$$4\,{}^{1}_{1}H \rightarrow {}^{4}_{2}He + 2\beta^{+} + 2\nu; \quad \Delta m = -0.028\,71 \text{ u}$$
$$= 26.7 \text{ MeV}$$

However, for such fusion reactions extremely high temperatures of the order of 10^8 K are needed for overcoming the Coulomb barrier. At such temperatures most atoms would be stripped of their electrons. Hence they are also referred to as *thermonuclear reactions*.

On the sun and stars, such reactions are going on eternally and the vast energy that we receive perennially from them is of this origin. Despite many planned efforts by eminent scientists it has not yet been possible to perfect the technique for generating atomic energy through nuclear fusion, apart from its uncontrolled devastating release in the so-called *hydrogen bomb*. However, the limited success in laboratory experiments, specially by the use of laser beams to effect the fusion of protons, provides a distant hope of a large scale controlled thermonuclear reaction in the future (see Sec. 5.10).

(b) *Via nuclear fission:* Very heavy nuclei of elements at the end of the Periodic Table, as Th, U and Pu of low $\bar{B}$, when excited mainly through the capture of a neutron, undergo *fission* into two fragments of medium masses of higher $\bar{B}$, *e.g.*

$$^{235}_{92}U + n \rightarrow \, ^{236}U \rightarrow \textit{fission fragments};$$
$$\Delta m = -\,0.2\,u$$
$$\simeq 200 \text{ MeV}$$

The phenomenon of *nuclear fission*, discovered by Hahn and Strassmann in 1939, has been studied since then in great depth. The fission fragments are $^{140}_{56}Ba + ^{94}_{36}Kr$, or similar pairs, and 2 or 3 free neutrons. The initially produced pair being radioactive decays further by β^- emission into stable nuclei. Some of the free neutrons, under proper conditions, can cause the fission of other U atoms resulting in chain reactions which release a vast amount of energy (see Chapter 7). The technique of generating atomic energy through nuclear fission on a commercial scale has been standardized more or less.[12-15] There are numerous electric power generating stations in the world today, including some in India.

References

(*where marked* (*), *see Bibliography*)

1. M. L. Glashan*
2. J. G. Stork and H. G. Wallace*
3. H. J. Arnikar and R. A. Kulkarni*
4. T. Urbansky, *Chemistry and Technology of Explosives*, Vol. 1, Pergamon Press, Oxford, 1964.
5. K. Rankama*
6. H. E. Suess and H. C. Urey, 'Abundance of Elements' *Revs. Mod. Phys.*, 1956, **28**, 53.
7. I. Kaplan*
8. E. Segrè* (1977).
9. R. D. Evans*
10. B. G. Harvey*, or J.H.E. Mattuch, W. Thiele and A.H. Wapstra, Nuc. Phys., 1965, **67**, 1.
11. H. E. White*
12. G. C. Wick, 'Range of Nuclear Forces in Yukawa's Theory', *Nature*, 1938, **142**, 993.
13. A. I. Simon*
14. S. Glasstone*
15. H. D. Smyth, 'Atomic Energy for Military Purposes', *Revs. Mod. Phys.*, 1945, **17**, 351.

Problems

(*Values of constants are given in Appendix III*)

1.1 A dc potential of 1000 V is applied to two parallel plates 5 cm apart. A small metal sphere with a charge of 3.8×10^{-9} C is held midway between the plates. Find (a) the field between the plates, (b) force in newtons per coulomb, and (c) the force on the metal sphere in newtons.

[(a) 2×10^4 V m^{-1}, (b) 2×10^4 N/C, (c) 7.6×10^{-5} N]

1.2 A metal sphere suspended by a silk thread is charged positively. If 2 µJ of energy are needed to carry a positive charge of 2.5×10^{-8} C from the ground to the sphere, what is the potential on the latter? [80 V]

1.3 Calculate the wavelength (a) of an electron of energy 10 eV, and (b) the wavelength of light emitted by an atom when an electron in it jumps from an outer to an inner orbit, the transition energy being 10 eV. Hint: $\lambda = h/\sqrt{2m_e E}$

[(a) 3.88×10^{-10} m, (b) 12.42×10^{-8} m]

1.4 What is the kinetic energy of an electron whose de Broglie wavelength is 10^{-10} m? [150.4 eV]

1.5 Calculate the de Broglie wavelength of (a) an oxygen nucleus of 120 MeV energy, and (b) a nitrogen nucleus of 140 MeV energy. Take the masses of the two nuclei to be 16 and 14 u respectively.

[(a) 6.56×10^{-16} m, (b) 6.49×10^{-16} m]

1.6 Sodium has a work function of 5.12 eV. Calculate (a) the threshold frequency and (b) the wavelength of light which can ionize a sodium atom, and (c) the energy of photo-electrons when light of wavelength 200 nm shines on it.

[(a) 1.24×10^{15} s^{-1}, (b) 2.42×10^{-7} m, (c) 1.08 eV]

1.7 Find the speeds of (a) alpha particles, (b) deuterons, and (c) protons of energy (i) 1 MeV and (ii) 2 MeV.

[(a) (i) 6.94, (ii) 9.82; (b) (i) 9.79, (ii) 13.84; (c) (i) 13.84, (ii) 19.57, all in units of 10^6 m s^{-1}.]

Comment on the close identity of answers between (a) (ii) and (b) (i), and (b) (ii) and (c) (i).

1.8 Boron is used as a rocket fuel, the enthalpy of combustion of boron to form B_2O_3 being -1278 kJ/mol. Find the energy of formation of one molecule of B_2O_3 in eV. [13.25 eV]

1.9 Calculate the mean binding energy of (a) ^{4}He and (b) ^{16}O atoms, given the masses: $H = 1.0078$ u, $n = 1.0087$ u, ^{4}He $= 4.0026$ u and ^{16}O $= 15.9949$ u.

[(a) 7.08 MeV, (b) 7.98 MeV]

1.10 Using part of the data of problem 1.9, explain why $^8_4$Be does not exist in nature: given the mass of ^{8}Be $= 8.0053$ u. [The mean binding energy of ^{8}Be is 7.064 MeV compared to 7.08 MeV in ^{4}He. The breaking up of ^{8}Be into two alpha particles is spontaneous.]

Chapter 2

Properties of Nucleons and Nuclei

2.1 The Nucleus, Its Size and Shape

Having listed the characteristics of the nucleons in Chapter 1, we proceed now to consider the mechanical and magneto-electrical effects due to the orbiting and spinning motions of individual protons and neutrons and the nuclei as a whole. We begin this with a brief discussion of the size and shape of atomic nuclei.

2.1.1 THE NUCLEAR RADIUS

It would not be possible to present a single definition for the nuclear radius which would hold good for all nuclear phenomena. Radii of *matter distribution* and of *charge distribution* would not be identical and neither *vis-a-vis* the range of the nuclear force. The variations, however, are known to be within 10–20 per cent, a situation better than in the case of atomic radii.

The constancy of the density of nuclear matter, ρ, having been well verified (Figs. 2.1 and 2.2) it is permissible to start with this as the basis, *viz.*

$$\rho \propto A/\tfrac{4}{3}\pi R^3 = constant \tag{2.1}$$

and hence

$$R = r_0 A^{1/3} \tag{2.2}$$

where r_0 is a constant, *the nuclear radius unit*. The problem is to evaluate r_0. A variety of techniques have been adopted for this which can be grouped under two categories.[1]

(i) Methods which depend, at least in part, on coulombic effects such as (a) probing the target nuclei with charged particles, as high energy electrons (100–200 MeV), protons and neutrons ($\sim$ 20 MeV) or muons and, (b) studying the angular distribution of the scattered particles. The radii are referred to as the *electromagnetic or coulombic radii*.

(ii) Methods which depend wholly on the nuclear force, such as the scattering of high energy α particles, half-lives of α emitters, scattering of fast neutrons and cross sections of nuclear reactions involving the

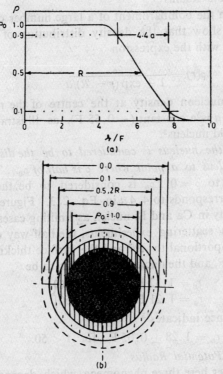

Fig. 2.1 The concept of the nuclear radius: the gold nucleus $^{197}_{79}$Au

    (a) Nucleon density distribution (ρ) as a function of distance (r)
        from the centre of the nucleus. Radius R is the distance from
        the centre ($\rho = \rho_0$) to the region ($\rho = 0.5\rho_0$). Surface thickness
        is the zone between ($\rho = 0.9\rho_0$) and ($\rho = 0.1\rho_0$) = 4.4a with
        $a \simeq 0.55$ F. (Hahn, Ravenhall and Hofstadter)[2]

    (b) Cross-sectional view of the atomic nucleus.

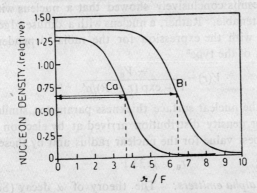

Fig. 2.2 Approximate limits of nucleon density distribution between
        a typically light nucleus (Ca) and a heavy one (Bi) (B. Hahn,
        D.G. Ravenhall and R. Hofstadter[2]).

emission of neutrons. The results are referred to as *nuclear force* or
potential radii. We shall consider the results of both the methods.

(i) The Coulombic Radius

Experiments on the bombardment of a large number of nuclei by high energy electrons show that the density distribution of nucleons, inside the nuclei, agrees with the expression

$$\rho(r) = \frac{\rho_0}{1 + \exp{(r - R)/a}} \qquad (2.3)$$

where ρ_0 is the nucleon density at the centre of the nucleus ($\simeq 0.165$ nucleons/F*, and a is a constant (~ 0.55 F), as illustrated in Fig. 2.1, for the typical gold nucleus[2].

The radius of the nucleus is considered to be the distance R from the centre of the nucleus to a point where ρ is half of ρ_0. The outer region from $\rho = 0.9\,\rho_0$ to $\rho = 0.1\,\rho_0$ is considered to be the *surface of the nucleus,* which corresponds to $4.4\,a$ in Eq. 2.3. Figure 2.2 illustrates the nucleon density in Ca and Bi nuclei, as limiting cases. On the basis of similar electron scattering experiments, the half-way density radius R is found to be proportional to $A^{1/3}$ and the surface thickness factor a to be to about 0.55 F, and the nuclear radius unit to be

$$\left. \begin{array}{l} r_0 = 1.32 \text{ F} \quad \text{for } A < 50 \\ r_0 = 1.21 \text{ F} \quad \text{for } A > 50 \end{array} \right\} \qquad (2.4a)$$

More recent evidence indicates[15]

$$r_0 = 1.28 \pm 0.05 \text{ F} \quad \text{for } A < 50. \qquad (2.4b)$$

(ii) The Nuclear Potential Radius

We shall consider here three phenomena which depend almost wholly on the interaction with the nuclear force and nearly independent of the Coulomb potential.

(a) *Scattering of high energy alphas and protons:* As intense beams of high energy particles (40 MeV alphas and 100–300 MeV protons) became available, studies on their scattering by heavy target elements were resumed. The results conclusively showed that a nucleus with a sharp boundary was untenable. Rather, a nucleus with a diffuse edge appeared to be consistent with the expression for the radial dependence of the nuclear potential, of the type[3]

$$V(r) = \frac{-V_0}{1 + \exp{(r - R)/a'}} \qquad (2.5)$$

Here again a' is the nuclear surface thickness parameter, similar to a in the expression for density distribution arrived at by electron scattering (Eq. 2.3). The best value for the nuclear radius unit by these studies is

$$r_0 = 1.33 \text{ F} \qquad (2.6)$$

(b) *Life-time of alpha emitters:* The theory of α decay (Sec. 4.6.5) provides an expression for the decay constant which involves the nuclear radius unit.

---

*This is same as 1.65×10^{38} nucleons/cm³, corresponding to a density of $\sim 10^{14}$ g cm⁻³ for the nuclear matter.

The expression for the α decay constant λ is a product of two factors: (i) a frequency factor λ_0 representing the number of times an α particle arrives at the nuclear border and (ii) an escape probability factor* P

$$\lambda = \lambda_0 P \qquad (2.7a)$$

The frequency factor is simply taken as the ratio $v_\alpha/2R$ where v_α is the velocity of the α particle *inside* the nucleus and R is the *effective* radius of the daughter nucleus. The probability factor P is of an exponential nature expressed here as

$$P = \exp{-[a - br_0^{1/2}]} \qquad (2.7b)$$

where a and b are constants. Assuming λ_0 to be $1.21 \times 10^{21} \, s^{-1}$, which is reasonable (see Sec. 4.6.5), Perlman and Ypsilantis arrived at the value[4]

$$r_0 = 1.48 \, F \qquad (2.8)$$

(c) *Scattering of fast neutrons*: For fast neutrons (10–20 MeV), the total cross-section** (Sec. 5.4.1 and 5.5.4) is given by

$$\sigma_t = 2\pi(R + \lambda^*)^2 \qquad (2.9)$$

where λ^* is the reduced de Broglie wavelength of the neutron. The bulk of experimental evidence tends to support the value for r_0 (involved in R in Eq. 2.9) to be

$$r_0 = 1.4 \pm 0.1 \, F \qquad (2.10)$$

Thus, it may be noticed that the nuclear force or potential radii tend to be 10–20 per cent larger than the values dependent on coulombic interactions. See Sec. 3.3.3 for other methods of evaluating the nuclear radius constant.[5,6]

2.1.2 THE SHAPE OF THE NUCLEUS

Most nuclides in the ground state, including all of the even-Z, even-N type (which are amongst the most abundant) may be considered to be spherical in shape. The actual deviation of a nucleus from sphericality is indicated by its electric quadrupole moment (Sec. 2.10). If this moment is zero, the nucleus is spherical, while positive or negative values of this moment indicate the extent of deviation from sphericality, towards prolate or an oblate type ellipsoid respectively (see Sec. 2.10.2). ^{176}Lu and ^{233}Pa appear to be the most distorted, the former having the highest positive quadrupole moment with an ellipticity for its prolate ellipsoidal shape of $+0.174$ and the latter having the highest negative quadrupole moment with an ellipticity for its oblate ellipsoidal shape of -0.06 (see Secs. 2.10.4 and 5).[7,8]

---

*A third numerical factor θ, where $(0.1 < \theta < 1)$, is included standing for the probability of prefabrication of the α particle inside the nucleus (see Sec. 4.6.5).

**The total cross section is the sum of cross sections for elastic and inelastic scattering, each equal to $\pi(R + \lambda^*)^2$. Here λ^* stands for $\lambda/2\pi$.

2.2 Mechanical Effects Due to Orbiting and Spinning of Nucleons

Like the electrons in the outer sphere of the atom, the protons and the neutrons in the nucleus are constantly orbiting around and spinning on their axes. Here, the angular momenta of individual nucleons due to these two motions, the nuclear quantum numbers and the laws governing them, their interactions leading to the resultant angular momentum of the nucleus and the magnetic effects arising therefrom are considered. The electric moments due to the spatial distribution of the proton charges in the nucleus, symmetry effects due to odd-even proton and neutron combinations, and the statistical behaviour of the assembly of nucleons are also briefly referred to.

2.2.1 ORBITAL ANGULAR MOMENTUM OF NUCLEONS

The *orbital motion* of nucleons, like those of electrons, is *quantized, i.e.* the angular momentum of a nucleon due to its orbiting motion can have only certain discrete values given by $\hbar [l (l + 1)]^{1/2}$ where $\hbar$ is the unit of action $(= h/2\pi)$ where h is the Planck's constant and l is a positive integer including zero.

Thus $l = 0, 1, 2, 3, 4, 5, 6, \ldots$ (2.11)

The observable maximum value of the orbital angular momentum is, however, $l\hbar$. The integer l is referred to as the *orbital angular momentum quantum number*. Alternatively and more conveniently, the serial numerical values are designated by spectroscopic symbols as shown below:

TABLE 2.1: Values of l and their spectroscopic symbols

Numerical	0	1	2	3	4	5	6	7
Spectroscopic symbol	s	p	d	f	g	h	i	j

2.2.2 SPIN ANGULAR MOMENTUM OF NUCLEONS

Besides orbiting around, each nucleon *spins* on its own axis. This *spin* motion is also *quantized*. The only value of angular momentum due to spin motion is given by $\hbar [s(s + 1)]^{1/2}$ where s *is $\frac{1}{2}$ for protons, and neutrons* (as also for electrons). The s used here to denote the spin quantum number should not be confused with the symbol s used for the orbital angular momentum quantum number $l = 0$, though unfortunately the same symbol is used for both. The observable maximum value of the spin angular momentum is, however, $s\hbar$.

2.2.3 TOTAL ANGULAR MOMENTUM OF A NUCLEON

The summation of the orbital and spin angular momenta of a nucleon is its *total angular momentum j* given by

$$j = l + s \tag{2.12}$$

The corresponding total angular momentum of the nucleon is given by $\hbar[j(j+1)]^{1/2}$. The observable maximum total angular momentum, is, however $j\hbar$, where j is referred to as the *total angular momentum quantum number*. Since the spin motion may either support orbital motion (both being parallel, *i.e.* both either clockwise or anticlockwise), or oppose the latter (one being clockwise and the other anticlockwise), *two* values of j for each value of l are possible (see Fig. 2.3). Thus

or
$$\left. \begin{array}{l} j = l + s \\ \\ j = l - s \end{array} \right\} \tag{2.12a}$$

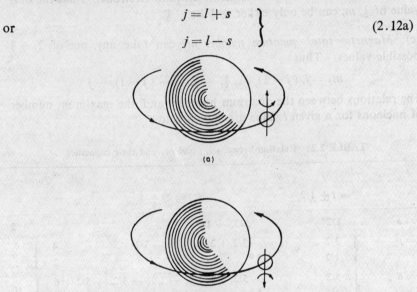

(a)

(b)

Fig. 2.3 The orientation of nuclear spin with respect to orbital motion
    (a)   Parallel orientation $j = l + s$
    (b)   Antiparallel orientation $j = l - s$

However, when $l = 0$ (s), j has a single value of $+\frac{1}{2}$ as j *can have only positive values*. Thus, the only values of j possible are positive half-integers, *i.e.*

$$j = 1/2,\ 3/2,\ 5/2,\ 7/2,\ 9/2\ \dots \tag{2.12b}$$

2.3 Magnetic Quantum Numbers

To each of the above described angular momentum quantum numbers (l, s, and j), there exists a magnetic analogue (m_l, m_s and m_j) representing the resolved component of the original quantum number along a specified direction, say that of the direction of an applied magnetic field. The magnetic quantum numbers are related to the corresponding quantum numbers as follows:

(a) *Magnetic orbital quantum number m_l* can take any one of $2l + 1$

possible positive and negative integral values lying between $+l$, and $-l$ including zero. Thus $m_l = l, (l-1)\ldots 1, 0, -1, \ldots -(l-1), -l$. If the orbital angular momentum quantum number l is $f(=3)$, m_l can have any one of the following seven $(=2l+1)$ values: $3, 2, 1, 0, -1, -2$ and -3. (Note that l can have only positive integral values including zero.)

(b) *Magnetic spin quantum number* m_s can have only one of two values $+s$ or $-s$. Since for protons, neutrons (and electrons), s has the only value of $\frac{1}{2}$, m_s can be only either $+\frac{1}{2}$ or $-\frac{1}{2}$.

(c) *Magnetic total quantum number* m_j can take any one of $2j+1$ possible values. Thus

$$m_j = j, (j-1), \ldots \frac{1}{2}, -\frac{1}{2}, \ldots -(j-1), -j$$

The relations between the quantum numbers and the maximum number of nucleons for a given l value are shown below:

TABLE 2.2: Relation between l, j and m_j and their capacities

l	j $= l \pm 1/2$	m_j $= 2j+1$	Total
$0 = s$	$1/2^*$	$1/2, -1/2$	2
$1 = p$	$3/2$ $1/2$	$3/2, 1/2, -1/2, -3/2$ **	4 2 } 6
$2 = d$	$5/2$ $3/2$	$5/2, 3/2, 1/2, -1/2, -3/2, -5/2$ **	6 4 } 10
$3 = f$	$7/2$ $5/2$	$7/2, 5/2, \ldots -5/2, -7/2$ **	8 6 } 14
$4 = g$	$9/2$ $7/2$	$9/2, 7/2, \ldots -7/2, -9/2$ **	10 8 } 18
$5 = h$	$11/2$ $9/2$	$11/2, 9/2, \ldots -9/2, -11/2$ **	12 10 } 22
$6 = i$	$13/2$ $11/2$	$13/2, 11/2, \ldots -11/2, -13/2$ **	14 12 } 26
$7 = j$	$15/2$ $13/2$	$15/2, 13/2, \ldots -13/2, -15/2$ **	16 14 } 30

*Since j can only have positive half-integral values, j has only one value of $1/2$ for $l = s$.

**As in the above for the same value of j.

2.4 Principal and Radial Quantum Numbers

There remain yet two more quantum numbers: the principal (n) and the

radial (v). These, however, do not play an independent role in determining the energy state of the nucleon.

(a) *The principal quantum number n* can have only positive integral values,
i.e. $n = 1$, 2, 3, 4, ... It is, however, less relevant as it does not
characterize the energy state of the nucleon. This is a situation very
different from that of electrons for which the field is coulombic and
central, where the principal quantum number can vary independently of
other quantum numbers and, as the name implies, it is the principal index
of the energy state of an electron.   In the case of the nucleus, where
the field is non-coulombic and non-central, n becomes relevant only as
a sum of the orbital angular momentum l and the radial quantum
number v, Thus,

$$n = l + v \qquad\qquad (2.13)$$

(b) *The radial quantum number* v arises as a consequence of the wave
equation of the nucleon. It stands for the number of loops in the wave
function of the nucleon, which can only be positive integers, *i.e.* $v = 1$,
2, 3, 4, ...   The number of loops is also obviously equal to the
number of nodes (zero amplitude) less by one (see Fig. 2.4).   As stated
before, v reveals itself only along with n and l.   Therefore, v $(= n-l)$
is sometimes the value used as the relevant quantum number in describing
the energy state of a nucleon, along with l and j values following a
convention introduced by Maria Goeppert-Mayer in 1949.[1,16]   Thus a
nucleon having the quantum numbers

$$n = 4,\; l = f \text{ and } j = l - s$$

will have v $(= n - l) = 1$ and would be represented as

$$1f_{5/2}$$

Let us repeat that the 1 appearing in the above designation is not the

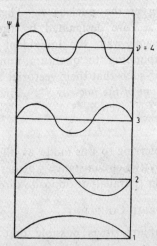

Fig. 2.4   The wave function ψ and the radial
quantum number v.

principal quantum number. It is rather $n - l$, or more simply the *first f state to appear* and similarly, $2f$ would stand for the *f state appearing for the second time,* corresponding to $n = 5$ and $l = 3$, and so on.

2.5 Total Angular Momentum of the Nucleus

So far we have discussed the orbital, spin and their sum, or the total angular momentum of *individual nucleons.* When two or more nucleons are able to come together to form a nucleus, the components of motion of individual nucleons interact with one another which leads to a resultant *total angular momentum of the nucleus* as a whole. This resultant determines the *nuclear level* or the energy state of the nucleus. The total nuclear angular momentum is given by $\hbar [I (I + 1)]^{1/2}$ where I is the corresponding *total nuclear angular momentum quantum number* which is sometimes inappropriately refered to as the *nuclear spin.* As in other cases, the observable maximum value of this total nuclear angular momentum is $I \hbar$.

The ways of coupling of the individual nucleon orbital and spin motions are not clearly understood. Two limiting cases are defined, as in atomic spectroscopy, with the recognition that the actual type of coupling may most probably lie in between. The two limiting modes are (i) the *LS* and (ii) the *jj*-coupling, the latter being dominant.

2.5.1 THE LS OR THE RUSSELL-SAUNDERS COUPLING

Under this type of coupling, the interaction between the orbital motion of a nucleon with its own spin motion is weak or negligible. On the other hand, the orbital motions of the different nucleons in the nucleus represented by the corresponding quantum numbers l_1, l_2, ... interact strongly with one another such that their vectorial sum gives the *resultant orbital angular momentum* of the nucleus L. The different numerical values of $L = 0, 1, 2, 3, \ldots$ are designated by the analogous symbols $S, P, D, F \ldots$. In the same way, the individual spin motions of the different nucleons corresponding to quantum numbers s_1, s_2, interact strongly with one another such that their vectorial sum gives *the resultant spin angular momentum of the nucleus S^**. Finally, the *total angular momentum of the nucleus I* is given by**

$$I = L \pm S \qquad (2.14)$$

which is the reason for referring to this mode as the *LS coupling.* The sign of S is determined by the circumstance whether S and L correspond both to the same direction (parallel) or opposite directions (antiparallel).

2.5.2 THE *jj* OR SPIN-ORBIT COUPLING

In contrast to the *LS* coupling, it is possible that the orbital and spin

---

*Here again this S should not be confused with the symbol S used to designate $L = 0$. The context in which the symbol is used will make the point clear.

**Sometimes the symbol J is used for I.

motions of the same nucleon may interact strongly and the different $j_1 (= l_1 \pm s_1)$, $j_2 (= l_2 \pm s_2) \ldots$ may then add together vectorially to give the *resultant total angular momentum of the nucleus I*.

$$I = \text{vectorial sum } \{j_1 + j_2 + \ldots\} \qquad (2.15)$$

This is the reason why this mode of coupling is referred to as the *spin-orbit* or *jj-coupling*. Obviously there is no L or S term under the *jj*-coupling.

As pointed out earlier, the LS and the *jj* represent limiting simplified modes of coupling, whereas in reality the actual coupling in a given nucleus may be neither one exclusively, but a mixture. Evidence seems to favour nearly *pure jj-coupling in heavy nuclei*, while in the light nuclei it is probably an intermediate mode.

2.5.3 THE TOTAL ANGULAR MOMENTUM (OR SPIN) OF THE NUCLEUS

Due to the pairing of nucleons, protons with protons and neutrons with neutrons, the individual orbital and spin angular momenta in a pair cancel out. This is evidenced by the fact that all stable nuclides of the *even-Z, even-N* type in the ground state*, without exception, have a zero nuclear spin (I)**. It is then only (a) the *odd-A nuclei* (odd-Z, even-N, or *vice-versa*), and (b) such *even-A nuclei* having *both Z and N odd*, that possess a resultant spin in the ground state, which is:

(a) $I = 1/2, 3/2, 5/2, \ldots$ for odd-A nuclei

(b) $I = 1, 2, 3, \ldots$ for odd-Z, odd-N nuclei

On what is known as the *single particle* model of the nucleus (to be considered later in Sec. 3.2.2), the paired protons and paired neutrons form the *core* of the nucleus with zero resultant spin. It is the single odd proton or neutron, of the outermost shell, which imparts its spin to the entire nucleus. We shall revert to this topic in Sec. 2.8.

2.6   The Magnetic Total Nuclear Angular Momentum Quantum Number

As in the case of the magnetic quantum numbers m_l, m_s and m_j of individual nucleons, we have the *magnetic total angular momentum quantum number m_I* for the nucleus as a whole. This stands for the resolved component of I in any specified direction, say in the direction of the applied magnetic field. As in the case of individual nucleon magnetic quantum numbers, the values of m_I for the nucleus can take any one of $2I + 1$ positive or negative values including zero, lying between $I, (I-1), \ldots 1, 0, -1, \ldots -(I-1)$ and $-I$.

---

*All the even-A nuclei, (both the even-Z, even-N and the odd-Z, odd-N types), in the *excited* state possess integral spins, 1, 2, 3, ...

**As pointed out earlier, the use of the term spin is not wholly correct when applied to the *total* (orbital + spin) angular momentum. However, it is widely used in this sense, on account of its brevity, perhaps.

2.7   The Magnetic Properties of the Nucleus

When a charged particle moves in a closed path it generates a magnetic field externally which is equivalent to the presence of a magnetic dipole at the centre of the loop. Hence, electrons, protons and neutrons,* by virtue of their charge and orbital and spin motions, behave as tiny magnets with the dipoles situated at the centre of their motion. We shall now proceed to calculate the magnetic dipole moment of a charged particle due to its orbital motion.

2.7.1   THE MAGNETIC DIPOLE MOMENT OF A CHARGED PARTICLE

The magnetic dipole moment** μ due to a charge e moving in a circular path of radius r, with an angular velocity of ω radians per second is given by

$$\mu = \pi r^2 i \tag{2.16}$$

where i is the resulting current given by charge times the frequency of its rotation

$$i = e\, \omega/2\pi$$

Hence,

$$\mu = \frac{e\, \omega\, r^2}{2} \text{ esu} \tag{2.17}$$

To convert the charge from electrostatic to electromagnetic units, we divide Eq. 2.17 by the velocity of light c.

Thus,
$$\mu = \frac{e\omega r^2}{2c} \text{ cgs.}$$

Next, to eliminate ω and r^2, we multiply by p which is the orbital angular momentum and divide by its value $p = mvr = m\omega r^2$.

Thus
$$\mu = \frac{ep}{2mc}$$

Since the orbital angular motion is quantized, p can have only the values $p = l\hbar$, i.e. the integral multiples of $\hbar$, including zero. Thus, we arrive finally at

$$\mu = \frac{l\hbar e}{2mc} \tag{2.18}$$

Equation 2.18 is a general expression in cgs units for the magnetic moment of any charged particle of charge e (in esu), mass m and angular momentum quantum number l. We now pass on to consider the magnetic moments of specific particles, the electrons, protons, neutrons and nuclei as a whole, and the units employed to express the same.

---

*The behaviour of the neutron, as if it had a negative charge in its periphery, leading to its magnetic moment as observed, is considered in Sec. 2.7.8.
**Referred to, in the case of nuclei, simply as nuclear magnetic moment, as *only* the dipole moment is involved.

2.7.2   THE BOHR AND THE NUCLEAR MAGNETONS

(a) The Bohr Magneton

Applied to the orbital motion of an electron of angular momentum quantum number $l = 1$, Eq. 2.18 reduces to the unit magnetic moment referred to as the *Bohr magneton*, a constant.

(i) *in cgs units*   (ii) *in SI units*

$$\mu_B = \frac{\hbar e}{2m_e c} \qquad\qquad \mu_B = \frac{\hbar e}{2m_e}* \qquad (2.19)$$

The values of the constants being

$\hbar = 1.054\ 60 \times 10^{-27}$ erg-s $\hbar = 1.054\ 60 \times 10^{-34}$ J-s

$e = 4.803\ 25 \times 10^{-10}$ esu $e = 1.602\ 19 \times 10^{-19}$ C

$m_e = 9.109\ 56 \times 10^{-28}$ g $m_e = 9.109\ 56 \times 10^{-31}$ kg

$c = 2.997\ 93 \times 10^{10}$ cm s^{-1}

The value of the Bohr magneton comes out to be

$\mu_B = 9.274\ 1 \times 10^{-21}$ erg/gauss

$\mu_B = 9.274\ 1 \times 10^{-24}$ J T^{-1} **
$= 9.274\ 1 \times 10^{-24}$ A m^2 ***

(b) The Nuclear Magneton

Applied to the motion of a proton or a neutron of unit angular momentum, Eq. 2.18 reduces to unit nuclear magnetic moment, referred to as the *nuclear magneton*, given by

(i) *in cgs units*   (ii) *in SI units*

$$\mu_N = \frac{\hbar e}{2m_p c} \qquad\qquad \mu_N = \frac{\hbar e}{2m_p}* \qquad (2.20)$$

The value of the constants are the same as in the Bohr magneton, except for the replacement of m_e by the mass of the proton:

$m_p = 1.672\ 61 \times 10^{-24}$ g $m_p = 1.672\ 61 \times 10^{-27}$ kg

The value of the nuclear magneton comes out to be

$\mu_N = 5.050\ 95 \times 10^{-24}$ ergs/gauss

$\mu_N = 5.050\ 95 \times 10^{-27}$ J T^{-1} **
$= 5.050\ 95 \times 10^{-27}$ A m^2 ***

Since the mass of a proton is 1836 times that of an electron, the nuclear magneton bears to the Bohr magneton the inverse ratio, *viz.* $\mu_N/\mu_B = 1/1836$.

*Note that c is missing from the denominator in the formulae for the magnetons in SI units, as in converting the charge from the esu to SI units the division by c had already taken place.

**1 tesla (T) $= 10^4$ gauss (G)

***The SI unit for the magnetic dipole moment directly reveals its dimensions, *viz.* area times current (*vide* Eq. 2.16).

2.7.3 THE NET MAGNETIC MOMENTS OF NUCLEI

Due to the pairing of nucleons, protons with protons and neutrons with neutrons, the individual magnetic moments in a pair cancel out, as do their spins. *Hence, all stable nuclides of the even-Z, even-N type have a zero magnetic moment.* It is then only (a) the *odd-A nuclei* (odd-Z, even-N, or *vice-versa*), and (b) such of the *even-A nuclei* (odd-Z, odd-N) which display a non-zero magnetic moment. The paired protons and the paired neutrons form the *core of the nucleus* with zero resultant spin and magnetic moment. It is the single odd proton or neutron which imparts its spin and magnetic moment to the entire nucleus. We shall revert to this topic under Sec. 2.8.

2.7.4 THE NUCLEAR g FACTOR

While the odd-*A* nuclei possess a nuclear spin *I* equal to that of the unpaired nucleon, their magnetic moments, however deviate from the value expected from the general expression (Eq. 2.18) *viz.*

$$\mu = \frac{\hbar e}{2m_p} I \tag{2.18}$$

Instead, the expression on the right side needs to be multiplied by g, *the nuclear factor*, whose value varies from nucleus to nucleus. Thus,

$$\mu = g \frac{\hbar e}{2m_p} I$$
$$= gI\mu_N \tag{2.21}$$

where μ_N is the nuclear magneton.

The origin of this deviation is not well understood. In the case of the nuclei it probably arises from the meson field and the charge exchange force which modifies the instant charge. Earlier the *g* factor was referred to as the *gyromagnetic ratio*. The latter term is now reserved for the ratio $\mu/\hbar I$. In fact, even the elementary particles as the electron, the proton and the neutron have non-unity *g* factors, for their *spin* components.

2.7.5 THE MAGNETIC MOMENT OF THE ELECTRON

The magnetic moment of an electron due to its *orbital* motion with $l = 1$, has the expected value of one Bohr magneton, implying $g_{orb} = 1$. In the case of the electron, its orbital angular momentum is quantized in terms of the principal quantum number $n = 1, 2, 3, \ldots$.

$$\mu_{e(orb)} = \frac{\hbar e}{2m_e} = -\mu_B{}^* \tag{2.19}$$

However, the magnetic moment of the electron due to its *spin* motion is more complicated, the observed value being 1.001 16 μ_B. Since the spin of the electron is 1/2, it implies that the $g_{spin} = 2.002\ 32$.

*Since the electron charge is $-1e$.

Hence,

$$\mu_{e(spin)} = -2.002\ 32 \times \tfrac{1}{2}\ \mu_B$$
$$= -1.001\ 16\ \mu_B \qquad (2.22)$$

2.7.6 The Magnetic Moment of the Proton

The spin magnetic moment of the proton $\mu_{p(spin)}$ is a very important quantity as all the magnetic moments of nuclei are referred to it. Extensively repeated investigations by numerous workers using different techniques place the value at

$$\mu_{p(spin)} = 2.792\ 68\ \mu_N \qquad [(2.23a)$$

The value commonly employed is $2.793\ \mu_N$. Since the maximum observable spin of the proton is 1/2, the corresponding g factor for proton spin magnetic moment is

$$g_{p(s)} = 5.586 \qquad (2.23b)$$

The value for the g factor for proton for orbital motion magnetic moment is however

$$g_{p(l)} = 1 \qquad (2.23c)$$

2.7.7 The Magnetic Moment of a Neutron

At first sight one would expect the neutron should have zero magnetic moment, the spinning particle being uncharged. However, experimentally, the neutron shows a large magnetic moment, the actual value being

$$\mu_{n(spin)} = -1.913\ 5\ \mu_N \qquad (2.24)$$

The corresponding $g_{(s)}$ factor is $-3.827\ 0$, the spin being 1/2: however, the orbital $g_{(l)} = 0$ for a neutron. The zero value of $g_{(l)}$ for a neutron implies that in its orbital motion, unlike in spinning, the neutron behaves as a simple uncharged particle. The negative sign for the neutron magnetic moment indicates the magnetic field is in a direction opposite to that of its spin angular momentum unlike in the case of a proton where the two are in the same direction (see Fig. 2.5)[9].

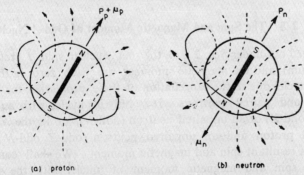

(a) proton   (b) neutron

Fig. 2.5 The orientation of spin momentum (p) and magnetic moment (μ) for
(a) Proton: p and μ are parallel,
(b) Neutron: p and μ are antiparallel.

34

ESSENTIALS OF NUCLEAR CHEMISTRY

The existence of a magnetic moment for the neutron suggests a complex structure for the particle. The neutron is believed to be made up of equal amounts of positive and negative charges but so distributed that the negative charge is on the average farther from the axis of spinning, which gives it a large negative magnetic moment. The large $g_{(s)}$ factors for the proton (5.586) and for the neutron (-3.827) lend support to a complex structure of charge distribution in these nucleons with meson clouds around them as envisaged in the Heisenberg exchange model (Sec. 1.5.5). Figure 2.6 shows the radial distribution of total charge in a proton and a neutron. It may be seen from the figure that

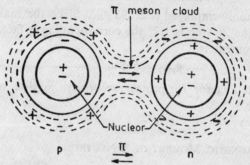

Fig. 2.6 Composite structure of nucleons showing the radial distribution of charges and the π meson cloud (from *Introduction to Atomic and Nuclear Physics* by H.E. White, Van Nostrand Rhinehold Co., 1964, with author's permission).

the proton and neutron differ only in the middle and the outermost regions of the nucleus, approximately between $0.25\,F$ and $1.5\,F$ from the centre. The proton is charged positively and the neutron negatively in the outermost diffuse region. The innermost cores of all the nucleons are alike. The electron, on the other hand, is considered a simple elementary particle with the centres of charge and mass coinciding, as evidenced by small g factors $g_{orb} = 1$ and $g_{spin} = 2.0032$.

2.8 The Spin and Magnetic Moment of Odd A Nuclei

As pointed out under Sec. 2.7.3, the net nuclear spin I (total angular momentum) and the magnetic moment are each zero in the even-Z, even-N nuclei due to the cancellation of these properties for the paired protons and paired neutrons. It is only in nuclei with an unpaired proton (odd-Z) or an unpaired neutron (odd-N), or in the case of an unpaired proton and an unpaired neutron (odd-Z, odd-N type) that there is a resultant spin and magnetic moment. We shall consider here how the spin and magnetic moment of nuclei with the single odd nucleon, of which over 100 are stable, are determined. The rules relating to the spin of nuclei with two odd nucleons being more complicated will be deferred for the present.

2.8.1 THE SPIN I

The spin I of the odd-A nuclide is same as the j $(= l \pm s)$ of the odd unpaired nucleon of the outermost level, as the level of this nucleon is reached in building progressively the nuclide in accordance with certain rules which will be considered while discussing the shell model of the nucleus (see Sec. 3.2.5 and Table 2.4).

2.8.2 THE MAGNETIC MOMENT μ_I

The general expression for the total magnetic moment (*orbit + spin*) of a nucleus with spin I is

$$\mu_I = (g_l \, l_z + g_s \, s_z) \, \mu_N \qquad (2.25)$$

where the gs are respective nuclear factors and l_z and s_z are the resolved components of the orbital and spin momentum quantum numbers along a given, say, the z direction. From this, Schmidt[1,17] derived the expressions for the expected value of the nuclear magnetic moment for the two cases where the odd particle is (a) a proton, and, (b) a neutron, and each again for two types where (i) $j = l + s$ and (ii) $j = l - s$. The *Schmidt limits*, as they are known, for the nuclear magnetic moments of the odd A-nuclides, are given in Table 2.3.

TABLE 2.3: Schmidt limits of nuclear magnetic moments of odd-A nuclides in units of μ_N

Odd nucleon	$I = l + s$	$I = l - s$
Proton	$I + 2.293$	$I - 2.293 \left(\dfrac{I}{I+1} \right)$
Neutron	-1.913	$1.913 \left(\dfrac{I}{I+1} \right)$

Table 2.4 lists values of spin, magnetic moments and electric quadrupole moments (described below) of some of the odd-A nuclides.

2.8.3 THE SPINS OF ODD-Z, ODD-N NUCLEI: THE NORDHEIM RULES

It was pointed out earlier that all except four of the odd-Z, odd-N nuclides are radioactive (Sec. 1.5.1). These nuclides have two unpaired nucleons, a proton and a neutron. The prediction of the spin and parity of such nuclei is less certain. However, the *Nordheim rules*[18] give in most cases the correct values of spin and parity. The rules are illustrated below.

Let the unpaired proton and neutron have l_1 and l_2 as their orbital angular momenta, and j_1 and j_2 as their total angular momenta (see Sec. 3.2.5). The net angular momentum of the nucleus (or spin) is given by

(a) $I = |j_1 - j_2|$ if the sum $(l_1 + l_2 + j_1 + j_2)$ is even, and

(b) $I = (j_1 + j_2)$ if the sum $(l_1 + l_2 + j_1 + j_2)$ is odd.

The rule regarding the parity of the nucleus is:

(a)   The parity is even if l_1 and l_2 are *both* even or *both* odd, and

(b)   The parity is odd if l_1 is even and l_2 is odd, or *vice-versa*.

As an example, let us consider the odd-Z, odd-N nucleus $_{33}^{76}As_{43}$. The unpaired nucleons are the 33rd proton and 43rd neutron, whose l and j values, as may be obtained from the spin-orbit coupling shell model (Sec. 3.2.5, Fig. 3.7) are $f_{5/2}$ and $g_{9/2}$. The sum of $(l_1 + l_2 + j_1 + j_2)$ being 14, is an even number, the spin of the nucleus is given by the difference $j_2 - j_1$, viz. 2. The parity is odd, since of the l_1 and l_2, one is odd and the other is even.

2.9   Nuclear Magnetic Resonance

If a nucleus with spin I is placed in an external magnetic field, the magnetic moment vector precesses in the direction of the applied field, the component of the magnetic moment in this direction being

$$\mu = m_I \, g \, \mu_N \qquad (2.21)$$

where $m_I = I, I-1, I-2, \ldots 0, \ldots, -(I-2), -(I-1). -I$ as mentioned earlier, and g is the nuclear factor. The potential energy of the nucleus due to the applied magnetic field of strength H is given by

$$E = -\mu H = -m_I \, g \, \mu_N \, H \qquad (2.26)$$

The spacing between two adjacent permitted energy levels is

$$\Delta m_I = \pm 1 \qquad (2.27)$$

Hence the energy of transition is

$$\Delta E = E_2 - E_1$$
$$= -[m_{I_2} - m_{I_1}] \, g \, \mu_N H$$
$$= \mp \, g \, \mu_N \, H* \qquad (2.28)$$

Let us consider hydrogen ^1H (protons) of spin 1/2 and nuclear magnetic moment 2.793 μ_N placed in a magnetic field of one tesla ($= 10^4$ gauss). The energy of transition for hydrogen (^1H) is given by Eq. 2.28.

$$\Delta E_{(H)} = 5.585 \, 4 \times 5.050 \, 9 \times 10^{-27} \times 1 \text{ joules}$$

$$= 28.211 \, 6 \times 10^{-27} \text{ J}$$

---

*The sign $\mp$ depends on whether energy is absorbed for transition from a lower to higher energy state or energy is released for the reverse transition.

where 5.585 4 is the g factor of ^{1}H given by $\mu/I\mu_N$. This energy ΔE is absorbed (or emitted) as radiation of frequency ν given by the general quantum theory

$$\Delta E = h\nu \tag{2.29}$$

Where h is Planck's constant. In other words, the frequency of nuclear magnetic resonance (NMR) for hydrogen atoms (^{1}H) in a field of one tesla is

$$\nu = \frac{\Delta E}{h} = \frac{28.118\ 5 \times 10^{-27}\ \text{J}}{6.626\ 2 \times 10^{-34}\ \text{Js}}$$
$$= 42.576\ \text{MHz}.$$

In other words, substances containing hydrogen atoms (^{1}H) in their molecules, when placed in an external magnetic field of one tesla, emit or absorb a radiation signal of frequency 42.576 MHz. This is referred to as the *NMR spectrum* for hydrogen. A similar calculation for ^{19}F with a spin 1/2 and nuclear magnetic moment 2.628 μ_N, and hence $g = 5.256$ shows, the NMR frequency in the same field of one tesla is 40.065 MHz.

It may be noted that these NMR frequencies are in the convenient microwave region for fields of the order of a tesla. The resonance condition (Eq. 2.28) is approached either by holding the magnetic field H constant and varying ν by an external radiofrequency supply, or by varying H for a fixed ν. All elements with non-zero nuclear spins in the ground state, display NMR spectra and this technique constitutes a powerful tool in the study of molecular structure. It has been most widely used in determining the different kinds of hydrogen atoms present in a molecule as OH, CH_2, CH_3 .., their relative numbers and the nature of electronic environment. Another additional advantage is that it is a non-destructive mode of analysis as the sample remains unchanged after the NMR spectrum has been recorded.

2.10 The Electric Quadrupole Moment of Nuclides

For an understanding of the structure of the nucleus, it is important to know how the protons in it are spatially distributed and the potential such an arrangement gives rise to at a given point outside the nucleus.

2.10.1 THE ELECTRIC MULTIPOLES

It is convenient to begin this study with a consideration of the potential due to a single point charge e situated at a distance r from the centre of the nucleus and with x, y, and z as its coordinates whose origin is also at the centre of the nucleus (Fig. 2.7) According to the laws of electrostatics, the potential ϕ at a point distance d from the centre of the nucleus is given by the sum of potentials due to *electric multipoles*:

$$\phi = \frac{e}{d'} = \frac{e}{d} + \frac{er}{d^2} \cos\theta + \frac{er^2}{d^3} \left(\tfrac{3}{2}\cos^2\theta - \tfrac{1}{2}\right) + ...^* \tag{2.30}$$

---

*d' is the distance of the point from the point charge (see Fig. 2.7).

where $\cos \theta = z/r$. The different terms constitute the electric multipoles as follows:

(i) The first term is the potential due to the *electric monopole, i.e.* just the total charge e. The external potential due to the monopole (or pole order 2^0) varies inversely as d.

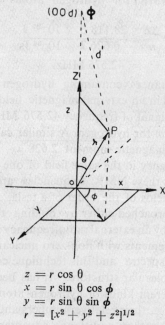

$$z = r \cos \theta$$
$$x = r \sin \theta \cos \phi$$
$$y = r \sin \theta \sin \phi$$
$$r = [x^2 + y^2 + z^2]^{1/2}$$

Fig. 2.7   The cartesian and polar
coordinates.

(ii) The second term is the potential due to the *electric dipole, i.e. er* (the product of charge and length). The external potential due to the dipole (or pole order 2^1) varies inversely as d^2.

(iii) The third term is the potential due to the *electric quadrupole, i.e. er²* (the product of charge and area). The external potential due to the electric quadrupole (or pole order 2^2) varies inversely as d^3.

(iv) The fourth and subsequent terms, not included in Eq. 2.30 give *electric octupole* (or pole order 2^3), the electric 16 pole (or pole order 2^4), *etc.* These are negligible as they depend inversely on higher powers ($\geqslant 4$) of d.

Thus, the presence of a single proton (charge e) displaced from the centre of the nucleus ($r \neq 0$) is equivalent to the presence of electric multipoles all of which generate an overall potential outside the nucleus as per Eq. 2.30. Finally, the total potential due to the Z protons in the nucleus is to be considered in relation to their spatial distribution inside the nucleus with both positive and negative values of r and $\cos \theta$. We can thus expect some mutual cancellations as clarified below.

It can be further shown that if the nucleus has an axis of symmetry in any direction and a plane of symmetry perpendicular to it, and if the centres of mass and charge coincide, all odd multipoles as 2^1 (dipole), 2^3 (octupole), 2^5 (32 pole) and so on must be zero. Thus, *only the monopole* (2^0) *and quadrupole* (2^2) *determine the total electric potential outside the nucleus.*

2.10.2 THE ELECTRIC QUADRUPOLE MOMENT

The coefficient of $1/d^3$ in Eq. 2.30 is the *electric quadrupole moment*

$$Q = er^2 \, (3/2 \cos^2 \theta - 1/2) \tag{2.31}$$

We shall now consider the quadrupole moments due to a single proton placed at different limiting positions in the nucleus (Fig. 2.8).[1]

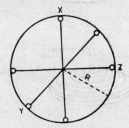

Fig. 2.8 The electric quadrupole moment due to a single proton placed at different limiting positions along the periphery of the nucleus.

(i) The single proton is along the axis (Z) of angular momentum at $z = r = R$; $x = y = 0$. From Eq. 2.31 it follows, remembering $\cos \theta = z/r$,

$$Q_{(z=R)} = eR^2 \tag{2.32}$$

(ii) The single proton is along the X axis, *i.e.* $x = r = R$ and $y = z = 0$

$$Q_{(x=R)} = -1/2 \, eR^2 \tag{2.33a}$$

(iii) Similarly for the proton along the Y axis, *i.e.* $y = r = R$ and $x = z = 0$,

$$Q_{(y=R)} = -1/2 \, eR^2 \tag{2.33b}$$

We thus see that the net quadrupole moment due to six protons placed spherically symmetrically, two at $\pm z$, two at $\pm x$ and two at $\pm y$ $(x = y = z = R)$ is zero. It is clear from Eq. 2.32, the quadrupole moment due to the 2 protons along the body (Z) axis is $+ 2 \, eR^2$ while the moment due to the other 4 protons in the plane perpendicular to the Z axis is $- 2 \, eR^2$, resulting in zero net quadrupole moment due to a symmetric disposition of the protons around the centre of the nucleus.

If now *an extra* proton were to be present *asymmetrically* in the nucleus it contributes to the net quadrupole moment making it $\lessgtr 0$. The sign corresponds to the type of spheroidal deviation. The resulting quadrupole moment has a positive sign, if the asymmetric distribution of protons is such that there is an elongation along the body (Z) axis and a *prolate spheroid* (egg shaped) results (Fig. 2.9a). On the other hand if the asymmetric distribution of protons is such that a flattening of the X or Y axis occurs an *oblate* or discus-like spheroid results (Fig. 2.9b). The resulting quadrupole moment in the latter case is negative. Thus the magnitude and sign of the quadrupole moment indicate the shape of the atomic nucleus, a zero value indicating a spherical shape while a positive value shows the nucleus is prolate and a negative value an oblate deviation from sphericality.

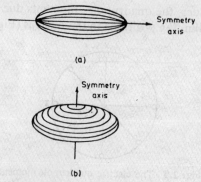

Fig. 2.9   Distortion of the shape of nucleus due to
           asymmetric distribution of protons.
           (a)   Prolate spheroid: $Q > 0$
           (b)   Oblate spheroid : $Q < 0$

2.10.3   THE UNITS OF QUADRUPOLE MOMENT

From the definition of the electric quadrupole moment (Eq. 2.31), Q has the dimensions of charge *times* area. However, it is customary to divide by the proton charge and express the *quadrupole moment in units of area only*. This convention will be followed in the rest of the text. The Q values of non-spherical nuclei vary from $\pm 10^{-28}$ to $\pm 10^{-30}$ m^2, where 10^{-28} m^2 = 1 barn which is roughly of the magnitude of the cross-sectional area of the nuclei.

2.10.4   QUADRUPOLE MOMENT AND NUCLEAR ELLIPTICITY

Let a nucleus with a finite quadrupole moment be represented by an ellipsoid with the semi-axis b parallel to the symmetry axis (Z) and the semi-axis a perpendicular to it (Fig. 2.10).

If the total charge Ze be assumed to be distributed uniformly over this volume, the quadrupole moment in the Z direction Q', or by convention, $Q\left(= \dfrac{Q'}{e}\right)$ is given by

$$Q = (2/5)\, Z\, (b^2 - a^2) \tag{2.34}$$

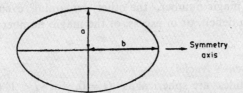

Fig. 2.10 Quadrupole moment (Q) and ellipticity (ϵ)
$$\epsilon = 2(b - a)/(b + a)$$
$$Q = 4/5\epsilon ZR^2$$
$$R = \text{nuclear radius}$$

Defining the mean radius

$$R = \frac{b + a}{2} \qquad (2.35)$$

and ellipticity

$$\epsilon = \frac{b - a}{R} = 2\frac{b - a}{b + a} \qquad (2.36)$$

The quadrupole moment, (Eq. 2.34) would now become

$$Q = 4/5 \, \epsilon ZR^2 \qquad (2.37)$$

Most nuclei have small ellipticities, the largest value being in the case ^{176}Lu with $\epsilon = + 0.174$ and $Q = 7b$, while ^{233}Pa has the lowest quadrupole moment of $-3b$ and an ellipticity of -0.06. Table 2.4 gives Q and ϵ values for typical nuclei.

2.10.5 RELATION BETWEEN NUCLEAR SPIN (I) AND QUADRUPOLE MOMENT (Q)

It was pointed out earlier (Sec. 2.7.3) that even-Z, even-N nuclei have in the ground state a zero spin and zero magnetic moment due to the cancellation of angular moment of paired nucleons and that it is only the presence of a single unpaired proton or/and unpaired neutron which imparts to the nucleus its spin and magnetic moment. It can be shown further that the quadrupole moment would be zero for nuclei with $I = 0$ (i.e., all even-Z, even-N nuclei), or indetectably small for nuclei with $I = 1/2$ (i.e. a large number of odd A-nuclei). In other words, for the nuclear quadrupole moment to be measurable, $I \geqslant 1$. This means that all nuclei with $I = 0$ or $I = 1/2$ are very nearly spherical in shape.

Besides the mutual cancellation of spin and magnetic moments between the paired protons and the paired neutrons, there is additional stability and symmetry in shape if both Z and N happen to be even numbers and one of them Z or N, (or both), happen to be equal to one of the numbers, 2, 8, 20, 50, 82, 126, which are also referred to as the *magic numbers*. On the *shell model of the nucleus* (see Sec. 3.5.1), if the number of protons Z in a nucleus happens to equal one of these magic numbers, they form a completely *closed shell*, the same also being true for the neutrons. The effects on quadrupole moment of Z (or N) being

(a) equal to a magic number, the other remaining even, and (b) of Z (or N) being in deficit, or in excess, of the magic number are described below.

(i) Even-Z, Even-N Nuclei

All such nuclides are spherical as $Q = 0$, for $I < 1$ (being actually zero).

(ii) Even-N, Odd-Z Nuclei

(a) $Z =$ magic number $- 1$: In those nuclei in which the number of protons is one less than a magic number, the proton shell is incomplete or has a hole in it. Such nuclei are elongated into a prolate (egg-like) ellipsoidal shape, as $Q > 0$. As an example may be cited $^{115}_{49}$In, which has one proton less than the nearest magic number 50 and has a positive quadrupole moment $(Q = + 1.16 \text{ b})$ and an ellipticity of $+ 0.056$.

(b) $Z =$ magic number $+ 1$: Nuclei in which the number of protons is one more than the magic number, i.e. there is an extra proton outside a completed shell, have $Q < 0$ and are of flattened oblate (discus-like) ellipsoidal shape. The quadrupole moment expected for such a nucleus with a single unpaired proton of total spin j and lying outside a closed shell is

$$Q_j = - \frac{2j - 1}{2(j + 1)} \frac{3}{5} \bar{r^2} \qquad (2.37 \text{ a})$$

where $\bar{r^2}$ is the mean of r^2 for the orbit*,[10] which is somewhat less than R^2. If this be the only unpaired nucleon, the nuclear spin I would be same as j. The experimentally observed values are, however, much higher than the values given by Eq. 2.37(a). As an example we have $^{123}_{51}$Sb with $Q = - 1.2$ b and an ellipticity of $- 0.053$. The quadrupole moment calculated by eq. 2.37(a) is $- 0.194$ b.

Thus the sign of Q changes from positive $(Z =$ magic no. $- 1)$, through zero $(Z =$ magic no.$)$ to negative $(Z =$ magic no. $+ 1)$. The maximum Q value $(+$ or $-)$ is for Z about half-way between two adjacent magic numbers. The variation of shapes of nuclei around the proton magic number of 50 is shown in Fig. 2.11.

(iii) Even-Z, Odd-N Nuclei

The situation is similar to (ii); here the value of Q is determined by

*This value is given by

$$\bar{r^2} = \frac{\displaystyle\int_0^\infty r^2 \, 4\pi r^2 \, \rho(r) \, dr}{\displaystyle\int_0^\infty 4\pi r^2 \, \rho(r) \, dr}$$

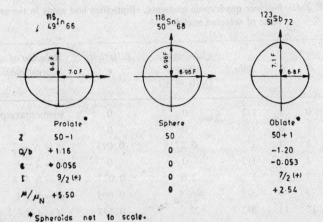

Fig. 2.11 Variation of shapes of nuclei around the proton magic number of 50.

the *total* number of protons.   Nuclei with one neutron less than needed to complete a shell have $Q > 0$ and nuclei with one neutron in excess of a completed shell have $Q < 0$.   The corresponding examples are $^{137}Ba_{81}$ and $^{143}Nd_{83}$, having $+ 0.28$ and $- 0.48$ b respectively as their quadrupole moments.

(iv) Odd-Z, Odd-N Nuclei

All the nuclides of this type are radioactive except the lightest four (^2H, ^6Li, ^{10}B, and ^{14}N) as pointed out earlier. The quadrupole moments of nuclides of this category do not follow simple rules and hence they are not considered here.

Figure 2.12 shows the variation of the quadrupole moment (Q/ZR^2) as a function of the number of odd nucleons.[11]

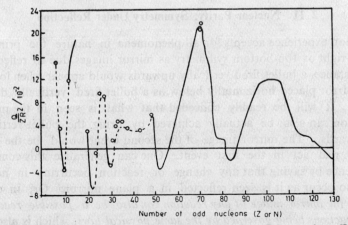

Fig. 2.12 Quadrupole moment (Q/ZR^2) as a function of the number of odd nucleons (C.H. Townes, H.M. Foley and W. Low[11]).

TABLE 2.4:   Nuclear quadrupole moments, ellipticities and spins in the ground
state of selected nuclides[1,7,8]

Nuclide	Z	N	Spin	Quadrupole moment $Q/10^{-30}$ m^2	Ellipticity ε	Relation of nucleus to nearest magic number
^1n	0	1	1/2	0	0	Elementary particle
^{1}H	1	0	1/2	0	0	,, ,, ,,
^{2}H	1	1	1	0.273	0.095	$Z = N = 2 - 1$
^{3}H	1	2	1/2	0	0	$Z = 2 - 1$
^{14}N	7	7	1	2.0	0.027	$Z = N = 8 - 1$
^{17}O	8	9	5/2	−0.5	−0.005	$N = 8 + 1$
^{25}Mg	12	13	5/2	22	0.137	$N = 14^* - 1$
^{27}Al	13	14	5/2	15.6	0.074	$Z = 14 - 1$
^{75}As	33	42	3/2	30	0.03	Z and N are very far from 20 and 50
^{87}Sr	38	49	9/2	30	0.026	$N = 50 - 1$
^{115}In	49	66	9/2	116	0.056	$Z = 50 - 1$
^{123}Sb	51	72	7/2	−120	−0.053	$Z = 50 + 1$
^{176}Lu	71	105	7	700**	0.174**	Z and N are very far from 82 and 126
^{209}Bi	83	126	9/2	−40	− 0.008	$Z = 82 + 1$
^{233}Pa	91	142	3/2	−300**	−0.06**	Z and N are very far from 82 and 126

*14 is considered a semi-magic number.

**^{176}Lu has the highest positive quadrupole moment and maximum ellipticity, while
^{233}Pa appears to have the maximum negative quadrupole moment.
(Partly from P.F.A. Klinkenberg[7] and *Nuclear Data*, Academic Press, New York,
1969, with permission.)

2.11   Nuclear Parity: Symmetry Under Reflection

Common experience accepts for all phenomena in nature the principle
of left-right or top-bottom symmetry as mirror images due to reflection.
For instance, a bullet fired vertically upwards would appear when looked
in a mirror placed horizontally below as a bullet fired vertically downwards. It will be readily conceded that what is seen in the mirror
reflection can also be actually achieved by firing the bullet vertically
downwards. The mirror image of the second event would be the same
as the real act in the first event. One can generalize this common
experience by saying that any change or reaction occurring in nature
can also occur as it is seen reflected in a plane mirror. Or, in other
words, *the mirror image of any reaction can also be a possible reaction,
both reactions being governed by the same physical laws,* which is also the
same as saying that the laws of nature are invariant under reflection.

2.11.1 THE WAVE FUNCTION AND ITS SIGN

In quantum-mechanics, the *wave function* ψ is involved in determining the energy state of a particle in terms of its space coordinates (x, y, z) about a given origin, by the Schrödinger equation

$$H \psi = E \psi \qquad (2.38)$$

where H is the Hamiltonian energy operator given by

$$H = - \frac{\hbar^2}{2m} \left[\frac{\partial^2}{\partial x^2} + \frac{\partial^2}{\partial y^2} + \frac{\partial^2}{\partial z^2} \right] + U$$

Let us now suppose that the signs of all the coordinates are simultaneously inverted with respect to the origin, *i.e.* $+x$, $+y$ and $+z$ are changed to $-x$, $-y$ and $-z$, as would happen with the image of the original particle when reflected by a set of three plane mirrors mutually at right angles. It is further assumed that the potential field is symmetrical, *i.e.* $V_{(x)} = V_{(-x)}$, *etc.* Such an inversion of the space coordinates will have either one of the following two possible effects on the wave function ψ describing the energy of the particle in the new location.

Case I: The wave function remains unaltered, *i.e.*

$$\psi_{(-x, -y, -z)} = \psi_{(x, y, z)} \qquad (2.39a)$$

Case II: The sign of the wave function also has to be reversed to describe the energy of the particle in the new situation, *i.e.*

$$\psi_{(-x, -y, -z)} = -\psi_{(x, y, z)} \qquad (2.39b)$$

We can combine the two equations in the form

$$\psi_{(-x, -y, -z)} = P \psi_{(x, y, z)} \qquad (2.40)$$

where $P = \pm 1$.

The *probability* of finding the particle in the element of space volume $dx.dy.dz$ is, however, unaffected by the sign of ψ, as this probability is given by $|\psi|^2$.

2.11.2 PARITY: A QUANTUM NUMBER

The quantity P in Eq. 2.40 is yet another *quantum number* known as *parity*, which governs the sign of the wave function when the signs of the space coordinates are inverted. Parity can have only one of the two values $P = \pm 1$. A particle or a system is said to have (i) *even (or +) parity* if Eq. 2.39a holds good for the wave function following an inversion of the signs of the coordinates, or (ii) *odd (or —) parity* if Eq. 2.39 b holds good. Unlike other quantum numbers, parity has no relation to any physical quantity. Parity is related only to the symmetry properties of the wave function.

2.11.3 PARITY AND ORBITAL ANGULAR MOMENTUM

All the *elementary particles*, as electrons, protons, neutrons and neutrinos are ascribed an *intrinsic even parity*. The π *mesons*, however, exhibit *odd intrinsic parity*. The parity of an odd-A nucleus is determined by the *orbital motion of the unpaired nucleon*. It is given by

$$P = (-1)^l \qquad (2.41)$$

where l is the orbital angular momentum of the single unpaired proton or neutron. Hence, nuclides for which l is even $(s, d, g, \ldots)$ will have *even* (*or* $+$) *parity*, while nuclides for which l is odd $(p, f, h, \ldots)$ will have *odd* (*or* $-$) *parity*. Of course, nuclides having no unpaired proton or neutron (even-Z, even-N type) have even (or $+$) parity. The case of odd-Z, add-N nuclides, as always, is complicated. If l_1 and l_2 be the orbital angular momenta of the two unpaired nucleons (proton and neutron), the parity of such a nucleus is (i) *even* (or $+$) if *both* l_1 and l_2 are even, or both are odd (*i.e.* $l_1 + l_2$ is even); (ii) the parity is *odd* (or $-$) if one of them l_1 or l_2 is even and the other is odd, (*i e.* $l_1 + l_2$ is odd).

It is customary to represent the nuclear spin (I) and parity (P) together. As mentioned earlier, I and P are determined by the j and l values of the odd nucleon respectively. Thus, in the nuclide $^{17}_{8}O$, the odd nucleon is the ninth neutron which on the shell model (see Sec. 3.2.2) occupies the level $1d\ 5/2$, *i.e.* its l value $= d$ (*i.e.* 2) and $j = 5/2$. Hence its spin and parity are shown as $5/2$ ($+$). Similarly, the 27th odd nucleon in $^{59}_{27}Co$ is a proton whose level is $1f\ 7/2$. Hence, its spin and parity are $7/2$ ($-$).

2.11.4 PARITY AND ITS CONSERVATION

In the same way as the energy and momentum of an *isolated system, its parity also remains conserved*. Being a constant of its motion, the parity of an isolated system cannot be altered as long as no interaction with the outside occurs in the form of emission or absorption of a photon or a particle. As long as the system remains isolated no internal changes in it can change its parity. As for the other quantum numbers, there are *selection rules involving change in parity* in a transition following the emission or absorption of a photon or a particle (see Sec. 4 8). Since parity can have either of only two values $+1$ or -1, *conservation of parity means the products of parities of reactants must equal the product of parities of the resultants*. If the initial parity product is even ($+$ 1), the final parity product also must be even ($+$ 1), or both the initial and final parities may be odd ($-$ 1).

As expected, parity is found to be conserved in all *strong interactions* involving the emission of (i) photons and (ii) nucleons. There is another type of interaction considered as *weak*, involving electrons, neutrinos and mesons, where there is evidence of a breakdown of the parity conservation. It was Lee and Yang[12] who first observed paradoxical results in reactions involving τ and θ mesons suggesting non-conservation of parity. To verify this, Lee and Yang[12]* Wu[13], and Wu, Ambler, Hayward, Hoppes and Hudson[14] studied the β⁻ decay of ^{60}Co in a strong magnetic field at the low temperature of 0.1 K. It was found that under these conditions the betas were emitted anisotropically clearly showing an absence of symmetry and hence a non-conservation of parity.

This is illustrated in Fig. 2.13. The case of isotropic (symmetrical) emission is shown in Fig. 2.13a. The mirror image also shows isotropic emission. The experiments, however showed that this did *not* happen

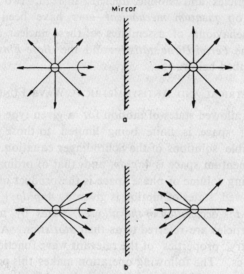

Fig. 2.13 Parity in β emission under a magnetic field
(a) Symmetric emission: Parity conserved
(b) Asymmetric emission: Parity not conserved
(e.g. β⁻ from ^{60}Co).

in the case of β⁻ decay of ^{60}Co in a magnetic field at 0.1 K, when the spins of all the nuclei were aligned along the direction of the external magnetic field. It was found that more betas were emitted in a direction *opposite* to that of the spin alignment, say Z (Fig. 2.13b) indicating the absence of symmetry. The mirror image also reveals an asymmetry of emission, but corresponding to more betas being emitted *in* the direction of the spin alignment. This was the first evidence of non-conservation of parity, in the case of a weak interaction.

Excepting in such weak interactions, parity is conserved in all other interactions.*

*(i) In the emission of a photon the force involved is proportional to the coupling constant, also known as *the fine structure constant*, a dimensionless quantity $e^2/\hbar c = 1/137.04 \simeq 10^{-2}$. (ii) In interactions involving nucleons the coupling constant is given by $f^2/\hbar c \simeq 1$. (iii) While in interactions involving electrons, neutrinos and mesons the coupling constant is given by $g^2/\hbar c \simeq 10^{-13}$. Because of the large difference in the magnitudes of these coupling constants (i) and (ii) are considered strong and (iii) a weak interaction.

2.12 Nuclear Statistics

The behaviour of an assemblage of a large number of particles is best described only statistically. For instance, the distribution of energies or velocities among the large number of molecules of a mole of a gas is satisfactorily described by the *Maxwell-Boltzmann statistics*. However, this type of statistics based on classical laws fails to describe the properties of assemblies of photons, electrons, protons, neutrons, other elementary particles and atomic nuclei. Instead, two new types of statistics based on *quantum mechanical laws* have been developed to describe the behaviour of assemblies of these nuclear and subatomic particles, *viz.* the *Fermi-Dirac statistics* and the *Bose-Einstein statistics*. These are described below.

2.12.1 Symmetrical and Antisymmetrical Wave Function

The number of allowed states of motion for a given type of particle in a unit volume of space is finite being limited to those wave functions which are possible solutions of the Schrödinger equation. If the volume element of momentum space is $4\pi p^2 dp$ and that of ordinary space is V, the corresponding volume of phase space is the product of the two. The number of allowed states of motion is given by $4\pi p^2 dp . V/h^3$. [15] Precise *rules governing the occupation of the allowed states* by mutually indistinguishable particles are referred to as their *statistics*. A consideration of the symmetry properties of the relevant wave function leads to two types of statistics. The following operation makes this point clear.

Consider an assembly of a large number of identical nucleons, numbered $1, 2, \ldots, i, \ldots, j, \ldots, n$. Each nucleon is described by a function of its three space coordinates, and the value of its spin whether it is $+ 1/2\, \hbar$ or $- 1/2\, \hbar$. Let the total coordinates of space and spin of these particles be designated by $\pi_1, \pi_2, \ldots, \pi_i, \ldots, \pi_j, \ldots, \pi_n$ (*i.e.* π_i stands for all the space and spin coordinates of the ith particle). Let us now try to interchange the positions of two of these identical particles i and j with respect to *all* their coordinates. Such an operation with the condition that the energy of the system as well as all other properties remain unaltered following the interchange would be possible only if the *wave function* of the system of particles is *either totally symmetrical or totally antisymmetrical*. Thus, two cases arise.

(i) *Case I: System with Symmetrical Wave Function*
Here the wave function of the system after the interchange of the ith and jth particles remains the same as before the interchange. Thus,

$$\psi\,(\pi_1, \pi_2, \ldots \pi_j, \ldots \pi_i \ldots \pi_n) = \psi\,(\pi_1, \pi_2, \ldots \pi_i \ldots \pi_j \ldots \pi_n) \qquad (2.42\,\mathrm{a})$$

The system with such a symmetrical wave function is said to obey the *Bose-Einstein statistics* and the particles making up this system are referred to as the *bosons*.

(ii) *Case II: System with Antisymmetrical Wave Function*

Here the wave function of the system after the interchange of the pair of particles is not the same as the initial one but *changes sign.* Thus,

$$\psi\,(\pi_1, \pi_2, \ldots \pi_j, \ldots \pi_i, \pi_n) = -\,\psi\,(\pi_1, \pi_2 \ldots \pi_i, \ldots \pi_j \ldots \pi_n) \qquad (2.42b)$$

The system with such an antisymmetrical wave function is said to obey the *Fermi-Dirac statistics* and the particles making up the system are referred to as the *fermions.*

2.12.2 THE FERMIONS

The fermions, an assemblage of which has antisymmetric wave function, and obeys the Fermi-Dirac statistics, include the following particles: electrons, positrons, protons, neutrons, neutrinos, μ mesons and all atomic nuclei with odd-A, $i\,e.$ having odd half-integral spin as $(1/2, 3/2, 5/2 \ldots)$. It follows from the antisymmetrical wave function of a system of fermions, *each completely specified quantum state can be occupied by only one particle.* or, in other words, no two particles can have all the four quantum numbers identical. For particles with spin, $s = \pm 1/2\,\hbar$ there can be a maximum of $2\,(= 2s + 1)$ particles per energy level. This is the *Pauli exclusion principle* applicable to all fermions.

2.12.3 THE BOSONS

The bosons, an assemblage of which has a symmetrical wave function and obeys the Bose-Einstein statistics, include the following particles: photons, π^+, π^- and π^0 mesons, deuterons, alpha particles and all atomic nuclei with even-A, *i.e.* having even integral spins as $(0, 1, 2, \ldots)$. Because of the symmetrical wave function of a system of bosons there is no restriction on the number of these that can enter a given quantum state. In other words, the Pauli exclusion principle does not apply to bosons.

References
(where marked (*), see Bibliography)

1. R.D. Evans*.
2. B. Hahn, D.G. Ravenhall and R. Hofstadter, 'High Energy Electron Scattering and the Charge Distribution of Selected Nuclei', *Phys. Rev.*, 1956, **101**, 1131.
3. E. Segrè (1977)*.
4. I. Perlman and T.J. Ypsilantis, 'Consistency of Nuclear Radii of Even-Even Nuclei from Alpha Decay Theory', *Phys. Rev.*, 1950, **79**, 30.
5. R. Hofstadter (Ed.), International Conference on 'Nuclear Sizes and Density Distributions', *Revs. Mod. Phys.*, 1958, **30**, 412.
6. L.R.B. Elton*
7. P.F.A. Klinkenberg, 'Tables of Nuclear Shell Structure', *Revs. Mod. Phys.*, 1952, **24**, 63.
8. *Nuclear Data*.

9.   H.E. White*.
10. B.L. Cohen*.
11. C.H. Townes, H.M, Foley, and W. Low, 'Nuclear Quadrupole Moments and Shell Structure', *Phys. Rev.*, 1949, 76, 1415L.
12. T.D. Lee and C.N. Yang, 'Parity Non-Conservation and a Two-Component Theory of the Neutrino', *Phys. Rev.*, 1957, 105, 1971.
13. C.S. Wu, 'Parity Experiments in Beta Decays', *Revs. Mod. Phys.*, 1959, 31, 783.
14. C.S. Wu, E. Ambler, R.W. Hayward, D.D. Hoppes and R.P. Hudson, 'Experimental Test of Parity Conservation in Beta Decay', *Phys. Rev.*, 1957, 105, 1413.
15. W.E. Burcham*.
16. M.G. Mayer, 'On Closed Shells in Nuclei II', *Phys. Rev.*, 1949, 75, 1969 L.
17. T. Schmidt, 'The Magnetic Moments of Atomic Nuclei', *Z. Physik.*, 1937, 106, 358.
18. L.W. Nordheim, 'Nuclear Shell Structure and β decay. II, Even A Nuclei', *Revs. Mod. Phys.*, 1951, 23, 322.

Problems

2.1 If the odd proton in a nucleus were in an f orbit, with its spin oppositely directed to l, what would be its nuclear (a) spin and parity and (b) magnetic moment?
                                                   [(a) 5/2 (−), (b) 0.8621 μ_N]

2.2 If the odd proton in a nucleus is in the g orbit with its spin parallel to l what would be its nuclear (a) spin and parity, and (b) magnetic moment?
                                                   [(a) 9/2 (+), (b) 6.793 μ_N]

2.3 On the basis of the shell model, assuming no cross-overs, predict the nuclear spin, parity and magnetic moment of (a) $^{137}_{55}$Cs and (b) $^{83}_{36}$Kr (consult text).
                                                   [(a) 5/2(+), 4.793 μ_N, (b) 9/2(+), −1.913 μ_N]

2.4 On the basis of the shell model predict the spin and parity of (a) $^{64}_{29}$Cu and (b) $^{86}_{37}$Rb, (consult text).
                                                   [(a) 1(+); (b) 2(−)]

2.5 The electric quadrupole moment of $^{175}_{71}$Lu is 5.9 b. Calculate (a) the ellipticity of the nucleus, and (b) the ratio of the axes b/a. Take the mean radius to be given by $R = 1.4\ A^{1/3}\ F$.
                                                   [(a) 0.170, (b) 1.1856]

2.6 Given that the nuclei $^{176}_{71}$Lu and $^{233}_{91}$Pa have extreme values of electric quadrupole moments of $+7$ and $-3b$ respectively, calculate (a) the ellipticity and (b) the ratio of axes b/a for the two nuclei. Take the mean radius to be given by $R = 1.4\ A^{1/3}\ F$.
                                                   [^{176}Lu: (a) 0.2001 and (b) 1.2224,
                                                   ^{233}Pa: (a) −0.0555 and (b) 0.946]

2.7 Given the ellipticity of $^{75}_{33}$As to be 0.03 calculate its electric quadrupole moment.
                                                   [0.2761b]

2.8 Calculate the frequency of (a) proton spin resonance and (b) electron spin resonance in a magnetic field of 1.5 tesla (take $g = 5.5854$ and 1 for proton and electron respectively).
                                                   [(a) 63.86 MHz, (b) 2.22 × 10^10 Hz]

2.9 Fluorine (^{19}F) is placed in an oscillating electric field of 40.2 MHz. Find the magnetic field for causing a resonance. Take g for ^{19}F to be 5.256.   [1.003 T]

2.10 Compare the *nmr* frequencies of ^{10}B and ^{14}N in a magnetic field of 1 tesla. Take the g values to be 5.4 and 4.01 for ^{10}B and ^{14}N respectively.
                                                   [ν ^{10}B = 41.16 MHz and ν ^{14}N = 30.56 MHz; ratio = 1.35]

Chapter 3

Nuclear Models

3.1 Historical

It was only after the discovery of the neutron by Chadwick in 1932 and the recognition that the nuclei of all atoms consist of protons and neutrons*[1] that our knowledge of the atomic nucleus really progressed. In the early stages (1932–36), it was generally believed that certain numbers of nucleons of one kind, protons or neutrons, formed *closed shells* and that the nucleons of one shell had no interaction with those in other shells in much the same way as the electrons in the different orbitals in the outer sphere of the atom.

The development of this independent particle model received a setback over the years 1936–48, when Niels Bohr and Frenkel, independently of each other, suggested an opposite view that all the nucleons in a nucleus interact strongly with one another irrespective of their charge. In other words, this model envisages the nucleus as a homogeneous entity with *strong interaction* amongst all the neighbour nucleons like the molecules of a *liquid drop*. The behaviour of the nucleus on this model could be understood only on a statistical basis, with no individual characteristics. When Bohr's theory was able to provide a mechanism for low energy nuclear reactions and provide a basis for the calculation of the mass of an atom and also subsequently explain the phenomenon of nuclear fission, the *liquid drop model* came to be accepted, even though it does have certain weaknesses.

However, interest reverted once again to the earlier independent particle model around 1948 as a result of the contributions of Maria Goeppert-Mayer who highlighted the numerous experimentally observed discontinuities in nuclear properties, as stability, abundance, binding energy, neutron absorption cross-section, *etc.*, recurring everytime the number of protons or neutrons reached the values of 2, 8, 20, 50, 82 and 126, the so-called *magic numbers*. These discontinuities demonstrate forcibly the independent movements of individual nucleons which are inconsis-

*The nuclei of all atoms consist of Z protons and N neutrons, the sole exception being the nuclide ^1H which consists of a single proton.

tent with a statistical model. Besides Goeppert-Mayer, Haxel, Jensen and Suess contributed significantly to the development of the independent particle or the *shell model* which envisages spin-orbit coupling of the nucleons in a shell but with no interaction with nucleons in other shells.

The success and the limitations of both the models had to be accepted, as each was able to explain certain phenomena only. Thus, the complimentary nature of the two models was recognized. Since then several attempts have been made, notably by Aage Bohr, (son of Niels Bohr), and Mottelson over the years 1948–50, to develop a *collective model* which treats the movement of the nucleons as a whole, as well as the movements of individual nucleons outside the closed shells, thereby combining the essential characteristics of the two models. We shall proceed now to consider the chief features of these and some other models.

3.2 The Shell Model

The shell model assumes that the nucleons are distributed in a series of discrete energy levels satisfying certain quantum-mechanical conditions, not unlike the electrons in the outer-sphere. As the capacity of each level is reached, a closed shell is formed, the protons and the neutrons being in separate shells. As on this model the motions of individual nucleons are considered, it is also referred to as the *single particle model*, and it is mainly applicable to the nucleus in the *ground* state. As pointed out earlier, the model is consistent with the observed periodicity in several nuclear properties, some of which are described below.

3.2.1 PERIODICITY IN NUCLEAR PROPERTIES: THE MAGIC NUMBERS

The periodic variation of properties of elements with the number of electrons in the atom, *viz.* 2, 10, 18, 36, 54 and 86* is well known, and this forms the basis of the Periodic Classification of elements. In an analogous manner, the nuclear properties are known to vary periodically, each period coming to an end when the number of protons, or neutrons in the nucleus equals 2, 8, 20, 50, 82 or 126, these numbers being popularly referred to as the *magic numbers*. We shall list here some of the discontinuities observed experimentally in nuclei in which Z or N equals one of these numbers.

(i) Tendency of Pairing

Even as electrons tend to pair up to form a stable bond, so do nucleons of the same kind, (neutrons with neutrons and protons with protons); such pairing adds to the stability of the nucleus. This is witnessed by the facts:

---

*Closed shells of electrons are formed in the outer sphere of the atoms when their number equals one of these values. These represent the numbers of electrons of the atoms of the rare gases of the atmosphere, or the zero group elements, He, Ne, Ar, Kr, Xe and Rn.

(a) Even-Z, even-N nuclides are the most abundant amongst stable nuclides in nature: 165 out of 274 (Sec. 1.5).

(b) The $(n+n)$; $(p+p)$;... rule for the formation of stable nuclides from ^{16}O to ^{35}Cl (Sec. 1.5.1) is another evidence. According to this rule all odd-Z elements have only one while even-Z elements have three stable isotopes over this region*, (Fig. 1.1).

(c) The heaviest stable nuclide in nature is ^{209}Bi with 126 neutrons.

(d) The stable end product of all naturally occurring radioactive series of elements is Pb with 82 protons.

(ii) *High Mean Binding Energy*

It was pointed out earlier that maxima occur in a plot of mean binding energy as a function of A, at the magic numbers of Z or N (Sec. 1.5.4). Where both Z and N are magic numbers, as in $^{4}_{2}$He$_2$, $^{16}_{8}$O$_8$, $^{40}_{20}$Ca$_{20}$, $^{208}_{82}$Pb$_{126}$ the binding energy per nucleon is particularly high.

(iii) *Abundance in Nature*

The most abundantly occurring nuclides in the universe, whether of terrestrial or cosmic origin are again those with a magic number of protons or neutrons, or both (*vide* Goldschmidt's curve[2] or Brown's Table[3]). Following nuclides occupy peak positions:

$$^{16}_{8}O_8, \quad ^{28}_{14}Si_{14}, \quad ^{118}_{50}Sn, \quad ^{88}Sr_{50}, \quad ^{89}Y_{50};$$

$$^{90}Zr_{50}, \quad ^{138}Ba_{82}, \quad ^{139}La_{82}, \quad ^{140}Ce_{82}, \quad ^{208}_{82}Pb_{126}.$$

The large fluctuations in the natural abundance of elements up to ^{19}F are attributed by geochemists to their preferential use up in the subsequent thermonuclear reactions in the prestellar stage.

(iv) *Number of Stable Isotopes and Isotones*

The number of isotopes of a given element (Z constant) which are *stable* is a reflection of the relative stability of that element. If this number is plotted as a function of Z, distinct peaks occur at $Z = 20$ (Ca), 50 (Sn) and 82 (Pb) compared with their immediate neighbours of Z value ± 1 of the above values; similarly for isotones (N constant), (*vide* Fig. 3.1 (a, b), also Table 3.1).[4]

(v) *α-Decay*

Since α-decay involves the emission of a helium nucleus consisting of two protons and two neutrons, it may be anticipated from the evidence marshalled above, that nuclides with 128 neutrons would be in a favoured position in regard to α-decay, as the resulting daughter would be left with a magic number of neutrons. Such nuclides (*e.g.* $^{212}_{84}$Po$_{128}$ and $^{213}_{85}$At$_{128}$)

_____

he rule ceases to be simple beyond ^{35}Cl.

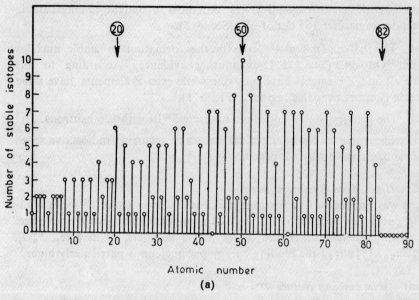

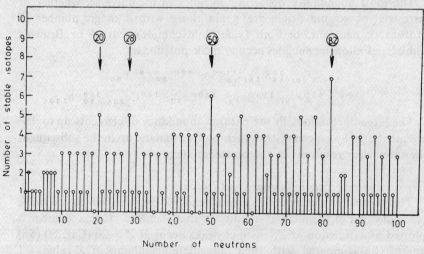

Fig. 3.1 Variation of the number of stable isotopes as a function of (a) proton number Z, and (b) neutron number N (B.H. Flowers[4], see Fig. 3.2).

TABLE 3.1: Number of stable isotopes of elements of $Z = 20$, 50 and 82 and their neighbours

Region around $\big/ Z$	Magic no. -1	Magic no.	Magic no. $+1$
Calcium	$_{19}$K : 2	$_{20}$Ca : 6	$_{21}$Sc : 1
Tin	$_{49}$In : 2	$_{50}$Sn : 10	$_{51}$Sb : 2
Lead	$_{81}$Tl : 2	$_{82}$Pb : 4	$_{83}$Bi : 1

would be very short-lived and emit α particles of high energy (*vide* the Geiger-Nuttal law: Sec. 4.6.4). On the contrary, α emitters already having just 126 neutrons, (*e.g.* $^{210}_{84}Po_{126}$ and $^{211}_{85}At_{126}$) would be expected to be relatively longer lived and emit α particles of lower energy. This is indeed the case, as revealed by the data given below.

(1) $^{212}_{84}Po_{128} \xrightarrow{\alpha} {}^{208}_{82}Pb_{126}$; $\tau = 46$ s; $E_\alpha = 8.78$ MeV

$^{210}_{84}Po_{126} \xrightarrow{\alpha} {}^{206}_{82}Pb_{124}$; $\tau = 138.4$ d; $E_\alpha = 5.31$ MeV

(2) $^{213}_{85}At_{128} \xrightarrow{\alpha} {}^{209}_{83}Bi_{126}$; $\tau = 0.11$ μs; $E_\alpha = 9.08$ MeV

$^{211}_{85}At_{126} \xrightarrow{\alpha} {}^{207}_{83}Bi_{124}$; $\tau = 7.2$ h ; $E_\sigma = 5.87$ MeV

(vi) β-*Decay*
A similar situation prevails amongst the β-emitters as well. The energy of the β would be specially high and the half-life relatively short if the resulting product has Z or N equal to a magic number. The energy discontinuity is around 2 MeV, *i.e.* about 25% of mean binding energy, in β disintegrations in the neighbourhood of magic numbers.

(vii) *Neutron Absorption Cross-Section*
A study of the variation of neutron absorption cross-section with the neutron number of nuclides brings out very well the significance of the magic numbers. The absorption cross section for 1 MeV neutrons is lower by a factor of 50–100 for nuclides containing 20, 50, 82 and 126 neutrons compared to their neighbour nuclides containing one neutron short of the magic number. The effect is even more pronounced in the

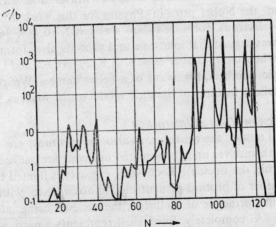

Fig. 3.2 Variation of thermal neutron capture cross section with the nuclear neutron number N. The minima occur at the magic numbers (from the *Nuclear Shell Model* by B.H. Flowers, in Progress in Nuclear Physics, Ed. O.R. Frisch, Vol. 2, Pergamon Press, Oxford, with permission).

case of thermal neutron capture cross-sections, as shown in Fig. 3.2 and illustrated by the following pairs of examples:

	Nuclide	σ/b
(i)	$^{88}_{38}Sr_{50}$	5.8×10^{-3}
	$^{87}_{38}Sr_{49}$	16
(ii)	$^{136}_{54}Xe_{82}$	0.16
	$^{135}_{54}Xe_{81}$	2.65×10^{6}

(viii) Separation Energy of a Neutron

The binding energy of the last neutron in a nuclide or its *separation energy*, is generally determined by measuring the net energy of a reaction of the type (γ, n) or (d, t). The energy needed to extract the *last* neutron from a nucleus is very much higher if it happens to be a magic number neutron, than if it were one in excess of the magic number as the following data show. Energy needed to remove the 126th neutron from $^{208}_{82}Pb_{126}$ is 7.38 MeV, while the energy needed to remove the 127th neutron from $^{209}_{82}Pb_{127}$ is only 3.87 MeV.

3.2.2 THE SALIENT FEATURES OF THE SHELL MODEL

It was to explain the periodicity observed in the above and other nuclear properties occurring at definite intervals with increasing proton or neutron number, that the *closed shell* or the *independent particle model* was proposed and developed by Maria Goeppert-Mayer and, independently, by Haxell, Jensen and Suess. Maria Goeppert-Mayer and J.H.D. Jensen were awarded the Nobel prize in Physics for this work in 1963. As in the case of electrons forming closed shells at 2, 10, 18, 36, 54 and 86 electrons, it was argued that neutrons and protons also form (separate) closed shells when their number equals, 2, 8, 20, 50, 82, and 126, referred to as the magic numbers, for want of a better name. We present here some of the salient features of the shell model of the nucleus.[5]

(i) Weak Nucleon-Nucleon Interaction

On the shell model, the neutrons, as also the protons, are believed to pair amongst themselves and these paired nucleons are packed into separate shells within the nucleus. Each shell capacity is limited to a certain maximum number of protons or neutrons, in accordance with quantum rules and Pauli's principle of exclusion, the nucleons being all fermions (Sec. 2.12.2). A completely filled shell represents a particularly stable configuration of low energy.

Every nucleon is assumed to move in its own orbit independent of other nucleons, but governed by a *common potential* due to the interaction of all the nucleons. This implies that in the ground state, or in some ofthe lowest excitation states, the nucleon-nucleon interaction is absent or is very feeble. This in its turn implies that the *mean free path* of a nucleon in the ground state is of the order of a nuclear diameter or more, so that a nucleon is able to orbit around about once before colliding with another nucleon (Fig. 3.3a). However, experimental results on nucleon-nucleon scattering do not support this concept. The scattering

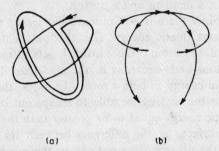

(a)   (b)

Fig. 3.3   Nucleon-nucleon collisions and nucleon mean free path λ: two models (a) λ $\simeq$ nuclear radius, (b) λ $\ll$ nuclear radius[7].

data suggest more frequent elastic collisions implying a mean free path very much shorter than the nuclear radius (Fig. 3.3b). It was Weisskopf who explained away this weak interaction paradox by invoking Pauli's principle of exclusion that not more than two protons or neutrons may be in the same orbit.[6] This limits severely the frequency of collisions amongst the nucleons in a nucleus.

(ii) *The Nuclear Potential*

The orbit or the quantum state of a nucleon is analogous to the quantum state of an electron in the outer sphere, with the difference that the orbit of the nucleon is determined by the *nuclear potential* which is the average total effect of interactions of all the nucleons with one another; hence the nuclear potential is same for all the nucleons. In regard to the nature of this potential it had been pointed out in Sec. 1.5.3: (a) that *all nucleons, irrespective of their charge, attract one another*, and (b) that *this attractive force is of short range*, operative inside the nucleus, falling rapidly to zero outside the nuclear boundary within a distance of about a fermi.

3.2.3 Forms of Nuclear Potential

We shall now consider some of the forms of the nuclear potential proposed, the magnitude of this potential and the nature of its variation with distance from the centre of the nucleus.

(i) *The Square-Well Potential*

Of the different forms of nuclear potential suggested, the simplest is the *square* or *rectangular well* described by

$$V_{(r)} = -V_0 \quad (r \leqslant R)$$
$$V_{(r)} = 0 \quad (r \geqslant R)$$
$$\left. \right\} \qquad (3.1)$$

where R is the radius of the nucleus (a few fermis) and the magnitude of $V_0 \sim$ 30–50 MeV, minus sign indicating an attractive potential. The deep minimum in the $V-r$ curve (Fig. 1.3) justifies the name *potential well*.

We shall now consider the conditions of penetration into and escape out of a nucleus for a neutron and a proton.

(a) *Neutron:* Since there is no Coulomb barrier for a neutron, even neutrons of the lowest kinetic energy (*i.e.* thermal neutrons) can penetrate the nucleus of any atom. Once inside it gets attracted to and by all the other protons and neutrons in the nucleus. This results in a drop of its potential energy to below zero. In order that this, or any other neutron inside the nucleus, be able to escape out of the nucleus, it should have a kinetic energy equal to or greater than the nuclear potential at the nuclear surface, *i.e.* the difference between its actual negative value and zero. If the neutron does not possess this much kinetic energy, it remains captured in the nucleus.

(b) *Proton:* For a proton, or any other positively charged particle, it should have enough kinetic energy equal to or greater than the maximum Coulomb barrier E_c before it can penetrate an atomic nucleus. If its kinetic energy is $E < E_c$, it will be reflected or scattered back the moment it approaches a point where the Coulomb barrier is equal to its kinetic energy* (Fig. 1.3). Once inside the nucleus by overcoming the Coulomb barrier, the proton will be attracted to and by all the other protons and neutrons, *i.e.* its potential energy drops below zero. A proton (the same that came in, or any other) to be able to escape out of the nucleus, should have kinetic energy equal to or greater than the maximum Coulomb barrier E_c: or else it remains captured* in the nucleus.

(c) *Other forms of potential:* Admittedly, it is unlikely that the potential would sharply change at a particular value of r from zero to a large negative value as implied in the square-well potential Eq. 3.1. To smooth out the discontinuity, different refined forms have been suggested for the nuclear potential. The more important of these are mentioned below.

(ii) *The Harmonic Oscillator Potential*

$$V(r) = -V_0 + \tfrac{1}{2}M\omega^2 r^2 \qquad (3.2)$$

where ω is the frequency of simple harmonic oscillation of the nucleon.

The energy levels are given by**

$$E_{(n_1,n_2,n_3)} = (n_1 + n_2 + n_3 + 3/2)\,\hbar\omega \qquad (3.3)$$

---

*This is true if wave-mechanical tunnel effect is not considered (Sec. 4.6.5).

**This is an extension of the one-dimensional expression for a simple harmonic oscillator $E_n = (n + 1/2)\,\hbar\omega$.

where n_1, n_2, n_3 are integers specifying the wave functions in the three dimensions. The *oscillator quantum number* N being the sum $n_1 + n_2 + n_3$, Eq. 3.3 may be written as

$$E_N = (N + 3/2)\, \hbar\omega \qquad (3.4)$$

which shows the energy levels are evenly spaced with $\Delta E = \hbar\omega$. The magnitude of ΔE is also given by $41/A^{1/3}$ MeV.

(iii) *The Exponential Potential*

This and the following forms of potential involve the range of the nuclear force $1/\mu$.

$$V(r) = -\, V_0\, e^{-\mu r} \qquad (3.5)$$

(iv) *The Gaussian Potential*

$$V(r) = -V_0\, e^{-\mu^2 r^2} \qquad (3.6)$$

(v) *The Yukawa Potential* (1937)

$$V(r) = -\, V_0\, \frac{e^{-\mu r}}{\mu r} \qquad (3.7)$$

$$= -\, \gamma^2\, \frac{e^{-\mu r}}{r}$$

where γ is a constant.

(vi) *The Woods-Saxon potential* (1954)

$$V(r) = \frac{-\, V_0}{1 + e^{(r-R)/a}} \qquad (3.8)$$

where $V_0 \simeq 57$ MeV, $R \simeq 1.25\, A^{1/3} F$ and $a = 0.65\, F$. In Fig. 3.4 are sketched some of these potentials.[8]

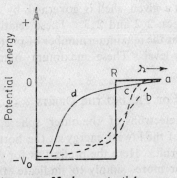

Fig. 3.4   Nuclear potentials
(a)   Rectangular or square well,
(b)   Harmonic oscillator,
(c)   Woods-Saxon, and
(d)   Yukawa.

3.2.4 ENERGY LEVELS IN A NUCLEAR POTENTIAL WELL

Studies of the scattering of protons and neutrons by a nucleus show that the potential well must have a depth of about 35–50 MeV for neutrons and some 5 MeV less deep for protons due to coulombic repulsions. The other experimental observation that to extract a proton or a neutron from a nucleus it needs ∼ 7–8 MeV energy, shows that not all the nucleons are at the bottom of the well. In fact it is known that the nucleons are distributed into a series of discrete energy levels, as sketched in Fig. 3.5, there being two separate sets of levels for the protons and

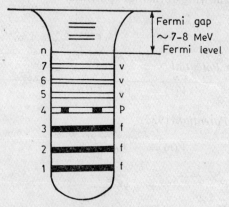

Fig. 3.5 Nuclear energy levels: the shell model
f: levels completely filled,
p: levels partly filled,
v: levels completely vacant.

the neutrons. The lowest levels are fully occupied. The one above these, is partly occupied and partly vacant while the levels above this last are wholly vacant. Each level represents a permissible solution to the wave-mechanical equation applicable. The maximum number of protons or neutrons in a given shell is governed by the quantum relations described in Secs. 2.2 and 2.3. These relations and the Pauli's exclusion principle limit the maximum number of protons and neutrons in a given orbit or energy level. These maximum numbers are given in Table 2.2.

3.2.5 THE SEQUENCE OF FILLING THE ORBITS

As in the case of the electrons of the outer sphere, the nucleons start filling from the orbit of the lowest energy at the bottom of the potential well, *i.e.* with the 1*s* orbit. Here the prefix 1 is for the radial quantum number $\nu (= n - l)$, or more simply to indicate that the *s* orbit is appearing for the first time. When the 1*s* orbit is filled, the orbit of the next higher energy, namely 1*p*, starts filling in, and then 1*d*. Once a *d* orbit is completed, the next *s*, viz., 2*s*, starts filling in. This is followed in order by 1*f*, 2*p*, 1*g* and 2*d* (prefixes 1 and 2 alternating). Again when the $2d$ is complete, the next s viz., $3s$ starts and this is followed by $1h$, $2f$, $3p$, $1i$; etc. (the prefixes 1, 2 and 3 coming by turns as shown below:

$$1s \to 1p \to 1d$$
$$\to 2s \to 1f \to 2p \to 1g \to 2d$$
$$\to 3s \to 1h \to 2f \to 3p \to 1i \to 2g \to 3d$$
$$\to 4s \to 1j \ldots$$

This is a simplified model which neglects spin-orbit coupling due to splitting of levels into $(l + \frac{1}{2})$ and $(l - \frac{1}{2})$ sublevels. The orbit capacities are as shown in Table 2.2, viz. $s = 2$; $p = 6$; $d = 10$; $f = 14$; $g = 18$; $h = 22$; $i = 26$ and $j = 30$. The sequence of filling on the different potential models is described below.

(a) Rectangular Well Potential Model

Figure 3.6(a) shows the level sequence for nucleons in a *deep rectangular well potential* (Eq. 3.1). The energy levels are unevenly spaced, getting closer at higher levels, as may be seen from the energy scale shown on the right, with zero at the bottom. When full, each level with $2(2l + 1)$ nucleons, constitutes a closed shell. The total numbers thus closing the shells are 2, 8, 18, 20, 34, 40, 58, 68, 90, 92, 106, 132 and 138. These numbers differ from the magic numbers: except for 2, 8 and 20; the higher magic numbers are all absent on this model.[9]

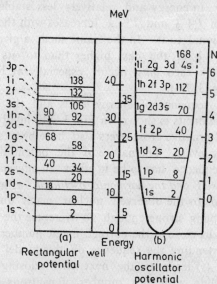

Fig. 3.6 Sequence of filling energy levels on the basis of (a) Rectangular well potential, (b) Harmonic oscillator potential. Most shells do not close at magic numbers under (a) and (b) (from *Nuclear Physics/An Introduction* by W.E. Burcham, Longman, London, 1973, with permission).

(b) Harmonic Oscillator Potential Model

On the other hand, if the nucleons are filled in a *harmonic oscillator* *potential well* (Eq. 3.4), a different picture emerges (Fig. 3.6b). Since on this potential the levels have to be evenly spaced ($\Delta E = \hbar\omega$), the shell closures occur with different numbers of nucleons as shown. Each closed shell on this potential corresponds to a different oscillator quantum number N beginning with $N = 1$ for the $1s$ shell*, $N = 2$ for the $1p$ shell and so on with $N = 7$ for the topmost shell comprising of $1i$, $2g$, $3d$ and $4s$ as shown in Fig. 3.6(b). The numbers of nucleons closing shells on the oscillator potential are 2, 8, 20, 40, 70, 112 and 168. These also differ from the nuclear magic numbers, except for 2, 8 and 20. The higher magic numbers 50, 82 and 126 are again missing.

(c) *Spin-Orbit Coupling Model*

In the previous two models only the orbital angular momentum of nucleons was considered and the spin momentum neglected, with the result that shell closures did not wholly correspond to the magic numbers. It was Maria Goeppert-Mayer and, independently, Haxel, Jensen and Suess who proposed a strong spin-orbit coupling pointing out that such a coupling involves a *non-central force* of a magnitude depending on the relative orientation of the orbital and spin momenta. The overall result is that each l level, (except the s), splits into two sublevels $j = l + \frac{1}{2}$, lower in energy and relatively more stable and $j = l - \frac{1}{2}$, higher in energy and relatively less stable. The amount of splitting between $l + \frac{1}{2}$ and $l - \frac{1}{2}$ increases with the value of l, being roughly proportional to it. In the same shell, a given $l - \frac{1}{2}$ level may be nearer to $l' + \frac{1}{2}$ of the next higher than to its own $l + \frac{1}{2}$ lower level. Cross-overs then *may* occur, especially at higher l values, as illustrated in Fig. 3.7(a).

The resulting sequence of energy levels and the order of filling of nucleons into the orbits is shown in Fig. 3.7(b) involving several cross-overs. Some alternative cross-overs also have been suggested specially at higher energy levels. The nature of the potential well in the spin-orbit coupling sequence has to be in effect an *intermediate one between the rectangular well and the harmonic oscillator*, as neither of the latter types corresponds to the observed nuclear magic numbers. Assuming a spin-orbit coupling strong enough to overcome the oscillator spacing of levels, the shells close at the correct magic numbers 2, 8, 20, (28), 50, 82 and 126. Extending the sequence on this model to beyond $3p$, *i.e.* ($1j$, $2g$, $3d$ and $4s$) leads to the next shell closing at 184 (Fig. 3.7), though no nuclide with this number of neutrons exists or has been made synthetically so far. The possibility of a *Super Heavy Element* (SHE) stable against all types of decay has been postulated with $N = 184$ and $Z = 114$.

---

*Some physicists begin with $N = 0$ for the $1s$ level and end with $N = 6$ for the topmost shell, on the assumption that $N (= n_1 + n_2 + n_3) \geqslant 0$ is permissible in Eq. 3.3.

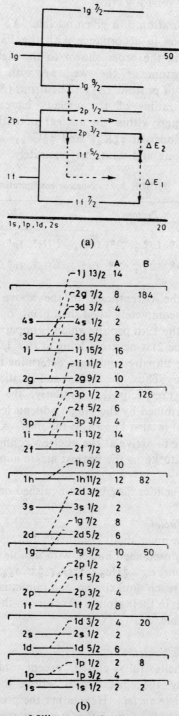

(a)

(b)

Fig. 3.7 Sequence of filling energy levels on the strong spin-orbit
coupling shell model: shells close at the magic numbers.

3.2.6   Nuclear Configuration

The nuclear configuration of a given nuclide $_Z^A X_N$ is obtained by adding neutrons and protons in accordance with the Pauli principle of exclusion to the levels in the order shown to the right of Fig. 3.7b, beginning from the bottom of the well, $i.e.$ with the $1s$ level, till the necessary numbers of protons (Z) and neutrons (N) are accomomodated. In the process the radius of the nucleus increases to permit all the nucleons to be bound within the nuclear potential. As examples, the nuclear configurations of $_{19}^{39}K_{20}$ and $_{20}^{41}Ca_{21}$ are shown below, in Table 3.2 for protons and neutrons separately.

TABLE 3.2:   Nuclear configuration

Nuclide	Protons	Neutrons
$_{19}^{39}K_{20}$	$[1s^2, 1p^6, 1d_{5/2}^6, 2s^2]\,1d_{3/2}^3$	$[1s^2, 1p^6, 1d_{5/2}^6, 2s^2, 1d_{3/2}^4]$
$_{20}^{41}Ca_{21}$	$[1s^2, 1p^6, 1d_{5/2}^6, 2s^2, 1d_{3/2}^4]$	$[1s^2, 1p^6, 1d_{5/2}^6, 2s^2, 1d_{3/2}^4]\,1f_{7/2}^1$

The terms within the parentheses in the above Table form completely closed shells, the incompletely filled shell being outside the parentheses. Thus in ^{39}K, it is the 19th proton which is unpaired lying at $1d_{3/2}$ level and in ^{41}Ca it is the 21st neutron, lying at the $1f_{7/2}$ level. The j and l values of the single unpaired nucleon determine the spin and parity of the entire nucleus. Thus, the spins and parities of ^{39}K and ^{41}Ca are 3/2 (+) and 7/2 (−) respectively. Similarly, the magnetic moment of the nucleus is determined by the single odd nucleon. This is the reason why the shell model is also known as the *single particle model*.

In actual practice to arrive at the nucleon configuration of any nuclide, it is necessary only to know the nearest magic numbers which the Z and N exceed by.

Three types of nuclides may be distinguished on the shell model[7].

(i)   Closed Shell Nuclei

Nuclei with some inner shells completely full and outer ones completely vacant constitute closed shell nuclei, with double magic numbers, *i.e.* for protons and neutrons, *e.g.* $_2^4He_2$, $_8^{16}O_8$, $_{20}^{40}Ca_{20}$ and $_{82}^{20}Pb_{126}$. Most nuclear properties reach a maximum or a minimum with these nuclides. They are analogous in their atomic structure to the zero group elements of the Periodic Table.

(ii)   Single Particle Nuclei

Nuclei with shells fully closed, except one shell with a single particle, occupying the lowest level above the filled shells, constitute the *single particle nuclei*. Here either the protons or the neutrons are in a magic number and the other is one in excess of a magic number, *e.g.* $^5_3Li_2$. $^{17}_8O_9$, $^{17}_9F_8$, $^{41}_{20}Ca_{21}$ and $^{41}_{21}Sc_{20}$. They are analogous to the alkali metals in their electron configuration.

(iii) *Single Hole Nuclei*

This type refers to nuclei with shells full or vacant except one shell which is incomplete for want of a single nucleon. This must be the topmost of the filled shells, *e.g.* $^{15}_8O_7$, $^{15}_7N_8$, $^{39}_{19}K_{20}$, $^{39}_{20}Ca_{19}$. Their analogues in the atomic world are the halogen elements.

3.2.7 NUCLEON HYBRIDIZATION

Due to the closeness of neighbour levels, specially at higher energy levels on the spin-orbit coupling potential, cross-overs occur as shown in the sequence of energy levels on this model. In addition between two very close lying shells, the transfer of a nucleon from a filled lower to an incomplete higher neighbour level may occur, leaving the odd unpaired nucleon in the *lower* level instead of in the higher level. This process may be referred to as *hybridization* of nucleons, by analogy with the electrons in the outer sphere of the atom. For instance, on the shell theory, the proton configuration of ^{19}F ought to be $[1s^2_{1/2}, 1p^4_{3/2}, 1p^2_{1/2}]$, $1d^1_{5/2}$, implying a spin and parity of the ninth odd particle and hence of the ^{19}F nucleus to be 5/2 (+). In reality the value is 1/2 (−). This would be the value if a proton from $p_{1/2}$ level is transferred to the $d_{5/2}$ level leaving the other proton unpaired in the $p_{1/2}$ level; thus $[1s^2_{1/2}, 1p^4_{3/2}, 1d^2_{5/2}]$, $1p^1_{1/2}$. Similarly, the spin and parity of $^{137}_{56}Ba_{81}$ predicted by the shell model is 11/2 (−) on the configuration for the 81st neutron $[1s^2_{1/2}...2d^4_{3/2}]$, $1h^{11}_{11/2}$. The actual spin and parity of ^{137}Ba is 3/2 (+) which would be the result if a neutron is assumed to be transferred from $2d_{3/2}$ to the $1h_{11/2}$ level, leaving the 81st odd neutron in the $2d_{3/2}$ level instead of in the $1h_{11/2}$ level thus $[1s^2_{1/2}...1h^{12}_{11/2}]$, $2d^3_{3/2}$.

3.2.8 MERITS OF THE SHELL MODEL

The success of the shell model arises from its ability, not only to explain the periodicity in the nuclear properties, but to predict the spins and parities of odd-*A* nuclides and to account for their electric quadrupole moments. These are reviewed below.

(i) *Periodicity of Nuclear Properties*

As described under Sec. 3.2.1, the numerous discontinuities in nuclear properties as stability, binding energy, abundance in nature, neutron absorption cross sections, *etc.* at magic numbers of neutrons or protons, find an explanation on the basis of shell closures occurring at the magic numbers of nucleons. This was in fact the starting point for the postulation of the shell model of the nucleus.

(ii) *Prediction of Total Angular Momentum*
Parity and Magnetic Momentum of a Nucleus

(a) *Odd-A nuclei:* The spin and parity of the odd-A nuclei are determined respectively by the j and l values of the odd nucleon, as mentioned earlier (Sec. 2.8.1). These characteristics of the odd nucleon are imparted to the nucleus as a whole. The examples of the spin and parity of ^{39}K and ^{41}Ca were presented under Sec. 3.2.5. In a large number of cases, the shell model correctly predicts the spin and parity of odd-A nuclides (Table 3.3).

Where Z or $N > 70$, *i.e.* in and beyond the level $1h_{11/2}$ high spins as 11/2 and 13/2 should be common; however there are very few nuclides with such high spins in the ground state. Cross-overs and hybridiza-

TABLE 3.3: Nuclear spins and magnetic moments of selected odd-A nucleli[7,10] (from *Nuclear Data*, 5, 443, 1969. Academic Press, reproduced with permission)

Nuclide	Odd nucleon	Level of the nucleon on the spin-orbit coupling model	Nuclear spin I and parity	Nuclear magnetic moment μ_N[7,10,11]
^{1}n	n	$1s_{1/2}$	1/2 +	-1.9131
^{1}H	p	$1s_{1/2}$	1/2 +	2.793
^{2}H*	p and n	$1s_{1/2}$	1 +	0.857
^{6}Li*	3rd p and 3rd n	$1p_{3/2}$	1 +	0.822
^{7}Li	3rd p	$1p_{3/2}$	3/2 −	3.256
^{13}C	7th n	$1p_{1/2}$	1/2 −	0.702
^{17}O	9th n	$1d_{5/2}$	5/2 +	-1.894
^{19}F	9th p	$1d_{5/2} \rightarrow 1p_{1/2}$**	1/2 −	2.629
^{25}Mg	13th n	$1d_{5/2}$	5/2 +	-0.855
^{27}Al	13th p	$1d_{5/2}$	5/2 +	3.641
^{31}P	15th n	$2s_{1/2}$	1/2 +	1.132
^{35}Cl	17th p	$1d_{3/2}$	3/2 +	0.822
^{37}Cl	17th p	$1d_{3/2}$	3/2 +	0.684
^{39}Ar	21st n	$1f_{7/2}$	7/2 −	-1.3
^{39}K	19th p	$1d_{3/2}$	3/2 +	0.391
^{41}Ca	21st n	$1f_{7/2}$	7/2 −	-1.595
^{59}Co	27th p	$1f_{7/2}$	7/2 −	4.62

*^{2}H and ^{6}Li are included here as they have an unpaired proton and an unpaired neutron (odd-Z, odd-N type).

**The energy levels being close to each other, a transfer of a nucleon between them is possibe, causing the odd nucleon to appear in the lower level (Sec. 3.2.6).

tion of nucleons between neighbour levels overcome this apparent breakdown of the shell model. The examples of spins of ^{19}F and ^{137}Ba were discussed earlier under Sec. 3.2.7.

Similarly, the magnetic moments of odd-A nuclides are determined by the single unpaired nucleon. The Schmidt limits for the magnetic moments of nuclides of the odd-A type, where the odd particle is a proton or a neutron, and again where the nuclear spin I equals $l + s$, or $l-s$, are presented in Table 2.3 (Sec. 2.8.2). The Schmidt limits serve as a rough guide. Here, as in the case of the nuclear spin and parity, cross-over effects of the odd nucleon have to be considered.

A knowledge of the correct spin and parity of nuclei is of great importance specially in β decay and in γ emission as the probability of decay depends on the difference between the total angular momenta and parities of the parent and the daughter nuclei. Predictions in regard to the degree of allowedness or forbiddenness of many β decaying nuclides made on this basis have been found to agree very well with experimental results (see Secs. 4.7.7 and 4.8.2).

(iii) *Correlation of Nuclear Isomerism with Magic Numbers*

If the number of long-lived isomers ($\tau > 1s$) in the case of odd-A nuclides is plotted *versus* the odd proton or odd neutron number, *islands of isomers* occur, *i.e.* they tend to concentrate between two magic numbers and the number of such isomers sharply falls to zero at the magic number itself and the isomers start reappearing as the next shell is about half-full. Nuclear isomerism appears when two neighbour energy levels in a nucleus have a large difference in spin, so that the transition becomes highly forbidden (see Sec. 4.8.3).

(iv) *Electric Quadrupole Moment*

As pointed out earlier, there is a strong correlation between the electric quadrupole moment of a nucleus and the proton, or neutron magic numbers. The electric quadrupole moment has the highest positive value when the last shell is about two-thirds full, and the value drops as the shell fills up, becomes zero at the magic number when the shell closes, and goes to negative values in shells with a few nucleons in the next incomplete shell. As the new shell begins to fill in, the value rises again crosses zero to reach a maximum positive value when the shell is two-thirds full to start the next cycle (Fig. 2.11).

3.3 The Liquid Drop Model

The liquid drop model is a statistical model developed by Niels Bohr and Wheeler and independently by Frenkel. The model is unconcerned about the motions of individual nucleons and treats the nucleus as a *homogeneous* entity consisting of a certain number of protons and neutrons as in an *ideal* solution, each nucleon interacting strongly with all its neighbours. In physical chemistry a solution is considered *ideal* if the particles of solute (s) and solvent (S) interact without distinction, *i.e.* the force $f_{s-s} \simeq f_{s-S} \simeq f_{S-S}$. The interaction force involved is assumed to be *a short range one* tending to *saturation* as the number of nucleons increases. It is further assumed that the interaction force is *charge and spin independent*, so that the energy of interaction amongst the nucleons is a continuous function of the mass of the nucleus and hence of the number of nucleons present.

3.3.1 ANALOGY WITH A LIQUID DROP

As the name suggests, the model is based on certain similarities in behaviour between the nucleus and the drop of a liquid. Following are some of the similarities.

(i) A liquid drop and an atomic nucleus both have a *large* number of particles*, molecules or atoms in the case of the liquid drop and protons and neutrons in the case of the nucleus.

(ii) Both the liquid drop and the nucleus are *incompressible* and *homogeneous*. Density**, charge and all other properties are same throughout the drop and the nucleus, except only at the surface boundary. This implies that

the nuclear volume $\propto$ mass $\propto A$.

Hence, the nuclear radius is given by

$$R = r_0 A^{1/3} \qquad (2.2)$$

where r_0 is a constant of the order of $1.2 - 1.5$ F (Sec. 2.1).

(iii) Considered as an ideal solution the force between all the nucleons is same, *i.e.*

$$f_{n-n} \simeq f_{n-p} \simeq f_{p-p} \qquad (3.9)$$

i.e. the nuclear force is charge and spin independent.

(iv) The nucleon interaction being only with the neighbours, the nuclear force is a *short range one and hence it saturates*, the interation energy being proportional to A. (If each nucleon interacted not with neighbours only, but with every other nucleon, the energy would be proportional to $A(A - 1) \approx A^2$, as in the case of Coulomb interaction between the protons in a nucleus (see Sec. 3.3.3).

(v) Analogous to the drop of a liquid, the atomic nucleus also displays *surface tension force*, proportional to the surface area of the nucleus, hence to $A^{2/3}$.

(vi) If the liquid drop or the nucleus is invaded by a high energy

---

*The term *large* is to be understood in the sense of number of particles per unit volume. Considering the volume of a drop of water to be 0.05 cm³, it would contain about 10^{21} molecules whereas the same volume of nuclear matter would contain 10^{37} nucleons, the density being 0.165 nucleon/F^3 (Sec. 2.1.1).

**The exceptionally high density of nuclear matter, $\sim 10^{14}$ g cm⁻³ was pointed out earlier (Sec. 1.3).

particle from the outside, the *particle* is captured with the formation of a *compound nucleus* (see Sec. 5.5). The excess energy of the captured particle is rapidly shared by all the particles in the drop or the nucleons in the nucleus. The time for this process of *thermalization of* energy in the case of the compound nucleus is of the order of $10^{-21}-10^{-17}$ s, depending on the velocity of the incoming nucleon.

(vii) *Deexcitation* of the drop or the compound nucleus may occur by one of the following processes, depending on the energy of excitation.

Drop	*Compound nucleus*
(a) by cooling, *i.e.* by radiating away heat;	(a) by emission of radiation;
(b) by evaporation of some particles;	(b) by the emission of one of more nucleons;
(c) in case of high excitation, by the rupture of the drop into two droplets.	(c) by nuclear fission into two nuclei.

(viii) The common observations of the tendency for the fusion of small drops into a larger one and the reverse, namely of rupture of a large drop when perturbed into smaller droplets have their analogues in nuclear fusion of light nuclei and nuclear fission of a large nucleus, both processes being exoergic. The fusion and fission of drops is best demonstrated with a drop of mercury on a glass surface.

3.3.2 Merits of the Liquid Drop Model

The great merit of the liquid drop model is the satisfactory explanation it provides for the behaviour of nuclei in *excited states* (unlike the shell model which applies to nuclei in the ground state). Besides providing plausible mechanisms of most low energy nuclear reactions, and explaining the phenomenon of nuclear fission, the liquid drop model provides the basis for the equation of Weizsacker for calculating the binding energies of nuclei and hence their atomic masses. This equation is presented below.[12]

3.3.3 The Semi-Empirical Mass Equation

As pointed out in Sec. 1.5.4, the atomic mass of an atom is given by

$$m\left({}^{A}_{Z}X\right) = Zm_H + Nm_n - \Delta m \tag{1.2b}$$

wher m_H is the mass of an H atom (= 1.007 825 u $\simeq$ mass of proton + mass of electron), m_n is the mass of a neutron (= 1.008 665 u) and Δm is the mass loss in the synthesis of the atom. Since the total binding energy of an atom is

$$B = 931 \ \Delta m \ \text{MeV}, \tag{1.4}$$

to be able to know the mass of an atom, it is necessary to know only its binding energy. On the basis of the liquid drop model, Weizsacker[12] had arrived at what is known as the *semi-empirical mass equation*, made up of five terms as follows:

$$B \quad = \quad B_v \quad + \quad B_s \quad + \quad B_c \quad + \quad B_a \quad + \quad B_p \qquad (3.10)$$
$$\text{total} \qquad \text{volume} \qquad \text{surface} \qquad \text{Coulomb} \quad \text{asymmetry} \qquad \text{pairing}$$

(i) Volume Energy

This is the most important energy term which is positive. This arises out of the attraction of every nucleon by all the nucleons around it. The volume energy is proportional to the nuclear volume and hence to A on the assumption of uniform nuclear matter of constant density. As the interaction is limited to neighbour nucleons only, the volume energy term saturates and is given by

$$B_v = a_v A \qquad (3.11)$$

where the value of the constant commonly accepted is

$$a_v = 14.1 \pm 0.02 \text{ MeV}$$

(ii) Surface Energy

The above volume energy term assumes that every nucleon is attracted by an *equal number* of nucleons. While it is true for the nucleons in the interior of the nucleus, it cannot be true for nucleons situated at the surface. On the average the surface nucleons interact with only half as many nucleons as do those in the interior. As a consequence of this surface tension effect, the binding energy is lowered proportional to the area of the nuclear surface

$$B_s = - a_s A^{2/3} \qquad (3.12)$$

The value of the constant is taken as

$$a_s = 13.0 \pm 0.1 \text{ MeV}$$

This term is particularly important for lighter nuclei where the proportion of nucleons at the surface to those in the interior is very high, unlike in heavy nuclei where the proportion is about half.

(iii) Coulomb Energy

The mutual repulsion of protons involves another negative term in the total binding energy. As each proton is repelled by $(Z-1)$ protons, the total Coulomb energy is proportional to $Z(Z-1) e^2/R$. This leads to

$$B_c = -3/5 \frac{Z(Z-1) e^2}{r_0 A^{1/3}}$$

$$= -a_c Z(Z-1) A^{-1/3} \qquad (3.13)$$

with the constant

$$a_c = 0.595 \pm 0.02 \text{ MeV}$$

Naturally, the Coulomb energy becomes more important as Z (and hence A) rises.

(iv) Asymmetry Energy or Neutron Excess Energy

With only the above three energy terms, the atomic masses calculated come out to be too low compared to experimentally observed values. It is known that in an isobaric series (*i.e.* A constant), in a majority of cases, there is a particular value of Z_s corresponding to a stable nuclide with maximum binding energy, while all the other values $\gtrless Z_s$ correspond to radioactive nuclides (see examples under Sec. 3.3.5). It had also been pointed out (Sec. 1.5.2) that in light stable nuclei ($A \leqslant 40$) the number of neutrons is about the same as the number of protons. However as Z rises above 20, the ratio of neutrons to protons (N/Z) rises (Table 1.3 and the Segrè chart in Fig. 1.2). The presence of excess neutrons brings in asymmetry as seen from the shell model of the nucleus (Sec. 3.2.5). Equal numbers of protons and neutrons fill all the lower levels, as per their capacity, while neutrons alone ($N-Z$ in number) have to occupy the higher levels, of larger kinetic energy and smaller potential energy. This is referred to as the *asymmetry or neutron excess energy* which lowers the binding energy.

Symmetry conditions show that the binding energy of a nucleus is maximum when $N = Z = A/2$. As the asymmetry ($N-Z$) increases, the binding energy decreases as a quantum-mechanical effect. The latter is related to the change in the total energy (potential + kinetic) of all pairs of interacting nucleons: Thus[7]

$$B_a = -[1/2 \, \Delta (\sum_i V_i) - \Delta (\sum_i T_i)] \qquad (3.14)$$

(Since each Coulombic repulsion between two particles is counted twice it is necessary to halve the summation. The sign of the energy of repulsion being positive that of attraction is negative.)

To evaluate these terms for a given nucleus ${}_Z^A X_N$ of asymmetry ($N-Z$), one may proceed with a symmetric nucleus ${}_{A/2}^A R_{A/2}$ and progressively convert proton after proton into a neutron till the required nucleus ${}_Z^A X_N$ is reached*. Assuming that the permitted orbits are evenly spaced in energy, as on the harmonic potential model, it can be shown

$$\left. \begin{array}{l} 1/2 \, \Delta (\sum_i V_i) = 27 \, (N-Z)^2 \, A^{-1} \, \text{MeV} \\[2mm] \text{and} \qquad \Delta (\sum_i T_i) = 6.3 (N-Z)^2 \, A^{-1} \, \text{MeV} \end{array} \right\}^{7} \qquad (3.15)$$

It follows

$$B_a = -20.7 \, (N-Z)^2 \, A^{-1} \, \text{MeV}$$

Writing in the general form of Eq. 3.10,

*As an example, to arrive at ${}_{28}^{60} \text{Ni}_{32}$, we begin with the symmetrical nucleus

$$ {}_{30}^{60} \text{Zn}_{30} \xrightarrow{p \to n} {}_{29}^{60} \text{Cu}_{31} \xrightarrow{p \to n} {}_{28}^{60} \text{Ni}_{32} $$

$$B_a = -a_a(N-Z)^2 A^{-1} = -a_a(A-2Z)^2 A^{-1} \qquad (3.16)$$

where the accepted value for asymmetry constant is 19.0 ± 0.9 MeV.

(v) Pairing Energy

Earlier it was observed that even-Z, even-N nuclides are the most abundant amongst the stable nuclides occurring in nature, amounting to 165 out of 274, while only four stable nuclides exist of the type odd-Z, odd-N (see Table 1.2). This is a result of the positive contribution to the binding energy due to the complete pairing of protons with protons and neutrons with neutrons (even-Z, even-N type). The contribution is equal in magnitude but *negative* in sign if a proton and a neutron both remain unpaited (odd-Z, odd-N type). The pairing energy vanishes if only a single proton or only a single neutron remains unpaired (even-Z, odd-N; or odd-Z, even-N type). Thus

$$B_p = \overset{+}{\underset{-}{\circ}} a_p A^{-1} \qquad
\begin{cases}
+ & \text{for even-}Z\text{, even-}N \\
- & \text{for odd-}Z\text{, odd-}N \\
\circ & \text{for odd-}A
\end{cases}
\qquad (3.17)$$

On the basis of the shell model, B_p appears to be roughly proportional to $(2j+1)/A$. The value of the constant is

$$a_p = 135 \text{ MeV}$$

However, Fermi had earlier suggested for the pairing term

$$B_p = \overset{+}{\underset{-}{\circ}} 33.5 \ A^{-3/4} \text{ MeV}.$$

(iv) The Total Binding Energy

The total binding energy of a nucleus is given by combining all the energy terms,

$$B = a_v A - a_s A^{2/3} - a_c Z(Z-1)A^{-1/3} - a_a(A-2Z)^2 A^{-1} \overset{+}{\underset{-}{\circ}} a_p A^{-1} \qquad (3.18)$$

Replacing the constants by their accepted values leads to

$$B = 14.1A - 13A^{2/3} - 0.595\,Z(Z-1)A^{-1/3} - 19(A-2Z)^2 A^{-1}$$
$$\overset{+}{\underset{-}{\circ}} 135 \ A^{-1} \text{ MeV} \qquad (3.19)$$

For high Z nuclides the Coulomb term is often simplified to $-0.6\,Z^2\,A^{-1/3}$.

The constants used in Eq. 3.19 are the old set of values, mostly due to Fermi. Several workers in recent times have proposed somewhat different values which lead to a better agreement with experimentally observed atomic masses, but still with an uncertainty of the order MeV/c^2 ($\simeq 1$ *mu*). Some recent values are shown in Table 3.4, together with the earlier values.

3.3.4 MEAN BINDING ENERGY

The mean binding energy per nucleon is given by

$$\bar{B} = B/A \qquad (3.20)$$

The variation of the mean binding energy with A is shown in Fig. 3.8.

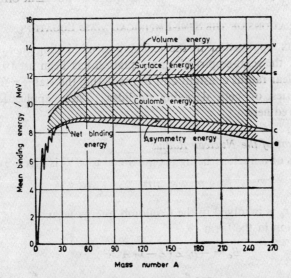

Fig. 3.8 Mean binding energy as a function of the mass number:
the contribution of the different terms:
(v) Volume, (s) Surface, (c) Coulomb and (a) Asymmetry.
(from *The Atomic Nucleus*, by R.D. Evans, © 1955.
McGraw-Hill, Inc., reproduced with permission).

TABLE 3.4: Values of the constants in the semi-empirical mass equation

Constant	Earlier values/MeV[13]	Mozer's values/MeV[14]	Segrè's values/MeV[8]
a_v	14.1	15.297	15.67
a_s	13.0	18.342	17.23
a_c	0.595	0.696	0.697
a_a	19.0		23.29
a_p	$33.5/A^{3/4}$ $135/A$		$12/A^{1/2}$

The top line *v* gives the binding energy due to the volume term (a constant of 14 MeV per nucleon), from which are subtracted the surface energy curve *s*, the Coulomb energy curve *c* and the asymmetry energy curve *a*. This is for odd *A* nuclides for which the pairing energy is zero. The variation of the mean binding energy with *A* had been broadly discussed under Sec. 1.5.4 for light, medium and heavy nuclides, and its relevance to the problem of releasing atomic energy by fusion of light and fission of heavy nuclides (Sec. 1.6).

From a knowledge of the binding energy as in Eq. 3.19, the mass of any atom can be calculated by Eq. 1.2. The masses thus calculated for a large number of nuclides agree reasonably with the values determined experimentally by mass spectrometry.

3.3.5   APPLICATIONS OF THE SEMI-EMPIRICAL MASS EQUATION

Apart from its application in the calculation of binding energies and atomic masses, the semi-empirical mass equation has been used in computing the nuclear radius constant and in predicting the stable nuclide of an isobaric series of beta decaying nuclides. These applications are briefly considered here.

(i)   *The Constant of the Nuclear Radius*
(a)   The radius of a nucleus being proportional to $A^{1/3}$ is given by

$$R = r_0 A^{1/3} \qquad (2.2)$$

Since the same r_0 is involved in the Coulomb energy term of the semi-empirical equation in the form

$$B_c = -a_c Z(Z-1) A^{-1/3}$$

where
$$a_c = 3/5 \frac{e^2}{r_0}, \qquad (3.13)$$

a careful determination of the Coulomb energy for a number of nuclides provides the value of the constant r_0. The value obtained by Green[15] by this method is

$$r_0 = 1.256 \ F$$

(b)   The radius constant has also been determined in a different way from the difference in the binding energy of a pair of *mirror nuclei* which are defined as a pair of isobars where the proton and neutron numbers are interchanged, with $|N-Z| = 1$, *e.g.* $^{31}_{15}P_{16}$ and $^{31}_{16}S_{15}$; $^{37}_{18}Ar_{19}$ and $^{37}_{19}K_{18}$. The binding energies of a pair of mirror nuclei as $^{A}_{Z}X_N$ and $^{A}_{N}Y_Z$ are given by

$$\left. \begin{array}{l} B(Z, N) = K - a_c Z^2 A^{-1/3} - a_a (A-2Z)^2 A^{-1} \\ B(N, Z) = K - a_c N^2 A^{-1/3} - a_a (A-2N)^2 A^{-1} \end{array} \right\} \qquad (3.21)$$

where K includes the terms involving A only and hence is the same for both nuclei.

The asymmetry energy term can be shown to be the same for the two nuclei by the following argument.

$A \equiv (N + Z)$ and for mirror nuclei $|N - Z| = 1$.

Hence, for the first nucleus: $(A - 2Z)^2 = 1$,

and for the second nucleus: $(A - 2N)^2 = 1$.

Hence,

$$\Delta B = B(Z, N) - B(N, Z) = a_c A^{-1/3} (N^2 - Z^2)$$

$$= a_c A^{-1/3} A \ (\because N - Z = 1)$$

$$= a_c A^{2/3} \qquad (3.22)$$

Replacing $a_c = \dfrac{3}{5}\dfrac{e^2}{r_0}$ in Eq. 3.13, we arrive at a relation connecting ΔB and r_0 in terms of known values of e and A:

$$r_0 = \frac{3}{5}\frac{e^2}{\Delta B}A^{2/3} \tag{3.22a}$$

The values of r_0 computed by this method are given in Table 3.5 and this appears to be of the same order of magnitude as obtained by the first method.

TABLE 3.5: Computation of r_0 from the binding energies of mirror nuclei

Mirror nuclei	$B(Z, N)/$ MeV	$B(N, Z)/$ MeV	$\Delta B/$ MeV	r_0/F
³¹P — ³¹S	262.916	256.688	6.228	1.37
³⁷Ar — ³⁷K	315.516	308.587	6.929	1.39

The value of r_0 obtained by Kofoed–Hansen[16], employing more recent values of the constant is

$$r_0 = 1.28\ F.$$

The concept of the nuclear radius and other methods of determining the constant had been presented earlier under Sec. 2.1.1.

(ii) β-Decaying Isobars

Since all β-decays end in nuclei isobaric with the parent, the binding energy expression (Eqs. 3.18 and 3.19) simplify to two terms involving Z and Z^2; thus *under condition of constant A*,

$$(B)_A = K - \frac{0.6Z^2}{A^{1/3}} - \frac{20}{A}(A^2 - 4AZ + 4Z^2)^*$$

$$= K' - \frac{0.6Z^2}{A^{1/3}} + 80Z - \frac{80Z^2}{A}$$

$$= K' - \frac{Z^2}{A}(0.6A^{2/3} + 80) + 80Z \tag{3.23}$$

where K and K' are constants involving terms with A only. Eq. 3.23 shows that, a plot of B, for constant A, *versus Z* would be parabolic. To find Z_s of maximum stability, we equate the derivative dB/dZ to zero and solve for Z_s

$$\left(\frac{dB}{dZ}\right)_A = \frac{-2Z_s}{A}(0.6\,A^{2/3} + 80) + 80 = 0$$

*Here the values of the constants a_c and a_a have been rounded of to 0.6 and 20 MeV respectively and $Z(Z-1)$ is replaced by Z^2 for simplifying calculations.

$$\therefore \quad Z_s = \frac{40A}{0.6A^{2/3} + 80} \tag{3.24}$$

Also graphically, Z_s would be at the vertex of the parabola, corresponding to maximum binding energy.

To illustrate this application of the semi-empirical mass equation it is more convenient to deal with the two cases of odd-A and even-A separately.

(a) *Parabola for odd-A isobars:* Figure 3.9 is typical of the plots of variation of the binding energy B, (rather B—constant), as a function of Z in an odd-A isobaric series. The binding energy is shown as increasing downwards for the series $^{141}_{55}$Cs to $^{141}_{62}$Sm. The vertex of the parabola represents Z_s the stable nucleus. All members on the left arm of the parabola decay by β^- and those on the right by β^+ or EC, ending in the stable nucleus ^{141}Pr, thus

$$^{141}_{55}\text{Cs} \rightarrow \text{Ba} \rightarrow \text{La} \rightarrow \text{Ce} \rightarrow {}_{59}\text{Pr} \leftarrow \text{Nd} \leftarrow \text{Pm} \leftarrow {}_{62}\text{Sm}$$
$$\rightarrow \beta^- \qquad\qquad\qquad \text{stable} \qquad\quad \leftarrow \beta^+ \text{ and/or } EC$$

The difference in the binding energies of adjacent nuclides on the parabola gives the $\beta^{\pm}$ decay energy. Thus, the binding energies of ^{141}Ba and ^{141}La are -480.8 and -477.9 MeV the difference being 2.9 MeV, while the β^- energy observed for the decay

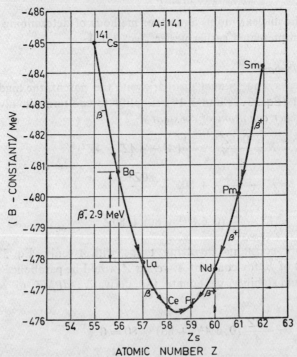

Fig. 3.9 Binding energy and β-decay of isobars[17] $A = 141$

(from *Introduction to Nuclear Physics and Chemistry*, by B.G. Harvey, © 1963. Prentice-Hall, Inc., reproduced with permission).

$$^{141}Ba \rightarrow {}^{141}La + \beta^- + \bar{\nu}$$

is 2.8 MeV.

Similar parabolae have been obtained for a large number of other odd-A β-decaying isobars, $e.g.$

$$^{87}_{35}Br \rightarrow Kr \rightarrow Rb \rightarrow {}_{38}Sr \leftarrow Y \leftarrow Zr \leftarrow {}_{41}Nb$$
$$\rightarrow \beta^- \qquad\qquad\qquad \text{stable} \qquad\qquad \leftarrow \beta^+ \text{ and/or EC}$$

$$^{73}_{30}Zn \rightarrow Ga \rightarrow {}_{32}Ge \leftarrow As \leftarrow {}_{34}Se$$
$$\text{stable}$$

$$^{65}_{28}Ni \rightarrow {}_{29}Cu \leftarrow Zn \leftarrow {}_{31}Ga$$
$$\text{stable}$$

$$^{131}_{51}Sb \rightarrow Te \rightarrow I \rightarrow Xe \rightarrow Cs \rightarrow {}_{56}Ba \leftarrow La \leftarrow {}_{58}Ce$$
$$\text{stable}$$

$$^{137}_{53}I \rightarrow Xe \rightarrow Cs \rightarrow {}_{56}Ba \leftarrow La \leftarrow Ce \leftarrow Pr \leftarrow {}_{60}Nd$$
$$\text{stable}$$

(b) *Parabolae for even-A isobars*: In the case of isobars of even-A, there will be two parabolae, one for the odd-Z, odd-N nuclides and the other for the even-Z, even-N nuclides, the former parabola being displaced from the latter by *twice* the pairing energy. The pairing energy, zero for odd-A nuclides, assumes two different values $+ 135/A$ for even-Z, even-N and $- 135/A$ for odd-Z, odd-N nuclides (*vide* Eq. 3.17), hence the two parabolae are separated by $270/A$ MeV.

There can be again two types: one stable nuclide, naturally on the vertex of the higher energy parabola (even-Z, even-N), or two stable nuclides both on the even-Z, even-N parabola. These two types are illustrated by the following examples and Figs. 3.10 and 3.11.

(i) *Single stable nuclide:* The even-A isobaric series $A = 140$

$$^{140}_{55}Cs \rightarrow Ba \rightarrow La \rightarrow {}_{58}Ce \leftarrow Pr \leftarrow Nd \leftarrow {}_{61}Pm$$
$$\rightarrow \beta^- \qquad\qquad\qquad \text{stable} \qquad\qquad \leftarrow \beta^+ \text{ and/or EC}$$

ends in $^{140}_{58}Ce$ as the stable nuclide, with Cs, La, Pr and Pm lying on the odd-odd parabola and Ba, Ce and Nd lying on the even-even parabola, as shown in Fig. 3.10.

(ii) *Two stable nuclides:* The even-A isobaric series with $A = 64$

$$^{64}_{27}Co \rightarrow {}_{28}Ni \leftarrow Cu \rightarrow {}_{30}Zn \leftarrow {}_{31}Ga$$
$$\qquad\quad \text{stable} \qquad\qquad \text{stable}$$

has two stable nuclides both lying on the even-Z, even-N parabola as in Fig. 3.11. Other examples:

$$^{92}_{38}Sr \rightarrow Y \rightarrow {}_{40}Zr \leftarrow Nb \rightarrow {}_{42}Mo \leftarrow {}_{43}Tc$$
$$\qquad\quad \text{stable} \qquad\qquad \text{stable}$$

$$^{102}_{41}Nb \rightarrow Mo \rightarrow Tc \rightarrow {}_{44}Ru \leftarrow Rh \rightarrow {}_{46}Pd \leftarrow Ag \leftarrow {}_{48}Cd$$
$$\qquad\qquad\qquad \text{stable} \qquad\qquad \text{stable}$$

$$^{108}_{44}Ru \rightarrow Rh \rightarrow {}_{46}Pd \leftarrow Ag \rightarrow {}_{48}Cd \leftarrow {}_{49}In$$
$$\qquad\qquad \text{stable} \qquad\qquad \text{stable}$$

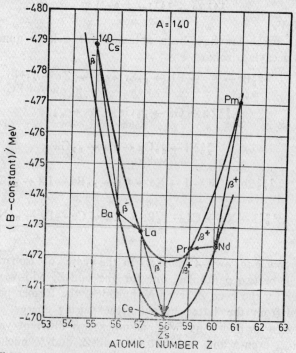

Fig. 3.10 Binding energy and β-decay of isobars[17] $A = 140$
(from *Introduction to Nuclear Physics and Chemistry*, by B.G. Harvey, © 1963.
Prentice-Hall, Inc., reproduced with permission).

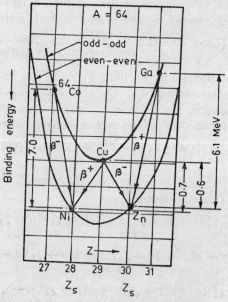

Fig. 3.11 Binding energy and β-decay of isobars $A = 64$.

The last four examples are typical of about 60 *pairs of stable* isobars of even-Z, even-N type, which differ in Z *by two units*. For odd-A isobars there can be only one stable nuclide, the sole exception being $^{113}_{48}$Cd and $^{113}_{49}$In, both stable.

Finally, as a direct application of Eq. 3.24, let us consider two isobars 64 and 125, chosen on account of their integral cube roots. We have

$$Z_s = \frac{40A}{0.6A^{2/3} + 80} \tag{3.24}$$

$A = 64$ leads to $Z_s = 28.6$ whereas the stable nuclides of this series are $_{28}$Ni and $_{30}$Zn; similarly with $A = 125$, we arrive at $Z_s = 52.6$ whereas the stable nuclide of this series is $_{52}$Te. Considering the rounding off of the constants to lead to a simple expression Eq. 3.24, the agreement is good.

3.3.6 Limitations of the Liquid Drop Model

While the liquid drop model explains satisfactorily the behaviour of a nucleus in the excited state, provides a mechanism for the low energy nuclear reactions, accounts for the phenomenon of fission and provides the basis for the semi-empirical mass equation, it suffers from the following major limitations.

(i) The charge independent model is inconsistent with the p-p and n-n pairing effects so prominently observed in the natural abundance of stable nuclides, and in the enhanced binding energy of even-Z, even-N nuclides, due to the positive contribution of the pairing term to the total binding energy.

(ii) The model is also incompatible with closed shell effects as revealed by the periodicity in a large number of nuclear properties recurring at magic numbers of protons or neutrons.

(iii) The model ignores independent motions of nucleons, the single particle spin, parity and magnetic moment effects.

(iv) Even in its application it is limited to medium mass nuclides; as in light nuclides $A < 20$, most nucleons are on the surface and in heavy nuclides $A > 150$, Coulomb effects cannot be ignored.

3.4 The Fermi Gas Model

Another statistical model of the nucleus is the Fermi gas model which treats the nucleus as a whole, disregarding independent motions of nucleons. The concept of the nuclear potential well is retained. Each level starting from the bottom of the well is completely filled, leaving no vacancies, the nucleus being in the lowest possible energy state, resembling a gas at the temperature of 0 K. When excited, some of the nucleons are promoted to vacant levels over the Fermi level (Fig. 3.5). As the number of possible states increases very rapidly with the energy of excitation, mixing of alternative configurations of a given spin and parity level occurs on a large scale. The number of permitted levels may be as high as 10^6 at 10 MeV excitation. These excited states play a dominant role in nuclear reactions and decay transitions. Because of the large number of states involved with frequent mixings, these can be studied only collectively on a statistical basis, as in the case of kinetic motions of the molecules of a gas, which is the reason for the name of the model. What is being considered large here is the number of possible energy levels or states, or the *level density*, at high energy of excitation. The level density $\rho(\varepsilon)$ is defined as the number of permitted levels between energy ε and $\varepsilon + d\varepsilon$. This is given by[17]

$$\rho(\varepsilon) = C \exp [2(\alpha\varepsilon)^{1/2}] \qquad (3.25)$$

with C and α as constants depending on A. Obviously, C and α have each the dimensions of reciprocal energy. Blatt and Weisskopf have computed the values of the constants for different A values.[18]

The reciprocal of ρ gives the corresponding energy spacing between two adjacent levels. Equation 3.25 also leads to the concept of *nuclear entropy* $S(\varepsilon)$ and *nuclear temperature* $T(\varepsilon)$ as follows:

$$S(\varepsilon) = \ln \rho(\varepsilon) = 2(\alpha\varepsilon)^{1/2} + \text{constant} \qquad (3.26)$$

$$\frac{dS(\varepsilon)}{d\varepsilon} = \left(\frac{\alpha}{\varepsilon}\right)^{1/2}$$

and

$$\frac{d\varepsilon}{dS(\varepsilon)} = \left(\frac{\varepsilon}{\alpha}\right)^{1/2} \qquad (3.27)$$

Though $d\varepsilon/dS$ is dimensionally a temperature, it is conventional to express nuclear temperatures in units of energy (MeV), as a product of the Boltzmann constant, i.e.

$$kT = \left(\frac{\varepsilon}{\alpha}\right)^{1/2}$$

or

$$\varepsilon = k^2\alpha T^2 \qquad (3.28)$$

This is an equation for the Fermi gas to which Fermi-Dirac statistics are applicable.

Let us apply Eq. 3.25 to calculate the level density in aluminium excited to 25 MeV above the Fermi level, as an illustration. The values of constants, given by Blatt and Weisskopf for $A = 27$ are $C = 0.5$ MeV^{-1} and $\alpha = 0.45$ MeV^{-1} respectively.

$$\rho = 0.5 \exp [2(0.45 \times 25)^{1/2}]$$
$$= 0.5 \exp (6.7082)$$
$$= 0.5 \times 819.098\ 2$$
$$= 409.6/\text{MeV}$$

and the level spacing $= 1/\rho = 2.44$ keV

The nuclear temperature

$$kT = (\varepsilon/\alpha)^{1/2} = 7.45 \text{ MeV}.$$

3.5   The Collective Model

The nuclear models considered hitherto have each several strong points in their favour and provide many important applications. However, no single model may be considered capable of explaining *all* aspects of known behaviour of nuclei both in the ground and excited states. There is some apparent antithesis between the shell model which attributes many nuclear properties to the single nucleon(s) lying outside the filled shells and the liquid drop model which disregards characteristics of individual nucleons. For years attempts have been in progress to over-come the dualism by incorporating the major features of the shell and the liquid drop models into a single model. This is largely achieved in the *collective model*, developed mainly by the efforts of Aage Bohr and B.R. Mottelson, (1951-53). This model treats the movement of the nucleus as a whole as well as the motions of unpaired nucleons. It thus conserves the essential features of the liquid drop model, besides retaining the concept of quantum numbers of the nucleons outside the filled shells.

3.5.1   NUCLEAR DEFORMATION DUE TO NUCLEONS OUTSIDE FILLED SHELLS

The starting point of the collective model appears to be the suggestion of Rainwater[19] (1950) that nucleons lying outside the closed shells exert a centrifugal pressure which deforms the shape of the nucleus from sphericality. A. Bohr and B.R. Mottelson showed that nuclei thus deformed should execute vibrational and rotational motions, the nucleus behaving as *one collective unit*, somewhat like the motions of a poly-atomic molecule. This implies periodic oscillations in the nuclear shape and size. Since the causative factor for these collective motions is the number of nucleons outside the filled shells, the effect should increase in magnitude farther N and Z are from magic numbers, and hence with the increase in the magnitude of electric quadrupole moment (Sec. 2.10 and 3.2.8). Actually the quadrupole moment of a highly deform-ed nucleus lying farthest from magic numbers is found to be many times larger than the value attributable to a single odd particle of spin j. The latter value Q_j is given by[7]

$$Q_j = - \frac{2j - 1}{2(j + 1)} \cdot \tfrac{3}{5} R^2 \tag{2.37a}$$

The ratio of the actual quadrupole moment to Q_j is a measure of the number of nucleons moving collectively. In one case this number was reported to be as high as 40.

Also on this model, nuclear excitation may consist not only in the transfer of a nucleon or a few nucleons to higher vacant levels, as en-visaged in the shell model, but in the collective motion of many nucleons lying outside together, *leading to higher rotational and/or vibrational quantum numbers* for *the group of nucleons as a whole.* Of the two, rotational motions have been better understood.

3.5.2 COLLECTIVE ROTATION: EVEN-EVEN NUCLEI

Rotational band energies for even-Z, even-N nuclides are given by

$$E_{rot} = \frac{\hbar^2}{2\mathscr{J}} I(I+1) \qquad (3.29)$$

where I is the total angular momentum of the nucleus with values 0, 2, 4, 6, 8... and even parity, and $\mathscr{J}$ is the moment of inertia of the deformed nucleus, whose magnitude increases with the extent of deviation from sphericity. The lowest excitation state is 2(+), the next 4(+) and so on. The ratios of the energy of the higher excitation states 4(+), 6(+), etc. to the lowest excitation state 2(+), as given by Eq. 3.29 are listed in Table 3.6, together with the values observed in the rotational bands of the nuclide $^{238}_{94}Pu_{144}$ (Fig. 3.12) which is typical of nuclides far removed from magic numbers in respect of both Z and N.

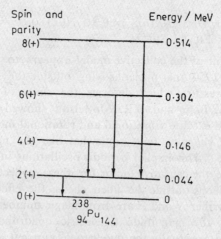

Fig. 3.12 Rotational levels in $^{238}_{94}Pu_{144}$: the collective model[17]

(from *Introduction to Physics and Chemistry*, by B.G. Harvey, © 1963.
Prentice-Hall, Inc., reproduced with permission).

TABLE 3.6:   Ratios of higher excitation energies to the lowest excitation energy in even-Z, even-N nuclides

Ratio	Value expected on Eq. 3.29	Value observed for ^{238}Pu (*Fig. 3.12*)
E_4/E_2	$(4\times5)/(2\times3)=3.33$	3.32
E_6/E_2	$(6\times7)/(2\times3)=7.0$	6.91
E_8/E_2	$(8\times9)/(2\times3)=12.0$	11.68

The value for the ratio E_4/E_2 observed in the case of several other even-even nuclides lying far from magic numbers also are close to the theoretical value of 3.33, as shown below in Table 3.7.

TABLE 3.7: E_4/E_2 ratios for some even-even nuclides[17]

Nuclide	$^{180}_{72}Hf_{108}$	$^{226}_{88}Ra_{138}$	$^{230}_{90}Th_{140}$	$^{250}_{98}Cf_{152}$
E_4/E_2	3.33	3.09	3.28	3.39

In sharp contrast to the above nuclides, the double magic number nuclide $^{208}_{82}Pb_{126}$ with minimum deformation has 1.2 for E_4/E_2 ratio, showing its hard to deform rigid structure.

3.5.3 COLLECTIVE ROTATION: ODD-A NUCLEI: ADDITIONAL QUANTUM NUMBERS

In the case of collective rotation of outer lying nucleons of an odd-A nucleus, the effective angular momentum cannot be taken as the j value of the single odd nucleon, as already mentioned. These nuclei deviate from the spherical shape to a prolate or an oblate spheroid, possessing an axis of symmetry all the same (Fig. 2.9.) The resultant angular momentum is given by the vector addition of the particle angular momentum j and *collective motion angular momentum R*, as shown in Fig. 3.13.[17] The projection of j and I on the symmetry axis gives the new quantum numbers Ω and K respectively. In a given rotational band, Ω and K retain constant values.

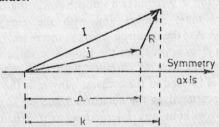

Fig. 3.13 Quantum number Ω and K in collective rotation

    j: Odd nucleon total angular momentum quantum number,

    R: Collective motion angular momentum quantum number,

    I: Resultant of vector addition of j and R,

    Ω: Projection of j on the symmetry axis,

    K: Projection of I on the symmetry axis.

(from *Introduction to Nuclear Physics and Chemistry*, by B.G. Harvey, © 1963. Prentice-Hall, Inc., reproduced with permission).

The energy of rotation of an odd-A nucleus is given by

$$E_{\text{rot}} = \frac{\hbar^2}{2\mathscr{J}}[I(I+1) - I_0(I_0+1)] \qquad (3.30)$$

where I may have values I_0, $(I_0 + 1)$, $(I_0 + 2)$, etc. and the ground state spin $I_0 = 3/2$, $5/2$, etc. The case of $I_0 = 1/2$ involves a more complicated treatment.

3.5.4 MERITS OF THE COLLECTIVE MODEL

In summarizing, the following merits of the collective model may be noted:

(i)   It accounts for the observed rotational energy levels of nuclei farthest removed from magic numbers.

(ii) It predicts the correct cross sections for coulombic excitation and for the probability of $E2$ transitions (vide Sec. 4.8.1).

(iii) It explains consistently several other nuclear properties as magnetic moments, high electric quadrupole moments and isomeric transitions of nuclei far from magic numbers.

3.6 The Optical Model

Some of the values of neutron cross sections observed at both high and low energies seem to violate Bohr's theory which expects the formation of the compound nucleus as soon as the particle reaches the surface of the target nucleus, within about 10^{-21}–10^{-17} s, implying *a mean free path for the particle smaller than the nuclear diameter.* On the basis of Bohr's statistical (liquid drop) model, the total cross section is given by*

$$\sigma_t = 2\pi(R + \lambda^*)^2 \tag{2.9}$$

where R is the nuclear radius ($\propto A^{1/3}$) and λ^* is the wavelength of the particle. Equation 2.9 requires a smooth variation of the cross section with the target mass number and with the energy of the neutron, (through λ^*)**. As the neutron energy increases, λ^* decreases and $(R + \lambda^*) \simeq R$, i.e. σ_t approaches the geometric value πR^2. Experimental results in many cases are at variance with this expectation. No compound nucleus is formed in these cases. Instead, the incident particle in many cases is scattered at the nuclear surface or sometimes, even after penetration, but without any interaction, as if it had a *mean free path longer than the nuclear diameter.*

The observation of lower cross sections for 90 MeV neutrons, compared to 25 MeV neutrons, observed by Cook and others[20], seems to suggest that at such high energies, the incident particle tends to interact with individual nucleons of the target nucleus rather than with the whole of it, displaying also a tendency for emerging out of the nucleus without any interaction (elastic scattering). This results in a greatly reduced yield of the compound nucleus.

Similarly, the data on low energy neutron cross sections, collected by

*See footnote to Eq. 2.9. (Sec. 2.1.1). Here $\lambda^* = \lambda/2\pi$.
**Since $\lambda^* = \hbar/p$ and $p = \sqrt{2mE}$.

Ford and Bohm[21] as well as by Barschall[22] clearly point to dual properties of the nuclear potential well, of its dispersive and absorptive abilities. Scattering effect implies that the *mean free path* of the particle is *longer than* the nuclear diameter. The target nucleus behaves much as a transparent crystal towards light which is almost wholly reflected or refracted without being absorbed. It was these scattering effects which paved the way to the development of the *optical* model for the nucleus by Fernbach, Serber and Taylor[23] (high energy version) and by Feschbach, Porter and Weisskopf[24] (low energy version).

The optical model attempts to combine the single particle and the compound nucleus behaviour. On this model, the formation of the compound nucleus is not always a certainty. Following four possibilities are envisaged for the incident particle:

   (i) It may be scattering at the surface of the target nucleus (shape elastic scattering),

   (ii) It may penetrate the the target nucleus, and after a finite time be ejected out without any interaction with the target nucleons (*compound elastic scattering*).

   (iii) It may penetrate and *directly react with one or more nucleons* of the target nucleus.

   (iv) It may form a true *compound nucleus*, but not necessarily as fast as implied in Bohr's theory.

The probabilities of (i), (ii), (iii) and (iv) occurring are each finite, and there is a finite life time for the particle after penetration wherein it retains its identity, the *pre-compound nucleus stage*. This picture is thus different from the theory of compound nucleus formation with a total certainty and within the natural nuclear time (defined as the time for the particle to traverse a distance equal to the nuclear diameter $\approx 10^{-21}$–10^{-17} s for neutrons) (Sec. 5.5.1).

The two principal projectile-target interactions, thus, are (a) scattering before or after penetration and (b) absorption leading to nuclear reaction directly or *via* the compound nucleus. The shell model rectangular well potential $V_{(r)}$ (Eq. 3.1), can account for scattering but not for absorption or collective effects. The optical model envisages a two term *complex nuclear potential* $U_{(r)}$ as made up of a real one $V_{(r)}$ and an imaginary one $iW_{(r)}$, i being $\sqrt{-1}$, thus

$$U_{(r)} = V_{(r)} + iW_{(r)} \tag{3.31}$$

Such a complex potential implies a wave function for the travelling wave whose amplitude falls as it advances, signifying partial absorption of the projectiles of the incident beam.

It is the imaginary term which thus allows for absorption. Values of -50 MeV and -5 MeV are typical of V and W components respectively.

Both V and W are energy dependent. Single particle elastic scattering is produced by V whereas the imaginary component W attenuates the incident wave. It also governs the mean free path of the particle in the target nucleus, larger the W, shorter the mean free path and higher the probability of absorption and compound nucleus formation.

On the analogy of light passing through a crystal, the imaginary component of the potential imparts to the clear crystal a certain amount of 'cloudiness' which enables absorption. Hence the optical model is sometimes referred to as the *cloudy crystal ball* model.

References
(*where marked* *, *see Bibliography*)

1. J. Chadwick, 'The Existence of a Neutron', *Proc. Roy. Soc.* (London), 1932, A136, 696.
2. K. Rankama*
3. H. Brown, 'Table of Relative Abundances of Nuclear Species', *Revs. Mod. Phys.*, 1949, **21**, 625.
4. B.H. Flowers, 'The Nuclear Shell Model', —*Progress of Nuclear Physics* (Ed. O.R. Frisch, 1952, **2**, 235, Pergamon Press, London).
5. M. Goeppert-Mayer and J.H.D. Jensen*
6. V.F. Weisskopf, 'The Nuclear Model', *Science*, 1951, **113**, 101.
7. B.L. Cohen*
8. E. Segrè (1977)*
9. W.E. Burcham*
10. P.F.A. Klinkenberg, 'Tables of Nuclear Structure', *Revs. Mod. Phys.*, 1952, **24**, 63.
11. *Nuclear Data**
12. C.F. von Weizsacker, *Z. Physik.*, 1935, **96**, 431.
13. R.D. Evans*
14. F.S. Mozer, 'Generalized Atomic Law', *Phys. Rev.*, 1959, **116**, 970.
15. A.E.S. Green, 'Nuclear Size and Weizsacker Mass Formula', *Revs. Mod. Phys.*, 1958, **30**, 569.
16. O. Kofoed-Hansen, 'Mirror Nuclei Determinations of Nuclear Size,, *Revs. Mod. Phys.* 1958, **30**, 449.
17. B.G. Harvey*
18. J.M. Blatt and V.S. Weisskopf*
19. J Rainwater, 'Nuclear Energy Level Argument for a Spheroidal Nuclear Model', *Phys. Rev.*, 1950, **79**, 432.
20. L.J. Cook, E.M. McMillan, J.M. Peterson and D.C. Swell, 'Total Cross Sections of Nuclei for 90 MeV Neutrons' *Phys. Rev.*, 1949, **75**, 7.
21. K.W. Ford and D. Bohm, 'Nuclear Size Resonances', *Phys. Rev.*, 1950, **79**, 745.
22. H.H. Barschall, 'Regularities in the Total Cross Sections for Fast Neutrons', *Phys. Rev.*, 1952, **86**, 431.
23. S. Fernbach, R. Serber and T.B. Taylor, 'The Scattering of High Energy Neutrons by Nuclei', *Phys. Rev.*, 1949, **75**, 1352.
24. H. Feschbach, C.E. Porter and V.F. Weisskopf, 'Model for Nuclear Reactions with Neutrons', *Phys. Rev.*, 1954, **96**, 448.

Problems

3.1 Find the Coulomb barrier for the penetration of a $^{232}_{90}$Th nucleus by (a) a proton and (b) an alpha particle. Take the nuclear radius constant to be 1.4 F.   [(a) 12.96 MeV, (b) 23.94 MeV].

3.2 Calculate the Coulomb barrier for the approach of (a) proton towards $^{112}_{50}$Sn and (b) an α particle towards $^{66}_{30}$Zn. Take the nuclear radius constant to be 1.4 F.   [(a) 8.84 MeV, (b) 10.96 MeV].

3.3 What is the closest distance of approach of an α particle of energy 6 MeV to a gold nucleus ($Z = 79$)?   [37.9 F].

3.4 On the basis of the semi-empirical mass equation, predict the stable nuclide of the isobaric series $A = 180$.   [$^{180}_{72}$Hf].

3.5 From the table of atomic masses of nuclides given below, calculate the binding energy of the (a) last proton and (b) last neutron in (i) ^{12}C and (ii) ^{28}Si.
[(a) (i) 15.95 MeV, (ii) 11.58 MeV;
(b) (i) 18.71 MeV, (ii) 17.17 MeV].

3.6 Suppose that starting from ^{12}C the nuclides (a) ^{14}N and (b) ^{16}O are formed by combination with appropriate nuclear particles. Calculate the energies released.   [(a) 10.27 MeV; (b) 7.16 MeV].

3.7 Calculate the binding energy of the last two neutrons in ^{37}Cl given the mass difference between ^{35}Cl and ^{37}Cl is 1.997 042 u.   [18.89 MeV].

3.8 Calculate the energies of the states (a) 4(+), (b) 6(+), (c) 8(+), and (d) 10(+) all being members of a rotational band in an even-even nucleus of which the energy of the 2(+) state is 44 keV.
[(a) 146.5 keV; (b) 308 keV; (c) 528 keV and (d) 805 keV].

3.9 The rotational band spectrum of ^{238}U is based on the 0(+) ground state. If the energy of the 2(+) state is 44.7 keV, what is the spin and parity of the state of energy 525 keV?   [12(+)].

3.10 A given even-even nucleus has in its rotational band spectrum following energy levels: 0(+) ground state, 2(+) 44 keV and higher states of 146, 304 and 514 keV respectively. Assign the spin and parity for the last three higher energy states.   [4(+), 6(+) and 8(+)].

Table of relevant atomic masses/u (^{12}C=12.000 000)

n	1.008 665	^{14}N	14.003 074
^{1}H	1.007 825	^{16}O	15.994 915
^{2}H	2.014 102	^{27}Al	26.981 535
^{4}He	4.002 603	^{27}Si	26.986 705
^{11}B	11.009 305	^{28}Si	27.976 927
^{11}C	11.011 433		

Chapter 4

Radioactivity

4.1 Discovery

The observation by Henri Becquerel (1896) of the blackening of a photographic plate placed close to a uranium preparation led perhaps to the greatest discovery of the century, namely *radioactivity*. The phenomenon which was then wholly *incomprehensible* led to a series of other spectacular discoveries necessitating the abandonment of some of the then well-accepted theories of matter. The new results formed the basis of modern concepts and the birth of nuclear science. The name *radioactivity* was proposed by a Polish pupil of Becquerel, Marie Sklodowska, who later became the illustrions scientist Marie Curie, the recipient of two Nobel Prizes.

The finding that the naturally occurring pitchblende was many times more radioactive than warranted by its uranium content, led Pierre and Marie Curie to the belief that there must be present in it some unknown element far more radioactive than uranium. With no previous experience of this type of work, with no financial support, but with faith in their reasoning, the Curies undertook to isolate this mysterious element. They worked in a shed with a simple electroscope for differentiating the 'active' fraction from the rest and they succeeded after agonizingly prolonged toil in separating not one but *two new* intensely radioactive elements, one named Polonium, after Marie's native country and the other Radium (1898). The isolation of these elements, present in no more than about a mg in a tonne of the ore, is not only a remarkable triumph of their prediction, but a chemical engineering achievement unparalled in the history of science.

Besides the Curies in France, Schmidt in Germany, Soddy, Rutherford and Ramsay in England and many other great scientists of the epoch contributed richly to the rapid development of the subject of radioactivity which, over the decades, led to the development of nuclear science. Today, a large number of radioactive elements, both naturally occurring and man-made are known and several types of radioactivity are recognized. The more important of these will be considered here, after presenting in brief the essential characteristics common to all forms of radioactivity.

4.2 Radioactive Elements

An element is said to be *radioactive* if the nuclei of its atoms keep *disintegrating spontaneously*, transforming thereby into a different element, emitting in the process nuclear particles and/or radiation. There seem to be about 1000 radionuclides, as against 274 stable ones.

4.2.1 TYPES OF RADIOACTIVE DECAY

Following are some of the important modes of nuclear decay.

Type	*General nuclear reaction*	*Example*
(i) α decay	$^{A}_{Z}X \rightarrow ^{A-4}_{Z-2}Y + \alpha$	$^{226}_{88}Ra \rightarrow ^{222}_{86}Rn + ^{4}_{2}He\ (\alpha)$
(ii) β⁻ decay	$\left. \begin{array}{l} ^{A}_{Z}X \rightarrow ^{A}_{Z+1}Y + \beta^- + \bar{\nu} \\ n \rightarrow p + \beta^- + \bar{\nu} \end{array} \right]$	$^{32}_{15}P \rightarrow ^{32}_{16}S + \beta^- + \bar{\nu}$
(iii) β⁺ decay	$\left. \begin{array}{l} ^{A}_{Z}X \rightarrow ^{A}_{Z-1}Y + \beta^+ + \nu \\ p \rightarrow n + \beta^+ + \nu \end{array} \right]$	$^{22}_{11}Na \rightarrow ^{22}_{10}Ne + \beta^+ + \nu$
(iv) Electron capture	$\left. \begin{array}{l} ^{A}_{Z}X + e \rightarrow ^{A}_{Z-1}Y + \nu \\ p + e \rightarrow n + \nu \end{array} \right]$	$^{55}_{26}Fe + e \rightarrow ^{55}_{25}Mn + \nu$

Electron capture (EC) generally accompanies β⁺ decay.

(v) Isomeric transition	$^{Am}_{Z}X \rightarrow ^{A}_{Z}X + \gamma$	$^{60m}_{27}Co \rightarrow ^{60}_{27}Co + \gamma$

4.2.2 DECAY SCHEMES

Taking cognizance of the fact that (i) an α particle is a helium nucleus ($^{4}_{2}He$), (ii) a β⁻ particle is an electron and (iii) β⁺ is a positron, their emissions lead to the formation of new elements which occupy (i) two places to the left (α decay), (ii) one place to the right (β⁻ decay) and (iii) one place to the left (β⁺ decay and electron capture) in the Periodic Table of elements. The *decay scheme* is a graphical representation of the nuclear transformation. A vertical transition signifies the emission of γ.radiation by a daughter nucleus in returning from an excited to the ground state in one or more steps in cascade. It could also represent an isomeric transition of the parent from its metastable to the ground state. The decay scheme presents a great deal of relevant data regarding the nuclear decay, as the half-life period of the decaying species, the energies of the particles and photons emitted and the propor-

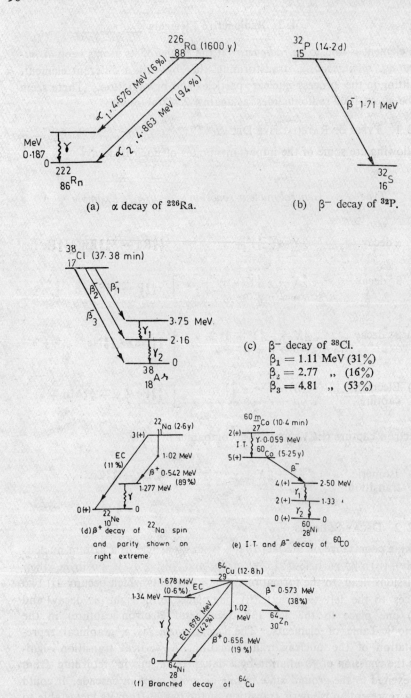

Fig. 4.1   Typical decay schemes representing α, β⁻, β⁺, EC, IT and
branched decay
(from D. Strominger, J.M. Hollander and G.T. Seaborg,[1]
reproduced with authors' permission).

tion of alternative modes of decay in the case of branched decay. Sometimes the spin and parity are also included for the nuclides involved.
Typical decay schemes are shown in Figs. 4.1 a–f.[1]

4.3   General Characteristics of Radioactive Decay

Some features common to all forms of radioactive decay are listed below.

4.3.1   MASS LOSS AND ENERGY RELEASE

The sum of the masses of the products of nuclear decay is always less
than the mass of the parent atom, *i.e.* a radioactive decay is always accompanied by a net loss of mass and it is this which makes the process
spontaneous and irreversible. The equivalent of the mass loss appears
as the recoil energy of the daughter atom and the kinetic energy of the
particles and the energy of the photons emitted during the process, *e.g.*

$$^{32}P \rightarrow {}^{32}S + \beta^- + \bar{\nu}$$

mass/u   31.973 908 $>$ 31.972 074 ; $\Delta m = -0.001\ 834$ u*

Total energy released $= \Delta m.\ 931$ MeV $= 1.705$ MeV. This energy
is shared between the recoil atom ^{32}S, the β^- and the $\bar{\nu}$. Because of the
continuous decay of atoms and energy release all radioactive samples
tend to keep warmer relative to the surroundings.

4.3.2   NUCLEAR RADIATIONS

During the decay of a radioactive nucleus, either helium ions (α decay),
or electrons (β^- decay), or positrons (β^+ decay) are emitted. These particles are in many cases accompanied by pure electromagnetic radiation
in the form of γ photons. Further, the $\beta^\pm$ particles are accompanied
invariably by neutrinos $\bar{\nu}$ (with β^-) and ν (with β^+). These radiations are
of high energy (10^3–10^6 eV) and have high penetrating power through
matter. The ranges of penetration through air by α, β particles and γ
photons of a given energy are in the order**

$$R_\gamma \gg R_\beta > R_\alpha$$

They ionize the atoms of the matter they pass through and thereby lose
their energy gradually, the ionizing power being in the reverse order

$$I_\alpha > I_\beta \gg I_\gamma.$$

---

*Here the mass of the electron is not included as one of the products, for the ^{32}S
  atom formed takes an electron from environment to form a neutral S atom and
  the mass shown is that of the neutral S atom. The antineutrino $\bar{\nu}$ has zero mass.
**The soft betas from ^3H, ^{14}C and ^{35}S of maximum energies 18, 155 and 167 keV
  have low ranges similar to α particles.

If the air through which the radiation passes be super-saturated with water vapour, the ions formed act as nuclei for the condensation of water. The droplets being visible can be photographed under proper conditions and the track of the water drops is also the track of the α or β radiation. A *cloud chamber* for photographing the tracks of α or β or other charged particles was first devised by C.T.R. Wilson in 1896. The α tracks are short and straight, nearly of equal length and end abruptly. The β tracks, on the other hand, are thinner, much longer but very irregular and zigzag (Fig. 4.2) while the γ radiation because of its feeble ionizing ability leaves hardly any track.

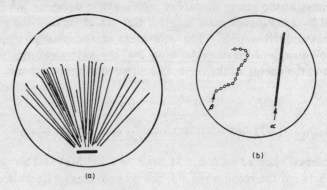

(a)   (b)

Fig. 4.2   Characteristics of (a) α and (b) β particles.

The nuclear radiations, because of their higher energy (10^3–10^6 eV), effect characteristic physical and chemical reactions in the matter they pass through, referred to as radiation damage, which form the subject of *Radiation Chemistry*. The blackening of the photographic plate observed by Becquerel is an instance. The possibility of using nuclear radiations for industrial purposes is discussed in Sec. 8.17.

The energy spectrum of these radiations are characteristic. The α and γ spectra consist of a few sharp monoergic *lines*, while the β spectrum is a *continuum* from nearly zero to a definite maximum. For instance, the alphas from $^{244}_{96}$Cm consist of four lines 5.508, 5.658, 5.763 and 5.805 MeV and the gammas are 0.292, 0.142 and 0.043 MeV, while the β spectrum from ^{210}Bi is a continuum from 0 to an upper limit of 1.17 MeV, with a broad peak around 0.1–0.3 MeV. These are discussed in detail later.

4.4   Decay Kinetics

Every reaction is characterized by a specific rate. A study of the reaction kinetics throws light on the mechanism involved. All radioactive decays are spontaneous and obey the same simple kinetic laws but follow different mechanisms. We shall first consider the decay characteristics and later the theories of the major types of radioactivity.

4.4.1 THE DECAY CONSTANT

The rate of decay of a radioelement at any instant is proportional to the number of its atoms present at that instant.* As the decay proceeds the number of the (parent) atoms diminishes and so does the rate of decay. The kinetics of dacay conforms strictly to what is referred to as the *first order rate law*, viz.

$$-\frac{dN}{dt} = \lambda N \tag{4.1}$$

where λ is a constant of proportionality, known as the *decay constant* having the dimension of [time^{-1}]. The integral forms of Eq. 4.1, which are more commonly used are

$$\left.\begin{array}{l} N = N_0 e^{-\lambda t} \\[2mm] \log \dfrac{N}{N_0} = \dfrac{-\lambda t}{2.303} \end{array}\right\} \tag{4.2}$$

or

where N_0 and N are the numbers of atoms of the parent element remaining at time zero and t respectively. The exponential nature of the decay rate is revealed by Fig. 4.3 wherein are plotted the variation of (a) N *vs.* t and (b) $\log N$ *versus* t, for the β^- decay of ^{24}Na into ^{24}Mg. The slope of the latter $(= -\lambda/2.303)$ gives the decay constant, in this case 0.0461 h^{-1}.

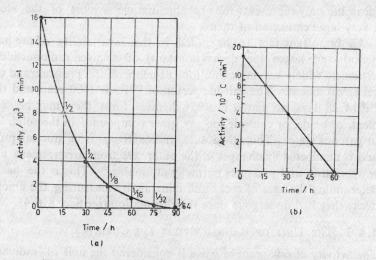

Fig. 4.3 Decay of ^{24}Na of half-life period 15.03 hours
(a) activity *vs.* time, (b) log activity *vs.* time.

4.4.2 THE HALF-LIFE PERIOD AND THE MEAN LIFE

A quantity more frequently used to characterize a radioelement is its

---

*This is similar to the rate of flow of water from a cylinder with a constant outlet at the bottom. The rate at any moment is proportional to the amount of water remaining in the vessel.

half-life period (τ or $t_{1/2}$), defined as the time needed for a given amount of the radioelement to decay exactly to half its value (provided only the number is large enough). Its relation to λ is revealed when we make $N = N_0/2$ in Eq. 4.2.

$$\lambda \tau = 2.303 \log N_0/N = 2.303 \log 2 = 0.693. \qquad (4.3)$$

Thus, in the previous example of ^{24}Na the half-life period is given by

$$\tau = \frac{0.693}{0.0461} \text{ h} = 15.03 \text{ h}.$$

Sometimes the *mean life* $\bar{\tau}$ is used. This represents the *average* life time of the radioelement and is given by

$$t_{1/2} = \frac{\ln 2}{\lambda} \qquad \bar{\tau} = \frac{1}{\lambda} = \frac{\tau}{0.693} = 1.443 \tau \qquad (4.4)$$

It may be mentioned here that the half-life periods (and hence the decay constants) vary over extremely wide limits for different radioelements, for instance from 10^{-6} s for ^{214}At to 10^{10} y ($\simeq 10^{17}$ s) for ^{232}Th.

Being a statistical phenomenon, the above kinetic equations are meaningful only as long as a very large number of the decaying atoms are present, at least about 10^{-18} mole ($\sim 10^6$ atoms). In other words, it is impossible to predict when a *given atom* would decay. It may decay immediately or not at all for an extremely long period. The mean life only represents the probable lifetime of most of the atoms in a very large collection of them.

An important fact to be noted is the invariability of the half-life period (and hence the decay constant) of a given radionuclide, over extremely widely varying conditions of temperature, pressure and chemical environment. The half-life period of ^{226}Ra is 1600 years and that of ^{32}P 14.28 days, no matter in what chemical form they may be, as element, or oxide, or chloride, or any other compound, in the solid, liquid or gaseous state. This is because radioactivity is a nuclear property and is unaffected by changes in the outer electron arrangement and by temperatures and pressures normally attainable.* This is the basis for determining the ages of rocks and minerals by measuring the amount of decay they had undergone since their formation (see Sec. 8.6.4).

4.4.3 THE UNIT OF RADIOACTIVITY: THE CURIE (Ci)

The activity of one gram of ^{226}Ra is considered the unit of radioactivity and is called the curie (Ci). Since 1 g of ^{226}Ra has $\dfrac{6.022 \times 10^{23}}{226}$ atoms and a fraction λ ($= 1.38 \times 10^{-11}$)** of this decays per second, the disinte-

---

*In the case of electron capture and internal conversion by elements of low Z, chemical environment may slightly alter the rate of decay, as actually observed in the L.capture of ^{7}Be of half-life 53.4 d, the ratio of τ_{BeF_2}/τ_{Be} being 1.000 84.[1a,b,c]
**The half-life of ^{226}Ra is 1600 y ($=1600 \times 3.16 \times 10^7$ s). Hence its decay constant is given by $\lambda = 0.693/1600 \times 3.16 \times 10^7 = 1.38 \times 10^{-11}$ s^{-1}.

gration rate of 1 g of radium (^{226}Ra), *i.e.*, one curie of activity is given by

$$1 \text{ Ci} = 1.38 \times 10^{-11} \times 6.022 \times 10^{23}/226 = 3.7 \times 10^{10} \text{ disintegrations/s.}$$

A radioactive preparation of any element which decays at this rate is said to have an activity of one curie. Fractions of the unit, as the mCi and μCi, and multiples as kCi and MCi are also used when necessary. The SI unit of radioactivity recently proposed is the *becquerel* (Bq), which is defined as the activity due to *one disintegration per second*. Hence, 1 Ci = 3.7×10^{10} Bq = 37 GBq. Radioactive preparations are priced on the basis of their activity.

The strength in curies is a measure of the absolute number of atoms of the element decaying per second, while the activity as measured by a detector, the actual counts per second, will be a fraction of the disintegrations/s, depending on the efficiency of the detector and the geometry employed, *i.e.* the fraction of the radiations (α, β or γ) actually reaching and interacting in the detector.

4.4.4 DECAY RATE OF A MIXTURE OF UNRELATED RADIONUCLIDES

Sometimes two ore more radionuclides, unrelated to one another, get mixed up, say in the neutron irradiation of sodium chloride when ^{24}Na, ^{38}Cl and to a less extent ^{35}S and ^{32}P are formed together by various nuclear reactions*. The total activity A at any moment t is given by

$$A = A_{1.0} \, e^{-\lambda_1 t} + A_{2.0}, \, e^{-\lambda_2 t} + \dots \qquad (4.5)$$

where $A_{1.0}$, $A_{2.0}$, *etc.* are activities at time zero of the components A_1 of decay constant λ_1, of A_2 of decay constant λ_2, *etc.* The components decay completely, in the order of their half-lives, the longest lived being the last to decay completely. A plot of log A versus t in the case of a mixture is a complex curve, concave upwards in the early stage and tending to linearity in the end. The slope of the end straight part gives the half-life of the longest lived component. This is illustrated in Fig. 4.4 for the decay of a mixture of ^{24}Na (15.03 h) and ^{38}Cl (37.2 min). The curve (a) gives the total activity of the two components, curve (b) is an extension of (a) to meet the activity axis. Curve (c) is the result of replotting the values of each ordinate of (a) from which the corresponding value of (b) has been subtracted. If (c) also shows a curvature in the early stage (not in this case), the presence of a third activity of still shorter life is indicated and the analysis is repeated till the final curve is linear all-through. The decay constant (and hence the half-life period) of each component is calculated from the slope of corresponding linear segment (slope = $-\lambda/2.303$).

---

*Following reactions are possible:
   ^{23}Na (n, γ) ^{24}Na; ^{37}Cl (n, γ) ^{38}Cl; ^{35}Cl (n, p) ^{35}S and ^{35}Cl (n, α) ^{32}P. The yields of the ^{35}S and ^{32}P are very small as they are due to fast neutrons. The other product ^{36}Cl from ^{35}Cl is not formed to any measurable extent for short periods of irradiation, its half-life being 3.0×10^5 y.

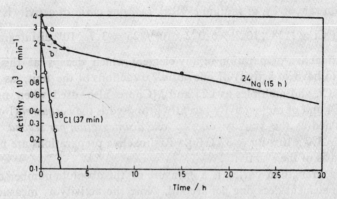

Fig. 4.4 Resolution of complex decay of a mixture of activities due to ²⁴Na (period 15.03 h) and ³⁸Cl (period 37.2 min).

4.5 Parent-daughter Decay-growth Relationships

When a radioactive nucleus decays, the resulting daughter nucleus may be stable or also radioactive with a half-life greater than, equal to or less than that of the parent. These cases are considered separately.

4.5.1 THE DAUGHTER NUCLEUS IS STABLE

In this case the radioactive parent decays continuously while the amount of the daughter grows at the same rate, till the parent decays completely, which happens for all practical purposes in about 6 to 8 half-lives*. This is also the time in which the daughter amount reaches a constant maximum equal to the initial amount of the parent. Both the decay and growth rates follow the same law**, *viz.*

$$-\frac{dN_1}{dt} = \frac{dN_2}{dt} = \lambda_1 N_1 \tag{4.1}$$

There can be no equilibrium between the parent and the daughter at any time. The numbers of atoms N_1 of the parent and N_2 of the daughter at time t are given by

$$\left.\begin{array}{l} N_1 = N_{1 \cdot 0}\, e^{-\lambda_1 t} \\ N_2 = N_{1 \cdot 0}\, (1 - e^{-\lambda_1 t}) \end{array}\right\} \tag{4.6}$$

where $N_{1 \cdot 0}$ is the initial number of parent atoms at time zero. To obtain the *activity* A_1 or the disintegration rate, of the parent at time t, the

---

*Normally one handles in radiochemical work 1–10 μCi which after 6 half-lives would have decayed to $(1/2)^6 = 1/64$ of the initial amount, *i.e.* 0.0156 to 0.156 μCi.

**In this and in subsequent sections, the *subscripts 1 and 2 will stand for the parent and the daughter respectively*, used along with the number of atoms N, activity A, decay constant λ or half-life τ.

number of atoms at the moment is multiplied by the decay constant λ_1.

$$A_1 = N_1\lambda_1 = \lambda_1 N_{1\cdot0}\, e^{-\lambda_1 t} \qquad\qquad (4.7)$$

Most of the artificially prepared radioelements are a one-stage process of this type, *e.g.*

$$^{60}\text{Co} \xrightarrow[5.27\ y]{\beta^-} {}^{60}\text{Ni (stable)}$$

Figure 4.5 shows the decay of ^{60}Co and the growth of ^{60}Ni.

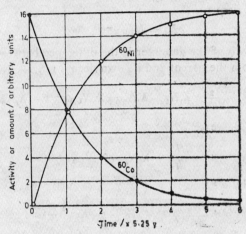

Fig. 4.5 Decay of ^{60}Co (period 5.27 y) and the growth of ^{60}Ni (stable).

4.5.2 CHAINS OF DISINTEGRATION

When a parent nucleus gives rise to a radioactive daughter nucleus, the latter further decays in one or more steps until a stable end product is finally reached. Chains of disintegration are common both in natural radioactivity, as in

$$^{234}\text{U} \xrightarrow{\alpha} {}^{230}\text{Th} \xrightarrow{\alpha} {}^{226}\text{Ra} \xrightarrow{\alpha} {}^{222}\text{Rn} \xrightarrow{\alpha} {}^{218}\text{Po} \xrightarrow{\alpha}$$

$$^{214}\text{Pb} \xrightarrow{\beta^-} {}^{214}\text{Bi} \xrightarrow{\beta^-} \ldots \rightarrow {}^{206}\text{Pb (stable)},$$

and amongst nuclear fission products, as in

$$^{90}\text{Sr} \xrightarrow{\beta^-} \text{Y} \xrightarrow{\beta^-} {}^{90}\text{Zr (stable)}$$

$$^{137}\text{Te} \xrightarrow{\beta^-} \text{I} \xrightarrow{\beta^-} \text{Xe} \xrightarrow{\beta^-} \text{Cs} \xrightarrow{\beta^-} {}^{137}\text{Ba (stable)}$$

All the intermediates of a given genetically related series are being continuously created from their immediate parents and are decaying into their immediate daughters, until finally a stable nuclide results. As the half-lives of radioelements differ, often widely, the growth and decay curves of the intermediate nuclides are complex and differ from system to system. We shall consider in what follows the decay and growth of a pair of parent and daughter only. We shall first consider a general expression for the number of daughter atoms N_2 as a function of time and later apply the same for different cases of (a) $\tau_p < \tau_d$ (b) $\tau_p \simeq \tau_d$ and (c) $\tau_p > \tau_d$; the subscripts p and d stand for parent and daughter.

4.5.3 GENERAL EXPRESSION FOR THE ACTIVITY OF A DAUGHTER NUCLIDE

Using the earlier notation (Sec. 4 5.1) we have for the number of atoms of the parent at time t

$$N_1 = N_{1 \cdot 0}\, e^{-\lambda_1 t} \tag{4.6}$$

The rate of growth of the daughter is the difference between the rates of its formation from the parent and its own decay, viz.

$$\frac{dN_2}{dt} = \lambda_1 N_1 - \lambda_2 N_2 = \lambda_1 N_{1 \cdot 0}\, e^{-\lambda_1 t} - \lambda_2 N_2 \tag{4.8}$$

Rewriting Eq. 4.8, we get

$$\frac{dN_2}{dt} + \lambda_2 N_2 = \lambda_1 N_{1 \cdot 0}\, e^{-\lambda_1 t}$$

On multiplying by $e^{\lambda_2 t}$,

$$e^{\lambda_2 t}\frac{dN_2}{dt} + \lambda_2 N_2 e^{\lambda_2 t} = \lambda_1 N_{1 \cdot 0} e^{(\lambda_2 - \lambda_1)t}$$

Writing the left side as the differential, we have

$$\frac{d}{dt}\left(N_2 e^{\lambda_2 t}\right) = \lambda_1 N_{1 \cdot 0}\, e^{(\lambda_2 - \lambda_1)t}$$

On integration

$$N_2 e^{\lambda_2 t} = \frac{\lambda_1}{\lambda_2 - \lambda_1}\, N_{1 \cdot 0}\, e^{(\lambda_2 - \lambda_1)t} + C$$

where C is a constant of integration. On dividing by $e^{\lambda_2 t}$

$$N_2 = \frac{\lambda_1}{\lambda_2 - \lambda_1}\, N_{1 \cdot 0}\, e^{-\lambda_1 t} + C e^{-\lambda_2 t} \tag{4.9}$$

The constant of integration may be evaluated by letting $N_2 = N_{2 \cdot 0}$ at $t = 0$.

$$N_{2 \cdot 0} = \frac{\lambda_1}{\lambda_2 - \lambda_1}\, N_{1 \cdot 0} + C$$

whence

$$C = -\frac{\lambda_1}{\lambda_2 - \lambda_1}\, N_{1 \cdot 0} + N_{2 \cdot 0} \tag{4.10}$$

On replacing C in Eq. 4.9 by its value obtained in Eq. 4.10, we finally arrive at

$$N_2 = \frac{\lambda_1}{\lambda_2 - \lambda_1}\, N_{1 \cdot 0}\,[e^{-\lambda_1 t} - e^{-\lambda_2 t}] + N_{2 \cdot 0}\, e^{-\lambda_2 t}. \tag{4.11}$$

Comprehensive
Heterocyclic
Chemistry
Vol. 4

If, as it more often happens, $N_{2\cdot0} = 0$, the second term on right side vanishes and *no. of daughter in clide at any time .*

$$N_2 = \frac{\lambda_1}{\lambda_2 - \lambda_1} N_{1\cdot0} [e^{-\lambda_1 t} - e^{-\lambda_2 t}] \qquad (4.12)$$

In terms of activity: *(of daughter nuclies)*

$$A_2 = \lambda_2 N_2 = \frac{\lambda_2 A_{1\cdot0}}{\lambda_2 - \lambda_1} [e^{-\lambda_1 t} - e^{-\lambda_2 t}] \qquad (4.13)$$

In terms of half-lives:

$$A_2 = \frac{\tau_1 A_{1\cdot0}}{\tau_1 - \tau_2} [e^{-0.693 t/\tau_1} - e^{-0.693 t/\tau_2}] \qquad (4.14)$$

It is useful to note that when $t = \tau$, $e^{-\lambda t} = e^{-0.693} = \frac{1}{2}$, and in general if $t = n\tau$, $e^{-\lambda t} = \left(\frac{1}{2}\right)^n$. Hence,

$$N = N_0 \left(\frac{1}{2}\right)^n \qquad (4.15)$$

Finally, Eq. 4.13 may be extended to any member of a chain of dis-integrations assuming at $t = 0$, $N_1 = N_{1\cdot0}$, and $N_{2\cdot0} = N_{3\cdot0} = \ldots N_{n\cdot0} = 0$ in the form of the Bateman equations,[2] viz.

$$N_n = C_1 e^{-\lambda_1 t} + C_2 e^{-\lambda_2 t} + C_3 e^{-\lambda_3 t} + \ldots C_n e^{-\lambda_n t} \qquad (4.16)$$

where

$$C_1 = \frac{\lambda_1 \lambda_2 \ldots \lambda_{n-1}}{(\lambda_2 - \lambda_1)(\lambda_3 - \lambda_1) \ldots (\lambda_n - \lambda_1)} N_{1\cdot0} \Bigg\}$$

$$C_2 = \frac{\lambda_1 \lambda_2 \ldots \lambda_{n-1}}{(\lambda_1 - \lambda_2)(\lambda_3 - \lambda_2) \ldots (\lambda_n - \lambda_2)} N_{1\cdot0}$$

$$\vdots$$

$$C_n = \frac{\lambda_1 \lambda_2 \ldots \lambda_{n-1}}{(\lambda_1 - \lambda_n)(\lambda_2 - \lambda_n) \ldots (\lambda_{n-1} - \lambda_n)} N_{1\cdot0}$$

we shall now consider the three cases (a) $\tau_p < \tau_d$, (b) $\tau_p \simeq \tau_d$ and (c) $\tau_p > \tau_d$.

4.5.4 PARENT SHORTER-LIVED THAN DAUGHTER ($\tau_p < \tau_d$)

In this case there can be no equilibrium. The rate of build-up of the daughter (= rate of decay of the parent) is faster than its own decay, with the result the daughter grows to a maximum in about the same time as the parent would have decayed nearly completely. The time needed at which the daughter activity grows to a maximum is given, as in the general case whether $\tau_p > \tau_d$ or $\tau_p < \tau_d$, by

$$t_{(N_2)\text{max}} = \frac{2.303}{\lambda_2 - \lambda_1} \log \frac{\lambda_2}{\lambda_1} * \qquad (4.17)$$

*This is a general expression for $t_{(N_2)\text{max}}$ obtained by setting $dN_2/dt = 0$ in Eq. 4.8 and solving for t.

This is also the time when the disintegration rates of the parent and daughter become momentarily equal. Once the parent has decayed completely, the daughter decays with its characteristic period. Some of the systems corresponding to this type are:

(i) $^{92}Sr \xrightarrow[2.7\,h]{\beta-} Y \xrightarrow[3.6\,h]{\beta-} {}^{92}Zr$ (stable)

(ii) $^{143}Ce \xrightarrow[33\,h]{\beta-} Pr \xrightarrow[13.7\,d]{\beta-} {}^{143}Nd$ (stable)

(iii) $^{210}Bi \xrightarrow[5d]{\beta-} Po \xrightarrow[138\,d]{\alpha} {}^{206}Pb$ (stable)

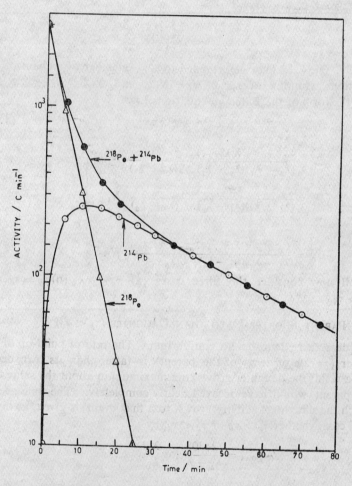

Fig. 4.6 Decay of shorter-lived parent ^{218}Po ($\tau = 3.05$ min) and longer-lived daughter ^{214}Pb ($\tau = 26.8$ min).

(iv) $^{218}Po \xrightarrow[3.05\,min]{\alpha} \, ^{214}Pb \xrightarrow[26.8\,min]{\beta^-} \, ^{214}Bi \, \cdot \longrightarrow \, \ldots$

Figure 4.6 shows the decay of ^{218}Po and daughter ^{214}Pb.

If the daughter has a very long life, the rate of its decay is negligible over observable periods, *i.e.* λ_2 is negligible relative to λ_1 (or τ_1 is negligible in relation to τ_2). Under these conditions, Eq. 4.13 becomes

$$A_2 = \frac{\lambda_2}{\lambda_1} A_{1\cdot0} \,(1 - e^{-\lambda_1 t})$$

or (4.18)

$$A_2 = \frac{\tau_1}{\tau_2} A_{1\cdot0} \,(1 - e^{-0.693\, t/\tau_1})$$

The half-life of the daughter may be obtained from the end linear part of the mixture, while the half-life of the parent is obtained by extrapolating this linear part back to zero time, subtracting the ordinates of this curve from those of the composite curve and replotting the difference, in the same manner as described under Sec. 4.4.4 for the resolution of a decay curve for a mixture of radionuclides.

4.5.5 PARENT AND DAUGHTER OF NEARLY THE SAME HALF-LIFE ($\tau_p \simeq \tau_d$)

The case of perfect equality of decay-rates of parent and daughter is almost non-existent. There are, however, some cases where the two decay rates are close to each other (see below). We shall consider here a limiting case of equal decay rates:

$$A \xrightarrow{\tau_1} B \xrightarrow{\tau_2} C$$

where $\tau_1 = \tau_2 = \tau$ and hence $\lambda_1 = \lambda_2 = \lambda$.

As in the other cases,

$$\frac{dN_2}{dt} = \lambda_1 N_1 - \lambda_2 N_2 \tag{4.8}$$

$$= \lambda N_{1\cdot0}\, e^{-\lambda t} - \lambda N_2$$

When $\lambda_1 = \lambda_2$, the general Eqs. 4.8 and 4.11–4.14 take an indeterminate form. To avoid this, the first term on the right side is replaced by its equivalent as shown in Eq. 4.8 (a).

$$\frac{dN_2}{dt} = A_{1\cdot0}\, e^{-\lambda t} - \lambda N_2 \tag{4.8a}$$

Integrating Eq. 4.8 (a) and assuming there is no daughter element at $t = 0$, we have

$$N_2 = A_{1\cdot0}\, t\, e^{-\lambda t} = \lambda N_{1\cdot0}\, t\, e^{-\lambda t}$$

$$\therefore \quad A_2 = \lambda^2 N_{1\cdot0}\, t\, e^{-\lambda t} = \lambda A_1\, t$$

$$= \frac{0.693\, A_1\, t}{\tau} \tag{4.19}$$

Time for the maximum growth of the daughter is the same as the mean life t for N_2 max $= \bar{\tau} = 1/\lambda = 1.443\,\tau$ (4.20)

Following are two systems where τ_1 and τ_2 are nearly equal:

(i) $^{181}\text{Ba}\ \xrightarrow[11.5\,\text{days}]{\text{EC}}\ \text{Cs}\ \xrightarrow[9.7\,\text{days}]{\text{EC}}\ ^{131}\text{Xe}\ (\text{stable})$

(ii) $^{214}\text{Pb}\ \xrightarrow[26.8\,\text{min}]{\beta^-}\ \text{Bi}\ \xrightarrow[19.7\,\text{min}]{}\begin{array}{l}\xrightarrow{\alpha}\ ^{210}\text{Tl}\ \rightarrow\ \cdots\\[4pt]\xrightarrow{\beta^-}\ ^{214}\text{Po}\ \rightarrow\ \cdots\end{array}$

Figure 4.7 shows the growth and decay of the system

$$^{131}\text{Ba}\ \xrightarrow{\text{EC}}\ ^{131}\text{Cs}\ \xrightarrow{\text{EC}}\ \text{Xe}\ (\text{stable}).$$

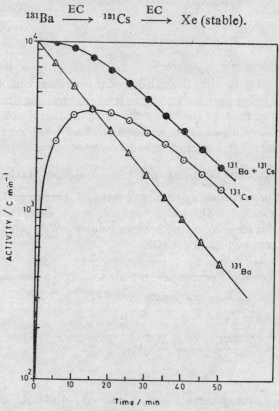

Fig. 4.7   Decay of parent ^{131}Ba $(\tau = 11.5\,\text{d})$ and daughter ^{131}Cs $(\tau = 9.7\,\text{d})$, a case of parent and daughter of nearly same half-lives.

4 5.6   PARENT LONGER LIVED THAN THE DAUGHTER $(\tau_p > \tau_d)$

This is an important case which leads to an *equilibrium* after a time between the amounts of the parent and the daughter.* Once an equilibrium is attained, the *relative amounts* of the daughter, as well as all the successive members of the disintegration series, provided they are all shorter

---

Radioactive equilibrium is *not* to be considered as a reversible chemical equilibrium as all radioactive decays proceed irreversibly. The equilibrium here implies only a constant ratio of the parent and daughter amounts, both decreasing with time at a constant rate equal to that of the parent.

lived than the original parent, *remain constant and all the descendent species decay with the half-life of the dynasty founder parent*. This is true, however, only as long as no component is removed or allowed to escape from the mixture. There are numerous examples of this phenomenon which include all the naturally occurring and artificially prepared radioactive series, as

$$\ldots \to {}^{226}\text{Ra} \xrightarrow[1600\ y]{\alpha} \quad {}^{222}\text{Rn} \xrightarrow[3.82\ d]{\alpha} \quad {}^{218}\text{Po} \xrightarrow[3.05\ min]{\alpha} \ldots,^*$$

or, in several fission disintegration series, as

$$\ldots \to {}^{140}\text{Ba} \xrightarrow[12.8\ d]{\beta-} \text{La} \xrightarrow[1.67\ d]{\beta-} {}^{140}\text{Ca (stable)}$$

or,

$$\ldots \to {}^{90}\text{Sr} \xrightarrow[28.1\ y]{\beta-} \text{Y} \xrightarrow[64.1\ h]{\beta-} {}^{90}\text{Zr (stable)}$$

Considering a longer lived parent-daughter pair, as

$${}^{226}\text{Ra (1600 y)} \xrightarrow{\alpha} {}^{222}\text{Rn (3.82 d), or } {}^{90}\text{Sr (28.1 y)} \xrightarrow{\beta-} {}^{90}\text{Y (64.1 h),}$$

Eqs. 4.12–4.14 apply for the growth and decay of daughter and its activity as a function of time. In the initial stage, when there is only the parent, N_1 remains much greater than N_2 for some time and the rate of the formation of the daughter ($\lambda_1 N_1$) exceeds that of its decay ($= \lambda_2 N_2$), though always $\lambda_2 > \lambda_1$. As the amount of the daughter builds up with time, a stage will be reached when its formation rate equals its decay rate. This corresponds to the establishment of an equilibrium between the parent and the daughter in respect of their relative amounts and rates of decay. Equilibrium is attained when the contribution of the term $e^{-\lambda_2 t}$ becomes insignificant. This implies in other words $e^{-\lambda_2 t}$ tends to zero with time and $\lambda_2 - \lambda_1$ may be approximately equated to λ_2. Under these conditions Eq. 4.12 simplifies to

$$N_2 = \frac{\lambda_1}{\lambda_2} N_{1\cdot 0}\, e^{-\lambda_1 t}$$

$$= \frac{\lambda_1}{\lambda_2} N_1$$

or

$$\boxed{\frac{N_2}{N_1} = \frac{\lambda_1}{\lambda_2} = \frac{\tau_2}{\tau_1} = \text{constant}} \qquad (4.21)$$

and

$$A_2 = \lambda_2 N_2 = \lambda_1 N_1 = A_1 \qquad (4.22)$$

The total activity after equilibrium

$$A_{\text{total}} = A_1 + A_2 = 2 A_1 \qquad (4.23)$$

Hence on the attainment of equilibrium, two results follow:

*See Appendix I for full disintegration series.

(i) the relative amounts of parent to daughter N_1/N_2 become constant independent of time and equal to the ratio of their half-lives.

(ii) Thereafter the rate of decay of the daughter equals that of the parent, as long as the parent species exists.

The radioactive equilibrium is not, however, reached abruptly, rather it is continuously approached, as $e^{-\lambda_2 t}$ tends to vanish. The *actual time for the* establishment of the steady state depends on *how close we propose to approach it**, *i.e.* on the value of $e^{\lambda_1 - \lambda_2}$. This depends on both the actual value of τ_2 and on the ratio of τ_1/τ_2. Overman and Clark have computed the times required for approaching the steady state to within (a) 0.1, (b) 0.05, (c) 0.01 and (d) 0.001 for different τ_1/τ_2 ratios[3] over the range 1 to 10.

4.5.7 SECULAR AND TRANSIENT EQUILIBRIUM

The radioactive equilibrium described above may be of two types: (a) *secular* and (b) *transient*. The former being a limiting case of the latter, the difference is only in degree. The one condition common to both secular and transient equilibria is that the parent's half-life be greater than that of the daughter. It is by how much τ_1 is greater than τ_2 *and in relation to the experimenter's observation time* (say 1–10 years or more) that permits a distinction to be made between the two types of equilibria, though arbitrarily to some extent. The other feature that after the attainment of the equilibrium, the daughter and descendents decay with the half-life of the parent holds good for both secular and transient equilibria. The more important features of distinction between the two types are listed in Table 4.1.

(a) *Examples of Secular Equilibrium*

(1) $^{238}U \xrightarrow[4.5 \times 10^9 \text{ y}]{\alpha} \, ^{234}Th \xrightarrow[24.1 \text{ d}]{\beta^-}$ disintegration series,

(2) $^{226}Ra \xrightarrow[1600 \text{ y}]{\alpha} \, ^{222}Rn \xrightarrow[3.82 \text{ d}]{\alpha}$ disintegration series,

(3) $^{90}Sr \xrightarrow[28.1 \text{ y}]{\beta^-} \, ^{90}Y \xrightarrow[64.1 \text{ h}]{\beta^-} \, ^{90}Zr$ (stable).

Figure 4.8 shows the decay and growth of the daughter ^{90}Y in secular equilibrium with the parent ^{90}Sr.

(b) *Examples of Transient Equilibrium*

(1) $^{234}Th \xrightarrow[24.1 \text{ d}]{\beta^-} \, ^{234}Pa \xrightarrow[1.18 \text{ min}]{\beta^-}$ disintegration series

---

*One can envisage approaching radioactive equilibrium to within a specified extent practicable. *Absolute equilibrium* can never be attained, for it implies that $dN_2/dt = dN_n/dt = 0$. It is clear that dN_1/dt can only approach zero, but can never be zero for that would be a negation of the radioactivity of the parent.

TABLE 4.1: Secular and transient equilibria

Secular equilibrium	Transient equilibrium
1. $\tau_1 \gg \tau_2$ and	$\tau_1 \gg \tau_2$ but
$\tau_2 \gg$ observation epoch	$\tau_i \leqslant$ observation epoch
2. As $\tau_1 \to \infty$ (or $\lambda_1 \to 0$)	τ_i is finite, so also λ_1
$e^{-\lambda_1 t} \to 1$	$e^{-\lambda_1 t} < 1$
3. The general equation	The general equation remains unchanged
$N_2 = \dfrac{\lambda_1 N_{1\cdot 0}}{\lambda_2 - \lambda_1} [e^{-\lambda_1 t} - e^{-\lambda_2 t}]$	
simplifies to	
$N_2 = \dfrac{\lambda_1}{\lambda_2} N_{1\cdot 0} (1 - e^{-\lambda_2 t})$	
4. Further, after a sufficiently long time	
$N_2 = \dfrac{\lambda_1}{\lambda_2} = N_{1\cdot 0} e^{-\lambda_1 t}$	$N_2 = \dfrac{\lambda_1}{\lambda_2 - \lambda_1} N_{1\cdot 0} e^{-\lambda_1 t}$
or	or
$\dfrac{N_2}{N_{1\cdot 0}} \left(\simeq \dfrac{N_2}{N_1} \right) = \dfrac{\lambda_1}{\lambda_2}$	$\dfrac{N_2}{N_1} = \dfrac{\lambda_1}{\lambda_2 - \lambda_1}$
5. In the case of a series	
$\dfrac{N_1}{\tau_1} = \dfrac{N_2}{\tau_2} = \ldots \dfrac{N_n}{\tau_n} = \text{constant}$	

(2) $^{222}\text{Rn} \xrightarrow[3.82\,\text{d}]{\alpha} {}^{218}\text{Po} \xrightarrow[3.05\,\text{min}]{\alpha}$ disintegration series

(3) $^{140}\text{Ba} \xrightarrow[12.8\,\text{d}]{\beta^-} {}^{140}\text{La} \xrightarrow[40\,\text{h}]{\beta^-} {}^{140}\text{Ce}$ (stable)

(4) $^{80m}\text{Br} \xrightarrow[4.4\,\text{h}]{\text{IT}} {}^{80}\text{Br} \xrightarrow[17.6\,\text{min}]{\beta^-} {}^{80}\text{Kr}$ (stable)

Figure 4.9a shows the decay and growth of the daughter ^{140}La in transient equilibrium with the parent ^{140}Ba. The daughter activity grows to a maximum after separation from the parent in time equal to its mean life $\bar{\tau}_2$ ($= 1.44\,\tau_2 = 57.6$ h).

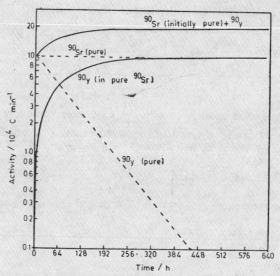

Fig. 4.8 Secular equilibrium between parent ^{90}Sr ($\tau = 28.1$ y) and daughter ^{90}Y ($\tau = 64.1$ h).

Thus, it is only the relative time scales which distinguish secular from transient equilibrium. If, for instance, some immortal agency were to measure and record the activities of ^{90}Sr and the daughter ^{90}Y in a sample, at intervals of 25 years over a period of 2 to 3 centuries, the activity curves would run down as in the case of transient equilibrium. On the other hand if the study of the system ^{140}Ba $\xrightarrow{\beta^-}$ ^{140}La were confined to a few days only, the activities being measured at intervals of one hour, the decay pattern would simulate secular equilibrium.

The different types of parent-decay, daughter-growth and equilibrium relationships can be demonstrated qualitatively by adjusting the rate of in-flow of water from one vessel (parent) to another (daughter) relative to the out-flow from the latter. This is illustrated in Fig. 4.9 b.

In the case of systems displaying secular equilibrium, the relation

$$\lambda_1 N_1 = \lambda_2 N_2 = \ldots = \lambda_n N_n \tag{4.22}$$

enables the calculation of the half-life period of any one member if that of any other member is known and the relative amounts of the two members in equilibrium are known, assuming no component of the system has been removed or allowed to escape. This is particularly helpful in assessing the half-life of a very long lived component. For instance, it is known that in naturally occurring uranium minerals, each g of ^{238}U is associated with 0.339 μ g of ^{226}Ra of half-life period 1600 y. Converting the amounts in grams to numbers of atoms, we have

$$\frac{N_U}{N_{Ra}} = \frac{226}{238 \times 0.339 \times 10^{-6}} = 2\ 801 \times 10^6$$

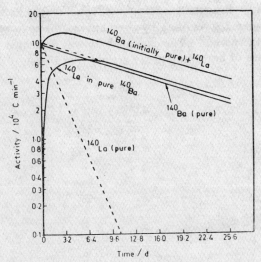

Fig. 4.9a Transient equilibrium between ^{140}Ba ($\tau = 12.8$ d) and daughter ^{140}La ($\tau = 1.67$ d).

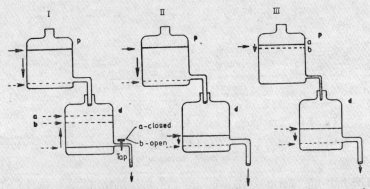

Fig. 4.9b A qualitative demonstration of parent decay and daughter growth in terms of levels and rates of flow of water from parent vessel (p) to daughter vessel (d). I: $\tau_p < \tau_d$, II: $\tau_p = \tau_d$, III: $\tau_p > \tau_d$.

and equating

$$\frac{N_U}{N_{Ra}} = \frac{\tau_U}{\tau_{Ra}}$$

and substituting

$$\tau_{Ra} = 1600 \text{ y}$$

$$\tau_U = 1600 \times 2.801 \times 10^6 = 4.48 \times 10^9 \text{ y}$$

4.5.8 BRANCHING DECAY

Though most radionuclides decay in a unique way, some nuclides are known to decay by two or more alternative modes. This is in addition to all β^+ active nuclides which have electron capture as an alternative mode of decay.   Branching decay by different modes happens whenever the daughter nuclides resulting by alternative paths have each a mass less than that of the parent.   The case of ^{64}Cu was presented in Fig. 4.1(f). Other examples of branching decay are given in Fig. 4.10.

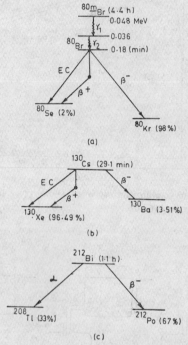

Fig. 4.10 Branching decays[1] (a) ^{80m}Br, (b) ^{130}Cs, and (c) ^{212}Bi

(from Strominger, J.M. Hollander and G.T. Seaborg[1], reproduced with authors' permission).

The half-life periods shown are the *net* half-life periods of all the branches of decay. For each branch of decay there is a characteristic *partial decay constant* ($\lambda_1, \lambda_2, \dots$) and the *total decay constant* is given by

$$\lambda_t = \lambda_1 + \lambda_2 + \dots + \lambda_n. \tag{4.24}$$

The corresponding *partial half-lives* are given by

$$\tau_1 = \frac{0.693}{\lambda_1}; \quad \tau_2 = \frac{0.693}{\lambda_2}; \quad \tau_n = \frac{0.693}{\lambda_n}, \text{ etc.}$$

and the *total half-life perod* τ_t is given by

$$\frac{1}{\tau_t} = \frac{1}{\tau_1} + \frac{1}{\tau_2} + \dots \frac{1}{\tau_n}$$

or

$$\tau_t = \frac{0.693}{\lambda_t} = \frac{0.693}{\lambda_1 + \lambda_2 + \dots \lambda_n} \tag{4.25}$$

The fraction f_i of the parent decaying by the ith mode is given by

$$\boxed{f_i = \frac{\lambda_i}{\lambda_t}}$$ (4.26)

We shall illustrate these statements with respect to the branching decay of ^{64}Cu (*vide* Fig. 4.1f).

Parent ^{64}Cu: mass $= 63.929\ 761$ u; $\tau_t = 12.8$ h; $\lambda_t = 0.0541$ h^{-1}.

Decay by:

Path 1 (β^-): 39%	*Path* 2 (β^+): 19%	*Path* 3 (EC): 42%
daughter: ^{64}Zn	daughter: ^{64}Ni	daughter: ^{64}Ni
mass: 63.929 145 u	mass: 63.927 959 u	mass: 63.927 959 u
$\Delta m = -616\ \mu$ u	$\Delta m = -1\ 802\ \mu$ u	$\Delta m = -1\ 802\ \mu$ u
$f_1 = 0.39$	$f_2 = 0.19$	$f_3 = 0.42$
$\lambda_1 = 0.021\ 1$ h^{-1}	$\lambda_2 = 0.010\ 3$ h^{-1}	$\lambda_3 = 0.022\ 7$ h^{-1}
$\tau_1 = 32.844$ h	$\tau_2 = 67.28$ h	$\tau_3 = 30.53$ h

4.6 Alpha Decay

Having considered some of the general features common to all types of radioactivity, the following modes of decay will be discussed here in detail. (a) α decay, (b) β^- decay (c) β^+ decay, (d) electron capture, (e) radiative deexcitation, (f) isomeric transition, and (g) internal conversion.

4.6.1 THE α ACTIVE NUCLIDES

In α decay, the parent nucleus $^A_Z X$ emits an α particle ($= ^4_2$He) leaving behind a daughter nucleus of four mass units less and charge two units less, $^{A-4}_{Z-2}Y$, *i.e.* shifting two places to the left in the Periodic Table of elements. Thus $^{226}_{88}$Ra $\xrightarrow[1600\ \text{y}]{}$ $^{222}_{86}$Rn $+ \alpha$; $^{239}_{94}$Pu $\xrightarrow[24\ 000\ \text{y}]{}$ $^{235}_{92}$U $+ \alpha$. ^{209}Bi being the heaviest stable nuclide in nature, all nuclides of $A \geqslant 210$ and $Z > 83$ tend to decay by α emission, and the very heavy nuclides $Z \geqslant 92$ do so in competition with the process of fission (*vide* Chapter 6). Of the stable elements in the middle of the Periodic Table there are some nuclides as $^{144}_{60}$Nd, $^{147}_{62}$Sm, $^{152}_{64}$Gd, $^{174}_{72}$Hf and $^{190}_{78}$Pt which are feebly α active with very long half-lives ranging from 10^{11} to 10^{15} y.

4.6.2 THE RANGE AND IONIZING POWER OF α PARTICLES

The α particles in radioactive disintegrations have a range of a few cm in air, and about 0.004 cm in aluminium. The term *range in air* refers to the distance in air from the source up to which practically all the α particles emitted traverse and beyond which their number abruptly falls. *The mean range R in air is related to the energy E of the particle by the relation*

(α)

$$R = 0.318 \ E^{3/2} \tag{4.27}$$

As an α particle passes through air, or any matter, it loses energy by exciting and ionizing the atoms of matter it collides with. On the average each α particle produces around 2500 ion pairs per mm path in the first 3 cm or so of air and the ionizing power rapidly increases to around 7000 ion pairs/mm towards the last few mm of the traject.

The *stopping power* of a medium is defined as

$$S = -dE/dx \tag{4.28}$$

It is given by the expression

$$S = KZ \ln \frac{2m_e \ v^2}{I} \cdot \simeq \frac{R_{air}}{R_{medium}} \tag{4.28a}$$

where K is a constant, Z the atomic number of the atoms of the medium, m_e the electron mass, v the velocity of the particle and I the mean excitation-ionization energy of the atom of the medium. The ratio of mean ranges in air to that in a medium gives the *approximate stopping power* of the medium.

4.6.3 The α Particle Energy Spectrum

The energy spectrum of α particles from a given nuclide consists of a few sharp monoergic lines corresponding to the decay of the parent nucleus to various excited and ground levels of the daughter nucleus,[4,5] Fig. 4.11 shows the α decay spectrum of ^{212}Bi[5]. The *maximum* energy of the decay is the equivalent of mass loss

$$E = [m_p - (m_r + m_\alpha)] \ 931 \ \text{MeV} \tag{4.29}$$

where m_r is the mass of the recoiling daughter nucleus. This energy E is shared between the recoil nucleus and the α particle as their kinetic energies in the inverse ratio of their masses

$$E = E_r + E_\alpha \tag{4.30}$$

and

$$E_r \ m_r = E_\alpha \ m_\alpha \tag{4.31}$$

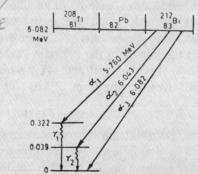

Fig. 4.11 α decay spectrum of ^{212}Bi

(from *Radiochemistry of Bismuth*, by K.S. Bhatki, NAS-NS-3061, Nuclear Science Series—National Research Council, 1977, reproduced with permission).

the last being a direct consequence of the conservation of linear momentum.

Since m_α is slight, being close to $4\,u$, most of the energy of the decay comes off as the kinetic energy of the α particle. Thus in the $^{232}Th \xrightarrow{\ \alpha\ } {}^{228}Rn$ decay, where $E = 4.07$ MeV, the kinetic energy of the α and the recoil nucleus are found to be 4.0 and 0.07 MeV respectively in agreement with Eq. 4.31.

4.6.4 GEIGER-NUTTAL'S LAW

An interesting relation has been observed between the energy (maximum) of the α particle emitted and the half-life period of the emitter. As the energy of the α-particle increases, from nuclide to nuclide, their half-lives diminish enormously rapidly. As the energy increases from about 4 MeV to 9 MeV, the half-life period decreases from 10^{10} y ($\approx 10^{17}$ s) to $\simeq 10^{-7}$ s, as shown below.

TABLE 4.2: Half-life and energy of α particles

α active nuclide	Energy of α/MeV	Half-life period/s
^{232}Th	4.0 (minimum)	4.31×10^{17} (maximum)
^{226}Ra	4.78	5.02×10^{10}
^{222}Rn	5.49	3.30×10^{5}
^{220}Rn	6.28	55.6
^{212}Po	8.78 (maximum)	3×10^{-7} (minimum)
Ratio: maximum/minimum	2.24	1.44×10^{24}

This extraordinary variation between the energy of alphas emitted from different nuclides and their half-lives was correlated by Geiger and Nuttal in the form of an empirical law known after them[6]. Using the decay constant in place of the half-life period ($\lambda = 0.693/\tau$) the law may be stated as

$$\log \lambda = A \log E + B \tag{4.32}$$

with A and B as constants. In Fig. 4 12 $\log \lambda$ *versus* $\log R$ (where the range $R = 0.318\,E^{3/2}$) for different α emitters are plotted. All the known α active nuclides of a given series fall on the same line; the three lines for the naturally occurring series $(4n + 0)$, $(4n + 2)$ $(4n + 3)$ are roughly parallel. The empirical law of Geiger and Nuttal remained inexplicable in the beginning, but later when an adequate theory of α decay was developed, the same law proved a strong evidence in its favour.

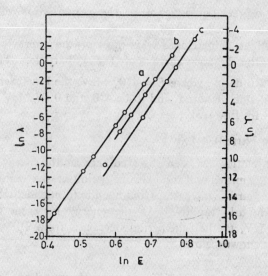

Fig. 4.12 α decay constant as a function of α range: the Geiger-Nuttal law
(a) the $(4n + 2)$ uranium series,
(b) the $(4n + 0)$ thorium series,
(c) the $(4n + 3)$ actinium series
(from *Nuclear Physics*, by I. Kaplan, © 1955, 1963. Addison-Wesley Publishing Co., Inc., reproduced with permission).

4.6.5 THE THEORY OF α DECAY

(a) α Decay: A Problem in Classical Physics

The spontaneously occurring α decay from a large number of nuclides remained a challenging problem in classical physics, for it was not clear how α particles of energy between 4 and 9 MeV are able to escape from nuclei against a large Coulomb barrier, of the order of ~ 30 MeV, which prevents the entry into the nucleus of α particles of similar energy from the outside. Rutherford's experiments clearly showed that when thin foils of different metals offering much lower Coulomb barriers* were bombarded by α particles of energy of the order 8–9 MeV, all of them were scattered outside the nucleus and none could penetrate the nucleus. While this result is to be expected, the energy of the α particles being much less than the Coulomb barrier, the reverse behaviour, *viz.* the escape of α particles of similar energy from inside the nucleus against the same barrier contravened known laws of physics. The anamolous situation is depicted in Fig. 4.13. The α decay would appear as anamolous as an elastic ball dropped from a certain height being able to rise during the rebound much above this height!

---

*The *maximum* Coulomb barrier between a nucleus and an α particle is given, in cgs units by $V_c = 2Ze^2/R'$, where Z is the atomic number of the nucleus, e, the unit charge and R' the sum of radii of the nucleus and of the α particle.

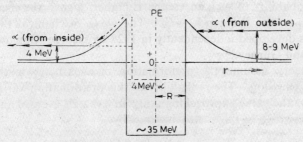

Fig. **4.13** The α decay puzzle.

(b) *A Wave-Mechanical Solution: The Tunnel Effect*

The problem of the α decay is similar to that of the particle in a box in wave mechanics, where the particle of energy less than the potential barrier at the box boundary can escape out of the box once in a way, *i.e.* with a small but finite probability. Classical laws expect always a node, *i.e.* zero amplitude for the particle at the wall of the potential barrier $(V > E$: Fig. 4.14a), whereas on wave mechanics, a small finite amplitude as shown in Fig. 4.14b is possible at the boundary, provided the potential barrier is not infinitely high, or infinitely wide.[8] As a result of this the particle is able to traverse the barrier once in a way as if it had found a tunnel in the barrier.

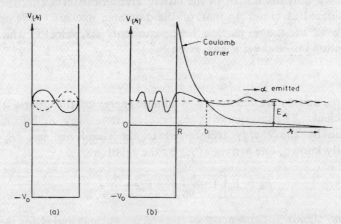

Fig. 4.14   The problem of α decay and the particle in a box
    (a) Classical model,
    (b) Wave-mechanical model: the tunnel effect,
(from Nuclear Physics/An Introduction, by W.E. Burcham
© 1973.   Longman   Group   Ltd., reproduced with permission).

Similarly, a solution to the Schrödinger equation for the α particle in a nucleus shows that there is a finite probability for the escape of the α particle, in spite of a high potential barrier $(V > E_\alpha)$, as a tunnel effect, provided the barrier is not infinitely high or infinitely wide.

The probability of such an escape is higher, higher the energy of the particle, *i.e.* less the gap $V - E_\alpha$. The wave mechanical theory of α decay was developed independently in 1928 by George Gamow[9] and by Condon and Gurney.[10]

The theory assumes the preformation of α particles in the nucleus before its emission. The probability of this preformation varies between 0.1 and 1, the value approaching unity in even-Z, even-N nuclei. The α decay constant on this theory is given by

$$\lambda = \theta\lambda_0 P \tag{4.33}$$

where θ is the preformation factor, λ_0 a frequency factor representing the number of times an α particle arrives at the nuclear border and P is the probability of escape. These are considered below.

The frequency factor: The frequency of arrival of the α particle at the nuclear border is simply the ratio of its velocity v_α to the effective diameter $2R$ of the nucleus, *i.e.*

$$\lambda_0 = v_\alpha/2R \tag{4.34}$$

The two terms v_α and R have to be carefully understood. If the parent nucleus is envisaged as surrounding the slightly smaller nucleus of the daughter (product of α decay), then for the release of the α particle it need reach only the border of the latter. Hence, the term *effective radius* is considered as closer to that of the daughter nucleus. The relevant velocity v_α of the α particle here represents its velocity while it is commuting inside the nucleus, given by

$$v_\alpha = \sqrt{2E_\alpha/m_\alpha}$$

where m_α and E_α are the mass and kinetic energy of the α particle inside the nucleus. The last quantity, E_α, exceeds its energy E_0 outside after emission by the energy transferred to the recoil nucleus. E_0 being generally known, one arrives at E_α by the relation

$$E_\alpha = E_0\left[1 + \frac{m_\alpha}{m_r}\right] = E_0\frac{A}{A-4} \tag{4.35}$$

where m_r stands for the mass of the recoil nucleus and A for the mass number of the parent.

The frequency factor λ_0 also stands for the decay constant in the absence of a potential barrier, *i.e.* $\lambda_0 = \lambda$ when $\theta = P = 1$. Applied as an example to ^{238}U which emits α particles of energy 4.22 MeV, the frequency factor comes to be 7.77×10^{20} s^{-1},* which means the α particle reaches the effective border of the nucleus 7.77×10^{20} times per second. What fraction of this results in the escape of the particle is given by the probability factor considered below.

*See footnote on next page.

The probability factor: The probability factor** representing the fraction of the arrivals of the α at the border resulting in its escape is given by

$$P = \exp - \left[\frac{4Z_\alpha Z_r e^2}{\hbar v_\alpha} (b - \sin b \cos b) \right] \qquad (4.36a)$$

where Z_α and Z_r are the nuclear charge numbers of the α particle $(= 2)$ and of the recoil nucleus $(= Z - 2)$, Z being that of the parent nucleus, and where

$$b = \cos^{-1} \left[\frac{m_\alpha v_\alpha^2 R}{4e^2 (Z - 2)} \right]^{1/2} \qquad (4.36b)$$

radius of parent nucleus

Replacing Z_α and Z_r by their values, Eq. 4.36a simplifies to

$$P = \exp - \left[\frac{8(Z - 2)e^2}{\hbar v_\alpha} (b - \sin b \cos b) \right] \qquad (4.37)$$

Because of the exponential nature of the probability factor, even small changes in the terms involved, v_α and R, alter the escape probability enormously.

Applied to the example of the α-decay of ^{238}U, one finds the probability factor is of the order of $e^{-88.8} = 2.72 \times 10^{-39}$ obtained by substituting the values of v_α, R and other constants in Eq. 4.36(b) and 4.37. We first calculate separately the factors making up the exponent of P (Eq. 4.37). It is simpler here to work in cgs units:

(i) $\quad \dfrac{8(Z - 2) e^2}{\hbar v_\alpha} = \dfrac{8 \times 90 \times (4.8)^2 \times 10^{-20}}{1.054 \times 10^{-27} \times 1.4357 \times 10^9} = 109.63$

(ii) The inverse cosine function

$$b = \cos^{-1} \left[\frac{m_\alpha v_\alpha^2 R}{4e^2(Z - 2)} \right]^{1/2} = \cos^{-1} \left[\frac{4 \times 1.66 \times 10^{-24} \times (1.4357)^2}{4 \times (4.8)^2 \times 10^{-20} \times 90} \times 10^{18} \times 9.2434 \times 10^{-13} \right]^{1/2}$$

$$= 1.1696$$

*We first convert E^0 $(= 4.22$ MeV) to E_α by Eq. 4.35

$$E_\alpha = 4.22 \times \frac{238}{234} = 4.2718 \text{ MeV}$$

$$= 6.8434 \times 10^{-13} \text{ J}$$

Next we obtain $v_\alpha = \sqrt{\dfrac{2E_\alpha}{m}}$

$$= \sqrt{\frac{2 \times 6.8434 \times 10^{-13}}{4 \times 1.66 \times 10^{-27}}} = 1.4357 \times 10^7 \text{ m/s}.$$

Lastly, the radius of the daughter nucleus ^{234}Th is given by

$$1.5 \times (234)^{1/3} \text{ F} = 9.2434 \times 10^{-15} \text{ m}.$$

Hence, the frequency factor

$$\lambda_0 = \frac{v_\alpha}{2R} = \frac{1.4357 \times 10^7}{2 \times 9.2434 \times 10^{-15}} = 7.77 \times 10^{20} \text{ s}^{-1}.$$

**The probability factor is also referred to as the *permeability* or *transparency* of the potential barrier.

(iii) $(b - \sin b \cos b) = 1.1696 - 0.9206 \times 0.39055 = 0.8100$

Hence $P = \exp\left[-\,(i) \times (iii)\right] = \exp\left[-\,109.63 \times 0.81\right]$

$$= \exp(-\,88.8) = 2.72 \times 10^{-39}$$

Finally, one arrives at the decay constant

$$\lambda = \theta\lambda_0 P = \frac{\theta v_\alpha}{2R} \exp -\left[\frac{8\,(Z-2)e^2}{\hbar v_\alpha}\right](b - \sin b \cos b) \qquad (4.38)$$

by substituting the values obtained for λ_0 and P in the above.

$$\lambda = 1 \times 7.77 \times 10^{20} \times 2.72 \times 10^{-39} = 2.11 \times 10^{-18}\ \text{s}^{-1}$$

whereas the value of λ for the α decay of ^{238}U as obtained from the observed half-life of 4.5×10^9 y is

$$= \frac{0.693}{4.5 \times 10^9 \times 3.6 \times 10^7}\ \text{s}^{-1} = 4.28 \times 10^{-18}\ \text{s}^{-1}.$$

Considering the approximate nature of Eq. 4.38, the agreement would appear to be good.

The close agreement makes the wave-mechanical theory of α decay by tunnel effect acceptable. The significance of $P \simeq 10^{-39}$ must be appreciated. The α particle of energy 4.22 MeV must knock at the border of the ^{238}U nucleus with the potential barrier of 28.7 MeV, some 10^{39} times before it can escape out of the nucleus. Higher the energy of the α emitted (hence also higher its velocity), smaller would be the negative exponent constituting the probability factor (Eq. 4.38) and hence a higher probability of escape or a larger decay constant, thus providing a qualitative basis of the empirical law of Geiger and Nuttal (Sec. 4.6.4).

Written in the logarithmic form, Eq. 4.38 becomes

$$\log \lambda = \log \theta\,\frac{v_\alpha}{2R} - \frac{8\,(Z-2)\,e^2}{2.303\,\hbar v_\alpha}\,(b - \sin b \cos b)$$

which can be simplified to the form

$$\log \lambda \simeq a - b\frac{(Z-2)}{v_\alpha} \qquad (4.39)$$

where a and b are constants, on the justifiable assumption that the variation of $\log \dfrac{v_\alpha}{2R}$ is small. The variation in both v_α and R for the α emitters are themselves small. Thus, a plot of $\log \lambda$ vs. $1/v_\alpha$ for a given Z, i.e. the α emitting isotopes of the same element should be linear, with a slope $= -8\,(Z-2)\,e^2 \times (b - \sin b \cos b)/2.303\,\hbar$. This may be considered as the theoretical basis for the Geiger-Nuttal law. The results of Kaplan for the α emitting isotopes of Po, Rn, Ra, Th, U, Pu and Cm confirm this expectation.[7]

The above wave-mechanical theory of α decay is limited to even-Z, even-N α emitters which have no resultant spin. Where Z or N or both are odd, the theory is less satisfactory due to centrifugal potential barrier, in addition to the coulombian, since these nuclei have a resultant spin.

4.7 Beta Decay

As pointed out under Sec. 4.2 there are three types of beta decay, β^-, β^+ and electron capture (EC).

4.7.1(a) β^- Decay ~ give off e

Under this type of radioactivity one of the neutrons in the parent nucleus transforms into a proton and in the process an electron (β^-) and an antineutrino* are emitted.

$$n \rightarrow p + \beta^- + \bar{\nu}$$

The daughter nucleus thus formed would appertain to an element one place to the right of the parent in the Periodic Table of elements. For example

$$^{24}_{11}Na \xrightarrow[15.03 \text{ h}]{} {}^{24}_{12}Mg \text{ (stable)} + \beta^- + \bar{\nu}$$

$$^{32}_{15}P \xrightarrow[14.28 \text{ d}]{} {}^{32}_{16}S \text{ (stable)} + \beta^- + \bar{\nu}$$

β^- decay is common over the entire range of nuclides and amongst the naturally occurring heavy radioactive nuclides and in fission products.

(b) β^+ Decay ~ gain e^-)

Here one of the protons of the nucleus of the parent atom transforms into a neutron, emitting in the process a positron and a neutrino

$$p \rightarrow n + \beta^+ + \nu$$

The daughter nucleus would belong to an element one place to the left in the Periodic Table of elements; e.g.

$$^{22}_{11}Na \xrightarrow[2.62 \text{ y}]{} {}^{22}_{10}Ne \text{ (stable)} + \beta^+ + \nu$$

$$^{45}_{22}Ti \xrightarrow[3.08 \text{ h}]{} {}^{45}_{21}Sc \text{ (stable)} + \beta^+ + \nu$$

(c) Electron Capture

Insofar as the parent-daughter relations are concerned, the process of electron capture (EC) is similar to that of β^+ decay, for in both cases a

---

*The *antineutrino* is an antiparticle of the neutrino differing only in its spin orientation with respect to the angular momentum vector. In what follows the term neutrino alone may be used.

nuclear proton is transformed into a neutron and the daughter element shifts one place to the left in the Periodic Table. The difference lies in the fact that in the electron capture process, as the name implies, an electron of the outer sphere of the same atom generally of the K, or less often, the L shell is captured by the nucleus leading to a transformation of a proton into a neutron.

$$p + e \text{ (from outer shell)} \to n + \nu$$

For example,

$$^{55}_{26}\text{Fe} \xrightarrow[2.6\,\text{y}]{\text{EC}} {}^{55}_{25}\text{Mn (stable)} + \nu$$

$$^{131}_{56}\text{Ba} \xrightarrow[12.0\,\text{d}]{\text{EC}} \nu + {}^{131}_{55}\text{Cs} \xrightarrow[9.7\,\text{d}]{\text{EC}} {}^{131}_{54}\text{Xe (stable)} + \nu$$

The outer electrons, now one less in number, just balance the nuclear charge which is also one less now. No other change is involved following electron capture, apart from the emission of X-rays when the outer electrons rearrange themselves in the process. Decay by EC occurs as an alternative to all β^+ decays, the converse is not true except under condition of the resulting mass loss exceeding two electron masses (*vide infra*).

4.7.2 THE ABSORPTION OF β PARTICLES AND THEIR RANGE THROUGH MATTER

The β particles being a few hundred times more penetrating and about as many times less ionizing than the α particles, their absorption is studied in denser media as metals, usually aluminium. The pattern of absorption of β particles and their range-energy relation depend on whether the particles are all of one energy or of a mixed energy spectrum. We shall consider the two cases separately.

(a) β Particles of Energy Continuum

To a good approximation, the number of β particles as they pass through matter decreases exponentially with the thickness of the absorber, thus

$$N_x = N_0 \exp(-\mu x) \tag{4.40}$$

where N_x and N_0 are the numbers of betas after passing through x and zero thickness of the absorber, and μ is the linear absorption coefficient of the latter. The thickness is more conveniently expressed in units of surface density of the absorber, *i.e.* mass per unit area (mg cm^{-2}). Besides being more easily determined, this way of expressing the thickness has the important advantage that the range or the distance traversed by the particles of a given energy is independent of the nature of the absorber. This is because the β particle range depends on the number of collisions the betas make with the atomic electrons of the absorbing medium, *i.e.* on the number of electrons per unit mass or on its Z/A value, which varies but slightly from substance to substance. For instance, in going from a light metal like Al to a heavy metal like Au, the variation in Z/A is from 0.48 to 0.40 and the ranges of 1 MeV betas in these two metals are 400 and 500 mg/cm² respectively.

(b)   *Monoergic β Particles*   → 1 kind (stage) — Energy β particle.

The variation with thickness of the absorption of monoergic betas of energy greater than 0.2 MeV is practically linear, unlike the exponential variation in the case of a beam of betas of mixed energies, described above.   The *effective range* is given by the intercept of the linear portion with the thickness axis. It should, however, be noted that even if a beam of betas be initially of one energy, they keep losing varying fractions of their energy in the successive collisions with the atomic electrons of the absorbing medium, giving rise to a straggling effect.   The range is thus less precisely defined in this case   The empirical range-energy relations proposed by Katz and Penfold are:[11]

$$R = 412\, E_0^{(1.265 - 0.0954\, \ln E_0)} \quad : E_0 < 2.5 \text{ MeV} \tag{4.41}$$

$$R = 530\, E_0 - 106 \qquad\qquad : E_0 > 2.5 \text{ MeV} \tag{4.42}$$

Here the range R is in mg/cm² and E_0 is the end point energy in MeV.

4.7.3   ENERGETICS OF BETA DECAY

In all the cases of beta decay (β⁻ or β⁺ or EC) the mass of the parent atom must be greater than that of the daughter atom, *i e.* there must be a net loss of mass

$$\Delta m = (m_{\text{parent}} - m_{\text{daughter}}) > 0 \tag{4.43}$$

Inspection of the β⁻, β⁺ and EC reactions, show following further conditions have to be fulfilled for the respective modes of β decay.

(a)   *β⁻ Decay*

As in the β⁻ process an electron is to be created, the condition for this process to be energetically possible is

$$m_{z\,(\text{parent})} > (m_{z+1\,(\text{daughter})} + m_e)$$

$$\Delta m = [m_z - (m_{z+1} + m_e)] > 0 \tag{4.44}$$

It is sometimes argued that the mass of the electron m_e should not be included here (Eq. 4.44), as the electron lost in the β⁻ process is compensated by the subsequent gain of an electron from space to fill the vacancy in the outer sphere.   This is true when atomic masses are used. This energy released ($= 931\,\Delta m$ MeV) is shared between the products of the decay, *viz.*

$$E_t = \Delta m\, c^2 = E_e + E_v + E_r \tag{4.45}$$

where E_t is the total energy, and E_e, E_v and E_r are the kinetic energies

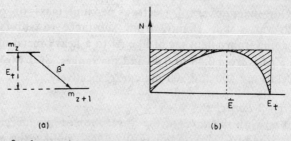

Fig. 4.15 β⁻ decay: (a) Energetics, (b) Energy spectrum: the β continuum.

of the electron, the neutrino and the recoil (daughter atom) (Fig. 4.15a). The energy of the recoil atom is, however, negligibly small being in the inverse ratio of the mass of the atom to that of an electron. Hence, it is fairly correct to write

$$E_t = E_e + E_\nu \tag{4.46}$$

Thus, practically the total energy of the decay reaction is shared between the electron and the neutrino as their kinetic energies in a continuous manner so that the energy spectrum of the electrons emitted is a continuum from zero to a maximum (E_{max} or E_t), also referred to as the *end point energy*. The neutrinos carry away the missing energy (shaded area of Fig. 4.15 b). The largest fraction of the electrons emitted have the mean energy $\overline{E}$, given by

$$\overline{E} = \frac{\displaystyle\int_0^{E_{max}} N(E)\,E\,dE}{\displaystyle\int_0^{E_{max}} N(E)\,dE} \tag{4.47}$$

The shape of the distribution curve and the value of $\overline{E}$ varies from system to system, $\overline{E}$ being generally round 30–80% of E_{max}.

The missing energy carried away by the neutrinos cannot be experimentally detected. The neutrinos being massless* and chargeless, the cross section of their interaction with atoms of matter is extremely low, being computed to be of the order of 10^{-48} m². Even the most efficient calorimeter would indicate only $\overline{E}$ as the energy per disintegration and not E_{max}. This was shown to be the case by Ellis and Wooster[12] in 1927 in their calorimetric experiment on the energy released in the decay of $^{210}Bi \xrightarrow{\beta^-} {}^{210}Po$, measured under conditions ensuring perfect absorption

---

*A calculation of the rest mass energy of the neutrino from the end point energy of β-decay in a large number of cases, shows it to be ~5×10^{-4} of an electron mass (= 25×10^{-8} u). This is considered as zero on account of the uncertainty associated with the measurement of end point energy.

of all the betas released and complete insulation. The calorimeter gave a value of 350 ± 40 keV per disintegration (which is $\bar{E}$), while E_t from mass loss is 1050 keV.

That the calorimetrically or otherwise observable value is $\bar{E} < E_t$ is well illustrated in the decay scheme for the transformation of $^{212}\text{Bi} \xrightarrow{\alpha,\ \beta^-} {}^{208}\text{Pb}$, which occurs *via* two alternative paths:

(i) $^{212}\text{Bi} \xrightarrow{\alpha} {}^{208}\text{Tl} \xrightarrow{\beta^-} {}^{208}\text{Pb}$ and

(ii) $^{212}\text{Bi} \xrightarrow{\beta^-} {}^{212}\text{Po} \xrightarrow{\alpha} {}^{208}\text{Pb}$

(see decay scheme Fig. 4.16).

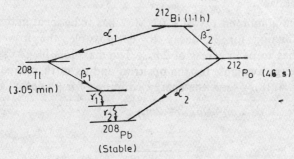

Fig. 4.16 Energetics of the transformation of ^{212}Bi into ^{208}Pb by alternative pathways.

Thermodynamically the total change in energy must be the same independent of the path. This holds good only if E_t values are used for the beta decays, and not the $\bar{E}$ values. Thus:

Path (i) (33%)		Path (ii) (67%)	
Process	*Energy/MeV*	*Process*	*Energy/MeV*
α_1	6.203	$\beta_2^- = E_{t_2}$	2.250
$\beta_1^- = E_{t_1}$	1.792	α_2	8.946
$\gamma_1 + \gamma_2$	3.200		
Total	11.195	Total	11.196

Until Pauli postulated the theory of the neutrino as a birth companion of the electron, the problem of the continuous spectrum of β-decay remained in the dark.

(b) β^+ *Decay*

On Dirac's theory, the creation of a positron (β^+ or e^+) involves the creation of an electron-positron pair. The electron is lifted out of the fully occupied negative states of energy while the hole left behind constitutes the positron. The minimum energy to be spent in the materialization of the pair of particles equals the sum of their rest mass energies

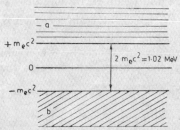

Fig. 4.17 Electron-positron pair production: Dirac's theory.

$(= 2m_e c^2 = 1.02$ MeV) where m_e is the electron $(=$ positron) rest mass (Fig. 4.17).

Since this minimum energy of 1.02 MeV has to be spent in the process of pair production for β^+ decay to be possible, the loss of mass $(m_z - m_{z-1})$ has to be in excess of $2m_e$. The mass loss in excess of $2m_e$ will be the energy available for the positron and its birth companion the neutrino (Fig. 4.18). Thus the energy condition for β^+ decay is   *Ask*

$$m_z - (m_{z-1} + 2m_e) > 0 \qquad (4.48)$$

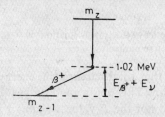

Fig. 4.18 Energetics of β^+ decay.

The net excess energy shared between the positron and the neutrino is given in units of MeV by

$$(m_z - m_{z-1} - 2m_e) \, 931 = E_{e^+} + E_\nu \qquad (4.49)$$

(c) Electron Capture

Since the only change occurring following electron capture is a re-arrangement of the residual electrons, for the process to be possible the energy condition required for EC is that the mass loss $(m_z - m_{z-1}) c^2$ be equal to the energy needed, E_K, for removing an electron from the K shell (K capture), or at least, the L shell E_L (L capture). The L captures being around 10 per cent of K capture, the capture of electrons from farther shells becomes less probable (see Fig. 4.19).

Since no other particle is emitted in the process, the energy of the reaction, less by E_K (or E_L) is wholly carried away by the neutrino and hence remains indetectable. Thus, for K capture, in units of MeV,

$$(m_z - m_{z-1}) \, 931 - E_K = E_\nu \qquad (4.50)$$

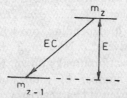

Fig. 4.19 Energetics of electron capture.

It should be noted that the neutrinos accompanying electron capture are all monoergic. The only observable energy change in EC is the emission of X-rays of the daughter nucleus, corresponding to the K or L shell being filled by electron jumps from outer levels.

Summarized below are the energy conditions to be fulfilled for the different beta decays to be possible.

(a) $0 < (m_z - m_{z+1})$ for β^- decay
(b) $0 < E_{K/L} < (m_z - m_{z-1})\, 931$ for EC   (4.51)
(c) $0 < 1.02 < (m_z - m_{z-1})\, 931$ for β^+

The above parent-daughter mass relations being so close to one another, in an isobaric series of nuclides (A constant, Z varying), all the isobars in the series would be radioactive, decaying successively by β^- or β^+ or EC into the neighbour nuclides till one (sometimes two)* stable nuclide(s) is reached which has a minimum mass or maximum binding energy. This is because as between two neighbour nuclides Z_A and $(Z \pm 1)_A$, the one or the other of the energy (conditions 4.51) would be fulfilled. Numerous examples of this have been cited in Sec. 3.3.5.

This is also evident by a look at the Segrè chart (Fig. 1.2) showing the zone of stability in the plot of N versus Z. Isobar lines cut the thin stability belt in such a way that nuclides above the belt are β^- active and those below are β^+ (or EC) active.

4.7.4 PROBLEMS OF β DECAY

It was the inexplicable problems associated with beta decay that necessitated the postulation by Pauli of the existence of the elusive neutrino, a particle of no mass and no charge but capable of having energy and angular momentum! The problem of *apparent non-conservation of energy* in β decay had already been mentioned. Though all β decays, whether of the $n \rightarrow p$ or $p \rightarrow n$ type, correspond to a finite energy release related to the mass loss $(m_z - m_{z \pm 1})$, the betas (e^- or e^+), come out with *all* values of energy from zero to a maximum, while energy conservation requires all the betas be monoergic, if neutrinos be not included.

A second problem associated with β decay concerns the *apparent non-conservation of spin*. As pointed out in Sec. 2.2 and 2.8, the elementary

---

*Two stable nuclides become possible in certain even A isobaric series (Sec. 3.3.5).

particles; electron, proton and neutron have each a spin of $1/2\ \hbar$, while the spins of nuclei are either 0, 1, 2,... *integral* times $\hbar$, or 1/2, 3/2, 5/2... semi-integral times $\hbar$, depending on whether the nuclei are of even-A or odd-A respectively*. Now in β decay, without involving neutrinos, the spin conservation breaks down, for in this type of decay, there is no change in the number of total nucleons A in the nucleus ($= N + Z$). The odd or even A characteristic of the daughter remains the same as that of the parent nucleus. Hence its total angular momentum must remain the same as that of the parent, or be less by an integral multiple of $\hbar$. Now when an e^- or e^+ is to be included as a product besides the daughter nucleus, conservation of spin breaks down, e.g.

$$^{35}S \;\rightarrow\; ^{35}Cl \;+\; e^-$$
$$\text{spin}\quad 3/2 \;\neq\; 3/2 \;+\; 1/2$$

$$^{24}Na \;\rightarrow\; ^{24}Mg \;+\; e^-$$
$$\text{spin}\quad 4 \;\neq\; 0 \;+\; 1/2$$

The integral spins 4 of ^{24}Na and 0 of ^{24}Mg are conserved. The non-conservation is only when a semi-integer is to be added to an integer on one side only.

There is yet another problem of beta decay, namely the *non-conservation of statistics*, if neutrinos were not involved. The total number of particles in the system after beta decay is either *one more* (β$^-$ and β$^+$) or *one less* (EC) compared to the initial system**. In other words, either an *odd* number of *total* particles becomes *even* after beta decay or *vice-versa*. This necessitates a change from either Fermi-Dirac to Bose-Einstein statistics, or *vice-versa*. In short, there is a non-conversation of statistics in all beta decays, unless a neutrino is postulated.

4.7.5 THE NEUTRINO

All the problems of non-conservation of energy, spin and statistics disappear with the creation of one more product species in β decay, *viz.* the neutrino of no mass and no charge but with a spin of $1/2\ \hbar$, and obeying Fermi-Dirac statistics.[13]

4.7.6 EXPERIMENTAL VERIFICATION OF THE EXISTENCE OF THE NEUTRINO

As mentioned earlier the peculiar properties of the neutrino make its

---

*As stated earlier (Sec. 2.6.3) in the ground state, even-Z, even-N nuclei have $I = 0$;
  odd-Z, odd-N nuclei have $I = 1, 2, 3, \ldots$ and
  odd-A (*i.e.* either Z or N is even and the other odd) nuclei have $I = 1/2, 3/2, 5/2, \ldots$.
**Thus, if neutrinos are not involved, in β$^-$: $n \rightarrow p + \beta^-$
                                              in β$^+$: $p \rightarrow n + \beta^+$ and
                                              in EC : $p + e \rightarrow n$.

direct detection almost impossible, as its cross section of interaction with matter is as low as 10^{-48} m². Though postulated as long back as 1931 by Pauli, it had not been possible to obtain experimental evidence of its existence till 1953, when Cowan and Reines, planned an inge-neous experiment to test the truth about the neutrino.[14,15]

If the reaction postulated by Pauli, *viz.*

$$p \rightarrow n + e^+ + \nu$$

be true, possibly the partial reverse of this, *viz.*

$$p + \nu \rightarrow n + e^+$$

also may be true, in which case it is only necessary to bring together protons and neutrinos in as high concentration (flux) as possible and search for the generation of neutrons and positrons both of which are easily identifiable.

A nuclear reactor in which a vast number of nuclear fissions take place all the time, and each fission event is accompanied by chains of beta decays, would be the proper source to provide antineutrinos in a high flux, if Pauli's hypothesis is correct, whereas a mass of water would provide a high concentration of protons.

All that was necessary was to place close to the reactor large tanks of water containing cadmium chloride in solution (A), the cadmium being for the detection of neutrons, sandwiched between larger tanks containing a liquid scintillator with many photomultipliers immersed to capture γ photons coming from different directions (B). The scintillator used was *popop* or terphenyl dissolved in triethyl benzene (see Fig. 4.20a).

If neutrinos existed, following reactions would be expected in the above arrangement:

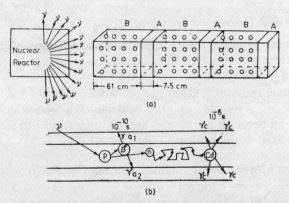

(a)

(b)

Fig. 4.20 The detection of the neutrino: the experiment of Cowan and Reines
(a) The experimental set up: (A) 200 litre tanks containing cadmium chloride solution, (B) 1600 litre tanks containing liquid scin-tillator and photomultipliers
(b) Paths of the products of ν + p interaction.

$$\underset{\substack{\nu \\ \text{from reactor}}}{\nu} + \underset{\substack{p \\ \text{from water}}}{p} \rightarrow e^+ + n \qquad (1)$$

The positron has a short life being an antiparticle: it reacts almost immediately (within $\sim 10^{-10}$ s) with an electron of matter and the two annihilate each other, producing in the process *two* prompt *gamma photons, each precisely of energy 0.51 MeV and proceeding in opposite directions*

$$e^+ + e^- \rightarrow \underset{0.51}{\gamma} + \underset{0.51 \text{ MeV}}{\gamma} \qquad (2)$$

This is the reverse of the process of pair production.
This is the *first event*.

The other product of reaction (1) is the neutron which takes appreciable time (1–10 μ s) to slow down through successive collisions with the hydrogen atoms of water molecules. Finally, the slowed neutron is captured by a cadmium atom on account of its very high cross section for this capture. The $^{114}Cd^*$ formed in returning to the ground state emits several γ photons of total energy ~ 9 MeV.

$$^{113}_{}Cd \, (n, \gamma) \, ^{114}Cd^* \rightarrow \, ^{114}Cd + \underbrace{\gamma + \gamma + \cdots \gamma}_{9 \text{ MeV}} \qquad (3)$$

The release of these *delayed* photons ($\sim 10^{-6}$ s later) of energy totalling ~ 9 MeV is the *second event* (see Fig. 4.20b). The photomultipliers in the experiment of Reines and Cowan did register the two prompt annihilation photons followed, after a lag of a few microseconds, by the capture photons, thereby providing for the first time experimental evidence for the existence of neutrinos. The experiment is reported to have lasted 52 days, with a mean difference in count rate between reactor on and off of 0.41 ± 0.20/min.

4.7.7 Fermi's Theory of Beta-Decay

It is important to note before considering any theory of beta decay, following aspects of this type of radioactivity.

(a) Formation of Electrons, Positrons and Neutrinos

The electrons, positrons, and the neutrinos are formed in the nucleus during $n \rightleftharpoons p$ interconversions and are emitted forthwith as these particles cannot exist in the nucleus.

(b) Relation between Decay Constant and the End Point Energy: Sargent's Curves

There is a relation between the decay constant (or the half-life period) of a beta-decaying nuclide and its end point energy. It was Sargent[16] who reported an empirical relation, which is analogous to the Geiger-Nuttal's law for α decay, viz. greater the end point energy E_{max}, larger the decay constant, although the range of variation in the values of the decay constant is not as wide as in alpha decay. Sargent showed that if log λ is plotted against log E_{max} for the different naturally occurring beta emitters, the points fall on two straight lines, or are close to them (Fig. 4.21).

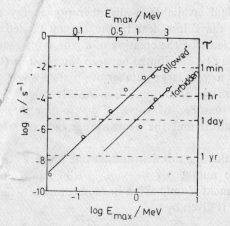

Fig. 4.21   β decay constant as a function of β energy: the Sargent curves for naturally occurring β emitters[16]
(from B.W. Sargent,[16] reproduced with author's permission).

For a given value of E_{max} the λ for the upper series is some 100 times more than the λ for the lower series, which empirical observation has been interpreted by referring to the β decays of the upper series as *allowed transitions* and of the lower series as relatively *forbidden transitions*. Later, curves similar to above had been obtained for artificially prepared β emitters.

We shall see how Fermi's theory of β decay explains these facts. To start with, it is necessary to understand the different concepts involved in this theory.[17]

(i)   *The nucleon-beta-neutrino interaction (The Fermi force G):*   Fermi, in 1934, introduced the concept of a new natural force governing the neutron-proton interconversions and their interactions with the electron or positron and the neutrino generated therefrom. This is also referred to as the *beta-neutrino field theory*. The constant of this force, *G*, is similar to the gravitational (*g*) and the Coulomb (*e*) constants except that *G* is very much weaker in magnitude than *g* or *e*. The value experimentally found for the Fermi force constant is

$$G = 10^{-60} \text{ J m}^3$$

(ii)   *The matrix element* | M_{if} |²: The *matrix element* | M_{if} |² governs the relationship between the properties of the parent, or initial, and the daughter or final nuclei. The matrix element thus involves the wave functions of the initial (i) and final (f) nuclear states, their spins, parities and nucleon arrangements. If the initial and final states do not differ very much (in their nucleon arrangements, spins and parities), the | M_{if} |²

large $|M_{if}|^2 \Rightarrow$ *easier of transition or decay const*

will have a large magnitude and the transition parent → daughter will be an easy one or, in other words, higher $|M_{if}|^2$, larger the decay constant (or shorter the half-life period).

(iii) *Ways of distribution of total energy E_0 between E_e and E_v*: dN/dE_0. The total available β disintegration energy E_0, related to the parent-daughter mass loss, less by the amount needed for the recoil of the daughter nucleus, for the creation of a pair, or extraction of an orbital electron (EC), may be distributed between the electron (or positron) and the neutrino in a very large number of possible ways, which affects the shape of beta energy spectrum. For the discussion here, the relevant quantity is the number of ways of distributing total available energy between the electron and the neutrino per unit of total energy E_0, *i.e.* dN/dE_0.

To obtain a value for this distribution one proceeds in two stages:

(a) To find the number of ways dn_e in which an *electron* may be in a given volume element V and having its momentum between p_e and $p_e + dp_e$. This number dn_e is given by

$$dn_e = 4\pi\, p_e^2\, V \frac{dp_e}{h^3} \qquad (4.52a)$$

(b) To find the number of ways dn_v in which a *neutrino* may be in the same volume element and having its momentum lying between p_v and $p_v + dp_v$. This number is similarly given by

$$dn_v = 4\pi\, p_v^2\, V \frac{dp_v}{h^3} \qquad (4.52b)$$

Finally, the number of ways dN in which the β decay leads to an electron having its momentum between p_e and $p_e + dp_e$ and the neutrino having its momentum between p_v and $p_v + dp_v$ both particles being in the same volume element, is given by the product of Eqs. 4.52a and 4.52b.

$$dN = dn_e \cdot dn_v = \frac{16\pi^2 V^2}{h^6}\, p_e^2 p_v^2\, dp_e\, dp_v. \qquad (4.53)$$

The relativistic momentum of a particle of rest mass m is given by

$$p = [E(E + 2mc^2)]^{1/2}/c.$$

Where m tends to zero, as in the case of a neutrino,

$$p = E/c.$$

The momentum of the neutrino is given by

$$p_v = \frac{E_v}{c} = \frac{E_0 - E_e}{c} \qquad (4.54)$$

and hence

$$dp_v = \frac{dE_0}{c} \qquad (4.55)$$

for a given E_e. Substituting the values of p_ν and dp_ν (4.53) becomes

$$\frac{dN}{dE_0} = \frac{16\pi^2 V^2}{h^6 c^3}(E_0 - E_e)^2 P_e^2\, dp_e \qquad (4.56)$$

(iv) *The Coulomb force contribution:* Lastly, one has to consider the role of the Coulomb barrier in letting out the electrons and positrons against it in β^- and β^+ decay. The Coulomb barrier aids the escape of positrons but hinders the escape of electrons. The effect of the Coulomb barrier depends both on the atomic number Z of the product nucleus and the energy of the electron or positron. This Fermi factor is simply represented by $F(Z, E_e)$ with Z positive for positrons and negative for electrons $F(Z, E_e)$ is a complex function and tables of its values may be referred to.[17a]

(v) *The probability of the emission of an electron of momentum $P(p_e)$:* Fermi's theory finally gives the probability of the decay with the emission of an electron having a given momentum p_e by the expression, which involves the nucleon-beta-neutrino force constant G, the matrix element $|M_{if}|^2$, and the function of the Fermi factor $F(Z, E_e)$

$$P(p_e) = \frac{4\pi^2}{hV^2}|M_{if}|^2 G^2 F(Z, E_e)\frac{dN}{dE_0} \qquad (4.57)$$

Replacing the value of dN/dE_0 from Eq. 4.56, we arrive at

$$P(p_e) = \frac{64\pi^4}{h^7 c^3}|M_{if}|^2 G^2 F(Z, E_e)(E_0 - E_e)^2 p_e^2\, dp_e \qquad (4.58)$$

Considering $|M_{if}|^2$ as a constant for a given parent-daughter transition, Eq. 4.58 simplifies to

$$P(p_e) = (\text{constant}) F(Z, E_e)(E_0 - E_e)^2 p_e^2\, dp_e. \qquad (4.59)$$

Obviously $P(p_e)$ varies smoothly from zero to a maximum, zero when $p_e = 0$ or $E_e = E_0$, *i.e.* when E_e is the end-point energy, as actually observed for all β decays.

(vi) *The Fermi-Kurie plot:* The equation for $P(p_e)$ shows that a plot of the quantity $\left[\dfrac{P(p_e)}{F(Z, E_e)\,p_e^2}\right]^{1/2}$ *versus* E_e should be linear. Such a plot is referred to as the Fermi-Kurie plot. Fig. 4.22 is a typical Fermi-Kurie plot for the beta decay of $^{32}\text{P} \rightarrow {}^{32}\text{S}$.[18]

Similar linear relations having been experimentally observed for many β decays, including the artificially prepared ones, the Fermi theory of β-decay appears to be reasonably well founded.

(vii) *The comparative half-life period:* Since the decay constant is the total probability that the nucleus would emit in unit time a β particle of *any* momentum, this would simply be the integral of $P(p_e)$ between the limits of zero and of maximum momentum corresponding to the maximum end point energy (E_0). Hence,

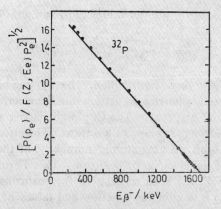

Fig. 4.22 The Fermi-Kurie plot[18] for ^{32}P
(from F.T. Porter, F. Wagner, Jr., and M.S. Freedman[18], reproduced with authors' permission).

$$\lambda = \int_0^{P_{e(\max)}} P(p_e) = \frac{64\pi^4}{h^7c^3} \, G^2 \, |M_{if}|^2 \int_0^{P_{e(\max)}} F(Z, E_e)\,(E_0 - E_e)^2\, p_e^2\, dp_e$$

$$\text{(4.60)}$$

$$= (\text{constant})\,|M_{if}|^2 \int_0^{P_{e(\max)}} F(Z, E_e)\,(E_0 - E_e)^2\, p_e^2\, dp_e$$

Here the matrix element is considered a constant, independent of p_e. Replacing the integral by f, we have, for allowed transitions:

$$f = \frac{\lambda}{(\text{constant})\,|M_{if}|^2} = \frac{0.693}{(\text{constant})\,t}\,|M_{if}|^{-2} \qquad \text{(4.61)}$$

Here the half-life period is shown simply as t, that being the convention in this context. The *product ft* is referred to as the *comparative half-life period. This is a constant for all β decays having the same matrix element, i.e.* involving the same changes in spin and parity between parent and daughter.

$$ft = (\text{constant})\,|M_{if}|^{-2} \qquad \text{(4.62)}$$

This is a great step towards the understanding of β-decay. The value of ft, or $\log ft$, gives an insight into the role of the matrix element. Eq. 4.62 shows that smaller is $\log ft$, greater is the value of the matrix element. Values of $\log ft$ vary *from 3* for *super-allowed transitions*, corresponding to the high matrix element, involving no change in spin and parity between the parent and daughter and hence of a short half-life, *to above 10* for *highly forbidden transitions*, corresponding to a low matrix element, involving large changes in spin and hence of a long half-life, involving sometimes a change in parity as well.

(viii) *Selection rules:* These concepts form the basis of *selection rules* governing β-decay. Two sets of selection rules have been suggested,

TABLE 4.3 Gamow-Teller selection rules for β-decay[12,19]

$\log ft$	$|M_{if}|^2$	Change in spin ΔI	Change in parity $\Delta \pi$	Type of transition	Examples (with $\log ft$ values in parentheses)[7]
2–3	very high	0	no	super-allowed or favoured	$n \xrightarrow[10.8\ \text{min}]{\beta^-} p\ (3.21)$; $^6\text{He} \xrightarrow[0.8\ \text{s}]{\beta^+} \text{Li}\ (2.74)$; $^{17}\text{F} \xrightarrow[66\ \text{s}]{\beta^+} 0^{**}$; $^{23}\text{Mg} \xrightarrow[12\ \text{s}]{\beta^+} \text{Na}^{**}$; $^{25}\text{Al} \xrightarrow[7.6\ \text{s}]{\beta^+} \text{Mg}^{**}\ (3.5)$
3–6	high	0 and ± 1 (but not $0\to 0$)*	no	allowed or normal	$^{64}\text{Cu}\ \xrightarrow{\beta^-} \text{Zn}\ (5.29)$; $\xrightarrow[12.8\ \text{h}]{\beta^+} \text{Ni}\ (4.94)$
6–10	low	$0, \pm 1, \pm 2$	yes	first (or once) forbidden	$^{115}\text{Cd} \xrightarrow[43\ \text{d}]{\beta^-} \text{Ag}\ (6.9)$
>10	very low	$\pm 2, \pm 3$ and higher also $0 \to 0$*	no	second (or twice) forbidden	$^{137}\text{Cs} \xrightarrow[30\ \text{y}]{\beta^-} \text{Ba}\ (12\text{–}13)$; $^{10}\text{Be} \xrightarrow[1.9\times10^6\ \text{y}]{\beta^-} \text{B}\ (13.7)$; $^{36}\text{Cl} \xrightarrow[3.0\times10^5\ \text{y}]{\beta^-} \text{Ar}\ (13.5)$; $^{40}\text{K} \xrightarrow[1.3\times10^9\ \text{y}]{\beta^-} \text{Ca}\ (17.6)$

The $0 \to 0$ transition is strongly forbidden on Gamow-Teller rules but is permitted on Fermi selection rules (i.e. if spins of the neutrino and electron are antiparallel).[17]

** Here the parent and daughter are mirror nuclei as described in Secs. 1.4 and 3.3.5.

viz. of (a) Gamow-Teller and (b) Fermi. The difference lies in regard to the relative spin orientations of the beta particle and the neutrino: if the spins of the two particles be assumed to be parallel the Gamow-Teller rules hold good, if they be assumed antiparallel, the Fermi rules are valid. The Gamow-Teller selection rules are tabulated in Table 4.3.

It should be pointed out that from the examples cited it should *not* be concluded that there is a rigidly regular relation between log *ft* and the actual half-life. There are innumerable deviations, *e.g.*

$$^{3}\text{H} \xrightarrow[12.33\text{y}]{\beta^{-}} \text{He}: \quad \log ft = 3.06$$

$$^{35}\text{S} \xrightarrow[88\text{ d}]{\beta^{-}} \text{Cl}: \quad \log ft \sim 4\text{–}5$$

$$^{97}\text{Zr} \xrightarrow[16.8\text{ h}]{\beta^{-}} \text{Nb}: \quad \log ft \sim 6\text{–}9$$

$$^{140}\text{Ba} \xrightarrow[12.8\text{ d}]{\beta^{-}} \text{La}: \quad \log ft \sim 6\text{–}9$$

4.8   Nuclear Deexcitation: Gamma Emission

It is common to find the daughter nucleus, resulting in any radioactive process, to be in an excited state and its deexcitation to the ground state may occur either by (a) photon emission, *i.e.* γ *transition* or, (b) by the ejection of electrons from the outer orbitals, i.e. by the process of *internal conversion*, or *Auger emission*. We shall briefly consider these two modes of nuclear deexcitation.

4 8.1   RADIATIVE DEEXCITATION: GAMMA TRANSITION

Unlike in α or β decay, it becomes necessary to indicate explicitly the spin and parity of the parent and daughter nuclides in γ transitions as the photons carry away integral units of angular momentum $l\hbar$ (with $l = 1$, 2, 3, . . .).

The probability of γ transition by the emission of a photon of given energy is governed by a term known as the *reduced transition probability*, whose value depends on the difference in the wavefunctions of the initial (ψ_i) and the final states (ψ_f) and hence on the changes in the spin and the parity following the photon emission. The single particle (shell) model as well as the collective model are able to explain the mechanism of the γ transitions satisfactorily. We shall present here only the mechanism based on the single particle model, first developed by Weisskopf[20] in 1951.

On the basis of the half-life of a γ transition, a distinction is made between those with $\tau < 10^{-7}$ s, *i.e.* the transitions are virtually instantaneous and those with $\tau > 10^{-7}$ s*. The latter are termed *isomeric*

---

*The distinction is the purely arbitrary. It may well be about 10 times on either side of the limit indicated here.

transitions (IT) between a *metastable parent* and daughter, *e.g.*
$^{60m}Co \xrightarrow[10.5 \text{ min}]{IT} {}^{60}Co$. The isomeric transitions will be considered later.

Every permitted state of the atomic nucleus, including the ground one, is a quantum state characterized by definite values of energy (E), spin (I) and parity (π). Theory attempts to correlate the probability of γ transition from one state to another in terms of the differences in E, I and π between the two states, initial and final.[17] The absorption or emission of radiation by a nucleus is due to the oscillations of its charge which may be the result of either:-

(a) *A to and fro motion of charges,* giving rise to what has been termed the *electric multipole radiation,* EL, or

(b) *A fluctuation in the electric current flowing in closed loops,* giving rise to the *magnetic multipole radiation,* ML. Here, L stands for the difference $|I_i - I_f|$. L is also the multipole order 2^L.

Thus:
$$L = 1: \text{dipole;}$$
$$L = 2: \text{quadrupole;}$$
$$L = 3: \text{octupole;}$$
$$L = 4: 16 \text{ pole; etc.}$$

Whether the radiation is of the electric or magnetic multipole origin is determined by the sum $\pi_i + \pi_f + L$, *wherein even parity is counted as* $+1$ *and odd parity as zero* (not -1). If this sum is even the emission is of the EL type; if odd it is of the ML type.

It must be noted that there is no difference between the photons themselves be they of the electric or the magnetic multipole origin; only the processes of emission are different.

Following the photon emission, a change in the nuclear characteristics must occur in the system, *viz.*

(i) *Change in energy:* $\quad \Delta E = E_i - E_f = E_\gamma = h\nu$ \hfill (4.63)

where the subscripts i and f stand for parent and daughter nuclei, *i.e.* the initial and final states.

(ii) *Change in spin:* $\quad \Delta I = |I_i - I_f| = L$ \hfill (4.64)

Theoretically, ΔI or L may have any integral value given by

$$(I_i + I_f) \geqslant L \geqslant |I_i - I_f|.$$

L given by Eq. 4.64 can only have integral values, as I_i and I_f are both integers (A even), or both semi-integers (A odd), and A does not change in a γ transition.

However, *the photon carries usually the minimum angular momentum permitted, viz.*

$$L = |I_i - I_f| > 0 \hfill (4.64a)$$

It is to be noted that L can have values of 1, 2, 3... but not 0, *i.e.* no photon emission is possible from systems where $I_i = I_f = 0$, as the minimum angular momentum of a photon is 1 $\hbar$. This is relevent to the theory of internal conversion (Sec. 4.8.4).

(iii) *Change in parity.* The process may or may not be accompanied by a change in parity. Thus there is no change in parity with L even for EL and L odd for ML. In the reverse cases there is a change in parity.

However, *in every case, the parity of the entire system,* the parent, radiation (photon) and daughter *is conserved.* The parity of the photon emitted depends on whether it is of EL or ML origin and whether L, the angular momentum associated with it is even or odd. These inter-relations are tabulated below.

TABLE 4.4:   Selection rules for γ transitions

Photon origin and its parity	*Angular momentum of photon or pole order* $L = \|I_i - I_f\|$.	
	L odd: 1, 3, 5 . . .	*L even: 2, 4, 6 . . .*
Electric multipole EL		
Photon parity $= (-1)^L$	-1	$+1$
Whether parity changes between		
π_i and π_f	Yes	No
Magnetic multipole ML		
Photon parity $= -(-1)^L$	$+1$	-1
Whether parity changes between		
π_i and π_f	No	Yes

(iv) *Some examples* are illustrated in Fig. 4.23 (a, b, c)[1].

The energy of the levels shown on the right are in MeV. The spin and parity are shown on the left. Only minimum values of L are shown.

(a) *System* $^{60m}\text{Co} \xrightarrow{\text{IT}} {}^{60}\text{Co} \xrightarrow{\beta-} {}^{60}\text{Ni}.$

In this system there are in all three γ emissions; γ_1 from ^{60m}Co by isomeric transition (see Sec. 4.83) and γ_2 and γ_3 from ^{60}Ni* to the ground state. Applying the above rules we arrive at the characteristics of the emissions as follows:

γ_1: $E = 0.059$ MeV: $L = 3$ (minimum),

    Type $= M3 (\because \pi_i + \pi_f + L = 1 + 1 + 3$ is odd).

γ_2: $E = 1.173$ MeV: $L = 2$ (minimum)

    Type $= E2 (\because \pi_i + \pi_f + L = 1 + 1 + 2$ is even)

γ_3: $E = 1.333$ MeV: $L = 2$ (minimum)

    Type: $E2 (\because \pi_i + \pi_f + L = 1 + 1 + 2$ is even)

(b) *System* $^{113m}\text{In} \xrightarrow{\text{IT}} {}^{113}\text{In}$

Here there is only one γ emission, namely in the IT.

$$\gamma: E = 0.392 \text{ MeV}: L = 4 \text{ (mimimum)}$$

Type: M 4 ($\because \pi_i + \pi_f + L = 0 + 1 + 4$ is odd).

(c) *System* $^{80m}\text{Br} \xrightarrow{\text{IT}} {}^{80}\text{Br} \xrightarrow{\beta^-} {}^{80}\text{Kr}$

In this system four γ emissions are theoretically possible; three in the isomeric transition from ^{80m}Br to ^{80}Br and one from $^{80}\text{Kr}^*$, with following characteristics, L being a minimum in every case:

$$\gamma_1: E = 0.049 \text{ MeV}, \ L = 3; \ \text{Type M3}$$

$$\gamma_2: E = 0.037 \text{ MeV}, \ L = 1; \ \text{Type E1}$$

$$\gamma_3: E = 0.086 \text{ MeV}, \ L = 4; \ \text{Type M4}$$

$$\gamma_4: E = 0.62 \ \text{ MeV}, \ L = 2; \ \text{Type E2}$$

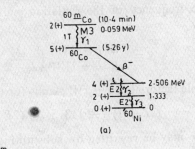

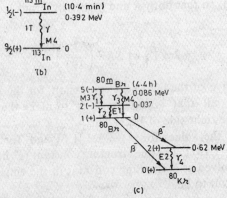

Fig. 4.23 Nuclear deexcitation by γ emission: electric and magnetic multipole emissions from ^{60m}Co, ^{113m}In and ^{80m}Br

(from D. Strominger, J.M. Hollander and G.T. Seaborg[1], reproduced with authors' permission).

4.8.2 GAMMA DECAY CONSTANT

The potential interaction of a particle of radius R and electromagnetic radiation of wavelength λ can be expressed in terms of a series of powers of $2\pi R/\lambda$ ($= R/\lambda^*$). Atomic nuclei absorb in the γ region of 1–5 MeV. Hence we have for nuclei-γ interactions:

$$R = 1.5 \times A^{1/3} \text{ fermis, } i.e. \text{ between 2–10 F; and}$$

$$\lambda^* = \frac{\hbar}{p} = \frac{\hbar}{h\nu/c} = \frac{\hbar c}{E} = \frac{1.054\ 6 \times 10^{-34} \times 2.997\ 9 \times 10^8}{E\,(\text{in MeV}) \times 1.602\ 2 \times 10^{-13}}$$

$$= \frac{1.973\ 3 \times 10^{-13}}{E} m = \frac{197}{E} \text{ F} \qquad (4.65)$$

With E in the 1–5 MeV region, λ^* comes to be in the range of 200–40 F and the ratio R/λ^* between 0.01 and 0.25*.

In the case of electric multipole emission (order 2^L), Blatt and Weisskopf derived the expression for the γ decay constant on the shell model[20].

$$\lambda_E = 2\pi\nu \left(\frac{e^2}{\hbar c}\right) S \left(\frac{R}{\lambda^*}\right)^{2L} \qquad (4.66)$$

where ν is the frequency of the radiation emitted and S is a statistical factor given by

$$S \equiv \frac{2(L+1)}{L\,[(2L+1)!!]^2} \left(\frac{3}{L+3}\right)^2 \qquad (4.67)$$

where the double factorial $(2L+1)!!$ stands for the product

$$(2L+1)!! \equiv 1.3.5 \ .\ .\ (2L+1).$$

Equation 4.66 may be rewritten by substituting λ^* by its value $197/E$, (with E in MeV), so that both R and λ^* are in fermis (see Eq. 4.65). Thus:

$$\lambda_E = 2\pi\nu \left(\frac{e^2}{\hbar c}\right) SR^{2L} \left(\frac{E}{197}\right)^{2L} \qquad (4.68)$$

In order to arrive at the final neat expression for the electric multipole decay constant, all that is necessary is to make the following simple operations to the right side of Eq. 4.68.

(a) Substitute the values for $\pi(= 3.141\ 6)$ and for the *fine structure constant* $(e^2/\hbar c = 1/137)$. The fine structure constant $(e^2/\hbar c)$ is a dimensionless quantity involved as a coupling constant in the emission of photons. Its value comes out to be

$$\frac{(4.8)^2 \times 10^{-20}}{1.054\ 6 \times 10^{-27} \times 2.997\ 9 \times 10^{10}} = 7.287\ 5 \times 10^{-3}$$

$$= 1/137.2 \quad (\text{see Sec. 2.11.4}).$$

The fine structure constant also represents the ratio of the feeble radiative decay of muons to their β decay[8]. (b) replace ν by its equivalent E/h, with E in MeV, (c) multiply and divide by 197 and (d) rearrange the

*With atoms and molecules $(R \sim 10^5$ F) absorbing in the visible and ultraviolet $(E \sim 10^{-6}$ MeV), λ^* comes to be in the range of 10^9 F and the ratio $R/\lambda^* \sim 10^{-3}$.

terms. Thus*

$$\lambda_E = 2.4 \times 10^{21} \ SR^{2L} \ (E/197)^{2L+1} \ s^{-1} \qquad (4.69)$$

The corresponding expression for the magnetic multipole emission is

$$\lambda_M = 0.55 \times 10^{21} A^{-2/3} \ SR^{2L} \ (E/197)^{2L+1} \ s^{-1} \qquad (4.70)$$

Thus, the decay constant for magnetic emission is smaller than the corresponding electric multipole emission by a factor of $4.4 \ A^{2/3}$.

The corresponding half-lives of emission are given by

$$\tau_E = 0.693/\lambda_E; \ \tau_M = 0.693/\lambda_M \text{ and } \tau_M/\tau_E = 4.4 \ A^{2/3}$$

The Blatt and Weisskopf equations (4.69) and (4.70) show how the γ-decay constant, whether by electric or magnetic multipole emission process, depends heavily on the angular momentum carried away by the photon, i.e. the change in the nuclear spin following the emission $L = | I_i - I_f |$, as L occurs *both* in the statistical factor and in the exponents of the nuclear size (R) and the energy of transition (E). The statistical factor diminishes by 10^{-2} per unit increase of L, as shown below:

TABLE 4.5: S values for $L = 1, 2, 3, 4, 5$ (calculated from Eq. 4.67)

L	1	2	3	4	5
S	2.5×10^{-1}	4.8×10^{-3}	6.0×10^{-5}	5.1×10^{-7}	3.0×10^{-9}

The overall effect of the increase of L by unity is to decrease the decay constant, (or increase the half-life of decay) by a factor of about 10^6, other factors as A (and hence R) and E remaining the same. Further, τ_E decreases both with E and with R. Further, ML is a more hindered process, the period being about 10^2 longer, compared to EL of the same order. These facts are well illustrated in Table 4.6, the values being calculated directly from Eqs. 4.69 and 4.70, and for a constant value of $A = 100$ (i.e. R about 7 F) and $E = 0.25$ MeV. Figure 4.24 also illustrates the variation of the half-life of decay by γ emission by both electric and magnetic multipole emissions, over the energy range 0.01 to 10 MeV[8].

4.8.3 NUCLEAR ISOMERISM AND ISOMERIC TRANSITION

We have seen in the preceding section how the half-life of a nucleus against γ decay varies over wide limits depending on the nuclear radius (hence on A), the energy and type of radiation and in particular on the difference in the spins and parities of the initial and final states. Where

*The right side of Eq. 4.68
$$= \frac{2 \times 3.141 \ 6 \times 1.602 \ 2 \times 10^{-6}}{137 \times 6.626 \ 2 \times 10^{-27}} \times 197 \ SR^{2L} \left(\frac{E}{197} \right)^{2L+1}$$
$$= 2.184 \ 6 \times 10^{21} \ SR^{2L} \ (E/197)^{2L+1} \ s^{-1}$$

TABLE 4.6: Values of decay constants and half-lives for γ emissions, calculated from Eqs. 4.69 and 4.70 for $R = 7\,F$ $(A = 100)$ and $E = 0.25$ MeV

Emission process	λ/s^{-1}	τ/s
E1	6.5×10^{13}	1.1×10^{-14}
M1	6.9×10^{11}	1.0×10^{-12}
E2	1.0×10^{8}	6.9×10^{-9}
M2	1.1×10^{6}	6.3×10^{-7}
E3*	1.6×10^{2}	4.3×10^{-3} IT$\downarrow$
M3*	1.7	4.1×10^{-1}
E4	7.5×10^{-5}	9.2×10^{3}
M4	7.9×10^{-7}	8.8×10^{5}

*As an example, the calculations involved in applying the Eqs. 4.69 and 4.70 are shown here for the case of E3 and M3 emission.

$A = 100$, hence $R = 7\,F$, $E = 0.25$ MeV, with $L = 3$, S is 6×10^{-5}, $R^{2L} = (7)^6 = 1.176 \times 10^5$.

$(E/197)^{2L+1} = (0.0013)^7 = 6.28 \times 10^{-21}$

$\lambda_{E3} = 2.4 \times 10^{21} \times 6 \times 10^{-5} \times 1.76 \times 10^5 \times 6.28 \times 10^{-21} = 1.6 \times 10^2\ s^{-1}$

$\tau_{E3} = 0.693/1.6 \times 10^2 = 4.3 \times 10^{-3}\ s$

$\lambda_{M3} = \lambda_E/4.4 \times 100^{2/3} = 1.6 \times 10^2/4.4 \times 21.54 = 1.7\ s^{-1}$

$\tau_{M3} = 0.693/1.7 = 4.1 \times 10^{-1}\ s.$

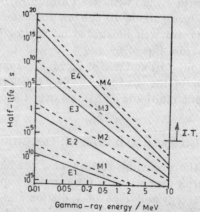

Fig. 4.24: Life-time *versus* energy relation for γ-emission by electric and magnetic multipole processes on the basis of the single particle formula of Weisskopf[8]

(from Nuclear Physics/An Introduction, by W.E. Burcham, © 1973. Longman Group Ltd., reproduced with permission).

the half-life is measurably long [the decay is considered as an *isomeric transition* (IT). Though what is *measurably long* cannot be rigidly stated; decay periods of a second and above are considered to come under isomeric transition. Nuclides which have identical Z and N (and hence A) values but which differ in their energy states, spins and parities are referred to as *nuclear isomers*. The parent isomer because of its relatively long life is described to be in a *metastable state*; the symbol signifying this is m, written beside the A value, e.g. (^{60m}Co, ^{80m}Br). Thus isomeric transition (IT) constitutes a regular type of radioactive decay.

Nuclear isomerism was first revealed in the (n, γ) reactions on natural bromine. As this element consists of two isotopes ^{79}Br and ^{81}Br, two radioactive products ^{80}Br and ^{82}Br would be expected following (n, γ) reactions. Curiously, *three* activities of periods, 4.42 h, 17.6 min and 35.34 h invariably resulted, and all the three activities were found to be due to the element bromine. It was this anomaly which first suggested the phenomenon of nuclear isomerism: in this case ^{80m}Br and ^{80}Br. Later ^{82m}Br with a half-life of 6·1 min has also been detected as an isomer of ^{82}Br.

It was Weizsacker[21] who first suggested in 1936 that the long life of the metastable isomer must be due to the large spin difference between the initial and final states, $(\Delta I) \geqslant (\pm 3)$. As pointed out earlier, each increase in ΔI of one unit, increases the half-life period by a factor of about 10^6. This theory of Weizsacker has been amply supported by experimental results in respect of isomeric transitions in all cases.

Some examples of nuclear isomerism and isomeric transition had already been presented under Sec. 4.8.1 together with their decay schemes, *viz.*

$$^{60m}_{2(+)}\text{Co} \xrightarrow[10·4 \text{ min}]{\text{IT}} {}^{60}_{5(+)}\text{Co}; \quad ^{80m}_{5(-)}\text{Br} \xrightarrow[4·4 \text{ h}]{\text{IT}} {}^{80}_{1(+)}\text{Br};$$

$$^{82m}_{2(-)}\text{Br} \xrightarrow[6·1 \text{ min}]{\text{IT}} {}^{82}_{5(-)}\text{Br}; \quad ^{113m}_{1/2(-)}\text{In} \xrightarrow[104 \text{ min}]{\text{IT}} {}^{113}_{9/2(+)}\text{In};$$

$$^{69m}_{9/2(+)}\text{Zn} \xrightarrow[14 \text{ h}]{\text{IT}} {}^{63}_{1/2(-)}\text{Zn}$$

One general observation is the more frequent occurrence of nuclear isomers of long life in the regions just below the magic numbers 50, 82 and 126 of neutrons or protons whichever is odd forming what has been described as 'islands of isomerism'.[22,23]

4.8.4 INTERNAL CONVERSION

It was pointed earlier that as an alternative to γ emission, the transition of a nucleus from an excited to the ground state may occur by the ejection of orbital electrons and this process goes by the name of *internal conversion*. In competition with the EL or ML radiative process of deexcitation, the excited nucleus expands and contracts alternately, interacting in the process with the orbital electrons. This is possible as the wavefunction of the electrons is not zero inside the nucleus. If the energy transferred to the electrons in this process exceeds the electron binding energy E_B, the electron is ejected with a kinetic energy:

$$E_e = E_\gamma - E_B \tag{4.71}$$

where E_γ is the same as the energy of γ in the alternative radiative mode of decay, being the excess energy of the initial over the final state. Thus, the conversion electrons display an energy spectrum consisting of discrete lines.

$$E_1 = E_\gamma - E_K,$$
$$E_2 = E_\gamma - E_{L_I},$$
$$E_3 = E_\gamma - E_{L_{II}},$$
$$E_4 = E_\gamma - E_{L_{III}}$$

representing the electrons ejected from the K $(1s_{1/2})$, L_I $(2s_{1/2})$, L_{II} $(2p_{1/2})$, L_{III} $(2p_{3/2})$ orbitals.

Each of the alternative modes of transition has a partial decay constant (and a corresponding half-life period) and the total decay constant is given by the sum of all the partial decay constants.

$$\lambda = \lambda_\gamma + \lambda_K + \lambda_L + \ldots \tag{4.72}$$

A quantity of importance is the *conversion coefficient* α defined for a given initial and final states as

$$\alpha = \frac{\text{Number of conversion electrons}}{\text{Number of photons}}$$

α is made up of the components representing the coefficients of different groups of conversion electrons

$$\alpha = \alpha_K + \alpha_{LI} + \alpha_{LII} + \alpha_{LIII} \tag{4.73}$$

The conversion coefficient varies as the third power of Z of the nucleus: hence the emission of conversion electrons as the competitive mode of deexcitation becomes important with heavy nuclides. Further, the coefficient decreases with increase of energy of transition. An approximate expression for the conversion coefficient is

$$\alpha_K \simeq C \frac{L}{L+1} Z^3 E^{-(L+5/2)} \tag{4.74}$$

where E is the energy of transition, L is the electric multipole order $(= 1, 2, 3 \ldots)$ and C a constant.

Earlier, the emission of conversion electrons was considered to be a two stage process; first the γ photon is emitted from the excited nucleus, and then some of these photons knocked off orbital electrons as a kind of photoelectric effect. Now it is known that this concept is wrong. Conversion electrons arise as a direct one stage process of deexcitation in competition with the photon emission. In addition to other evidences, this is well brought out in the ejection of conversion electrons from systems where both the initial and final states have zero spin. Since no photon emission is possible from $0 \to 0$ transitions (Sec. 4.8.1), (the minimum angular momentum of a photon being $1\hbar$), the emission of conversion electrons is the only mode of deexcitation in this case. It is thus a direct one-stage process. In this context, the experiments of Ellis and Wooster[24] on RaB (^{214}Pb) and of Cooper, Hollander and of Rasmussen[25] on ^{90}Nb are of interest.

4.8.5 THE AUGER EFFECT

Both in the process of electron capture and ejection of conversion electrons, vacancies are created in the inner electron orbitals, usually in the K or L shells. A vacancy deep inside is energetically unstable, as the ionization energy of outer electrons is very much less, the value falling rapidly farther the electron is from the nucleus. The inner vacancy therefore gets rapidly filled by the successive transfer of electrons from the outer orbitals. This process of vacancy filling gives rise to two distinctive effects (i) radiation emission and (ii) electron emission (the *Auger effect*).

(i) *Radiation Emission (The Fluorescence Mode)*

As an outer electron jumps into an inner vacancy, monochromatic X-rays corresponding to the energy

$$h\nu_1 = E_X = E_{B_1} - E_{B_2} \qquad (4.75)$$

are emitted where E_{B_1} and E_{B_2} are the binding energies of the inner and outer level electrons. The vacancy is thus pushed outward and the process goes on till each vacancy is filled by the jumping in of the next outer electron, emitting at each stage corresponding radiation

$$h\nu_i = E_{Bi} - E_{Bi+1} \qquad (4.75a)$$

This purely radiative process leaves the atom finally in a state of $+1$ charge, the vacancy having migrated from inner to the valency shell. The total photon yield is termed the *fluorescence yield*.

(ii) *Electron Emission (The Auger Effect)*

Alternatively, the excess energy (E_X in Eq. 4.75) may be non-radiatively transferred to the *next outer electron* causing its ejection, similar to the process of internal conversion. If we designate the electron initially lost from the innermost shell (by EC or emitted during internal conversion) as e_1, and the electron which jumped in to fill the vacancy as e_2, the electron *now* ejected as e_3, the kinetic energy of this (the second to be lost) is given by

$$E_3 = E_{B_1} - (E_{B_2} + E_{B_3}) \qquad (4.76)$$

where E_{B_3} is the binding energy of the electron e_3. Obviously, the ejection of e_3 would be possible only if $E_{B_1} > (E_{B_2} + E_{B_3})$ so that the kinetic energy of e_3 has a finite positive value. At this stage the atom has a charge of $+2$. This process of emission of further electrons e_4, e_5...e_n from successive outer orbitals can go on as long as the value of E_n is positive. The successive emission of electrons by such a process is named the *Auger effect in* honour of the discoverer, Pierre Auger[26].

Just as in the act of filling one inner vacancy two vacancies resulted in the outer orbital, the filling of these two vacancies leads to the creation of four vacancies in the next outer orbital, and the atom now has a charge of $+4$. This process repeats on the principle that the filling of one inner vacancy results in two vacancies in the outer orbital. Thus:

$$K \quad \leftarrow \quad LL \quad \rightarrow$$

1 *K* initial	$\rightarrow$	2 *L* vacancies after the process:
vacancy		one *L* electron goes to fill the *K*
		vacancy and the second *L* electron
		is ejected

Similarly,

$$L \quad \leftarrow \quad MM \quad \rightarrow$$

$\therefore$ 2 *L* vacancies before $\rightarrow$ 4 *M* vacancies, and so on.

The vacancy *cascades* (a term proposed by Snell and Pleasanton[27]) outwards to the valency shell, and the atom is left in a highly positively charged state. Figure 4.25 illustrates the Auger emission. The formation of highly positively charged species of atoms following electron capture, isomeric transition and internal conversion processes are common. For example, in the $^{80m}Br \xrightarrow[4.42\text{ h}]{\text{IT}} {}^{80}Br$ reaction the product species ^{80}Br

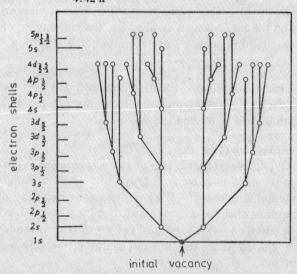

Fig. 4.25 The vacancy cascade: the Auger effect. The formation of Xe^{20+} by the loss of Auger electrons following initial internal conversion accompanying the isomeric transition of ^{133m}Xe

(from F. Pleasanton and A.H. Snell,[27] reproduced with authors' permission).

appears, as evidenced by mass spectral analysis, in all charge states from $+2$ to $+11$, the most abundant species being $^{80}Br^{+7}$. Similarly in the isomeric transition of ^{131m}Xe, of half-life 20 days, the charge spectrum of the product ^{131}Xe varies from $+1$ to $+23$, with a peak at $+8$.

The charging time has been computed to vary between 10^{-17} and 10^{-15} s, which is less than the time for an atomic vibration in a molecule. When a high positive charge builds up on a single atom (the product of nuclear decay), a rapid redistribution of the charge to other atoms in the molecule takes place, the ionization potentials of radicals bound to the atom being less than that of the multiply charged atom. This redistribution is also over in a time less than that of vibration of atoms in a molecule. The overall effect is a molecule in which several atoms are positively charged and this results in a coulombic explosion and the molecule breaks down into different fragments[28].

4.9 Artificial Radioactivity

In a series of experiments, soon after the discovery of the neutron, Irène and Frédéric Joliot-Curie studied the effects of bombarding light elements as boron, aluminium and magnesium with high energy alpha particles from polonium. In all cases they observed the emission of neutrons and positrons. There appeared to be some anomalies. First, in the case of aluminium, the recoil product had to be a light isotope of phosphorus, ^{30}P, to conserve mass and charge; thus,

$$^{27}_{13}Al + ^{4}_{2}\alpha \rightarrow ^{1}_{0}n + ^{30}_{15}P$$

but no such isotope of phosphorus was known at that time, the natural element being monoisotopic (^{31}P). Secondly, the moment the α source was removed, the emission of neutrons stopped, but that of *the positrons continued over well measurable periods*. Actually, the intensity of the positron emission was observed to decay exponentially with time with a half-life of about 3 minutes, as if from a true radioactive source! These inferences were subjected to chemical analysis which confirmed the formation of radiophosphorus ^{30}P from aluminium. The arrangement used is shown in Fig. 4.26. The α bombarded aluminium foil was dissolved in hydrochloric acid and the hydrogen evolved was collected in a thin walled glass tube which exhibited β^+ aciivity due to ^{30}P swept into it as PH_3 along with the hydrogen*.[29,30] The β^+ activity was found to decay with a half-life of 3 min. Thus, artificial radioactivity was discovered in 1934 by Irène and Frédéric Joliot-Curie who were awarded the Nobel Prize in 1935 for this discovery.

---

*The elegant set-up used in the discovery of artificial radioactivity is preserved in the Palace of Discoveries in Paris.

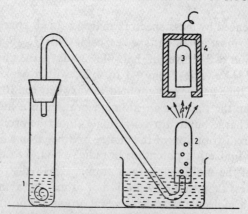

1. α-bombarded Al target in HCl solution   3. Counters
2. Thin walled glass tube   4. Shielding

Fig. 4.26 The discovery of artificial radioactivity: Evidence for the transformation of aluminium into radiophosphorus.[29]

The sequence of reactions in their experiments are

$$^{27}_{13}\text{Al}\,(\alpha, n)\,^{30}_{15}\text{P}\xrightarrow[3\text{ min}]{\beta^+}\,^{30}_{14}\text{Si}$$

Similarly, in the case of magnesium and boron resulting in the formation of radiosilicon and radionitrogen respectively, the reactions are

$$^{24}_{12}\text{Mg}\,(\alpha, n)\,^{27}_{14}\text{Si}\xrightarrow[5\text{ s}]{\beta^+}\,^{27}_{13}\text{Al}$$

$$^{10}_{5}\text{B}\,(\alpha, n)\,^{13}_{7}\text{N}\xrightarrow[10\text{ min}]{\beta^+}\,^{13}_{6}\text{C}$$

Immediately after this discovery, Fermi and his collaborators succeeded in producing 37 other radioelements by bombarding elements with neutrons from a Ra + Be source, i.e. by (n, γ) reactions on elements.

Today it is possible to obtain most elements, with a few exceptions, in the form of their radioactive isotopes by one or the other process as (n, γ) reaction in a nuclear reactor, bombardment with cyclotron accelerated high energy particles, as p, d, α, or other heavy ions as N^{6+}, O^{6+}, etc. or from fission fragments, so that radioactivity is no longer restricted to the few naturally occurring elements, as Ra, Ac, Th and U. Modes of obtaining a large number of useful radioisotopes and their ever-increasing applications in research, medicine, and industry are described in Chapter 8.

References

(where marked*, see Bibliography)

1. D. Strominger, J.M. Hollander and G.T. Seaborg, 'Tables of Isotopes', Revs. Mod. Phys., 1958, 30, 585.

    (a) R. Bouchez, P. Daudel, R. Daudel and R. Muxart, "Variation of the

Period of the Nuclide [7]Be as a Function of the Degree of Ionization of the Atom", *J. Phys. Radium*, 1947, **8**, 336; 1949, **10**, 201.

(b) E. Segrè and C. Wiegand, 'Experiments on the Effect of Atomic Electrons on the Decay Constant of [7]Be,' *Phys. Rev.*, 1949, **75**, 39.

(c) M. Haissinsky*

2. H. Bateman, 'The Solutions of a System of Differential Equations Occurring in the Theory of Radioactive Transformations,' *Proc. Cambridge Phil. Soc.*, 1910, **15**, 423.

3. R.T. Overman and H.M. Clark*

4. G. Gamow, 'Fine Structure of Alpha Rays', *Nature*, 1930, **126**, 397.

5. K.S. Bhatki, *Radiochemistry of Bismuth* (Energy Research and Development Administration, NAS-NS, 3061, Springfield, VA).

6. H. Geiger and J.M. Nuttal, 'The Ranges of the Alpha Particles from Various Radioactive Substances and a Relation between Range and Period of Transformation', *Phil. Mag.*, 1911, **22**, 613; 1912, **23**, 439 and 1912, **24**, 647.

7. I. Kaplan*

8. W.E. Burcham*

9. G. Gamow, 'Zur Quantentheorie des Atomkernes' *Z. Phys.*, 1928, **51**, 204.

10. R.W. Gurney and E.U. Condon, 'Quantum Mechanics and Radioactive Disintegration', *Nature*, 1928, **122**, 439; *Phys. Rev.*, 1929, **33**, 127.

11. L. Katz and A.S Penfold, 'Range-Energy Relations for Electrons and the Determination of Beta Ray End-Point Energies by Absorption', *Revs. Mod. Phys.*, 1952, **24**, 28.

12. C.D. Ellis and W.A. Wooster, 'The Average Energy Distribution of Radium-E', *Proc. Roy. Soc. (London)*, 1927, **A117**, 109.

13. J.S. Allen, *The Neutrino*, (Princeton Univ. Pr., Princeton, N.J., 1958).

14. F. Reines and C.L. Cowan, Jr , 'Detection of Free Neutrino', *Phys. Rev.*, 1953, **92**, 830.

15. C.L. Cowan, Jr., F. Reines, F.B. Harrison, Kruse and McGuire, 'Detection of the Free Neutrino: A Confirmation,' *Science*, 1956, **124**, 103.

16. B.W. Sargent, 'The Maximum Energy of the Beta Rays from Uranium-X and Other Bodies', *Proc. Roy. Soc. (London)*, 1933, **A139**, 659.

17. B.G. Harvey*
    (a) H.A. Enge*

18. F.T. Porter, F. Wagner, Jr., and M.S. Freedman, 'Evidence for Small Deviations from the Allowed Shape in Comparison of the Beta Spectra of [24]Na and [32]P' *Phys. Rev.*, 1957, **107**, 135.

19. R.D. Evans*

20. J.M. Blatt and V.F. Weisskopf*

21. C.F. von Weizsacker, 'Metastabile Zustände der Atomkerne', *Naturwiss.*, 1936, **24**, 813.

22. E. Segrè and A.C. Helmholtz, 'Nuclear Isomerism' *Revs. Mod. Phys.*, 1949, **21**, 271.

23. M. Goldhaber and R.D. Hill, 'Nuclear Isomerism and Shell Structure', *Revs. Mod. Phys.*, 1952, **24**, 179.

24. C.D. Ellis and W.A. Wooster, 'The Atomic Number of a Radioactive Element at the Moment of the Emission of Gamma Rays', *Proc. Cambridge Phil. Soc.*, 1925, **22**, 844.

25. J.A. Cooper, J.M. Hollander and J.O. Rasmussen. 'Effect of the Chemical State on the Life-time of the 24 second [90]Nb', *Phys. Rev. Lett.*, 1965, **15**, 680.

26. P. Auger, "The Compound Photoelectric Effect", *J. Phys. Radium*, 1925, **6**, 205. *Ann. Phys.* (Paris), 1926, **6**, 183.

27. A.H. Snell and F. Pleasanton, 'Ionization Following Internal Conversion in Xenon' *Proc. Roy. Soc. (London)*, 1957, **A241**, 141.

28. S. Wexler, 'Primary Physical and Chemical Effects Associated with Emission of Radiation in Nuclear Processes'—*Actions Chimiques et Biochimiques des Radiations,* (Ed. M. Haissinsky, Mason et cie, Paris, 1965).

29. I. Curie and F. Joliot, 'Un Nouveau Type de Radioactivité' *Comptes rendus.* (Paris), 1934, **198**, 254.

30. F. Joliot and I. Joliot-Curie, *Nobel Lectures in Chemistry*, 1935 (Elsevier Publishing Co., Amsterdam, 1966).

Problems

4.1   It is known that 1 g of ^{226}Ra emits 11.6×10^{17} atoms of radon per year. Given the half-life period of Ra to be 1600 y, compute the value of the Avogadro constant. $[5.8 \times 10^{23}]$

4.2   Natural potassium contains 0.0119 weight per cent of ^{40}K which decays by β^- emission with a half-life of 1.3×10^9 y. Calculate the specific activity of natural potassium in disintegrations per minute.

$[1030 \text{ dis min}^{-1} \text{ g}^{-1}]$;

4.3   Calculate the mass and the number of atoms in a mCi of (a) ^{24}Na (15 h) (b) ^{32}P (14.3 d); and (c) ^{226}Ra (1600 y). The figures in parentheses are the half-lives.   [(a) 1.15×10^{-10} g, 2.88×10^{12} atoms;

(b) 3.51×10^{-9} g, 6.6×10^{13} atoms;

(c) 1 mg, 2.65×10^{18} atoms]

4.4   Find the specific activity of tritium gas (^{3}H$_2$) at STP in curies per cm^3. The half-life of ^{3}H is 12.3 years. $[2.64 \text{ Ci cm}^{-3} \text{ at STP}]$

4.5   There is a steady level of ^{14}C (half-life; 5736 y) in the atmosphere corresponding to 16.1 disintegrations g^{-1} min^{-1}. Calculate the ratio of ^{14}C/^{12}C in the atmosphere. $[1.37 \times 10^{-12}]$

4.6   In an extremely delicate experiment to produce the β^+ active nuclide ^{18}F of half-life 110 min, only 10 disintegrations per minute were obtained. What is the number of ^{18}F atoms obtained and its mass?

$[1590 \text{ atoms}, 4.74 \times 10^{-20} \text{ g}]$

4.7   If one curie of pure ^{32}P is stored for 24 h, what weight of ^{32}S would result at the end of that period? (Half-life of ^{32}P is 14.3 d)

$[0.166 \text{ } \mu\text{g}]$

4.8   What fraction of a freshly prepared radon of half-life period 3.82 days decays at the end of (a) 1 day, (b) 5 days, (c) 10 days and (d) in 6 half-lives? (e) By what time or in how many half-lives would 99.9% of the radon have decayed?

[(a) 16.6%,   (b) 59.6%,   (c) 83.7%,   (d) 98.4%,

(e) 38.1 days or 10 half-lives]

4.9   The half-life of ^{22}Na is 2.6 y. 89% of it decays by β^+ emission and the rest by EC. Calculate (a) the partial decay constants and (b) the half-lives for each mode of decay.

[(a) $\lambda_{\beta^+} = 0.2372$ y^{-1}, $\lambda_{EC} = 0.0293$ y^{-1}

(b) $\tau(\beta^+) = 2.92$ y, $\tau(EC) = 23.65$ y]

4.10 ^{64}Cu decays with a half-life of 12.8 h as follows: 42% by EC, 19% by β^+ and the rest by β^-. Find the partial decay constant and half-life for each mode of decay.

[EC $\lambda = 2.27 \times 10^{-2}$ h^{-1}; $\tau = 30.53$ h,

$$\beta^+ \; \lambda = 1.03 \times 10^{-2} \, h^{-1}; \quad \tau = 67.28 \, h,$$
$$\beta^- \; \lambda = 2.11 \times 10^{-2} \, h^{-1}; \quad \tau = 32.84 \, h].$$

4.11 Calculate the proportions of ^{238}U, ^{226}Ra and ^{232}Rn in an ore which has attained equilibrium, the half-lives of these nuclides being 4.47×10^9 y, 1600 y and 3.82 days respectively.

[Rn: Ra: U::1:1.53 $\times 10^5$:4.27 $\times 10^{11}$]

4.12 A radioactive species X of half-life 2 h decays to a species Y which in its turn decays with a half-life of 1 h to species Z (stable). A mixture of X and Y to start with has equal activities of the two components. Find the proportion of the activity in the mixture due to Y at the end of 4 hours.
(*Hint*: express the time in units of τ_x and τ_Y).

[Y activity in the mixture = 63.6% after 4 h]

4.13 Given the filiation relation

$$^{140}Ba \xrightarrow[\text{12 d}]{\beta^-} \; ^{140}La \xrightarrow[\text{10 h}]{\beta^-} \; ^{140}Ce \; \text{(stable)}$$

find the activity due to ^{140}La at the end of (a) 12 h (b) 24 d if we had pure ^{140}Ba only initially with an activity of 2000 disintegrations per second.
(*Hint*: express time in units of half-lives of species)

[(a) 1111 d/s, (b) 526 d/s]

4.14 ^{92}Sr ($\tau = 2.7$ h) decays into ^{92}Y ($\tau = 3.6$ h). Find (a) the time when the daughter activity reaches a maximum and (b) the time when the parent and daughter activities equal each other.

[(a) 4.48 h, (b) the same]

4.15 ^{210}Bi is shorter lived than the daughter ^{210}Po ($\tau = 138$ d). If the parent and the daughter are found to decay at the same rate exactly at the end of 24.86 d compute the half-life of the parent.
(*Hint*: take $\ln x = 2 \, (x - 1)/(x + 1)$.)

[4.33 d]

4.16 ^{210}Bi decays by emitting β^- particles of mean energy 0.34 MeV with a half-life of 5 d. What is the rate of energy emission in watts from a 4 mg sample of the isotope?

[1.0 W]

4.17 Calculate the kinetic energy and the velocity of the ^{240}Pu recoil atom in the ground state produced in the α decay of ^{244}Cm, given the mass loss in the decay to be 0.006 332 u.   [$E_{Pu} = 0.0966$ MeV, $v = 2.79 \times 10^5$ m s^{-1}]

4.18 The irradiation of common salt in the Apsara reactor produces ^{24}Na at a steady rate of 10 million atoms per second. The half-life of ^{24}Na is 15 h. If a sample of salt is irradiated for 30 h and then allowed to stand for 45 h what would be the residual activity of the sample?
(Neglect the formation of activities other than ^{24}Na).

[9.38 $\times 10^5$ dis/s]

4.19 Mention the multipole type and order in the γ emissions due to the following transitions:

(a) 11/2 (+) → 7/2 (−);   (b) 2 (+) → 0 (+)
(c) 1/2 (−) → 3/2 (+);   (d) 0 (+) → 0 (+).

[(a) M 2, (b) E 2, (c) E 1 (d) not possible]

Chapter 5

NUCLEAR REACTIONS

5.1 Bethe's Notation

[handwritten: Definition]

A nuclear reaction, as the name implies, refers to a transformation of a target atomic nucleus, usually at rest, by bombarding it with projectiles of light nuclei, or free nucleons, or photons of adequate energy. A nuclear reaction is generally represented by an equation indicating the nuclear characteristics of the reactants and resultants, as

$$^{A_1}_{Z_1}X + ^{A_2}_{Z_2}a \rightarrow ^{A_3}_{Z_3}b + ^{A_4}_{Z_4}Y$$

where X stands for the *target* nucleus, a for the *projectile* effecting the reaction, b for the *particle ejected*, or the ejectile, and Y for the *product* nucleus or recoil. Except when the nuclear charge conservation is to be emphasized ($Z_1 + Z_2 = Z_3 + Z_4$), the Zs are omitted in the equation, as these values are unique for each chemical element. Similarly, A_2 and A_3 are omitted if the particles a and b are otherwise uniquely distinguishable. A shorter form of writing a nuclear reaction is due to Bethe, on which notation the above reaction is more elegantly represented by

[handwritten: Things usually be omitted]

[handwritten: Short form of NR.]

$$^{A_1}X(a, b)^{A_2}Y.$$

Here, the target nuclide is written first and the product last, with the projectile and ejectile particles inside the parenthesis, in the same order but separated by a comma, *e.g.*

   (i) ^{24}Mg(d, α) ^{22}Na;   (ii) ^{35}Cl(n, p) ^{35}S;

   (iii) ^{23}Na(n, γ) ^{24}Na;   (iv) ^{63}Cu$(p, p3n9\alpha)$ ^{24}Na.

The last example shows how, sometimes, many particles all shown to the right of the comma, may be emitted.

5.2 Types of Nuclear Reactions

One way of designating a nuclear reaction is merely by naming (a, b) on the target. Thus, (ii) and (iii) in the above examples are referred to as (n, p) reaction on ^{35}Cl and (n, γ) reaction on ^{23}Na, respectively. Based on the nature of a and b following types are distinguished.

5.2.1 ELASTIC SCATTERING

Here $a = b$ and $X = Y$, e.g. ^{9}Be (n, n) ^{9}Be: the incoming particle strikes the target nucleus, loses a fraction of its kinetic energy in translating the latter. There is no change in total potential energy and the *kinetic energy is conserved*. Such a process is known as *elastic scattering*. The amount of energy transferred to the target in setting it in motion (translation) is given by the relation

$$E_M = \frac{4\, mM \sin^2 \theta/2}{(m + M)^2}\, E_m \qquad (5.1)$$

where E_m is the initial kinetic energy of the incident particle of mass m, and E_M the kinetic energy gained by the target nucleus of mass M and θ is the angle between the initial and the final paths of the particle. If E'_m is the residual kinetic energy of the incident particle, the conservation of energy leads to

$$E_m = E_M + E'_m \qquad (5.2)$$

The slowing down of fast neutrons by a moderator in a nuclear reactor is mainly by elastic scattering.

5.2.2 INELASTIC SCATTERING

A process of scattering is considered *inelastic* if some of the kinetic energy of the particle is used up in raising the potential energy of the target in some way or other, as in exciting it to a higher energy level. Here the kinetic energy of the system, as such, is not conserved, e.g.

$$^{107}\text{Ag}\,(n, n')\ ^{107m}\text{Ag} \xrightarrow[44.3\ \text{s}]{\text{IT}} \ ^{107}\text{Ag}$$

Here the incoming neutron of high energy, excites the target nucleus ^{107}Ag to an excited state which in this case has a long life of 44.3 s and in this process the scattered neutron has considerably less kinetic energy. This is indicated by priming the outgoing neutron as shown.

5.2.3 PHOTONUCLEAR REACTIONS

Nuclear reactions induced by X-ray or γ photons of high energy (> 1 MeV) are referred to as *photonuclear* reactions. Here $a = \gamma$ and b is more often n or p and, with some very high energy photons, b may be d, t or α or even a mixture of particles, e.g.

  (i) ^{9}Be (γ, n) ^{8}Be $\rightarrow$ 2α;

  (ii) ^{2}H (γ, n) ^{1}H.

It is by reaction (i) that neutrons are obtained from an Sb–Be laboratory neutron source. The 2.5 MeV γ from ^{124}Sb brings about the (γ, n) reaction on beryllium as shown.

5.2.4 RADIATIVE CAPTURE

Here the particle on capture leads to the emission of radiation in the form of one or more γ photons, i.e. $b = \gamma$. The most common are (n, γ)

reactions in which the product is an isotope of the target element one mass unit higher as in:

$$^{23}\text{Na}(n, \gamma)\,^{24}\text{Na}; \quad ^{31}\text{P}(n, \gamma)\,^{32}\text{P}; \quad ^{179}\text{Au}(n, \gamma)\,^{180}\text{Au}.$$

(n, γ) reactions have been realized with a very large number of target nuclides. There are also some (p, γ) reactions, as

$$^{19}\text{F}(p, \gamma)\,^{20}\text{Ne}; \quad ^{27}\text{Al}(p, \gamma)\,^{28}\text{Si}.$$

5.2.5 OTHER TYPES OF NUCLEAR REACTIONS

A large variety of other types of nuclear reactions is known as (p, n), (n, p), (n, α), (α, n), (d, p), (d, n), (α, t). Some of these will be considered later.

5.2.6 SPECIAL NUCLEAR REACTIONS

In all the above nuclear reactions, the product nucleus differs from the target nucleus only by a few units of A and/or Z. There are on the other hand many reactions involving high energy projectiles in which the target nucleus is partly torn apart yielding products lighter by several units. Some of these are listed below in the order of violence of disruption.

(i) *Evaporation*

When several nucleons, and/or their combinations as alphas, leave the nucleus, the process is referred to as *evaporation, e.g.*

$$^{133}\text{Cs}(\alpha, 4n)\,^{133}\text{La}; \quad ^{27}\text{Al}(d, p\alpha)\,^{24}\text{Na}.$$

(ii) *Spallation*

This is more violent than evaporation, and a large number of nucleons are thrown out and the product nucleus is very much lighter than the parent, *e.g.*

$$^{63}\text{Cu}(p, p\,3n\,9\alpha)\,^{24}\text{Na}; \quad (E_p \geqslant 70 \text{ MeV}),$$

$$^{79}\text{Br}(p, p\,7n\,7\alpha)\,^{44}\text{Sc}; \quad (E_p \geqslant 180 \text{ MeV}).$$

(iii) *Fission*

Fission is the process in which a nucleus excited by a neutron or by other means breaks into two fragments of comparable sizes, *e.g.*

$$^{235}\text{U} + n \rightarrow {}^{236}\text{U}^* \rightarrow {}^{137}\text{Te} + {}^{97}\text{Zr} + 2n.$$

Nuclear fission is considered in detail in Chapter 6.

(iv) *Fragmentation*

When a nucleus on heavy excitation, around 0.5 GeV splits into a light and a heavy fragment having about the same N/Z ratio as in the parent, the process is referred to as *fragmentation*. The excitation energy not being equally distributed between the light and the heavy fragments, the former decays by β⁻ and the latter by evaporation.

(v) *Stripping reactions*

In some cases, the projectile does not react as a whole with the target nucleus, but one or more constituents of the projectile (into which it splits in the joint Coulomb field of target and projectile), alone are captured by the target nucleus. In this way, products *heavier* than the target are produced.

With accelerated deuterons as projectiles they behave as if they are made up of a proton and a neutron, of which either alone is captured, more often the neutron, *e.g.*

$$^{63}Cu + d(=n + p) \rightarrow {}^{64}Cu + p$$

With 125 MeV $^{14}N^{6+}$ ions as projectiles they behave as if they are stripped into $n + p + 3\alpha$ in the Coulomb field of the target of which some alone are captured by the target. Thus with ^{27}Al as the target, following reactions have been observed (see Sec. 5.7.2 e).

$$^{27}Al \xrightarrow{+p} {}^{28}Si$$

$$\xrightarrow{+\alpha} {}^{31}P$$

$$\xrightarrow{+2\alpha} {}^{35}Cl$$

$$\xrightarrow{+3\alpha} {}^{39}K$$

5.3 Conservation in Nuclear Reactions

The conservation of nuclear charge, *e.g.* the number of protons (Z), the number of neutrons (N), and hence of A, the conservation of momentum, linear as well as angular, and of energy, during nuclear reactions are considered below.[1]

5.3.1 CONSERVATION OF PROTONS AND NEUTRONS

In all low energy nuclear reactions, the number of protons (Z), and of neutrons (N), and hence A, in the initial and final systems, remain *separately* constant, except in β-decay. In other words, the nuclear charges as well as the mass numbers of reactants balance those of the products.

e.g. in the reaction $^{24}Mg\,(d,\,\alpha)\,^{22}Na$

$$\Sigma Z_{reactants} = \Sigma Z_{products} = 13$$

$$\Sigma N_{reactants} = \Sigma N_{products} = 13$$

However, in the case of β± decay and *EC*, as well as in reactions induced by very high energy particles $(E \geqslant 0.3$ GeV), involving the formation of π mesons and antiparticles, the conservation of Z and N

separately will not hold but together will be constant, *i.e. A* as a whole is conserved; *e.g.* in the reaction

$$^{63}\text{Cu}\,(\,p,\,p\pi^{+})\ ^{63}\text{Ni}$$

$$\Sigma\, Z_{\text{react.}}\,(=30) \neq \Sigma\, Z_{\text{pr.}}\,(=29)$$

$$\Sigma\, N_{\text{react.}}\,(=34) \neq \Sigma\, N_{\text{pr.}}\,(=35)$$

but
$$\Sigma\, A_{\text{react.}}\,(=64) = \Sigma\, N_{\text{pr.}}\,(=64).$$

The position is similar in β± decay and *EC* reactions.

5.3.2   CONSERVATION OF MOMENTUM

(a)   *Linear momentum*

The initial momentum of the incident particle *a* (mass *m* and velocity *v*), is equal to that of the compound nucleus (*X + a*) (see Sec. 5.5).

$$mv = (m + M)\,V \qquad\qquad (5.3)$$

where *M* is the mass of the target nucleus (initially stationary) and *V* the velocity of the compound nucleus (see Sec. 5.5). From the conservation of linear momentum it follows that

$$V = \frac{m}{m + M}\,v \qquad\qquad (5.4)$$

It further follows that the three trajectories, of the incident projectile (*a − X*), of the particle emitted (*X − b*) and of the residue nucleus (*X − Y*) must be coplanar (Fig. 5.1).

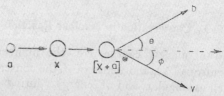

Fig. 5.1   Coplanar trajectories of the projectile, the ejectile and the recoil nucleus.

A further conclusion of importance which emerges out of the conservation of momentum is that not the entire kinetic energy of the projectile would be available for exciting the target nucleus leading to the nuclear reaction, but only a fraction of this, as the following consideration shows. Since the compound nucleus (*X + a*) has been set in motion with a velocity *V*, its kinetic energy is given by

$$T_r = \tfrac{1}{2}\,(m + M)\,V^2$$

Substituting the value of *V* from Eq. 5.4, we have

$$T_r = \frac{m}{m + M}\,T_a \qquad\qquad (5.5)$$

where T_a is the kinetic energy of the incident particle. (The kinetic energy of particles is sometimes symbolized by *T*.)

Since this amount T_r is used up in translation, the energy available for exciting the target nucleus is only

$$(T_a - T_r) = \frac{M}{m+M} T_a \qquad (5.6)$$

The component $\left(\dfrac{M}{m+M} T_a\right)$ is also referred to as the kinetic energy of the *projectile and the target* on the *centre of mass system* (CMS)*. In other words, the entire kinetic energy *on CMS* is available for effecting the nuclear reaction.

(b) *Angular momentum*

Besides linear momentum, nuclear reaction conserves total angular momentum. If the orbital angular momentum of the projectile particle is l and its spin s, the total angular momentum which the particle brings in is $I = l \pm s$ which together with the total angular momentum I' of the target nucleus must balance the sum of the total angular momenta of the particle(s) emitted and of the residual nucleus. This problem is best treated by bringing in the wave mechanical aspects of the system.

A free particle with momentum p and having no rotatory motion is associated with a plane wave of wavelength $\lambda^* = \hbar/p$ and wave number $k = 1/\lambda^* = p/\hbar$.** The angular momentum which the projectile transfers to the target nucleus depends on the *impact parameter*, (r) *i.e.* the distance of the point of impact from the centre of the nucleus. Here the target nucleus is considered as a penetrable sphere permitting some of the impacts to be in its *interior*. A head on collision at the centre of the target $(0 < r < \lambda^*)$ results in the particle being deflected by an angle close to 0 and this does not impart any rotatory motion to the target. As the point of impact moves farther $(r > \lambda^*)$ it tends to confer a rotatory motion to the target nucleus, larger the impact parameter, greater is the orbital angular momentum transferred (Fig. 5.2). However, orbital angular momentum, being quantized, can assume only discrete values of $l\hbar$ with

*For theoretical purposes it is found more convenient to adopt a new system of reference known as the *Centre of Mass System* (CMS). On the common Laboratory System (LS), the projectile alone moves, the target and the observer with his equipment being stationary: whereas on the CMS, both the projectile and the target are assumed to move towards each other with relative velocities of $(v-V)$ and V. Since on the CMS the momentum of the target is always equal and opposite to that of the projectile,

$$m(v-V) - MV = 0.$$

Hence, $V = \dfrac{m}{(m+M)} v$, which is the same as the velocity of the *compound nucleus* on the LS, (Eq. 5.4)[2].

**The momentum p is given in terms of the kinetic energy by the relation $p = \sqrt{2\mu E}$, where μ is the *reduced mass* of the target mass M and projectile mass m, given by $\mu = \dfrac{mM}{m+M}$.

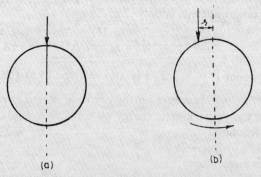

Fig. 5.2 Impact parameter (r) and transfer of angular momentum $(\Delta l \hbar)$
(a) $0 < r < \lambda^*$; $\Delta l \hbar = 0$ (b) $r > \lambda^*$; $\Delta l \hbar > 0$

$l = 0, 1, 2, \ldots$ the amount transferred also has to be an integral multiple of $\hbar$, including zero. This condition necessitates that the impact parameter also be in effect quantized, given by

$$r = l\lambda^*, \text{ with } l = 1, 2, 3, \ldots$$

or

$$\left. \begin{array}{l} r = \hbar/p, \ 2\hbar/p, \ \ldots \\ = \lambda^*, \ 2\lambda^*, \ \ldots \end{array} \right\} \tag{5.7}*$$

According to Blatt and Weisskopf,[3] the plane wave associated with the incident particle is resolvable into a set of partial waves, each corresponding to a different l value, thus $l = 0$ (s wave), $l = 1$ (p wave), $l = 2$ (d wave), and so on. The beam of monoergic particles appears to the

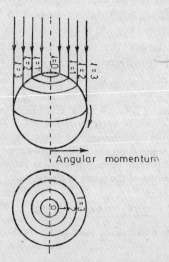

Fig. 5.3 Concept of projectile partial waves, impact parameter and transfer of angular momentum.

*The shortest impact of parameter is λ^* (see footnote to Table 5.1).

target nucleus as split into *concentric cylindrical zones* each with a different impact parameter and corresponding to a different cross section on the nuclear surface, and each partial wave transfers a different amount of angular momentum to the target nucleus in the zone of interaction (Fig. 5.3). Table 5.1 lists the characteristics of the different zones.

TABLE 5.1: Cross sections of partial waves

Zone		Partial wave	Impact parameter = associated wavelength	Crosssection of zone†
0	central	s $(l = 0)$	$1 \lambda^*$††	$\pi\lambda^{*2}$
1	next	p$(l = 1)$	$2\lambda^*$	$3\pi\lambda^{*2}$
2	next	d$(l = 2)$	$3\lambda^*$	$5\pi\lambda^{*2}$
l		l	$(l + 1)\lambda^*$	$(2l + 1)\pi\,\lambda^{*2}$

†Area of the ring shaped zone is given by

$$\pi\,\lambda^{*2}\,[(l + 1)^2 - l^2] = (2l + 1)\pi\,\lambda^{*2}.$$

††Over the central zone, (the *s* wave), the *geometrical* value of *r* varies from 0 to λ^*, but no impact parameter shorter than the associated wavelength can be visualized.

The total angular momentum brought in by accelerated particles can be sometimes very high. As the total angular momentum of the product nucleus can be only a few units of ℏ, the excess angular momentum brought in has to be carried away by the particles and photons emitted.[2,4]

5.3.3 CONSERVATION OF ENERGY

In every nuclear reaction, the total energy, being the sum of the rest mass energies and kinetic energies of reactants and resulting products, must be conserved. Thus in the reaction

$$X + a \to b + Y$$

We have

$$(m_X + m_a)\,931 + E_a = (m_b + m_Y)\,931 + E_b + E_Y \qquad (5.8)$$

where 931*m* stands for rest mass energy and *E* for kinetic energy, all in MeV units, presuming the target nucleus had no kinetic energy, being stationary. Rearranging Eq. 5.8 we arrive at

$$(m_X + m_a - m_b - m_Y)\,931 = E_b + E_Y - E_a = Q$$

$$Q = 931\,\Delta m \qquad (5.9)$$

where Δm is the mass loss. Here the term Q stands for the *energy of the reaction*, which is the equivalent of the enthalpy in a chemical reaction. Thus, Q (positive) signifies a loss of mass on reaction and the reaction is *exoergic* while a negative Q implies the reverse and stands for an *endoergic reaction*, the sign convention being the reverse for enthalpy in thermodynamics. Usually the term E_Y is difficult to measure directly, and Q is more often calculated from Δm.

5.3.4 THRESHOLD ENERGY FOR A NUCLEAR REACTION

For exoergic reactions, it would appear that there need be no threshold, but often through the operation of certain energy barriers, a minimum threshold exists. In the case of endoergic reactions the threshold has to be at least equal to $-Q$, the mass to be created. This has to come only in the form of the kinetic energy of the projectile. As pointed under Sec. 5.3.2, a fraction $\left(\dfrac{m}{m + M}\right)$ of E_a the kinetic energy of the projectile has necessarily to be used for the translation of the compound nucleus for conserving momentum. Hence the reaction to be possible

$$\left(\frac{M}{m + M}\right) E_a \geqslant Q$$

or threshold $$E_0 \geqslant \left(1 + \frac{m}{M}\right) Q \qquad (5.10)$$

Thus, if deuterons accelerated to 8 MeV energy (LS) strike a magnesium target, the energy available for effecting the nuclear reaction $^{24}Mg\,(d, \alpha)$ ^{22}Na is only $\dfrac{24}{2 + 24} \times 8 = 7.38$ MeV, which is the same as the kinetic energy on CMS (Sec. 5.3.2).

5.4 Reaction Cross Section

A very important quantity in nuclear reactions is the *reaction cross section*. This has the dimensions of area and is shown by σ_i in units of barns*, the subscript i indicates the *particular reaction*. σ_i represents the *number of reactions* of the type shown by i that *take place per cm² per second under conditions of unit density of target nuclei* and *unit flux of the incident particles*. In other words, the cross section σ_i is a measure of the probability of reaction i occurring, or its yield under the above set of conditions. For each reaction and for a given energy of the projectile, the reaction cross section has to be experimentally determined from the measured reaction yield and known surface density of target nuclei (N_0 cm⁻²) and the projectile flux (ϕ cm⁻² s⁻¹).

5.4.1 CROSS SECTION AND REACTION RATE

Consider a thin sheet of target containing N_0 (spherical) nuclei per unit area, and a beam of projectiles considered to be points passing through the sheet normally. Let the beam consist of n particles per cm³ all

*A barn ($= 10^{-28}$ m²) is the unit of reaction cross section. For convenience, areas are often expressed in units of cm², thus 1 b $= 10^{-24}$ cm².

travelling with a velocity v (cm s^{-1}). This is equivalent to a projectile flux of $\phi = nv$ projectiles cm^{-2} s^{-1}. The collision rate between the projectiles and target nuclei would be given by:

$$\text{Collision rate} \propto nvN_0$$
$$= \sigma\phi N_0 \text{ cm}^{-2} \text{ s}^{-1}$$

where σ is the reaction cross section. It follows that

$$\sigma \text{ (in cm}^2) = \frac{\text{collision cm}^{-2} \text{ s}^{-1}}{\phi \text{ cm}^{-2} \text{ s}^{-1} \quad N_0 \text{ cm}^{-2}} \tag{5.11}$$

5.4.2 The Geometric and Reaction Cross Section

[handwritten: 1 Fermi = 10^{-15} m]

The *geometric cross section* of a spherical nucleus is simply πR^2 where R is its radius given by $1.4 \times A^{1/3}$ F where A is the mass number. Obviously, for isotopic nuclides and nuclides of closeby elements R varies but very slightly. The nuclear radius just doubles from 4.2 F for ^{27}Al to 8.4 F for ^{216}Po. This corresponds to geometric cross sections of 0.554 and 2.217 b for the two nuclei. The reaction cross section is almost always *unrelated* to the geometric cross-section which varies but slightly amongst nuclides. On the other hand, the reaction cross section varies very widely from 10^{-3} to 10^6 b amongst reactions. The σ varies from reaction to reaction between the same pair of reactants, and for the same reaction often with the energy of the particle. It is therefore necessary to indicate the specific reaction by a subscript as σ_s for elastic scattering, σ_i for inelastic scattering, σ_a for absorption, $\sigma_{(n, f)}$ for neutron induced fission, or as $\sigma_{(d, p)}$, $\sigma_{(d, n)}$, $\sigma_{(d, \gamma)}$ for the specific reactions. Usually, σ_t stands for total of all processes between the two reactants. For instance, thermal neutrons interact in two ways with ^{233}U: (i) radiative capture (n, γ) with $\sigma_r = 53$ b and (ii) fission (n, f) with $\sigma_f = 531$ b which means in a total of 584 interactions only 53 or 9% are of (n, γ) type. Similarly, in the ^{232}Th $+ d$ interaction following reactions are possible (d, γ), (d, n), $(d, 2n)$, $(d, 3n)$ and (d, p). The total cross section σ_t is 2 b. This total target area is interpreted as being divided into areas $\sigma_{(d, \gamma)}$, $\sigma_{(d, n)}$.... The area σ_i assigned to the ith reaction is a measure of the *probability of that reaction* occurring. Thus, in the previous example given $\sigma_t = 2$ b and $\sigma_{(d, \gamma)} = 1$ mb, it means that out of 2000 deuterons striking the ^{232}Th target only one will be captured radiatively.

A few values of thermal neutron capture or specific reaction cross sections are given below to show the range of variation of reaction cross sections. The cross sections for xenon isotopes show the effect of magic number of 82 of neutrons. *[handwritten: (→ stable)]*

^{6}Li (n, α) T; $\sigma = 940$ b; $^{134}_{54}$Xe$_{80}$; $\sigma_c = 0.25$ b;

^{7}Li: $\sigma_c = 0.037$ b; $^{135}_{54}$Xe$_{81}$; $\sigma_c = 2.65 \times 10^6$ b;

Cd $\sigma_a = 19910$ b; $^{136}_{54}$Xe$_{82}$; $\sigma_c = 0.16$ b;

5.4.3 VARIATION OF NEUTRON CAPTURE CROSS SECTION WITH ENERGY : THE 1/v LAW

Generally, the slow neutron capture cross section varies inversely as the neutron velocity, which is referred to as the $1/v$ law. In other words, σ varies inversely as the square root of neutron energy. Fig. 5.4(a) shows this variation for the ^{10}B (n, α) ^{7}Li reaction. Here log σ is plotted against log neutron energy. In many cases, beyond a limit, the curve for the $1/v$ law gets superimposed by sharp peaks at definite values of neutron energy. Fig. 5.4(b) and (c) show this effect for the (n, γ) reactions in silver and zirconium respectively. These peak absorptions are referred to as resonance captures, considered in the next section.

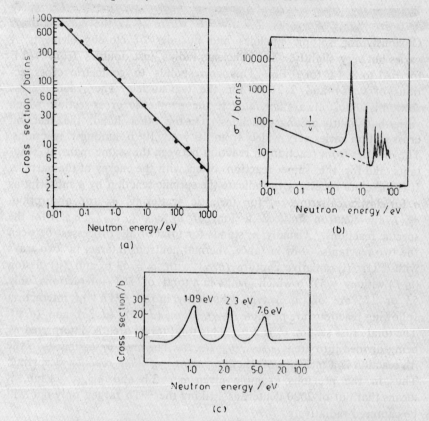

(a)

(b)

(c)

Fig. 5.4 Variation of neutron cross-section with energy: the $1/v$ law (a) $^{10}B(n, \alpha)$ ^{7}Li reaction[6] (b) ^{109}Ag (n, γ) ^{110}Ag reaction[6]. In the latter case, the $1/v$ law up to 1 eV is followed by resonance captures. (c) Neutron resonance capture in zirconium[7]

(from (a) *Introductory Nuclear Physics*, by D. Halliday, © 1950, 1955. John Wiley & Sons, Inc., reproduced with permission.

(b) Nuclear and Radiochemistry, by G. Friedlander, J.W. Kennedy and J.M. Miller, © 1964. John Wiley & Sons, Inc., reproduced with permission.

(c) W.H. Havens, C.S. Wu, L.J. Rainwater and C.L. Meaker[7], reproduced with permission of the Columbia University).

The de Broglie wavelength of slow neutrons of energy 1 eV is 2.86×10^{-11} m, which is many times greater than the dimensions of the target nucleus. The de Broglie wavelength of a particle is given by $\lambda = \dfrac{h}{p} = \dfrac{h}{\sqrt{2mE}}$ where m is its mass and E the energy. Substituting $E = 1$ eV $= 1.6 \times 10^{-19}$ J and values of other constants,

$$\underset{\text{(1 eV neutron)}}{\lambda} = \frac{6.6262 \times 10^{-34}}{(2 \times 1.009 \times 1.66 \times 10^{-27} \times 1.6 \times 10^{-19})^{1/2}} \text{ m}$$

$$= 2.86 \times 10^{-11} \text{ m}.$$

For an increase of neutron energy by a factor of 10^2, the wavelength decreases by a factor of 10. Thus, λ (1 MeV neutron) $= 2.86 \times 10^{-14}$ m, which approaches the nuclear dimension.

This means a neutron wave of 1eV energy surrounds a very large number of target nuclei, hence a great capture cross section. As the neutron energy increases, the wavelength diminishes and the number of nuclei encompassed by it falls rapidly and hence the decrease of σ as per $1/v$ law[8].

5.4.4 RESONANCE CAPTURE

The compound nucleus (see below), has several excitation levels above the ground level. If the capture of a neutron of a particular energy excites the compound nucleus precisely to one of its excited levels, then the capture of neutrons of that particular energy will be highly favoured. This is termed the *resonance capture*. If the neutron energy be slightly greater or less than this value the corresponding σ falls from the peak value (Figs. 5.4(b) and (c)). There may be more than one resonance absorption. ^{238}U has resonance absorption of neutrons of energy 6, 20, 38 eV. Similarly, the reaction ^{14}N $(n, p)^{14}$C shows resonances at 495, 639, 998, 1120 and 1211 keV.

5.5 The Compound Nucleus Theory

Based on the liquid drop model of the atomic nucleus, Bohr proposed a theory of nuclear reactions in 1936 which envisages the formation of a *compound nucleus* between the target nucleus and the projectile. The basic concepts of this theory are presented below.

5.5.1 THE CONCEPT OF THE COMPOUND NUCLEUS

(a) Under favourable conditions, the projectile particle and the target nucleus fuse together to form a *compound nucleus* C^*, thus:

$$^{A_1}_{Z_1}X + ^{A_2}_{Z_2}a \rightarrow ^{A_1+A_2}_{Z_1+Z_2}C^*$$

e.g.

$$^{24}Mg + d \rightarrow ^{26}Al^*$$

$$^{60}\text{Ni} + \alpha \rightarrow \ ^{64}\text{Zn}^*$$

$$^{63}\text{Cu} + p \rightarrow \ ^{64}\text{Zn}^*$$

This last shows how the same compound nucleus may be formed from two (or more) sets of reactants.

(b) The compound nucleus would be in an *excited state*, the excitation energy being the *sum* of the binding energy of the projectile particle in the compound nucleus and the kinetic energy of the projectile on CMS (Sec. 5.3.2).

(c) The excess or excitation energy brought in by the incoming particle will be very quickly shared by the nucleons of the compound nucleus in a *random* way. The time (t) for this is just the time needed for the particle (of velocity v) to traverse a diameter ($2R$) of the target nucleus.

$$t \simeq \frac{2R}{v}$$

Thus, with *fast neutrons* of energy 1 MeV, the velocity is $\sim 10^7 \text{ m s}^{-1}$ and taking the nuclear diameter to be $\sim 10^{-14}$ m, the time for energy randomization is $\sim 10^{-21}$ s. With slow neutrons of $v \sim 10^3 \text{ m s}^{-1}$, t is about 10^{-17} s. This is referred to as the *natural nuclear time*. The excess energy distribution is a random process. This means that the distribution is such that it keeps varying with time in such a way that at some moment one set of nucleons may have a large share of this energy and if a particular nucleon, or a small group of nucleons, come to possess energy in excess of the *Fermi gap* (~ 8 MeV per nucleon), that nucleon or group of nucleons succeed in separating from the compound nucleus, resulting in a nuclear reaction of a certain type.

(d) Thus the overall nuclear reaction $X(a, b) Y$ is a *two-step process*, *viz.* the formation of the compound nucleus and its subsequent decay to give products. The occurrence of the second stage of the nuclear reaction of one kind or another referred to above is a *relatively slower process*, involving times of the order of $10^{-15} - 10^{-14}$ s, compared to the *natural nuclear time* ($10^{-17} - 10^{-21}$ s). This means the compound nucleus has a *relatively long life*.

This concept has significant implications:

(i)   The same compound nucleus may be formed in more than one way, *i.e.* from different sets of target and projectile pairs.

(ii) Because of its long life, the compound nucleus forgets its parentage, *i.e.* how it was formed.

(iii) The subsequent decay of the compound nucleus is independent of the mode of its earlier formation, and the decay may occur also in more than one way, the relative yields depending on the energy of excitation.

(iv) Being an independent process, the products of the decay of the compound nucleus, may be emitted isotropically (*i.e.* nearly uniformly in all directions), without relation to the direction of the incident particle.

The following reactions studied by S. N. Ghoshal make these points clear[9].

$$\text{Target} + \text{projectile} \rightarrow \text{compound nucleus} \rightarrow \text{decay products}$$

$$\left.\begin{array}{c} {}^{60}\text{Ni} + \alpha \\[20pt] {}^{63}\text{Cu} + p \end{array}\right] \rightarrow \quad {}^{64}\text{Zn*} \quad -\left[\begin{array}{l} \rightarrow n + {}^{63}\text{Zn} \\ \rightarrow 2n + {}^{62}\text{Zn} \\ \rightarrow p + n + {}^{62}\text{Cu} \end{array}\right.$$

As further examples, we have the reactions studied by Alexander and Simonoff[10]

$$\left.\begin{array}{c} {}^{139}\text{La} + {}^{16}\text{O} \\ {}^{140}\text{Ce} + {}^{15}\text{N} \\ {}^{144}\text{Nd} + {}^{11}\text{B} \end{array}\right] \rightarrow \quad {}^{155}\text{Tb*} \quad \rightarrow 6n + {}^{149}\text{Tb}$$

and the reactions, studied by the French group at Saclay:

$$\left.\begin{array}{c} {}^{59}\text{Co} + {}^{20}\text{Ne} \\ {}^{63}\text{Cu} + {}^{16}\text{O} \end{array}\right] \rightarrow \quad {}^{79}\text{Rb*} \quad \rightarrow p + {}^{78}\text{Kr}$$

5.5.2   THE EXCITATION STATES OF THE COMPOUND NUCLEUS

(a)   *The Energy of Excitation*

The total energy of excitation of a compound nucleus is the result of two contributions.

(i)   The kinetic energy of the projectile on the CMS (see Sec. 5.3.2), and

(ii)   The binding energy of the particle in the compound nucleus.

The following example illustrates the calculation. The reaction is the bombardment of magnesium by 8 MeV deuterons, the compound nucleus formed being ${}^{26}\text{Al*}$ whose excitation energy is the sum of two terms:

(i)   The kinetic energy of the deuteron in striking ${}^{24}\text{Mg}$ nucleus on CMS *viz.* (Eq. 5.6) $= (24/26) \times 8 = 7.38$ MeV, and

(ii)   The binding energy of the deuteron in the ${}^{26}\text{Al}$ given by:

$$[m({}^{24}\text{Mg}) + m({}^{2}\text{D}) - m({}^{26}\text{Al})]\ 931$$

$$= (23.985\ 045 + 2.014\ 102 - 25.986\ 900)\ 931$$

$$= 0.012\ 247 \times 931 = 11.40\ \text{MeV}$$

Hence, the energy of excitation of ${}^{26}\text{Al*} = 7.38 + 11.40 = 18.78$ MeV.

(b)   *Distribution of the Excitation Energy*

As mentioned earlier the total excitation energy is distributed randomly between the nucleons of the compound nucleus. The probability of a uniform distribution is the lowest. For instance, in the $(\text{Mg} + d)$ reaction described above, if the excitation energy of 18.78 MeV were to be uniformly distributed over the 26 nucleons of the compound nucleus, each nucleon would get about 0.72 MeV which is too low to effect any nucleon emission. In such a case, the nuclear deexcitation can occur only by emitting radiation.

A large excitation energy of several MeV results in many nucleons being raised to energy levels much higher than their ground state, besides the presence of considerable rotational and vibrational energy. The distribution of this energy among the nucleons is random, implying a continuous variation, as a result of incessant interactions amongst them (possible on the liquid drop or the gas model). The excess energy may be concentrated on a given group of nucleons at one instant and on another group at another instant. Each distribution corresponds to filling of certain energy levels which vary from moment to moment. Such a distribution is a *quasi-stationary* or a chaotic state. There will be a large number of closely spaced energy levels the widths of which are greater than the energy separation between the levels. In other words, these levels overlap and no discrete energy level characteristic of a single well-defined quantum state can be distinguished: it is practically a continuum. While the total energy and angular momentum remain constant, there may be a vast number of ways of distributing this amongst the nucleons of the compound nucleus and the latter keeps oscillating between these configurations. Such a system can be treated statistically on the Fermi gas model of the nucleus (see Sec. 3.4). In a nucleus like ^{63}Cu excited to 25 MeV, the density of energy levels is as high as 4×10^5 per MeV, corresponding to a mean separation of 2.5 eV between two adjacent levels. These high energy close-spaced levels constitute the *virtual levels* as distinct from well separated discrete levels lying mostly below the top of the nuclear well and referred

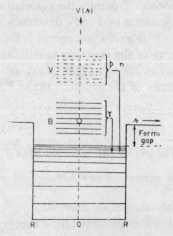

Fig. 5.5 Nuclear excitation
B: bound levels;
V: virtual levels.

to as the *bound levels* (Fig. 5.5). Deexcitation from the bound levels results by *photon emission*, while deexcitation from the *virtual levels* happens by the *emission of a particle,* as an *n*, or *p*, or a group of particles as 2*n*, *d*, α, often accompanied by γ. For the particle emission to occur, the particular nucleon, or a small group of nucleons, should receive the necessary energy (*i.e.* the separation energy of about 8 MeV per nucleon + Coulomb* and other barrier energies involved), concentrated by chance on the group during the random and incessant redistributions. This cannot be very frequent. However, once such a favoured configuration is reached, the nucleon emission follows without delay (energy being > separation energy), rather similar to the process of ionization of an atom once the atom is excited above the ionization potential.

Under low excitation (energy < separation energy) photon emission is the dominant mode of deexcitation.

5.5.3 DEEXCITATION OF THE COMPOUND NUCLEUS: LIFE TIMES AND LINE WIDTHS

Every excitation level has some line width (Γ), measured at half-height (Fig. 5.6), which varies from about 0.1 to about 10^4 eV, depending on

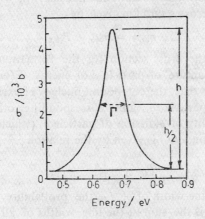

Fig. 5.6 Resonance capture of 0.65 eV neutrons by irridium, showing the line width Γ.

the energy of excitation and the mass number of the nucleus. Also each excited state has a mean life time ($\bar{\tau} = 1/$decay constant). By the principle of uncertainty, the product of the uncertainties of the two is ℏ, thus for the level *i*,

$$\Delta \Gamma_i \, \Delta \bar{\tau}_i = \hbar = 1.054\,4 \times 10^{-34} \text{ Js} \qquad (5.12)$$

The mean life time is given by

*There is no Coulomb barrier for neutron emission.

where Γ is in eV. As Γ varies from 0.1 to 10^4 eV, $\bar{\tau}$ varies from 10^{-15} to 10^{-20} s. Since each mode of decay has a different line width,

$$\Gamma_{total} = \Gamma_\gamma + \Gamma_n + \Gamma_{2n} + \Gamma_{p} + \Gamma_\alpha + \dots \tag{5.13}$$

where $\Gamma_\gamma \Gamma_n \dots$ are line widths for individual modes of decay, os radiation or photon width Γ_γ, neutron width Γ_n, etc. Each term is a measure of the probability of emission per second of the particle indicated by the subscript.

5.5.4 THE YIELD OF A NUCLEAR REACTION $X(a, b)\ Y$: THE BREIT-WIGNER FORMULA

The main problem in nuclear chemistry is to be able to calculate the yield of a given reaction $X(a, b)\ Y$ in terms of known characteristics of the target and the projectile particle and the energy and angular momentum of the latter. The solution to this is provided in the Breit-Wigner formula, whose derivation being complicated, we propose to approach it in two stages[11].

On Bohr's theory, a nuclear reaction, $X(a, b)\ Y$ is a two-step process: (i) The formation of the compound nucleus: $X + a \rightarrow [X + a]^*$ and (ii) the decay of the compound nucleus: $[X + a]^* \rightarrow b + Y$. The overall reaction cross section is given by

$$\sigma_{(a, b)} = \sigma_{c(a, E)}\ P_{(b, \varepsilon)} \tag{5.14}$$

where $\sigma_{c(a, E)}$ is the cross section for the formation of the compound nucleus by the capture of particle a of energy E (on CMS) and $P(b, \varepsilon)$ is the probability that the compound nucleus of excitation energy ε will decay yielding particle b, and corresponding other products. The relative probability of emission of particle b (which may be a photon, neutron, or proton, etc.) is given by the relation

$$P_{(b, \varepsilon)} = \frac{\Gamma_b}{\Gamma_t} \tag{5.15}$$

where Γ_b is the line width of b, i.e. the probability of emission of b in unit time and Γ_t is the sum of the line widths of all possible eimssions. This leads to

$$\sigma_{(a, b)} = \sigma_{c(a, E)} \frac{\Gamma_b}{\Gamma_t} \tag{5.16}$$

We shall now consider the two factors making up $\sigma_{(a, b)}$ separately.

(a) Cross section for the Formation of the Compound Nucleus

As pointed out earlier, the projectile beam appears to the target nucleus as a combination of partial waves each corresponding to a given orbital angular momentum quantum number, $l = 0, 1, 2, 3, \dots$ (Fig. 5.3). Under the action of the strong attractive force of the nucleus, a fraction of the particles of each partial wave is drawn in as in refraction and the rest scattered back as in reflection. The fraction of particles penetrating a given zone to the total number of particles incident is the *transmission coefficient* T_l of the zone l, given by

$$T_l = \frac{4kK}{(k + K)^2} \qquad (5.17)$$

where k and K are wave numbers *inside* and *outside* the nucleus of the particles constituting the l wave. The wave numbers are given by

$$\left. \begin{array}{l} k = \dfrac{1}{\lambda^*_{in}} = \dfrac{p_{in}}{\hbar} = [2\mu (E + V)]^{1/2}/\hbar \\[2mm] K = \dfrac{1}{\lambda^*_{out}} = \dfrac{p_{out}}{\hbar} = [2\mu E]^{1/2}/\hbar \end{array} \right\} \qquad (5.18)^*$$

For the s wave ($l = 0$), landing on the central zone, $k = K$ and hence $T_s = 1$, *i.e.* all the particles incident over this zone penetrate the nucleus.

The $\sigma_{c,l}$ for a given l value is given by (*vide* Eq. 5.7(a) and Table 5.1)

$$\sigma_{c,l} = \pi \lambda^{*2} (2l + 1)T_l$$

hence,

$$\sigma_c = \pi \lambda^{*2} \sum_{l=0}^{\infty} (2l + 1)T_l \qquad (5.19)$$

As the energy of the particle increases, T_l for all values of l tends to approach unity. Under these conditions the nucleus behaves as a *black body* absorbing all the incident nucleons. Also when the energy is high, the particle wavelength becomes very short, such that $R > l\lambda^*$, and the summation in Eq. 5.19 is limited to a maximum value of $l = R/\lambda^*$ thus,

$$\sigma_c = \pi \lambda^{*2} \sum_{l=0}^{R/\lambda^*} (2l + 1) \qquad (5.19\ a)$$

T_l being almost equal to unity.

For very large values of l, Eq. 5.19 (a) becomes

$$\sigma_c = \pi (R + \lambda^*)^2 \qquad (5.20)$$

We can simplify Eq. 5.20 under two extreme cases:
(i) for high energy particles $R \gg \lambda^*$

$$\sigma_c = \pi R^2 \qquad (5.21)$$

the cross section is simply equal to the geometric cross section; and
(ii) for very low energy particles (thermal neutrons) $R \ll \lambda^*$

$$\sigma_c = \pi \lambda^{*2} \qquad (5.22)$$

which is many times larger than the geometric cross section.

---

*In the general expression $\lambda^* = \dfrac{\hbar}{p} = \dfrac{\hbar}{\sqrt{2mE}}$, the mass m is changed to reduced mass $\mu = \dfrac{mM}{m + M}$ and for the particle inside, the resultant energy $E + V$ is used for the total energy due to the nuclear potential.

(b) *Probability of the Decay of the Compound Nucleus P (b)*

The decay probability of the compound nucleus by a particular mode, say by emitting particle b, is itself made up of two factors, *viz.*

(i) the resonance factor and (ii) the emission probability.

(i) *The resonance factor*:   In general, a plot of capture cross section as a function of particle energy (or velocity) follows the $1/v$ law (Sec. 5.4.3) with sharp peaks at specific energy values namely the *resonance* values (Fig. 5.4 b and c).   Let E_o be the nearest resonance energy for a given energy of excitation E of the compound nucleus.   The *resonance factor* is given by

$$\frac{1}{(E - E_o)^2 + (\Gamma/2)^2} \tag{5.23a}$$

where Γ is, the sum of all the partial line widths.   Obviously as E approaches E_o, the resonance factor increases to its maximum value of $4/\Gamma^2$, which is also the condition for the maximization of σ_c.

(ii)   *The emission probability P (b, ϵ)*:   The probability of emission of the particle b is given by the product

$$\Gamma_a\, \Gamma_b \tag{5.23b}$$

where Γ_a is the line width for the emission of the *incident* particle a itself, *in the reverse reaction* of the compound nucleus reverting to the original system

$$X + a \leftarrow [X + a]^*$$

Finally, combining the expressions for the cross-section of the formation of the compound nucleus (Eq. 5.20) and those for the probability of decay, (Eqs. 5.23 (a) and (b)) one arrives at the expression for the overall reaction cross section,

$$\sigma_{(a,b)} = \pi\,(R + \lambda^*)^2\, \frac{\Gamma_a\, \Gamma_b}{(E - E_o)^2 + (\Gamma/2)^2} \tag{5.24}$$

which is one of the simplest forms of the expression derived by Breit and Wigner in 1936 and known after them.   Under conditions of resonance capture, $(E = E_o)$ the overall cross section has a maximum value[11-13]

$$\sigma_{(a,b)\mathrm{max}} = \frac{4\pi\,(R + \lambda^*)^2\, \Gamma_a\, \Gamma_b}{\Gamma^2} \tag{5.25}$$

5.6   Experimental Evidence of Bohr's Theory: Experiments of Ghoshal and of Alexander and Simonoff

On Bohr's theory of nuclear reactions, the formation of the compound nucleus and its subsequent decay are independent processes.   Because of the appreciable time lag between the formation and decay, the compound nucleus forgets how it was formed.   This concept of independence of decay implies that if *the same compound nucleus* be obtained in two or more different ways, and *if the state of excitation be the same* in all cases, the decay products not only should be the same but their yields be also quantitatively comparable. In other words, if two reactions $X + a$ and $X' + a'$ lead to the same compound nucleus C* and if the latter decays partly into $b + Y$ and partly into $b' + Y'$, and *provided the excitation energy is the same* in the two cases, theory requires that

$$\frac{\sigma_{(a,\ b)}}{\sigma_{(a,\ b')}} = \frac{\sigma_{(a',\ b)}}{\sigma_{(a',\ b')}} \tag{5.26}$$

As shown in Sec. 5.5.1, the same compound nucleus can be obtained in different ways. Following examples were cited to illustrate this,

(a) ^{64}Zn* from ^{60}Ni $+ \alpha$, or from ^{63}Cu $+ p$;

(b) ^{155}Tb* from ^{139}La $+ ^{16}$O, or ^{140}Ce $+ ^{15}$N, or ^{144}Nd $+ ^{11}$B;

(c) ^{79}Rb* from ^{59}Co $+ ^{20}$Ne, or ^{63}Cu $+ ^{16}$O.

It is only necessary to ensure that the compound nucleus obtained by alternative reactions is in the same state of excitation. The excitation energy (Sec. 5.5.2) is made up of two terms:

(i)   The binding energy of the projectile particle in the compound nucleus: the value of this is fixed for each pair and this cannot be changed.

(ii)   The kinetic energy of the particle (on CMS) which is variable within wide limits. The value of this can be adjusted to match the difference in the binding energies in the two modes.

For instance, the binding energy of α in ^{64}Zn is 7 MeV less than the binding energy of p in the same compound nucleus. Hence, if the kinetic energy of α be made 7 MeV more than that of the proton, the resulting compound nucleus ^{64}Zn* will have the same excitation energy in the two cases. Under this condition, one should compare the yields of the corresponding decay products obtained from the ^{60}Ni $+ \alpha$ and ^{63}Cu $+ p$ reactions for different excitation energies. This was just what the Indian nuclear physicist, S. N. Ghoshal did in 1950[9]. As mentioned earlier (Sec. 5.5.1) the compound nucleus ^{64}Zn* decays in three principal ways (i) $n + ^{63}$Zn, (Fig. 5.7 (a) curves 1, 2), (ii) $2n + ^{62}$Zn (curves 3, 4) and (iii) $n + p + ^{62}$Cu (curves 5, 6). Ghoshal found that the yields of the products of these three modes of decay are sensibly the same from the compound nucleus prepared from ^{60}Ni $+ \alpha$ or ^{63}Cu $+ p$, over a range-excitation energies, as shown in Fig. 5.7 (a) where the reaction cross section is plotted as a function of energy of the particle for the different modes of decay of ^{60}Ni $+ \alpha$ (curves 1, 3, 5) and ^{63}Cu $+ p$ (curves 2, 4, 6) reactions. To help direct comparison the energy scale for α is displaced by 7 MeV to the left to match it with that for p.

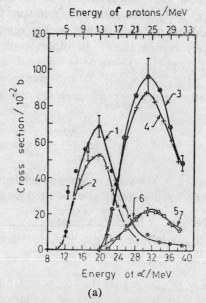

(a)

Fig. 5.7 Evidence for the compound nucleus theory:
(a) ^{64}Zn* from ^{60}Ni + α (curves 1, 3, 5) and
^{63}Cu + p (curves 2, 4, 6)
products: n + ^{63}Zn (curves 1, 2)
2 n + ^{62}Zn (curves 3, 4)
n + p + ^{62}Cu (curves 5, 6)

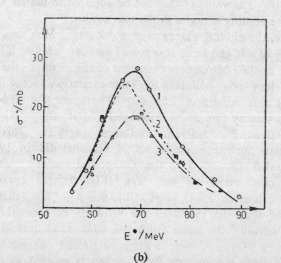

(b)

5.7 (b) ^{155}Tb* from ^{144}Nd + ^{11}B (curve 1); ^{140}Ce + ^{15}N (curve 2) and ^{139}La + ^{16}O
(curve 3): products: 6 n + ^{149}Tb
(from (a) S.N. Ghoshal[9], reproduced with permission from the author and the
University of California, Lawrence Berkeley Laboratory.
(b) and (c) J.M. Alexander and G.N. Simonoff[10], reproduced with authors' permission.

Alexander and Simonoff had similarly verified the compound nucleus theory in the case ^{155}Tb* formed by three different modes (^{144}Nd + ^{11}B; ^{140}Ce + ^{15}N; and ^{139}La + ^{16}O) and of ^{156}Dy* formed by two modes (^{144}Nd + ^{12}C and ^{136}Ba + ^{20}Ne). The yields of the products in the two cases, *viz.* ^{149}Tb + $6n$ and ^{150}Dy + $6n$, are comparable, as shown in Fig. 5.7 (b) and (c) respectively[10].

Another case of interest to which the Breit-Wigner formula applies with great success is the reaction ^{27}Al(p, α) ^{24}Mg and its reverse ^{24}Mg (α, p) ^{27}Al, with ^{28}Si* as the compound nucleus, studied by Kaufman, Goldberg, Koester and Mooring[14]. *If the compound nucleus obtained from either direction is to have the same excitation energy:*

$$E_{p(CMS)} + S_p = E_{\alpha(CMS)} + S_\alpha.$$

Hence,

$$E_\alpha - E_p = S_p - S_\alpha$$

where the E's are bombarding particle energies on CMS and the S's are the binding energies of the particles in the compound nucleus. The values of S_p and S_α in ^{28}Si are found from the table of mass excesses to be 11.575 and 9.981 MeV respectively. Hence, the kinetic energy of the alpha particle needs to be 1.59 MeV higher than the kinetic energy of the proton in order that the resulting ^{28}Si* be in the same state of excitation in the two cases. Under these conditions of excitation, the Breit-Wigner theory requires

$$\frac{\sigma_{(p,\alpha)}}{\sigma_{(\alpha,p)}} = \frac{\lambda^{*2}_\alpha}{\lambda^{*2}_p} \tag{5.27}$$

Hence, resonances should occur at the same excitation energies for both the direct and reverse reactions. Figure 5.8 confirms this, where the

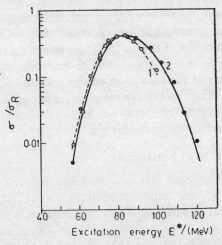

(c)

Fig. 5.7 (c) ^{156}Dy from ^{144}Nd + ^{12}C (curve 1) and ^{136}Ba + ^{20}Ne (curve 2) products: $6n + {}^{150}$Dy.

yields (proportional to cross sections) are plotted as a function of the kinetic energy of the particles, that of α being displaced to the left by 1.6 MeV.

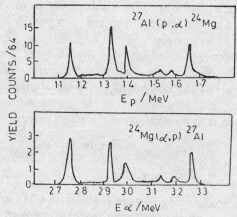

Fig. 5.8   Yields of the reverse nuclear reactions ^{27}Al $+ p \leftrightarrow \alpha + {}^{24}$Mg as a function of the excitation energy
(from S.G. Kaufman, E. Goldberg, L.J. Koester and F.P. Mooring[14], reproduced with authors' permission).

5.7   Specific Nuclear Reactions

Some of the material presented under this Section is based on Blatt and Weisskopf's classification of nuclear reactions on the basis of (i) the nature of the incident particle: n, p, d, t, α, heavy ions; or photons, (ii) the energy of the particle: low (< 1 keV); intermediate or ($1 - 500$ keV); high ($0.5 - 10$ MeV); or very high (> 10 MeV); (iii) the mass of the target nucleus: light (< 25 A); medium ($25 - 80$ A); or heavy (> 80 A)[3]. Of these, nuclear reactions with light target nuclei do not reveal any special trend permitting generalization. In fact, Bohr had recognized the limitation of the compound nucleus theory in respect of light nuclei which do not contain enough nucleons to permit sufficient random distribution of the excitation energy. Of the rest of the nuclear reactions with medium and heavy mass target nuclei, only some general trends observed will be pointed out here. Examples are cited only where the type is relatively less occurrent.

5.7.1   REACTIONS WITH NEUTRONS

Being free from Coulomb barrier, reactions induced by neutrons of different energies are not only the most numerous but very important both from the point of theoretical and applied aspects.

(a)   *Low Energy Neutrons $E < 1$ keV*

The principal types of reactions possible with low energy neutrons and with target nuclei of medium mass $25 < A < 80$ are (n, n); (n, γ)

and (n, r)* in decreasing order of their cross sections. With heavy nuclei $(A > 80)$, also the same types of reactions occur in the main, but in the order (n, γ), (n, n) and (n, r).

(b) *Intermediate Energy Neutrons* $1 < E \lessdot 500$ keV
  The principal reactions are still the same as with low energy neutrons, the cross sections decreasing in the order (n, n); (n, γ) and (n, r) with all target nuclei $A > 25$.

(c) *High Energy Neutrons* $0.5 < E < 10$ MeV
  The principal reactions with high energy neutrons are (n, n); (n, α) and (n, p) with medium mass nuclei and (n, n); (n, p) and (n, γ) with heavy mass nuclei. Examples of (n, α) are $^{35}Cl (n, \alpha)$ ^{32}P; $^{203}Tl (n, \alpha)$ ^{200}Au. An example of (n, p) is $^{35}Cl (n, p)$ ^{35}S.

(d) *Very High Energy Neutrons* $E > 10$ MeV
  The principal reactions with very high energy neutrons with nuclei $A > 25$ are $(n, 2n)$; (n, n); (n, p); (n, np); $(n, 2p)$; (n, α) and (n, m)**. Examples of $(n, 2n)$: $^{79}Br (n, 2n)$ ^{78}Br; $^{12}C (n, 2n)$ ^{11}C; examples of (n, m): $^{65}Cu (n, n\alpha)$ ^{61}Co; $^{63}Cu (n, \alpha 2n)$ ^{58}Co.

5.7.2 REACTIONS WITH CHARGED PARTICLES

No nuclear reaction is possible with charged particles as projectiles unless their energy is high enough to overcome the Coulomb barrier which increases with the charge Z (and hence the mass number A) of the target nucleus. The principal types of reactions are listed below in decreasing order of cross section.

(a) *Reactions with Protons*

		Medium mass nuclei	Heavy mass nuclei
(i)	Intermediate energy $(1 < E < 500$ keV)	$(25 < A < 80)$ (p, n); (p, γ); $[^{27}Al (p, \gamma)^{28}Si]$; (p, α); (p, r)	$(A > 80)$ energy not adequate for any reaction
(ii)	High energy $(0.5 < E < 10$ MeV)	$(25 < A < 80)$ (p, n); (p, p); (p, α); (p, r).	$(A > 80)$ (p, n); (p, p); (p, γ)
(iii)	Very high energy $(E > 10$ MeV)	$(p, 2n)$; (p, n); (p, p);	same as in the case

---

*We are abbreviating *resonance* capture or resonance scattering as (n, r).
**We are abbreviating the process of the *evaporation of multiple nucleons* as (n, m).

(p, np); $(p, 2p)$; (p, α); of medium mass
(p, m) nuclei
^{63}Cu $(p, 2p \, 6n\alpha)$ ^{52}Fe
^{65}Cu (p, pn) ^{64}Cu
^{209}Bi $(p, 8n)$ ^{202}Po

(b) Reactions with Deuterons

Reactions induced by accelerated deuterons are of special interest on account of the characteristics of this particle, *viz.*

(i) It is the simplest and most loosely bound nucleus with a mean binding energy of 1.115 MeV as against 7–8 MeV in most other nuclei.

(ii) It is unsymmetrical in respect of charge distribution, with a quadrupole moment of $+0.002\,74$ b (Sec. 2.10).

(iii) It is a triplet in the ground state, *i.e.* with parallel spins for the proton and the neutron.

It is doubtful whether a compound nucleus is formed at all in reactions with deuterons, especially in the class of *stripping reactions,* wherein the deuteron is stripped of one of its nucleons and the other is captured by the target nucleus, as in (d, p) and (d, n) reactions possible with intermediate and high energy deuterons:

$$^{A}_{Z}X + d \rightarrow {}^{A+1}_{Z}X + p \quad e.g. \quad ^{81}Br\,(d, p)\,^{82}Br$$

or

$$^{A}_{Z}X + d \rightarrow {}^{A+1}_{Z+1}Y + n \quad e.g. \quad ^{57}Fe\,(d, n)\,^{58}Co.$$

Of these the (d, p) reactions possible even at low energies, are known as the *Oppenheimer-Phillips* reactions, as these were first explained by them. As the projectile deuteron approaches a target nucleus, it orients itself such that the neutron faces the target and is drawn in, being free from Coulomb barrier and the proton is left out.

Other nuclear reactions induced by deuterons of higher energy are listed below which are similar for target nuclei of both medium and heavy masses. As before they are listed in the order of decreasing cross sections.

High energy $(0.5 < E < 10$ MeV$)$

Stripping reactions (d, p); (d, n); (d, pn);

$(d, 2n)$; $^{75}As\,(d, 2n)\,^{75}Se$

(d, α): $^{24}Mg\,(d, \alpha)\,^{22}Na$

Very high energy $(E > 10$ MeV$)$

(d, p); $(d, 2n)$; (d, pn); $(d, 3n)$; (d, d);

$(d, t) \begin{cases} ^{7}Li\,(d, t)\,^{6}Li \\ ^{31}P\,(d, t)\,^{30}P \end{cases}$

(d, m): $^{75}As\,(d, p6n)\,^{70}As$

(c) Reactions with Tritons

Nuclear reactions effected by tritons are similar to those effected by deuterons. The Oppenheimer-Phillips reactions take the form of (t, p) and (t, d), *e.g.*

$$^{12}\text{C}\,(t,\,p)\,^{14}\text{C};\ \ ^{59}\text{Co}\,(t,\,p)\,^{61}\text{Co};\ \ ^{63}\text{Cu}\,(t,\,d)\,^{64}\text{Cu}$$

Other reactions are $(t,\,n)$, $(t,\,2n)$ and $(t,\,\alpha)$,

e.g.

$$^{16}\text{O}\,(t,\,n)\,^{18}\text{F};\ \ ^{32}\text{S}\,(t,\,n)\,^{34}\text{Cl};$$

$$^{76}\text{Ge}\,(t,\,2n)\,^{77}\text{As};\ \ ^{7}\text{Li}\,(t,\,\alpha)\,^{6}\text{He}$$

(d)   *Reactions with Alpha Particles*

Alpha particles from naturally occurring radioelements were the first projectiles to be used in effecting nuclear reactions, the classical experiment of Rutherford in 1919 being the first one

$$^{14}\text{N} + \alpha \ \rightarrow \ p + {}^{17}\text{O}$$

Because of the limited energy and low flux of alphas available from natural radioelements, their applications have been limited to mainly studying elastic scatterings (α, α) which experiments actually led to the postulation of the nuclear atom by Rutherford. With the development of particle accelerators, much higher energy $^{4}\text{He}^{2+}$ ions and of higher flux have been available and these have been used in the study of a larger number of nuclear reactions. We shall list here only the types of reactions due to high and very high energy helium ions, which are same with both medium and high mass target nuclei.

High energy $(0.5 < E < 10 \text{ MeV})$ *Very high energy* $(E > 10 \text{ MeV})$

(α, n): $^{109}\text{Ag}\,(\alpha, n)\,^{112}\text{In}$ $(\alpha, 2n)$: $^{109}\text{Ag}\,(\alpha, 2n)\,^{111}\text{In}$;

(α, p); (α, α); (α, γ). (α, n); (α, p); (α, np); $(\alpha, 2p)$; (α, d);

$$(\alpha, m) : \begin{cases} ^{239}\text{Pu}\,(\alpha, 5n)\,^{238}\text{Cm} \\ ^{239}\text{Pu}\,(\alpha, p2n)\,^{240}\text{Am} \end{cases}$$

(e)   *Reactions with Heavy Ions*

Since for a given charge to mass ratio of an ion and acceleration, the kinetic energy of the ion is greater larger the mass, it would be advantageous to employ heavy ions for effecting nuclear reactions. Once machines capable of accelerating heavy ions (mass greater than that of a helium ion) became available, ions as $^{7}\text{Li}^{3+}$, $^{9}\text{Be}^{4+}$, $^{12}\text{C}^{6+}$ and some others have been used since the mid 1950s. Particularly the $6+$ ions as $^{12}\text{C}^{6+}$, $^{14}\text{N}^{6+}$, $^{16}\text{O}^{6+}$ and $^{20}\text{Ne}^{6+}$ have yielded valuable results. The special feature of the $6+$ ions is that they are accelerated in a cyclotron set for accelerating $2+$ ions of the same mass by the principle of the *third* *harmonic acceleration.** In addition, linear accelerators have also been used to deliver ion beams of fixed energy of 4 or 10 MeV per nucleon. These ions have been also accelerated to energies of the order of 100 MeV, and used to bombard targets of both light and heavy nuclei. The principal results are given below.

(i) *Production of neutron deficient nuclides.*

e.g. $^{65}Cu\,(^{12}C,\,3n)\,^{74}Br;\;^{115}In\,(^{14}N,\,3n)\,^{126}Ba$

Generally, reactions ejecting multiple neutrons and a proton have a higher cross section. These neutron deficient nuclei arrive at stability by one or more electron captures

$$^{74}Br \xrightarrow{EC} \;^{74}Se \text{ (stable)}$$

$$^{126}Ba \xrightarrow{EC} Cs \xrightarrow{EC} \;^{126}Xe \text{ (stable)}$$

(ii) *Production of high-Z transactinides*: One of the interests in nuclear reactions due to heavy ions has been the possibility of obtaining high Z elements well beyond uranium, an addition of 6 to 10 protons being possible.

Examples : $^{238}_{92}U\,(^{12}C,4n)\,^{246}_{98}Cf,$

$^{238}_{92}U\,(^{14}N,6n)\,^{246}_{99}Es,$

$^{238}_{92}U\,(^{16}O,\,xn)\,^{254-x}_{100}Fm,$

$^{246}_{96}Cm\,(^{12}C,\,6n)\,^{252}_{102}No,$

$^{252}_{98}Cf\,(^{11}B,\,xn)\,^{263-x}_{103}Lw,$

Other high-Z nuclides reported to be synthesized are

$$Z = 104 \text{ by } _{94}Pu + _{10}Ne \text{ reaction,}$$

$$= 105 \text{ by } _{98}Cf + _7N \quad\text{,,}$$

$$= 106 \text{ by } _{98}Cf + _8O \quad\text{,,}$$

Most of these high-Z-nuclides decay by spontaneous fission and α decay.
(iii) *Buckshot capture products*: Walker, Fremlin and Chackett[17,18] suggested that in reactions due to heavy ions and light or medium mass nuclei, the
projectile particle appears to be split into its components in the joint field,

---

*In a cyclotron most of these heavy ions get stripped to 6+ state. Once the machine
is tuned for 2+ ions, the 6+ ions also would be in correct phase for getting
accelerated, the 6+ ions traversing with thrice the angular velocity as 2+ ions of
the same mass. This is clear from the expression for the period of phase change in
a cyclotron, viz.

$$t = \frac{2\pi m}{Bq}$$

where B is the magnetic induction and m and q are mass and charge of the particle.
The period t for a 6+ particle is 1/3 that for a 2+ particle of the same mass;
hence the resonance condition is the same for both.[15]

some of which alone are captured by the target nucleus, hence the name of *buckshot hypothesis*. Thus, Al bombarded by 125 MeV $^{14}N^{6+}$ ions yields a large number of products, as, in decreasing yields: ^{32}P, ^{18}F, ^{34}Cl, ^{38}K, ^{30}P, ^{35}S, ^{24}Na, ^{31}Si, ^{27}Mg, ^{13}N, and ^{11}C. It is believed that instead of forming a compound nucleus, the projectile behaves as a bunch of 5 particles, $3\alpha + n + p$, one or more of which alone are captured by the target nucleus as described earlier (Sec. 5.2.6), leading to its disintegration in a variety of ways (Fig. 5.9).

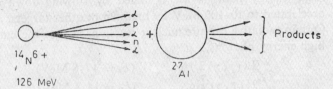

$^{14}N^{6+}$

126 MeV

^{27}Al

Fig. 5.9 'Buckshot' capture hypothesis in the heavy ion induced nuclear reaction: $^{14}N^{6+} + Al$.

Similar results had been reported for the bombardment of the same target (Al) by accelerated $^{16}O^{6+}$ ions, the products observed being: ^{38}K, ^{34}Cl, ^{32}P, ^{30}P, ^{24}Na and ^{18}F, which were common to the Al + ^{14}N reaction.

Since then the study of nuclear reactions induced by heavy ions has received considerable attention employing powerful accelerators capable of delivering beams of 100–200 MeV ions as heavy as Ne, and even more energetic ions of Br, I and Xe. Side by side there has been great progress in the techniques of detecting and analysing on-line the recoil products of a few seconds' half-life.

This is achieved by stopping the recoils in helium gas where they are absorbed on particles of 0.1 to 1.0 μ diameter. These particles are added as an aerosol, or produced by radiation polymerisation of an impurity in the He gas. The recoils can be transported over distances of 20–100 m, by laminar flow through capillary tubes of 1 to 2 mm internal diameter, where on-line chemical separations can be performed within seconds.

Newton and his group at Manchester have been studying, among others, the reactions of 100–200 MeV neon ions on niobium. The recoil products detected range from yttrium to silver and fall into two groups. The products close to the composite system $^{113}_{51}Sb$ ($^{93}_{41}Nb + ^{20}_{10}Ne$) are formed at low energies (100 to 150 MeV) through the compound nucleus mechanism; the products close to the target are formed at high energies (150–200 MeV) and seem to be formed by a deep-inelastic process. This is a reaction mechanism which has been observed by several groups in the last decade only and theories are not sufficiently advanced to explain the experimental observations. With the development of new accelerators deep-inelastic reactions will be studied in more detail[19].

5.8   Photonuclear Reactions

The excitation of a nucleus leading to its disintegration may be brought about not only by high energy particles, charged or otherwise, but also by the capture of high energy photons. Reactions of the latter type are known as *photonuclear reactions* which are briefly considered here[20].

5.8.1   SOURCES OF HIGH ENERGY PHOTONS

(a) High energy photons are obtained by slowing down electrons accelerated to 10–100 MeV by tungsten or other targets.

(b) Certain radiative capture nuclear reactions lead to the emission of high energy photons, *e.g.*

$$^{7}\text{Li}\,(p,\gamma)\,2\,^{4}\text{He}; \qquad (E_{\gamma} = 17.6 \text{ MeV})$$
$$^{3}\text{H}\,(p,\gamma)\,^{4}\text{He}; \qquad (E_{\gamma} = 14.8 \text{ MeV})$$

(c) Annihilation gammas are obtainable from thick targets bombarded by high energy electrons which lead to electron-positron pair formation and the pair on annihilation yield two γ photons each of 0.51 MeV energy.

5.8.2   TYPES OF PHOTONUCLEAR REACTIONS

Principal types of photonuclear reactions are

(a) (γ, γ'), *i.e.* excitation of the nucleus followed by its deexcitation by radiation emission. These are similar to (n, n') or (p, p') reactions.

e.g. $\qquad\qquad ^{115}\text{In}\,(\gamma, \gamma')\,^{115}\text{In}.$

(b) (γ, p), (γ, n) and $(\gamma, 2n)$ reactions. In the excited nucleus, the energy is concentrated on a proton or a neutron and if the value exceeds the separation energy (7-8 MeV) that nucleon is emitted. Though the Coulomb barrier may be expected to hinder (γ, p) reaction, in reality $\sigma(\gamma, p)$ is found to be greater than $\sigma(\gamma, n)$. This may be due to a direct transfer of the photon energy to a proton, before being shared by other nucleons.

(c) (γ, α) reactions, *e.g.* $^{51}\text{V}\,(\gamma, \alpha)\,^{47}\text{Sc}$; $^{16}\text{O}\,(\gamma, \alpha)\,^{12}\text{C}$

(d) (γ, m) reactions, *i.e.* photon capture followed by multiple evaporation of nucleons. For example,

$$^{12}\text{C}(\gamma, 3\alpha); \ ^{16}\text{O}(\gamma, 4\alpha); \ ^{19}\text{F}(\gamma, 2n)\,^{17}\text{F}; \ ^{24}\text{Mg}(\gamma, \alpha pn)\,^{18}\text{F};$$
$$^{75}\text{As}(\gamma, \alpha p\,2n)\,^{68}\text{Zn}; \ ^{107}\text{Ag}(\gamma, ^{8}\text{Li})\,^{99}\text{Ru}.$$

(e) *Fragmentation:* Some nuclei on bombardment with high energy photons have led to their fragmentation into several nuclei of similar masses.

5.8.3   SOME SPECIAL FEATURES OF PHOTONUCLEAR REACTIONS

Following are some special features:

(a) Photonuclear reactions of the (γ, n) type have been extensively studied on nearly all elements. A careful measurement of the photon threshold gives the binding energy of the last neutron in a nucleus.

(b) The (γ, n) reactions yield monoergic neutrons.

(c) The resonance widths, *i.e.* the σ at half-height in some cases are abnormally large; *often of the order of a few MeV*. This is referred to as *giant resonance*. In other words, it means the cross section remains at the peak value over a wide range of energy of incident photons. Fig. 5.10 shows the variation of σ for the emission of photoneutrons from ¹⁸¹Ta by photons over the energy range 11–18 MeV.

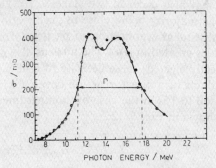

Fig. 5.10 High energy (γ, n) photonuclear reaction on ¹⁸¹Ta showing 'giant resonance'.[21] (from E.G. Fuller and M.S. Weiss[21], reproduced with author' permission)

5.9 Direct Nuclear Reactions

We had noticed some of the limitations of the compound nucleus theory of nuclear reactions, in the case of $(d, p)(d, n)$ and other stripping reactions. In some high energy spallation and fragmentation reactions and in the 'buckshot' type capture reactions due to heavy ions and light target nuclei.

Reactions due to ultra-high energy particles ($E > 50$ MeV and going into GeV range), constitute a type where the compound nucleus is not formed; instead, a large fraction of the energy of the incoming particle is transferred to one or a few nucleons of the target nucleus lying in its path. These nucleons are ejected promptly, as they have received energy in excess of what is needed to overcome all barriers. The incident particle continues colliding with more nucleons some of them being ejected and others raised to excited levels in the residual nucleus. In this process there is a distinct excess of nucleons emitted in the *initial direction* of the incident particle and the emissions are thus non-isotropic, unlike in the case where a true compound nucleus is formed and lives long enough to forget its mode of formation. A direct ($p, p3n$) nuclear reaction is sketched in Fig. 5.11.

Another characteristic of direct high energy reactions is that the reaction cross section varies very slightly with the energy of the projectile particle. Resonance peaks are nearly absent.

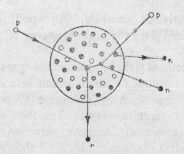

Fig. 5.11 A direct $(p, p3n)$ reaction.

Direct reactions may also occur in two stages: (i) The prompt emission of nucleons, the majority being close to the direction of the incident particle, and (ii) subsequent evaporation of particles from the residual nucleus with the holes created in (i). The nucleus also contains nucleons excited but not directly ejected; these deexcite to a new ground state.

Further, the products of a direct reaction cover a wide range of mass numbers, as from 60 to 15 in the case of bombardment of copper by 5.7 GeV protons shown in Fig. 5.12.

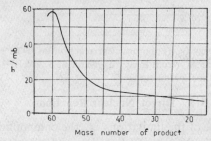

Fig. 5.12 Wide range distribution of products in the ultra-high energy reaction of 5.7 GeV protons on copper[22] (from *Spallation* by B.G. Harvey in *Progress in Nuclear Physics*, Ed. O.R. Frisch, Vol.), 1959. Pergamon Press Ltd., reproduced with permission).

5.10   Thermonuclear Reactions

The energy released per atom in nuclear reactions being about a million times larger than the energy available from chemical reactions (Sec. 1.2), the tapping of nuclear energy for every day use presents itself as a tempting proposition. Such an effort appears all the more relevant as the present day major resources of energy, *viz.* the fossil fuels, threaten to get depleted in the next few decades. Further, the fact that the vast amounts of energy coming from the Sun and stars is wholly the result of nuclear reactions of fusion of light nuclei, lends additional hopeful support for the need to explore the possibility of harnessing nuclear energy. The other mode of obtaining nuclear energy by the fission of heavy nuclei, the technology of which has been adequately perfected, is considered in Chapter 7.

It was pointed out earlier (Sec. 1.6) that the mass loss resulting in the fusion of four protons into a helium nucleus, going on perpetually in the Sun and the stars is 0.028 71 u, corresponding to 26.7 MeV per He nucleus formed. Our Sun radiates around 3.8×10^{20} MJ of energy per second and this is indeed a very large amount of energy! In the process, the Sun suffers a mass loss at the rate of 4.2×10^6 tonnes per second. This staggering mass loss of the Sun, however, corresponds to just 10^{-5} per cent per million years of its present mass ($\sim 2 \times 10^{27}$ tonnes). There are, however, formidable difficulties to be overcome before this process can be reproduced on the earth and the energy harnessed for practical purposes. The more important of these obstacles are pointed out below.

The closest distance of approach of two protons where the nuclear force of attraction balances the coulombian force of repulsion is about 7F. The potential barrier at this distance is about 0.2 MeV and the probability of penetration of the barrier is 10^{-13} for protons of energy 10 keV. The Maxwellian temperature corresponding to this mean energy is $\sim 10^8$ K*, a temperature inaccessible at present.

5.10.1   THE 4 H → He FUSION REACTION IN THE SUN AND STARS

In the interior of the Sun and the stars due to enormous gravitational pressures such high temperatures prevail permitting several types of thermonuclear reactions of which the $4\,^1H \rightarrow\,^4He$ is the dominant one. The mechanism most likely for the fusion reaction is believed to be either the proton-proton chain or the carbon-nitrogen cycle, outlined below.

(a)   *The Proton-Proton Chain*

$$[^1H + {}^1H \quad \rightarrow \quad {}^2H + \beta^+ + \nu; \quad E = 1.42 \text{ MeV}] \times 2 \qquad (a)$$

$$[^1H + {}^2H \quad \rightarrow \quad {}^3He + \gamma; \qquad E = 5.4 \text{ MeV}] \times 2 \qquad (b)$$

$${}^3He + {}^3He \quad \rightarrow \quad {}^4He + 2\,^1H; \quad E = 12.8 \text{ MeV} \qquad (c)$$

Reaction (a) is the slowest with a mean life of $7 - 15 \times 10^9$ years.

(b)   *The Carbon-Nitrogen Cycle***

$${}^{12}C + {}^1H \quad \rightarrow \quad {}^{13}N + \gamma; \qquad (d)$$

$${}^{13}N \quad \rightarrow \quad {}^{13}C + \beta^+ + \nu \qquad (e)$$

$${}^{13}C + {}^1H \quad \rightarrow \quad {}^{14}N + \gamma \qquad (f)$$

$${}^{14}N + {}^1H \quad \rightarrow \quad {}^{15}O + \gamma \qquad (g)$$

$${}^{15}O \quad \rightarrow \quad {}^{15}N + \beta^+ + \nu \qquad (h)$$

---

*This follows by equating kinetic energy with kT. The temperature corresponding to a mean kinetic energy of 1 eV is 1.16×10^4 K.

**The C—N cycle was first proposed by Bethe in 1939.

$$^{15}N + {}^1H \quad \rightarrow \quad {}^{12}C + {}^4He \tag{i}$$

Here, reaction (g) is the slowest with a mean life of 3.2×10^8 years.

In addition, other mechanisms have also been suggested involving nuclei as Li, Be, B and F, but these reactions are all too fast, and incompatible with the age of the Sun which is around 5×10^9 y and having about as much to go. Ninety per cent of the solar matter is known to consist of hydrogen and helium; other elements, mostly light, constitute the rest of the matter. Hence, the p-p chain is considered as the more likely mechanism of solar energy, while in the stars which are far more luminous and hotter than the Sun, the C—N cycle may be the probable mechanism. The net reaction of any mechanism is the fusion of four protons into an alpha particle

$$4\,{}^1H \quad \rightarrow \quad {}^4He + 2\beta^+ + 2\nu + 2\gamma; \quad \Delta m = 0.028\,71\text{ u}$$
$$= 26.7\text{ MeV}$$

As the neutrinos carry away 0.5 MeV, the net energy released is 26.2 MeV per He nucleus formed. The synthesis of other elements follows the formation of helium.[24]

5.10.2 THERMONUCLEAR REACTIONS ON THE EARTH

Apart from the problem of the enormously high temperature, the extremely slow rate of the starting reaction (a) is another obstacle. The mean life of this reaction is 7-15×10^9 y at a temperature of 1.5-2.0×10^7 K. However, other thermonuclear reactions are possible with the heavier isotopes of hydrogen (^2H and ^3H). Of these, deuterium (D) constituting one part in about 6000 parts of hydrogen, is plentifully available, while tritium (T) has to be generated by the $^6Li\,(n, \alpha)$ T reaction, requiring ^6Li in large amounts to be obtained by isotopic separation from natural lithium which is 92.6 per cent ^7Li and 7.4% ^6Li. The reactions involving all the hydrogen isotopes are as follows:

$$H + H \quad \rightarrow \quad D + \beta^+ + \nu; \quad E = 1.40\text{ MeV} \tag{j}$$

$$H + D \quad \rightarrow \quad {}^3He; \qquad\quad E = 5.40\text{ MeV} \tag{k}$$

$$H + T \quad \rightarrow \quad {}^4He; \qquad\quad E = 19.83\text{ MeV} \tag{l}$$

$$D + D \quad \rightarrow \quad H + T; \qquad E = 4.00\text{ MeV} \tag{m}$$

$$\rightarrow \quad {}^3He + n; \quad\; E = 3.26\text{ MeV} \tag{n}$$

$$\rightarrow \quad {}^4He; \qquad\quad E = 28.83\text{ MeV} \tag{o}$$

$$D + T \quad \rightarrow \quad {}^4He + n; \quad E = 17.50\text{ MeV} \tag{p}$$

$$T + T \quad \rightarrow \quad {}^4He + 2n; \quad E = 11.17\text{ MeV} \tag{q}$$

Of these, D — D and D — T reactions (o and p) are the most important. Even with these the yields are extremely low for energies below 10 keV ($T = 10^8$ K), as may be see from Fig. 5.13 showing the fusion cross section as a function of temperature and the deuteron energy.[25] Theory

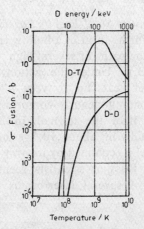

Fig. 5.13 Fusion cross sections for D–D and D–T reactions as a function of temperature   (from *Project Sherwood—The U.S. Program in Controlled Fusion*, by A.S. Bishop, © 1958. Addison-Wesley Publishing Co., Inc., reproduced with permission).

shows that the minimum critical temperature for the reaction to be self-sustaining is 4×10^8 K for the $D - D$ and 4.5×10^7 K for the $D - T$ reaction, hence the latter has a distinct edge over the former, which is, however, partially offset by the expensive process involved in the isotopic separation of ^{6}Li, needed for producing tritium.

The only way a thermonuclear reaction has been realized by man is in the form of a hydrogen bomb which is itself triggered by a fission bomb. The vast amount of the fusion energy is released in the explosion with all its horrendous destructive effects and fallouts. Apart from this, determined efforts have been in progress over the past 25 years in developing devices designed to bring about a controlled thermonuclear reaction. Of the techniques reported to be promising in exploiting the $D - T$ reaction, we shall refer to three here.

(i) *Magnetic Confinement of the Plasma*

A mixture of the gases deuterium and tritium is admitted into a taurus shaped vessel at a low pressure of the order of 10–100 pascals (1 atm $= 1.01 \times 10^5$ pascals) and is completely ionized under the action of a discharge. The plasma (a homogeneous and electrically neutral mixture of electrons and positive ions) continuously heats up to extremely high temperatures. As no material container can remain solid at these temperatures, the plasma is confined as a narrow ribbon along the axis of the taurus and prevented from touching the walls under the action of a magnetic field all along the taurus, hence the name of the technique. The fuel confinement has to be for a duration of the order of a second for significant burn up (D–T reaction) to be achieved. Before this, however, the plasma gets wriggles due to twisting and after this it becomes very unstable and tends to diverge. This has been the obstacle in this technique making headway.

(ii) *Inertial Confinement of Solid Fuel by Lasers*

The fuel, $(D + T)$ is in the form of a hollow ring-like solid pellet which is held at the focus of the paths of several high energy high flux laser* beams (Nd-glass or CO_2). Under the action of several laser beams the surface of the pellet heats up to very high temperatures and an ablation occurs, which simultaneously compresses the pellet to a density some 1000 times higher than the normal. In the resulting implosion the fuel burns up very rapidly in about 10^{-9} s before the particles of the pellet diverge. The fuel is confined by its own inertia; hence the name of the technique. The Russian scientists seem to favour this method, though the generation of several laser beams of the required power is expensive at present.

(iii) *Inertial Confinement of the Solid Fuel by Electrons*

This technique is similar to the previous one in all respects, except that high energy flux electron beams are used along with low energy lasers. The mechanism of heating and compression resulting in the implosion of the solid fuel is very similar to the one obtaining with lasers. The propagation of the intense electron beam on to the target pellet is proposed to be effected by a low energy laser along the axis of the plasma channel, which guides the electron beam to the surface of the pellet by its own magnetic field (Fig. 5.14). This technique of inertial

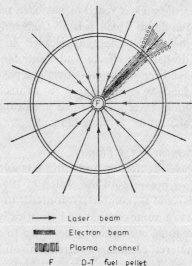

→   Laser beam

▬▬▬   Electron beam

▆▆▆▆▆▆   Plasma channel

F   D-T fuel pellet

Fig. 5.14 Principle of inertial confinement of the D–T
fuel pellet and the propagation of the electron
beam thereto.

*A laser, (discovered in 1960), is a beam of light of one frequency in which all the photons are *coherent*, *i.e.* they are all in one phase which results in a very high reinforcement of amplitudes and hence in intensity and energy. It is an abbreviation of light amplification by stimulated emission of radiation.

confinement by an electron beam is favoured by the American scientists of the Laurence Livermore Laboratory, the fusion facility being named *Shiva*. Attempts are also being made to use proton or other positive ion beams in place of electrons.

It is also planned to recover some of the tritium by surrounding the neutrons released in D—T reaction by a blanket of lithium. However, it is not before the late 80s or 90s that any significant progress in the realization of thermonuclear fusion is expected.[27]

References
(where marked *, see Bibliography)

1. R.D. Evans*
2. B.G. Harvey*
3. J.M. Blatt and V.S. Weisskopf*
4. M. Lefort*
4. (a) D. Halliday
5. H.H. Goldsmith, H.W. Ibser and B.T. Feld, 'Neutron Cross Sections of the Elements', *Revs. Mod. Phys.*, 1947, **19**, 259.
6. G.F. Friedlander, J.W. Kennedy and J.M. Miller*
7. W.W. Havens, C.S. Wu, L.J. Rainwater and C.L. Meaker 'Slow Neutron Velocity Spectrometer Studies—II: Au, In, Ta, W, Pt and Zn', *Phys. Rev.*, 1947, **71**, 165.
8. E. Amaldi. O.D'Agostino, E. Fermi, B. Ponteeorvo, F. Rasetti and E. Segrè, 'Artificial Radioactivity Produced by Neutron Bombardment', *Proc. Roy. Soc.* (London), 1935, **A149**, 522.
9. S.N. Ghoshal, 'An Experimental Verification of the Theory of the Compound Nucleus', *Phys. Rev.*, 1950, **80**, 939.
10. J.M. Alexander and G.N. Simonoff,
    (a) 'Average Energy and Angular Momentum Removed from Dy Compound Nucleus by Neutrons and Photons', *Phys. Rev.* 1964, **133B**, B93.
    (b) 'Angular Momentum Effects on Neutron Emission by Dy and Tb Compound Nuclei'. *Phys. Rev.*, 1964, **133B**, B104.
11. G. Breit and E. Wigner, 'Capture of Slow Neutrons', *Phys. Rev.*, 1936. **49**, 519.
12. G. Breit, 'Schematic Treatment of Nuclear Resonance', *Phys. Rev.*, 1946, **69**, 472.
13. E. Wigner, 'Resonance Reaction and Anomalous Scattering', *Phys. Rev.* 1946, **70**, 15.
14. S.G. Kaufman, E. Goldberg, L.J. Koester and F.P. Mooring, 'Energy Levels in ^{28}Si Excited by Alpha Particles on ^{24}Mg', *Phys. Rev.*, 1952, **88**, 673.
15. D. Walker, J.H. Fremlin, W.T. Link and K.G. Stephens, 'The Acceleration of Heavy Ions in Fixed Frequency Cyclotron', *Brit. J. Appl. Phys.*, 1954, **5**, 157.
16. (a) G.T. Seaborg*
    (b) G.T. Seaborg, 'Elements beyond 100, Present Status and Future Prospects', *Rev. Nuc. Sci.*, 1968 **18**, 53.
17. D. Walker and J.H. Fremlin, 'Acceleration of Heavy Ions to High Energies', *Nature* (London), 1953, **171**, 189.
18. K.F. Chackett, J.H. Fremlin and D. Walker, 'Nuclear Reactions Produced by Fast Neutrons', *Proc. Phys. Soc.* (London), 1953, **A66**, 495.
19. G.W.A. Newton (results to be published).
20. D.H. Wilkinson, 'Nuclear Photodisintegration', *Ann. Rev. Nuc. Sci.*, 1959, **9**, 1.

21. E.G. Fuller and M.S. Weiss, 'Splitting of Giant Resonance for Deformed Nuclei', *Phys. Rev.*, 1958, **112**, 560.

22. B.G. Harvey, 'Spallation', *Progress in Nuclear Physics*, Vol. 7 (Ed. O.R. Frisch, Pergamon Press, London, 1959).

23. J.M. Miller and J. Hudis, 'High Energy Nuclear Reactions', *Ann. Rev. Nuc. Sci.*, 1959, 9, 159,

24. E.M. Burbidge, G.R. Burbidge, W.A. Fowler and F. Hoyle, 'Synthesis of Elements in Stars', *Revs. Mod. Phys.*, 1957, **29**, 547.

25. A.S. Bishop*

26. A.I. Simon*

27. Yonas, 'Fusion, Power with Particle Beam's', *Scientific American*, 1978, **239**, 40.

Problems

5.1 ^{7}Li target is bombarded by protons of energy 5 MeV. Calculate (a) the energy of protons scattered elastically through an angle of 90°. (b) the energy of protons observed at 90° after they have excited the lithium to a level of 0.48 MeV.
[(a) 3.91 MeV, (b) 3.53 MeV].

5.2 If the threshold for the reaction A (p, n) B is 2.4 MeV, what is the mass difference between A and B?
$[m_A - m_B = -1212\ \mu u]$

5.3 (a) What is the threshold energy of γ which can create a proton-antiproton pair?

(b) What is the energy of γs of proton-antiproton annihilations?
[(a) 1.88 GeV; (b) 0.94 GeV]

5.4 The reactions (a) ^{9}Be (p, n) ^{9}B and (b) ^{18}O (p, n) ^{18}F have threshold energies of 2.059 and 2.590 MeV respectively. Find their Q values.
[(a) -1.86 MeV, (b) -2.45 MeV]

5.5 Given the Q values for the reactions (a) ^{11}B (d, p) ^{12}B and (b) ^{13}C (p, n) ^{13}N to be 1.136 and 3.236 MeV respectively, find the threshold energies of these reactions.
[(a) 1.343 MeV, (b) 3.485 MeV]

5.6 (a) From the following data calculate the binding energy of the last two neutrons in ^{56}Fe:

^{54}Fe (n, γ) ^{55}Fe; $Q_1 = 9.28$ MeV   (i)

^{55}Fe $\xrightarrow{\text{EC}}$ ^{55}Mn; $Q_2 = 0.21$ MeV   (ii)

^{55}Mn (n, γ) ^{56}Mn; $Q_3 = 7.25$ MeV   (iii)

^{56}Mn $\xrightarrow{\beta^-}$ ^{56}Fe; $Q_4 = 3.63$ MeV   (iv)

[20.37 MeV]

(b) Given the mass difference between ^{56}Fe and ^{54}Fe is 1.995 311 u, calculate the binding energy of the last two neutrons in ^{56}Fe and compare the answer with that of problem 5.6 (a).   [20.50 McV]

5.7 What is the excitation energy of the compound nucleus resulting in the bombardment of ^{27}Al by α particles of energy 6 MeV (LS)?   [14.89 MeV]

5.8 Calculate the excitation energy of ^{210}Bi formed when ^{209}Bi captures (a) a thermal neutron, and (b) a 1.4 MeV neutron.   [(a) 4.63 MeV, (b) 6.02 MeV]

5.9 ^{14}N has an excited state at 12.8 MeV. At what energy of the incident particle (LS), would resonance capture occur in the case (a) ^{10}B (α, n) ^{13}N and (b) ^{12}C (d, p) ^{13}C reactions?
[(a) 1.667 MeV, (b) 2.955 MeV]

5.10 What must be the frequency of the oscillating potential to be applied to the dees of a cyclotron to accelerate deuterons, the magnetic induction being 2.5 T?

[19.21 MHz]

5.11 An oscillating potential of 8.6 MHz is applied to the dees of a cyclotron. Calculate the magnetic field to accelerate (a) protons, (b) $^{14}N^{6+}$ ions.

[(a) 0.56 T, (b) 1.31 T]

5.12 The cross section for the ^{23}Na $(n, \gamma)^{24}$ Na reaction is 0.56 b. What activity of ^{24}Na of period 15 h would result when 2.5 mg of sodium chloride are bombarded for 12 h by thermal neutrons of flux 10^{13} n cm^{-2} s^{-1}?

[6.25×10^7 dis.s^{-1}]

5.13 Given that 0.1189 weight fraction of a given boron rod (^{10}B) disappears per year due to continuous exposure to slow neutrons of flux 10^{16} m^{-2} s^{-1}, find the cross section for the neutron capture by ^{10}B. [3836 b]

5.14 On irradiation of a thin gold foil by slow neutrons ($nv = 10^{18}$ n m^{-2} s^{-1}) for 24 h, 0.0852% of it is transmuted into ^{198}Au of period 2.7 days. Find (a) the cross section for the reaction, (b) the activity resulting at the end of 24 h of irradiation and (c) the saturation activity possible.

[(a) $\sigma = 98.61$ b, (b) 6.82×10^{12} dis.g^{-1} s^{-1}, (c) 3.01×10^{13} dis.g^{-1} s^{-1})]

5.15 A 0.02 cm thick gold foil is irradiated by thermal neutrons of flux 10^{20} n m^{-2} s^{-1} for 5 min. The product ^{198}Au has a half-life of 2.7 days. The density of gold is 19.3 t m^{-3} and its cross section for neutron capture is 98.7×10^{-28} m^2. Find (a) the number of radiogold atoms produced at the end of 5 min of irradiation and (b) the specific activity of the foil in Ci per cm^2.

[(a) 1.037×10^{12} dis. s^{-1}; (b) 28.03 Ci cm^{-2}]

Relevant atomic masses/u

n	= 1.008 665	^{27}Al	= 26.981 535
^{1}H	= 1.007 825	^{31}P	= 30.973 763
^{2}H	= 2.014 102	^{54}Fe	= 53.939 621
^{4}He	= 4.002 604	^{56}Fe	= 55.934 932
^{10}B	= 10.012 939	^{209}Bi	= 208.980 417
^{14}N	= 14.003 074	^{210}Bi	= 209.984 110

Chapter 6

Nuclear Fission

6.1 Nuclear Fission

The discovery of nuclear fission by Otto Hahn and F. Strassmann in January 1939 marks the beginning of the nuclear age. In contrast to the tiny chippings of atoms that take place in natural or artificial radio-activity, it became possible for the first time to break right through the atomic nucleus, annihilating in the fission process a significant amount of matter and releasing the corresponding energy on a scale totally unknown before, though most regrettably this took the form of horrendous atom bombs in the first instance. This apart, a large number of peaceful uses for the atomic energy also became a reality, which include the generation of electric power on a commercial scale and the production of numerous radioisotopes for use in basic research, medicine, agriculture and industry. Applications of radioisotopes are considered in Chapter 8. Here we shall present a brief account of the discovery of the phenomenon of nuclear fission and its basic characteristics.

6.1.1 The Discovery of Nuclear Fission

The discovery of nuclear fission has its origin in the experiments on the interaction of the then recently discovered neutrons (by James Chadwick in 1932) with uranium, the heaviest element found in nature. The discovery is the culmination of results of three groups of workers, (i) Enrico Fermi in Italy, (ii) The Joliot-Curies and Savitch in France and (iii) Otto Hahn and Strassmann in Germany. Their results of relevance are given below.[1]

(i) *Fermi's Experiments* (1934–38)

Fermi carried out a series of experiments in which uranium compounds were bombarded with slow neutrons, hoping thereby to produce artificially transuranic elements ($Z > 92$). He expected that the capture of a neutron by uranium would lead to a neutron rich isotope which by β^- decay would result in element $Z = 93$, and by successive neutron captures and β^- decays, other transuraniens as $Z = 94, 95, 96 \ldots$ would result; thus

$$^{238}_{92}U \xrightarrow{(n,\gamma)} {}^{239}U^* \xrightarrow{\beta^-} (Z=93) \xrightarrow{\beta^-} (Z=94) \xrightarrow{\beta^-} (Z=95)\ldots$$

On analysis of the products of $U + n$ interaction, Fermi found several activities, and he believed them all to be due to different transuraniens ($Z = 93, 94, 95\ldots$). Later studies, however, proved that only two of them, *viz.* the 23 minute and 2.33 day activities resulted in real transuraniens, which have since then been named neptunium ($Z = 93$) and plutonium ($Z = 94$). The other activities observed by Fermi were not due to transuraniens.

(ii) *Experiments of the Joliots and Savitch* (1934–38)

Irène and Frédéric Joliot-Curie and Savitch, who were also investigating the same phenomenon, reported a strange result. The chemical behaviour of one of the activities resulting from $U + n$ interaction seemed to be closer to that of lanthanum ($Z = 57$), far from uranium ($Z = 92$) in the Periodic Table, rather than to that of the neighbour element actinium ($Z = 89$)* as might have been expected. This remained an anomaly. Could they have asserted that the element under study *was* lanthanum, instead of saying *very much like* it, probably they would have been credited with the discovery of fission.

(iii) *Experiments of Hahn and Strassmann* (1934–38)

Otto Hahn and F. Strassmann who were also engaged in the same investigation were confronted with a similar anomaly, *viz.* that one of the activities appeared to be due to an element very similar to barium ($Z = 56$) rather than to a pre-uranien radium ($Z = 88$), as might be expected**. Further investigations revealed that while the new activity could be chemically separated from radium, it *could not be separated from barium*. This led Hahn and Strassmann to declare that as chemists they were forced to state that one of the products of $U + n$ interaction was barium, far removed from uranium, though as physicists, it was difficult to explain how barium could result from uranium[2]. *This was the discovery of nuclear fission* indicating the splitting of the nucleus of an atom like uranium ($Z = 92$) into two roughly equal fragments, one of $Z = 56$ (barium) and the other consequently of $Z = 36$ (krypton).

6.2   The Process of Nuclear Fission

Soon after the announcement of the discovery of fission by Hahn and Strassmann, Lise Meitner and O. R. Frisch developed a theory for the phenomenon in terms of the distortion of the excited nucleus following

---

*The electron configurations of the two elements are
$_{57}$La: $(5s^2, 5p^6)\, 5d^1, 6s^2$ and $_{89}$Ac: $(6s^2, 6p^6)\, 6d^1, 7s^2$
**The electron configurations of the two elements are
$_{56}$Ba: $(5s^2, 5p^6)\, 6s^2$ and $_{88}$Ra: $(6s^2, 6p^6)\, 7s^2$

neutron capture to a point of overcoming the force of surface energy and resulting in a splitting of the nucleus into fragments of compara- ble masses, the path a, b, c, d of Fig. 6.1. Alternatively, a fraction of the excited nuclei may deexcite radiatively followed by α-decay, the path a', b'. This is discussed later.

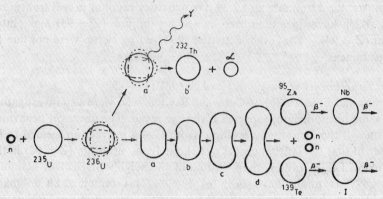

Fig. 6.1   Alternative modes of decay of ^{236}U
Path a, b, c, d: fission,
Path a', b' : α decay.

6.3   Fission Fragments and their Mass Distribution

The fission fragments F_1 and F_2 are *not* a unique pair but could be one of about 30 possible pairs such that the mass number of the lighter fragment (say F_1) ranges from about 85 to 105 and that of the heavier fragment (F_2) from about 150 to 130. These limits refer to fission yields of 1 per cent and above.   Following are some possibilities:

(a) $^{236}_{92}U$ → $^{94}_{36}Kr + ^{140}_{56}Ba + 2n$
(b) $^{236}_{92}U$ → $^{95}_{38}Sr + ^{139}_{54}Xe + 2n$
(c) $^{236}_{92}U$ → $^{96}_{40}Zr + ^{137}_{52}Te + 3n$
(d) $^{236}_{92}U$ → $^{99}_{41}Nb + ^{133}_{51}Sb + 4n$ and so on

Figure 6.2 shows the approximate limits of the fission modes.

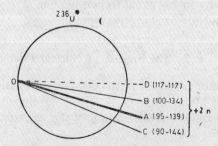

Fig. 6.2   Probable fissioning sections
OA: most probable fission,
OD: least probable fission.
OB–OC: limits of fission with yields > 1%.

It must be noted that all the primary fission fragments have invariably excess neutrons compared to their stable isotopes as per their position in the Periodic Table and the N/Z stability chart. Hence the primary fission fragments display β^- activity and continue to decay by successive β^- emissions till a stable nuclide isobaric with the primary fragment is reached. This is shown for a typical fission fragment pair thus:

$$^{236}_{92}U \longrightarrow \begin{cases} ^{99}_{41}Nb \xrightarrow{\ \beta^-\ } {}_{42}Mo \xrightarrow{\ \beta^-\ } {}_{43}Tc \xrightarrow{\ \beta^-\ } {}^{99}_{44}Ru \ (stable) \\[2ex] ^{133}_{51}Sb \xrightarrow{\ \beta^-\ } {}_{52}Te \xrightarrow{\ \beta^-\ } {}_{53}I \xrightarrow{\ \beta^-\ } {}_{54}Xe \xrightarrow{\ \beta^-\ } {}^{133}_{55}Cs \end{cases}$$

A term frequently employed in describing mass distribution between the fragments is the *cumulative chain fission yield* defined as

$$Y(A) = \frac{\text{Number of product nuclei of mass number } A}{\text{Total number of nuclei fissioned}} \times 100$$

A typical fission mass yield curve as a function of the mass number A is shown in Fig. 6.3. Experimentally, the yield of any mass number is given by the yield of the *final stable* isotope of that mass number. It may be noted that a majority of the fissions are asymmetric, *i.e.* $A_1 \neq A_2$*. The mass distribution curve shows that yield $\geqslant 1\%$ range from 85–105 for A_1 and 150–130 for A_2, as stated before. The maximum yields of close on seven per cent are 90–100 for A_1 and 144–134 for A_2 with an average loss of 2.5 neutrons per fission. It is interesting to note the

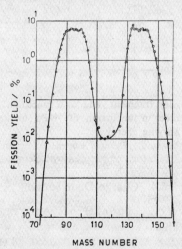

Fig. 6.3 Fission fragment yield as a function of mass number in the fission of ^{235}U by neutrons
(from *Introduction to Atomic and Nuclear Physics*, by H.E. White, © 1964. Van Nostrand Rhinehold Co., reproduced with author's permission).

*We shall designate throughout this chapter the lighter fragment properties by the subscript 1 and the heavier fragment properties by the subscript 2, thus A_1 and A_2, Z_1 and Z_2, and E_1 and E_2 for the mass, charge numbers and energies of the lighter and heavier fragments respectively.

presence of two spikes at 100 and 134 for A_1 and A_2 respectively. It should further be noted that the yield of *symmetrical fission*, i.e. $A_1 = A_2 = 117$ is the lowest being around 0.05 per cent. This is true for fission by thermal or low energy neutrons. However, as the energy of the particle effecting fission increases, the depth of the valley between the two peaks diminishes and the two peaks approach till there is a single peak of symmetric fission. Fig. 6.4 shows this effect in the fission of ^{239}Pu by deuterons of increasing energy from 9.3 MeV (distinctly asymmetric and similar to ^{235}U (n, f)) to 23.4 MeV (symmetric) fission.[3,4]

While fission into two fragments is more common, *tripartite* fission into three fragments has also been observed, e.g. fission of ^{226}Ra by 11 MeV protons and 14.5 and 21.5 deuterons[5a,b].

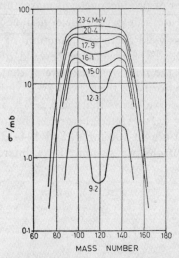

Fig. 6.4 Fission fragment yield as a functuion of mass
number in the fission of ^{239}Pu by deuterons
of varying energy
(from Introduction to Nuclear Physics and Chemistry, by B.G. Harvey, © 1963.
Prentice-Hall, Inc., reproduced with permission).

6.4 Charge Distribution

Each isobaric series (i.e. A constant) has only one stable nuclide of atomic number Z_s. This corresponds to the Z of maximum binding energy $B_{(max)}$ given by Eq. 3.24 (see Sec. 3.3.5). Let Z_1 and Z_2 be the atomic numbers of the most stable nuclides calculated from Eq. 3.24 for the two primary fragments of fission of mass numbers A_1 and A_2, i.e. Z_1 and Z_2 will be the *chain enders* of successive β^- decays. It is now required to deduce the most probable charges Z_1^0 and Z_2^0 of the *initial* or *primary* fragments of fission. These cannot be directly observed due to the series of β^- decays, mostly of very short half-lives. The most probable values of Z_1^0 and Z_2^0 are, however, deduced *assuming the theory of equal charge displacement*, i.e. Z_1^0 and Z_2^0 shall be equidistant from their final stable values Z_1 and Z_2 for the given isobaric series A_1 and A_2. In other words, this theory expects

$$Z_1 - Z_1^0 = Z_2 - Z_2^0 \qquad (6.1)$$

Initial charge conservation necessitates

$$Z_1^0 + Z_2^0 = Z_f \qquad (6.2)$$

where Z_f is the charge of the parent fissioning nucleus. In the case of uranium, $Z_f = 92$. Combining Eqs. 6.1 and 6.2, one arrives at the values of the initial charge distribution

$$Z_1^0 = \tfrac{1}{2}(Z_f + Z_1 - Z_2)$$
$$Z_2^0 = \tfrac{1}{2}(Z_f + Z_2 - Z_1) \qquad (6.3)$$

Thus, in the case of fission of high probability into fragments of $A_1 = 90$ and $A_2 = 144$, plus two free neutrons, Z_1 and Z_2 calculated from Eq. 3.24 are 39.11 and 59.68 respectively. Substituting these values into Eq. 6.3 and replacing Z_f by 92 we obtain,

$$Z_1^0 = \tfrac{1}{2}(92 + 39.11 - 59.68) = 35.72 = 36 = Kr$$

and similarly,

$$Z_2^0 = \tfrac{1}{2}(92 + 59.68 - 39.11) = 56.28 = 56 = Ba$$

Extending the procedure, it is possible to map out the ranges of Z_1^0, and Z_2^0 corresponding to primary fragments of A_1 ranging from 90 to 100 and of A_2 from 144 to 134. These are shown in Table 6.1.

The fraction of the independent yield of a fragment of atomic number Z and mass number A of the total chain yield for mass A is given by the Gaussian equation in the case of fission by thermal neutrons

$$\frac{P(Z, A)}{\Sigma(PZ_1, A + PZ_2, A + \ldots)} = 0.565 \exp [Z - Z_p(A)]^2 \qquad (6.4)$$

where $Z_p(A)$ is the charge of the fragment formed in the highest yield for the mass number A.

6.5   Ionic Charge of Fission Fragments

As the two fragments tear off the fissioning nucleus, a large fraction of the orbital electrons is shed as a result of internal conversion and other shake up processes, with the result that the fission fragments come out as highly positively charged ions as Sr^{20+}, Ba^{22+}, etc. As the fragments pass through air, or through other matter, they lose energy through excitation and ionization proportional to $\bar{z}^2 Z / m\bar{v}^2$ where $\bar{z}$ is the mean ionic charge on the fragment at the moment and Z is the atomic number of the medium, m and $\bar{v}$ being the mass and velocity of the fragment. The initial ionic charge of the fragment falls along its track due to capture of electrons into its vacant orbitals for which the Bohr electron velocity is greater than the fragment velocity. Thus, as the fragment slows down more electrons are captured and its ionic charge falls.

Some of the relevant properties of the ^{235}U (n, f) fragments are listed in Table 6.1.

TABLE 6.1:   Some properties of ^{235}U (n, f) fragments[6]

Property	Light fragment	Heavy fragment
A (limits)	90—100	144–134
$Z°$ (initial)	36 (Kr)—39 (Y)	56 (Ba)–53 (I)
Z (final, stable)	40 (Zr)—44 (Ru)	60 (Nd)–56 (Ba)
E (initial)/MeV	∼ 95	∼ 67
v (initial)/10^7 m s^{-1}	∼ 1.4	∼ 0.93
z (initial ionic charge)	20 +	22 +

It is repeated again that the mass and charge distributions shown in Table 6.1 apply to *limiting cases of high yield chains of fission*. There being many other possible chain starters, with varying lower yields, the overall products of nuclear fission get mixed up and identification of the true primary fragments becomes almost impossible, the position being made worse by the long chains of β⁻ decay from each starting fragment and the half-lives of some of the members being very short.

6.6   Fission Energy

As in all radioactive decays, nuclear fission is accompanied by a mass loss and the liberation of corresponding amount of energy. In fact, the value of mass loss in nuclear fission comes to around 0.2 u which is roughly 100 times greater than the mass loss observed in all other types of radioactive decays. It is this staggering amount of the energy release in fission that makes the process of special interest from the point of generating atomic energy for practical purposes. Let us illustrate this with respect to the fission of ^{235}U caused by thermal neutrons, into fragments of mass numbers 95 and 139, for which the fission yield is relatively high. Representing only the *initial reactants* and the *final products* and their masses, we have

$$^{235}_{92}U + n \;\rightarrow\; ^{95}_{42}Mo + ^{139}_{57}La + 2n + 7\beta^- + 7\bar{v} + x\gamma$$

$$u\;\; 235.043\,9 + 1.008\,7 \qquad\qquad 94.905\,7 + 138.906\,1 + 2.017\,4$$

$$\underbrace{}_{236.052\,6} \qquad\qquad \underbrace{}_{235.829\,2}$$

Mass loss $\Delta m = 0.223\,4\,u$

Fission energy $= 931\Delta m \simeq 208$ MeV.

The values calculated for other fission pairs are similar.

We also arrive at a similar magnitude for the fission energy from a different consideration. The mean binding energy $(\bar{B} = B/A)$ for the heavy fissile elements as of uranium and plutonium $(A > 200)$ is around 7.5 MeV per nucleon, while the value for the products of fission, being of medium mass $(A \simeq 100\text{--}150)$ is about 8.4 MeV per nucleon. It means that a nucleus of binding energy 7.5 MeV/nucleon changes by fission into two nuclei of binding energy 8.4 MeV/nucleon. Hence, the net increase in binding energy, due to mass loss, which is the fission energy, is around 0.9 MeV/nucleon. Allowing for the loss of 2–3 neutrons per fission, the fission energy comes to $0.9 \times 233 \simeq 210$ MeV, a value of the same magnitude as computed before. Careful calorimetric determinations of the total fission energy of ^{235}U gave values ranging from 175 ± 5 to 190 ± 5 MeV. Remembering that the energy carried away by the neutrinos accompanying the betas escapes the calorimeter, the agreement with theory is indeed very good. The results obtained for the fission of ^{233}U and ^{239}Pu are also of the same order of magnitude, *viz.* ~ 200 MeV.

This total energy of about 200 MeV is found to be distributed between the products of fission somewhat as follows:

Light fragment	:	100 $\Big\}\pm 5$ MeV
Heavy fragment	:	67
2.5 Neutrons each of 2 MeV energy	:	5
γ photons	:	12
β^- and neutrinos	:	16
Total		200 ± 5 MeV

The total kinetic energy carried by the two fission fragments has to be shared between them in the inverse ratio of their masses. This is a consequence of the conservation of linear momentum. Fig. 6.5 gives the distribution of energy of the fission fragments.[7]

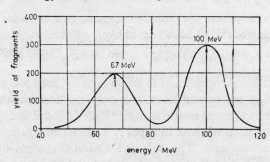

Fig. 6.5   Energy spectrum of fragments of fission of ^{235}U by thermal neutrons
(from W.E. Stein[7], reproduced with author's permission).

If we remember that the energy released even in the most powerful chemical reactions is well below 20 eV per atom or molecule reacting (Sec. 1.6), the staggering magnitude of fission energy of the order of 2×10^8 eV per fissioning nucleus and the possible applications of the same can be well imagined.[8,9]

6.7 Fission Cross Sections and Thresholds

It should be remembered that nuclear fission is only one of the possible alternatives of interaction between a heavy nuclide and a neutron. Apart from the simple (n, n) type of scattering, the neutron may be captured to form a *compound nucleus* in an excited state. The energy of excitation in the case of capture of a thermal neutron is just the binding energy of the neutron in the compound nucleus. The latter may deexcite either radiatively followed by α decay, or by fission. Thus, in the case of ^{235}U, the possible reactions are:

(i) $^{235}U + n \rightarrow n + {}^{235}U$ scattering

(ii) $^{235}U + n \rightarrow {}^{236}U^*$ compound nucleus

(iii) $^{236}U^* \quad \rightarrow h\nu + {}^{236}U \rightarrow {}^{232}Th + \alpha$ α decay (18%)

(iv) $^{236}U^* \quad \rightarrow F_1 + F_2 + 2\text{–}3\ n$ fission (72 %)

Other modes of deexcitation by neutron evaporation and spallation are considered later.

Though a large number of heavy nuclides, both naturally occurring and artificially made, undergo fission by thermal neutrons, most of them are of no practical importance either because they are short-lived, or have very low fission cross sections for thermal neutrons, as in the cases of

$$^{232}Pa\ (\tau : 1.32\ \text{d};\ \sigma_f = 700\ \text{b})$$

$$^{241}Am\ (\tau : 433\ \text{y};\ \sigma_f = 3.2\ \text{b})$$

Also of less interest, from the point of fission, are nuclides requiring high energy neutrons (1–2 MeV or above), or accelerated particles or photons of high energy (> 5 MeV). These are briefly described in a separate section.

Setting aside the short-lived and low fission yield nuclides, as well as those needing high energy excitation, the only nuclides capable of undergoing fission by thermal neutrons are ^{233}U, ^{235}U and ^{239}Pu. The isolation and concentration of these isotopes is a matter of strategic importance in the nuclear age. The relevant fission characteristics of these nuclides are presented in Table 6.2. Included in the table are also the data for the naturally occurring uranium (^{238}U : 99.3 %, ^{235}U : 0.7 %) for comparison.

TABLE 6.2: Fission by thermal neutrons[10,11]

Property	U (*natural*)	^{233}U	^{235}U	^{239}Pu
α decay half-life/y	4.47×10^9	1.59×10^5	7.04×10^8	2.44×10^4
α decay σ_r/b	3.5	53	101	286
**Fission σ_f/b	4.18	531.1	582.2	742.5
Ratio $a = \sigma_r/\sigma_f$	0.84	0.1	0.17	0.39
Neutrons emitted per fission: ν	2.5‡	2.51	2.44	2.89
†Neutrons emitted per neutron used up: η	1.36	2.28	2.07	2.08

*Based partly on I. Kaplan: *Nuclear Physics*, 1963. Addison-Wesley,Publishing Co., with permission, Brookhaven National Laboratory Report, 325–1958, 1960, and *Karlsruher Nuklidkarte*, 4 Auflage 1974.

**The fission cross section, as well as the number of neutrons emitted per fission increases with energy of the neutron initiating fission. The σ_f and ν values given here are for *thermal* neutrons of energy ~ 0.025 eV, or velocity: 2.2 km s^{-1}.

†This number η is important and is given by the expression

$$\eta = \nu/(1 + a) \text{ where } a = \sigma_r/\sigma_f; \text{ or } \eta = \nu\sigma_f/(\sigma_f + \sigma_r)$$

‡Figure 2.5 results from the ν fission of ^{235}U $(= 2.44)$ multiplied by the fast fission factor of 1.03 due to fission of ^{238}U by fast neutrons.

6.8.1 Fission Neutrons

As pointed earlier, the fissioning nucleus has a high neutron/proton ratio than needed for the stable end isobars of the fission fragments. This situation is responsible for the primary fission fragments undergoing a series of β^- decays to bring down the N/Z ratio. In addition to this process, the fissioning nucleus ejects 2–3 neutrons directly at the moment of fission. The direct ejection of neutrons becomes possible as the fissioning nucleus in the excited state has adequate energy to overcome the Fermi gap of about 7–8 MeV per neutron. The number of these neutrons emitted per fission is shown in Table 6.2.

The emission of neutrons during fission may be qualitatively demonstrated by comparing the neutron flux around a small neutron source* placed in a vessel filled with a solution of a uranium salt with the same when filled with an inert solution of ammonium nitrate of same density.[12]

Since not all the neutrons initially captured lead to fission, the net number η of neutrons emitted per neutron used up is more relevant and this is given by

*Small neutron sources convenient for a number of experiments in the laboratory may be a Ra + Be or ^{238}Pu + Be or ^{241}Am + Be which are available in the market.

$$\eta = \nu/(1 + a) = \frac{\nu \, \sigma_f}{\sigma_f + \sigma_r} \qquad (6.5)$$

Table 6.2 includes the η values.

These neutrons of fission origin are of very great practical importance as these can sustain chains of fission reactions once initiated. This is the basis of the working of nuclear reactors, which are considered in the next chapter.

6.8.2 THE PROMPT AND THE DELAYED NEUTRONS

Not all the fission neutrons are emitted at one instant. Over 99 per cent are emitted almost instantaneously in a time of the order of 10^{-14} s. These are the *prompt* neutrons having an energy spectrum from about 0.05 to 17 MeV, with a broad peak around 0.75 MeV. The energy distribution is given by

$$N(E) = e^{-E} \sinh(2E)^{1/2} \qquad (6.6)$$

The rest of the fission neutrons, forming less than one per cent of the total, are referred to as the *delayed* neutrons. These are emitted in groups after varying time lags. The number in each group falls exponentially with time, *i.e.* with a characteristic half-life period, as in radioactive decay, ranging from about 0.2 s to about 2 min. Table 6.3 gives the half-lives of the different groups of delayed neutrons with their energies.

TABLE 6.3 Delayed neutrons[13*]
(from G.R. Keepin, T.F. Wimmett and R.K. Zeigler[13], reproduced with authors' permission)

Half-life/s	Energy/MeV	% yield of total fission neutrons		
		[233]U	[235]U	[239]Pu
0.2	—	0.009	0.027	0.009
0.6	0.42	0.013	0.074	0.018
2.1	0.45	0.072	0.253	0 068
5·6	0.41	0.066	0.125	0.046
22	0.46	0.078	0.140	0 063
55	0.25	0.022	0.021	0 007
Total		0.26	0.64	0.21

A small group of extremely delayed neutrons with a half-life of the order of 2 h has also been reported in the case of uranium fission.

The emission of delayed neutrons, though less than one per cent of the total number of fission neutrons, plays a significant role in the functioning of reactor control system (see Sec. 7.7).

6.8.3 The Origin of Delayed Neutrons

The delayed emission of fission neutrons is attributed to such fission fragments (Z, N) whose β^- decay energy is in excess of the binding energy of the last neutron in the daughter product $(Z + 1, N - 1)$. The emission of this neutron would be delayed and would correspond to the half-life of the precursor β^- emitter. Careful investigations show the 55 s group of neutrons to be due to ^{87}Br ($\tau = 55.7$ s); Thus:

$$\text{Primary fission fragment} \rightarrow {}^{87}Br \xrightarrow[55.7\,s]{\beta^-} {}^{87}Kr^*_{51} \rightarrow {}^{86}Kr_{50} + n \text{ (delayed)}$$

Similarly, the 22 s neutrons originate in the β^- decay of ^{137}I ($\tau = 24.2$ s),

$$^{137}I \xrightarrow[24.2\,s]{\beta^-} {}^{137}Xe^*_{83} \rightarrow {}^{136}Xe_{82} + n \text{ (delayed)}$$

6.9   Theory of Nuclear Fission

(i) Nuclear Shape Distortion Following Excitation

Soon after the discovery of nuclear fission, Meitner and Frisch as well as Bohr and Wheeler proposed a theory for the phenomenon in 1939 based on the liquid drop model of the nucleus.[14–16] On this model, the atomic nucleus is considered analogous to a drop of incompressible liquid whose size is proportional to number of nucleons present (A) and the shape is determined by two opposing forces: The Coulomb force tending to distort the shape due to inter-proton repulsion, and the surface tension tending to restore the spherical shape. When the nucleus is excited by the capture of a neutron or by other means, oscillations are set up in the nucleus and a periodic distortion of shape takes place as in Fig. 6.1. If the excitation energy is not high enough, the nucleus reverts to the initial near spherical shape and the excess energy is lost radiatively and may be followed by α decay (Fig. 6.1, path a', b'). Alternatively, if the excitation energy is high enough the distortion increases from ellipsoidal to dumb-bell shape till a *critical deformation* is reached when the two halves separate out as fission fragments, each nearly spherical again (Fig. 6.1, paths a, b, c, d). The Bohr-Wheeler theory expresses the potential energy of the nucleus as a function of deformation at every stage leading to fission, in terms of a length parameter r, representing the separation between the likely centres of the two fragments.

(ii) Fission Energy versus Fission Barrier

Suppose a nucleus of mass $^A_Z m$ breaks into two halves yielding identical fragments $^{A/2}_{Z/2} m^*$. The energy released in the *symmetric fission* is given by

$$E_f = [^A_Z m - 2\, ^{A/2}_{Z/2} m] \; 931 \text{ MeV} \tag{6.7}$$

---

*The condition of fission into two identical fragments is not essential to the argument, as E_f for asymmetric fission differs only slightly.

The value of the fission energy depends on A and Z and may be calculated from the *semi-empirical mass equation* (Eq. 3.19). $p\,72$

It may be seen from a plot of E_f as a function of A (Fig. 6.6) that spontaneous fission becomes energetically possible for $A \geqslant 85$, *i.e.* E_f becomes positive* and the value for the symmetrical fission of ^{238}U is 170 MeV. However, a vast number of nuclides with $A \geq 85$ are stable without undergoing fission. In fact, it is not before A approaches 230 that spontaneous fission becomes discernible. This is due to the potential barrier opposing fission. Unless this barrier is overcome there can be no fission though it may be energetically possible. Fig. 6.6 also shows the variation of the barrier energy E_b as a function of A. It may be noted that it is only for $A \geqslant 235$ that $E_f > E_b$ and spontaneous fission does take place in the case of such heavy nuclides.[17]

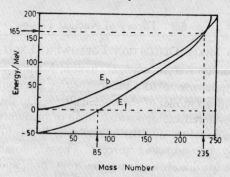

Fig. 6.6　Variation of the fission energy E_f and Coulomb barrier E_b with the mass number of nuclides
(from *Introductory Nuclear Physics*, by D. Halliday, © 1955. John Wiley & Sons, Inc., reproduced with permission).

To understand the fission barrier, let us now consider the process of fission in the reverse sense, *i.e.* the parent nucleus $^A_Z m$ as the result of fusion of two fragments characterized by A_1, Z_1 and A_2, Z_2. Thus

$$^{A_1}_{Z_1}m + ^{A_2}_{Z_2}m \underset{\text{fission}}{\overset{\text{fusion}}{\rightleftarrows}} ^A_Z m \qquad (6.8)$$

such that

$$Z_1 + Z_2 = Z \text{ and } A_1 + A_2 = A$$

(The 2 or 3 neutrons emitted during fission are neglected here.)

When the two fragments are far apart, *i.e.* the distance separating their centres $r \to \infty$, the Coulomb energy is zero, and as the fragments are made to approach each other the Coulomb energy increases as r^{-1}.

*This may be illustrated by computing E_f for two nuclei on either side of $A=85$, as ^{80}Kr and ^{108}Cd. The values are:

$$^{80}_{36}Kr \to 2\,^{40}_{18}Ar \;;\; E_f = -7.8 \text{ MeV};$$
$$^{108}_{48}Cd \to 2\,^{54}_{24}Cr \;;\; E_f = +24.4 \text{ MeV}.$$

When the two fragments are just in contact the limiting Coulomb barrier is

$$E_b = \frac{Z_1 Z_2 e^2}{R_1 + R_2} \tag{6.9}$$

where R_1 and R_2 are the radii of the two fragments. Figure 6.7 shows the variation of potential energy for a given nucleus of mass number A, as a function of r.

The limiting value of the potential at $r = R_1 + R_2$ is the fission barrier E_b of Eq. 6.9 which has to be overcome before a nucleus can undergo fission. The variation of E_b as a function of the atomic mass number A was shown in Fig. 6.6, besides the variation of E_f. It should further be noted that the energy available for fission E_f is also the potential energy at $r = 0$.

Any approach of the two fragments closer, i.e. $r < (R_1 + R_2)$ somehow, would mean nuclear *fusion* into the parent nucleus of a distorted shape. The total potential energy over the region $0 < r < (R_1 + R_2)$ is no longer purely coulombian, but a sum of coulombian and surface tension. The total energy varies with the degree of distortion and mass of the fused nucleus, and this is difficult to calculate. Theoretically, four types of curves, a, b, c and d are possible for the region $0 < r < (R_1 + R_2)$ as shown in Fig. 6.7, curve a meeting the energy axis (at $r = 0$) above E_b, curve b at E_b and curves c and d below E_b. The intercept on the energy axis E_f at $r = 0$ is important as it represents *the energy of the parent nucleus in the ground state, which is available for causing fission.* The value of E_f depends on the mass of the nucleus as shown in Fig. 6.6. The different cases lend to the following interpretation.

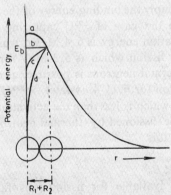

Fig. 6.7 Potential energy of a pair of fission fragments as a function of the distance between their centres

(from *Introductory Nuclear Physics*, by D. Halliday, © 1955. John Wiley & Sons., Inc., reproduced with permission).

(i) *Curve a:* $E_f > E_b$

Here the energy available in the nucleus in the ground state is greater than the fission barrier and the nucleus can undergo spontaneous fission, without external excitation. This applies to very heavy nuclides with $A \geqslant 240$, *i.e.* nuclides beyond plutonium.

(ii) *Curve b: $E_f = E_b$*

This is the limiting case representing the threshold for spontaneous fission. $A \simeq 235$.

(iii) *Curve c: $E_f < E_b$*

Here the energy available for fission from the parent nucleus in the ground state falls short *slightly* of the fission barrier with $(E_b - E_f)$ $\sim$ 5-6 MeV. Certain nuclides close to uranium, notably ^{233}U, ^{235}U and ^{239}Pu come under this category. On classical theory, these nuclides cannot undergo spontaneous fission due to this energy gap. In reality, however, these nuclides do suffer spontaneous fission; though with small cross sections corresponding to very long half-lives in the range 10^{11}-10^{17} y. This is explainable as a tunnel effect by quantum mechanics, as in α decay.

Alternatively, the nuclides of this group may be made to undergo fission by providing them with the *activation energy*, which is the difference between the barrier and fission energy available, *i.e.* $E_b - E_f$, which as pointed out above, is only of the order of $\sim$ 5-6 MeV. The necessary excitation is possible by the capture of a *thermal* neutron in the case of ^{233}U, ^{235}U and ^{239}Pu, while ^{232}Th, ^{238}U and some others need a greater excitation as in the capture of a fast neutron of energy $>$ 1 MeV or highly accelerated α, d, etc.

The excitation energy due to the capture of a thermal neutron (kinetic energy $\ll$ 1 eV) is simply the binding energy of the latter in the compound nucleus formed. In the case of ^{235}U capturing a thermal neutron to form ^{236}U* the excitation energy is 6.4 MeV†, which is greater than the activation energy for fission which is 5.3 MeV for this nucleus. Hence fission of ^{235}U by thermal neutrons is possible, as observed.

A similar calculation for ^{238}U $+ n$ (slow) $\rightarrow$ ^{239}U* shows the excitation energy is 4.75 MeV which is less than the activation energy $(=5.5$ MeV) hence ^{238}U cannot be fissioned by thermal neutrons, but fast neutrons; $(E \geqslant 1$ MeV) can do this.

(iv) *Curve d: $E_f \ll E_b$*

Here the energy available for fission falls far short of the barrier energy by about 50 MeV or more. Nuclides of this type cannot undergo spontaneous fission, nor on capturing thermal neutrons. All nuclides of $A < 225$ come under this category. Fission in some relatively

†The excitation energy is given in MeV by 931 times mass loss in the equation:
$$[m\,(^{235}\text{U}) + m\,(n) - m\,(^{236}\text{U})]\ 931$$
$$= (235\ 043\ 9 + 1.008\ 7 - 236.045\ 7)\ 931 = 6.42\ \text{MeV}$$

heavier ones can be effected with a low cross-section by bombarding them with very high energy particles or photons.

Values of activation energy $(E_b - E_f)$ needed for inducing fission and the excitation energy provided by the capture of thermal neutrons are listed in Table 6.4 for nuclides around uranium (type c above).

TABLE 6.4: Fissionability data for thermal neutrons*[10]

Nuclide	Activation energy for fission $E_{ae} = (E_b - E_f)/$ MeV	Excitation energy following thermal neutron capture, $E_{ex}/$MeV	$(E_{ex} - E_{ac})/$ (MeV)	Fission cross-section $\sigma_f/(b)$
^{231}Pa	5.1	5.4	+ 0.3	0.01
^{232}Th	6.5	5.1	− 1.4	3.9×10^{-5}
^{233}U	4.6	6.6	+ 2.0	531.1
^{235}U	5.3	6.4	+ 1.1	582.2
^{238}U	5.5	4.75	− 0.75	2.7
^{237}Np	4.2	5.0	+ 0.8	0.019
^{239}Pu	4.0	6.4	+ 2.4	742.5

*Based partly on I. Kaplan: *Nuclear Physics*, 1963. Addison-Wesley Publishing Co., with permission, ed. 1963, p. 630) Also Broohaven National Laboratory Report–325, 1958, 1960 and *Karlsruher Nuklidkarte*, 4 Auflage 1974.

The positive values of $E_{ex} - E_{ac}$ for ^{231}Pa and ^{237}Np are not compatible with their very poor fission cross sections. This suggests a limitation of the Bohr-Wheeler theory of fission which appears to go awry in these cases. It is believed that the theory best applies to nuclides with an odd number of neutrons which therefore favour neutron capture, while those already having an even number of neutrons as $^{231}_{91}$Pa$_{140}$, $^{232}_{90}$Th$_{142}$, $^{238}_{92}$U$_{146}$ and $^{237}_{93}$Np$_{144}$ have a poor tendency for capturing a neutron. In fact, this fits with the general finding that the excitation energy of a compound nucleus formed by the capture of a neutron in the case of a nucleus with an odd number of neutrons (so that the odd neutron can get paired in the compound nucleus), is greater than in the case of a nucleus with an even number of neutrons, by about twice the pairing energy Eq. 3.17 $(2B_p \simeq 1 \text{ MeV})$. This is in accord with the observation that while a thermal neutron $(E < 1 \text{ eV})$ can initiate fission in ^{233}U and ^{235}U having 143 and 145 neutrons respectively, a fast neutron $(E \geqslant 1 \text{ MeV})$ is needed to induce fission in ^{238}U having 146 neutrons.

Another aspect which militates against the liquid drop model theory of fission is the dominance of asymmetric fission while theory anticipates symmetric fission.

(v) *Shell closure effects*

An improved theory of fission results by associating shell closure effects. The total fission potential, according to Strutinsky should be the sum of the liquid drop, the shell model and the pairing energy terms[18].

Similarly, the extensive experimental data on the mass distribution of fission fragments lend support to the theory of '*hard core*' preformation prior to fission, developed by Wahl[19a]. As the nucleus gets increasingly deformed following excitation, the total nucleons tend to gather in the two end regions, asymmetrically. While one end collects a double magic number of 132 nucleons (*i.e.* 82 neutrons and 50 protons), the other end collects a magic number of 50 neutrons and, most of the, 34 protons, as observed in the neutron-induced fission of a large number of nuclides from thorium to californium[19b]. The formation of these hard cores, with shell structure closures, and hence of almost spherical shape, demands a minimum deformation of the parent nucleus. The rest of the nucleons, 20 (12 neutrons and 8 protons), in the case of ^{236}U fission, form a loose bridge between the two hard cores. At the moment of actual scission, these bridge nucleons get randomly shared between the two fragments, leading to asymmetric fission (Fig. 6.7(a)).

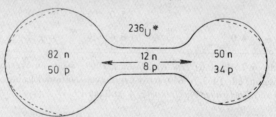

Fig. 6.7(a)   Hard core preformation theory of fission.

6.10   Other Types of Fission

Besides thermal neutron induced fissions of ^{233}U, ^{235}U and ^{239}Pu and spontaneous fissions of heavy nuclides beyond plutonium ($A > 240$), a variety of high energy particles and photons have been used to effect fission in not only heavy nuclides as Pb, Bi and beyond, but also in some of the medium mass elements. Phenomena rather similar to fission, but different in mechanism, as neutron evaporation and more generally nucleon evaporation, or spallation have also been studied over the years. Some of these will be described here.

6.10.1   SPONTANEOUS FISSION

It was Petrjak and Flerov[29] who first reported spontaneous fission in uranium in the unexcited state in 1940 and estimated the half-life for the process to be $\sim 10^{15}$ y. Now it is known that nearly all the heavy nuclides with $A \triangleright 230$ suffer spontaneous fission due to the large coulombic repulsion in nuclides of high Z. The half-lives vary over wide limits being related to the *fission parameter* Z^2/A. Actually the Coulomb term is $\propto Z^2/A^{1/3}$. The half-life decreases exponentially with Z^2/A, while the half-life for the competing mode of decay by γ and α emission varies in an inverse way. The ratio τ_{sf}/τ_α is 10^{-11} for ^{234}U while it is 70 for ^{256}Fm. When log half-life for spontaneous fission is plotted *versus* Z^2/A for even-even nuclides from ^{232}Th to ^{254}Fm a straight line results, though some of the isotopes of these elements fall away from the line (Fig. 6.8)[21]. The half-lives of odd A nuclides are several orders of magnitude longer.

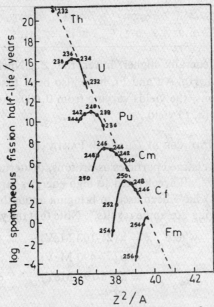

Fig. 6.8 Half-life of spontaneous fission as a function of
Z^2/A for even-Z, even-N nuclides
(from I. Halpern[21], reproduced with author's permission).

The mass, charge and energy distributions between the two fragments of spontaneous fission are similar to those in ^{235}U(n, f). The average number of neutrons emitted per spontaneous fission increases with A from 1.24 for ^{232}Th to 4 for ^{254}Fm.

The extrapolation of the curve in Fig. 6.8 to correspond to zero half-life or $10^{-20}\,s$ gives the critical maximum value of Z^2/A to be around 45. This hypothetical nuclide is referred to as *cosmium*. No nuclide of $Z^2/A > 45$ can exist as it would fission off instantaneously. Assuming A/Z to be around 2.59 in this region, cosmium would correspond to $Z = 116$ and $A = 300$. The heaviest nuclide synthesized is $Z = 105$ and $A = 262$ with a half-life of 40 s.

6.10.2 FISSION BY HIGH ENERGY NEUTRONS

While thermal neutrons ($E = 0.025$ eV or $v = 2.2$ km s^{-1}) induce fission in nuclides of the type ^{235}U with a high yield ($\sigma_f = 582$ b), the yield goes down as the neutron energy increases according to the $1/v$ law. In the case of ^{238}U, the major constituent of natural uranium (99.3%), fission is possible only with fast neutrons of energy ~ 1 MeV. This is also true for most other heavy nuclides which fall on the curve c of Fig. 6.7. The threshold neutron energies needed to cause fission in some of the heavy nuclides of this type are listed below in Table 6.5.

TABLE 6.5:   Neutron fission threshold energies[23]

Nuclide	^{237}Np	^{238}U	^{234}U	^{231}Pa	^{232}Th	^{230}Th	^{209}Bi
E/MeV	0.25	0.92	0.28	0.45	1.05	1	15

The threshold is generally higher, lower the Z. Nuclides of lower Z than Bi, as Pb, Tl, Hg, Au and Pt, have also been fissioned by the use of 84 MeV neutrons, the yields varying from 0.0009 for Pt to 0.02 for Bi, relative to Th (n, f) yield.

6.10.3   FISSION INDUCED BY CHARGED PARTICLES

Besides neutrons, charged particles as protons, deuterons, alpha particles, heavy ions as $^{12}C^{6+}$, all accelerated to high energies and even negatively charged pions (π^-) have been used in bringing about the fission of several nuclides. Following are some results. Note that the yields are very low.

$$^{238}U\ (x, f) \quad \text{where} \quad x = \alpha\,(21\text{-}100\ \text{MeV}): \qquad \sigma_f = 1.5\ \text{b:}$$
$$= p\,(\ 7\text{-}490\ \text{MeV}): \qquad \sigma_f = 2.0\ \text{b:}$$
$$= d\,(\ 8\text{-}193\ \text{MeV}): \qquad \sigma_f = 1.3\ \text{b:}$$
$$= {}^{12}C^{6+} \qquad\qquad\qquad \sigma_f = 0.1\ \text{b.}$$
$$^{232}Th\,(x, f) \quad \text{where} \quad x = \alpha\,(23 - 37.5\ \text{MeV}): \qquad \sigma_f = 0.6\ \text{b;}$$
$$= d\,(193\ \text{MeV}) \qquad : \quad \sigma_f = 1.2\ \text{b.}$$

Other fissions reported are of Bi, Pb, Tl, Ta and Au by 380 MeV alphas and 190 MeV deuterons.

When very high energy particles are employed, effects due to spallation (see below) are superimposed. Fissions by high energy particles, whether neutrons or others tend to be symmetrical (Fig. 6.4).

There are also reports of fission of U, Bi and W by negative pions (π^-) of energy in the range 70–120 MeV. It is believed that the pion is first captured by a proton or a neutron of the nucleus of the target atom and this nucleon gets excited to a very high energy state and this induces fission, though some doubts have been expressed about such a mechanism.

6.10.4   PHOTOFISSION

The 6.3 MeV γ photons from the reaction $^{19}F\ (p, \gamma)^{20}Ne$ have been found capable of fissioning a number of heavy nuclides and this is termed *photo-*

fission. The threshold energy is found to be nearly constant, between 5.2 and 5.4 MeV for the photofission of ^{232}Th, ^{233}U, ^{235}U, ^{238}U and ^{239}Pu. This threshold corresponds to fission by neutrons. The yields reported are 3.5 and 1.7 mb for ^{238}U and ^{232}Th by photons of 6.3 MeV. Photofission of Bi and Au nuclei has also been accomplished employing much higher energy photons, *viz*, 85 and 315 MeV respectively.

The primary process of radiation absorption is believed to be the production of pions which are then captured by nucleons which in their turn effect fission, as described earlier.

6.11 Neutron Evaporation and Spallation

Neutron evaporation, or more generally *nucleon* evaporation, and *spallation* are two high energy processes which lead to results similar to fission.

6.11.1 NEUTRON EVAPORATION

Here, according to Meitner, the excited fissile nucleus, which always has an excess of neutrons relative to its fragment products, ejects or lets evaporate a large number of neutrons in one lot and the residual nucleus then breaks into two *similar* fragments both having nearly the same N/Z ratio. These fragments further decay by β^- emission till stable end isobaric nuclei are formed, as in fission. Thus, in the case ^{209}Bi (d, f), Meitner proposed the following stages.

$$
\underset{(190\ \text{MeV})}{^{209}\text{Bi} + d} \rightarrow 12n + {}^{199}\text{Po}^* \xrightarrow{\text{Symmetric fission}} {}^{99}_{41}\text{Nb} + {}^{100}_{41}\text{Nb}
$$

$$
{}^{99}_{41}\text{Nb} \downarrow 3\beta^- \qquad {}^{100}_{41}\text{Nb} \downarrow \beta^-
$$

$$
\underset{\text{stable}}{{}^{99}_{44}\text{Ru}} \qquad \underset{\text{stable}}{{}^{100}_{42}\text{Mo}}
$$

It is not certain whether a compound nucleus ^{211}Po* is momentarily formed or not in such high energy reactions. It may be noted that the two fission fragments have each nearly same excess neutrons over the nearest magic number. In this case ^{99}Nb$_{58}$ and ^{100}Nb$_{59}$ have 8 and 9 neutrons in excess of 50.

6.11.2 SPALLATION

Here a large number of nucleons, as neutrons, protons and even α particles evaporate from the highly excited nucleus, leaving behind a much smaller residue akin to a product of fission. Thus in the bombardment of ^{63}Cu by 70–340 MeV protons, two of the more important products observed are ^{38}Cl and ^{24}Na, besides some others. These products may be the result of spallation or direct fission: it is not easy to decide; thus

$$
\left. \begin{array}{l} ^{63}\text{Cu}\,(p,\ pn6\ \alpha)\ ^{38}\text{Cl} \\[6pt] ^{63}\text{Cu}\,(p,\ p3n9\alpha)\ ^{24}\text{Na} \end{array} \right\} \quad \textit{Spallation}
$$

and

or

$$^{63}Cu + p \rightarrow\ ^{64}Zn^* \left\langle \begin{array}{l} ^{38}Cl + ^{25}Al + n \\ ^{24}Na + ^{39}K + n \end{array} \right\} fission$$

Some of the other products of spallation of copper by 370 MeV neutrons studied by Marquez[22] are listed in Table 6.6 together with their cross sections.

TABLE 6.6: Products of spallation of ^{63}Cu by 370 MeV neutrons[22]

Product	Reaction	Cross section	Product	Reaction	Cross section
^{64}Cu	(n, γ)	56.6	^{59}Fe	$(n, \alpha p)$	2.44
^{62}Cu	$(n, 2n)$	37.1	^{52}Fe	$(n, \alpha p7n)$	0.134
^{61}Cu	$(n, 3n)$	15.1	^{56}Mn	$(n, 2\alpha)$	2.81
^{57}Ni	$(n, 6pn)$	0.54	^{52}Mn	$(n, 2\alpha 4n)$	4.68
^{61}Co	$(n, 2pn)$	3.78	^{49}Cr	$(n, 2\alpha p6n)$	0.35
^{58}Co	$(n, \alpha 2n)$	23.2	^{45}Ti	$(n, 3\alpha p6n)$	0.078

The threshold for spallation of the type described above is around 170–110 MeV which is much higher than that for direct fission which for these reactions is around 50 MeV. Similar spallations have been studied in a number of nuclides of the type: Br, Ag, Sn and Ba yielding products of the type ^{24}Na, ^{66}Ga, ^{72}Ga and ^{61}Co, though some of these could be considered as fission products as well.

References
(where marked *, see Bibliography)

1. H.D. Smyth, 'Atomic Energy for Military Purposes' (Princeton Univ. Pr. Princeton, N.J. 1945). *Revs. Mod. Phys.*, 1945, **17**, 351.
2. O. Hahn and F. Strassmann, 'Uber den Nachweis und das Verhaltan der beider Behstrahlung des Uran Mittels Neutronen Erdalkali Metalle', *Naturwiss*, 1939, **27**, 11; 89.
3. B.G. Harvey*
4. S. Katkoff, 'Fission Product Yields from U, Th and Pu', *Nucleonics*, 1958, **16**, 78; *Revs. Mod. Phys.*, 1946, **18**, 513; *J. Amer. Chem. Soc.*, 1946, **68**, 2411.
5. (a) R.C. Jensen and A.W. Fairhall, 'Fission of Radium-226 by 11 MeV Protons', *Phys. Rev.*, 1958, **109**, 942.
    (b) R.C. Jensen and A.W. Fairhall, 'Fission of Radium-226 by Neuterons and Helium Ions', *Phys. Rev.*, 1960, **118**, 771.
6. R.D. Evans*
7. W.E. Stein, 'Velocities of Fragment Pairs from ^{233}U, ^{235}U and ^{239}Pu Fission', *Phys. Rev.*, 1957, **108**, 94.

8. J.S. Wahl, 'Energy Distribution of Fragments from the Fission of ^{235}U, ^{238}U and ^{239}Pu by Fast Neutrons; *Phys. Rev.*, 1954, **95**, 126.

9. J. Jungerman and S.C. Wright, 'Kinetic Energy Release in Fission of ^{238}U, ^{235}U, ^{232}Th and ^{209}Bi by High Energy Neutrons', *Phys. Rev.*, 1949, **76**, 1112.

10. I. Kaplan*

11. R.W. Lamphere, 'Fission Cross Sections of the Uranium Isotopes: 233, 234, 236 and 238 for Fast Neutrons', *Phys. Rev.*, 1956, **104**, 1654.

12. H. von Halban, F. Joliot and L. Kowarski 'Liberation of Neutrons in the Nuclear Fission of Uranium', *Nature*, 1939, **143**, 470; 680.

13. G.R. Keepin, T.F. Wimmett and R.K. Zeigler 'Delayed Neutrons from Fissionable Isotopes of Uranium, Thorium and Plutonium', *Phys. Rev.*, 1957, **107**, 1044.

14. N. Bohr and J.A. Wheeler, 'The Mechanism of Nuclear Fission', *Phys. Rev.*, 1939, **56**, 426.

15. L. Meitner, 'Fission and Nuclear Shell Model,' *Nature*, 1950, **165**, 561.

16. B.G. Harvey,*

17. D. Halliday*

18. V.M. Strutinsky, *Nuc. Phys.*, 1967, A **95**, 420; 1968, A**122**, 1.

19. (a) A.C. Wahl *Proc. I.A.E.A. Symp.*, Salzburg, 1965; Vienna, 1969; (b) J.P. Unik Rochester, 1973.

20. K. Petrjak and G. Flerov, *Doklady Akad-Nauk*, SSSR, 1940, **28**, 500.

21. I. Halpern, 'Nuclear Fission', *Ann. Rev. Nuc. Sci.*, 1959, **9**, 245.

22. L. Marquez, 'Spallation of Copper with High Energy Neutrons', *Phys. Rev.*, 1952, **88**, 225.

23. M. Haissinsky*

Problems

6.1 Show that $^{130}_{52}$Te should be unstable in respect of symmetric fission. Explain why this does not, however, take place. Find the fission energy E_f, the barrier energy E_b and activation energy E_a needed to effect this fission;
— given the atomic masses:

$$^{130}\text{Te} = 129.906\ 7 \text{ u},\ ^{65}\text{Cu} = 64.927\ 8 \text{ u, and } r_0 = 1.5\,\text{F}.$$
$$[E_f = 47.6 \text{ MeV};\ E_b = 80.7 \text{ MeV};\ E_a = 33.1 \text{ MeV}]$$

6.2 (a) What is the barrier energy against the symmetric fission of $^{114}_{50}$Sn? (b) What is the activation energy needed to effect this fission? Given the atomic masses of ^{114}Sn = 113.9030 u; ^{57}Mn = 56.9383 u and $r_0 = 1.5\,\text{F}$.
$$[\text{(a) } E_b = 77.95 \text{ MeV; (b) } E_a = 53.39 \text{ MeV}]$$

6.3 In the fission of $^{239}_{94}$Pu the fragments have the mass numbers 100 and 138, whose stable isobars are $^{100}_{42}$Mo and $^{138}_{56}$Ba what are the primary fragments?
$$[^{100}_{40}\text{Zr and } ^{138}_{54}\text{Xe}]$$

6.4 In the fission of $^{235}_{92}$U the end stable products are $^{94}_{40}$Zr and $^{140}_{58}$Ce, what are the primary fragments?
$$[^{94}_{37}\text{Rb and } ^{140}_{55}\text{Cs}]$$

6.5 Two sets of products of fission of $^{239}_{94}$Pu by thermal neutrons are
(a) ^{108}Pd + ^{129}Xe + 3n and (b) ^{155}Gd + ^{81}Br + 4n.

Find the energy released in the two cases, given the following atomic masses:

$$^{239}\text{Pu} = 239.052\ 2 \text{ u,} \quad ^{129}\text{Xe} = 128.904\ 8 \text{ u}$$
$$^{108}\text{Pd} = 107.903\ 9 \text{ u,} \quad ^{155}\text{Gd} = 154.922\ 0 \text{ u}$$
$$^{81}\text{Br} = 80.916\ 3 \text{ u,} \quad \text{and } n = 1.008\ 7 \text{ u}$$
$$[\text{(a) } 210.52 \text{ MeV, (b) } 174.85 \text{ MeV}]$$

6.6   Assuming symmetric fission of $^{250}_{100}$Fm, find (a) the fission barrier and (b) the fission energy released, given the atomic masses:

$$^{250}Fm = 250.0795 \text{ u}$$
$$^{125}Sn = 124.9077 \text{ u}$$

[(a) 240 MeV; (b) 245.88 MeV]

6.7   Compute the energy released in the following fission:

$$^{249}_{99}Es + n \rightarrow {}^{161}_{64}Gd + {}^{87}_{35}Br + 2n$$

given the following atomic masses:

$$^{249}Es = 249.076\ 2 \text{ u}; \quad {}^{161}Gd = 160.928\ 6 \text{ u}$$
$$^{87}Br = \ 86.022\ 0 \text{ u}; \quad\quad n = \ 1.008\ 7 \text{ u}$$ [1040 MeV]

Chapter 7

Nuclear Reactors

7.1 The Fission Energy

The twin characteristics of nuclear fission as described in the previous chapter are:

(i)   That each neutron induced fission of a uranium nucleus releases a staggering amount of energy; and

(ii) That each fission sets free on the average two or three neutrons.

These two characteristics are of great significance as they reveal the atom as a new source of energy. Of the 2.5 neutrons regenerated in each fission, *if one is utilized* in bringing about the fission of another atom of uranium, atomic energy may be said to have been harnessed, for in such a system, for every neutron used up in fissioning the uranium nucleus, another is made available for causing a fresh fission and in this way a *steady state* of self-propagated fission chains gets established. The number of fissions per second would be constant, releasing energy at a constant rate till all the uranium fuel is burnt up.

The situation is realized in a device known as the *nuclear reactor*.

If, however, *more than one of the fission neutrons is used* in causing further fissions in their turn, the fission chains multiply fast. The number of neutrons utilized, the fissions occurring and hence the energy released in unit time increase exponentially with time. Here most of the fissile material is burnt up and a terrific amount of energy is released in an extremely short time and this corresponds to a *divergent state*. This is what happens in an atom bomb. On the contrary, if *less than one* of the fission neutrons on the average is utilized in causing fresh fissions, the chains become shorter and shorter after growing to some length. Less and less neutrons become available for fission with time than are used up and the entire process is quenched. This corresponds to a *convergent state* which is of no practical interest.

Now let us look into the magnitude of fission energy when a kilogram of ^{235}U gets completely fissioned. As pointed out in the previous chapter, each fissioning nucleus releases roughly about 200 MeV energy. In terms of familiar units this is equivalent to 2×10^7 megacalories or nearly 1000 MW-day per kilogram of uranium fissioning per day. The calculation follows the definition of an electron volt:

$$1 \text{ eV} = 1.6 \times 10^{-19} \text{ volt-coulomb or joule,}$$

$$\therefore \quad 1 \text{ MeV} = 1.6 \times 10^{-19} \text{ MJ}$$

$$\therefore \quad 200 \text{ MeV} = 3.2 \times 10^{-17} \text{ MJ}$$

Since in 1 kg of ^{235}U there are $\dfrac{6 \times 10^{23} \times 10^3}{235}$ atoms of ^{235}U, the fissioning

of all these atoms releases at 200 MeV per fission, a total energy of

$$= 3.2 \times 10^{-17} \times 6 \times 10^{26}/235 \text{ MJ}$$

$$= 8.17 \times 10^7 \text{ MJ} \simeq 2 \times 10^7 \text{ Mcal.}$$

If the kilogram of ^{235}U fissions during the course of 1 day $(24 \times 3600 \text{ s})$,

the rate of energy release $= \dfrac{8.17 \times 10^7}{24 \times 3600} \text{ MW}$

Power $\simeq 950$ MW.

To produce this much of energy, 2.5×10^6 kg of coal of the best quality would have to be burnt. In short, the nuclear fuel to coal mass ratio is about $1 : 10^6$. Or in terms of destructive capacity, the fissioning of one kg of ^{235}U corresponds to 20 kilotonnes of TNT. Hence, the proposition of harnessing atomic energy appears attractively challenging. As long back as 1935, Professor Joliot-Curie, in his Nobel prize lecture, had predicted the possibility of obtaining energy by setting up chains of nuclear reactions, and that was before the discovery of fission.[1]

7.2   The Natural Uranium Reactor

Following considerations show how not all the two or three fission neutrons emitted in a fission would be available for the propagation of fission chains in natural uranium. First, the fission neutrons are of high energy (0.5-17 MeV) and the fission cross section of ^{235}U for fast neutrons is small, decreasing with the increase of neutron energy (the $1/v$ law) (Sec. 5.4.3 and Fig. 7.1).[2] Further, the total amount of this isotope in natural uranium is very small being 0.72 per cent. No doubt the fast neutrons can fission the ^{238}U nucleus, forming the bulk (99.28%) of natural uranium, but the cross section for ^{238}U fission is small, being around 0.01 b for 2 MeV neutrons. The few fast neutron fissions with ^{238}U would of course constitute a small positive factor which will be counted upon. These are the reasons why it becomes necessary *to thermalize* the neutrons, *i.e.*, to slow them down from MeV to less than eV range. This is realized by dispersing the uranium in a matrix of an inert substance, called the *moderator*, which slows down the fast neutrons through a series of elastic collisions.

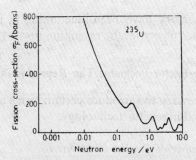

Fig. 7.1 Fission cross section of ^{235}U by slow neutrons
as a function of neutron energy, showing the
$1/v$ law and resonance peaks[2]
(from *Nuclear Physics/An Introduction*, by W.E. Burcham, © 1973.
Longman Group Ltd., reproduced with permission).

The earliest positive experiments of this type, with uranium oxide dispersed along different geometries in water, and later in heavy water, were due to Joliot-Curie, Halban and Kowarski.[3]

During moderation, however, some of the neutrons are invariably lost by capture by the atoms of the moderator itself. A second source of loss of neutrons is by what is termed the *resonance capture* of neutrons at a definite energy, around 6 eV, by the ^{238}U leading to the formation of the transuraniens, Np and Pu (Sec. 6 1). There are further losses of thermal neutrons due to their capture by other materials which must be necessarily present, as the container walls, coolant and the fission fragments accumulating all the time. Lastly, some of the neutrons, both fast and slow, leak out of the system on reaching the surface. Ultimately, some thermal neutrons survive all the above modes of loss and reach atoms of ^{235}U and a fraction of these succeed in causing the fission in the second generation and thus help sustain fission chains from generation to generation.

The designing of a nuclear reactor must be such that a precise, optimum and efficient use is made of the fission neutrons of each generation by minimizing losses by all factors, so that self-propagating fission chains from generation to generation become possible. At the same time an automatic control for preventing over-optimization must be built into the reactor so that the *rate* of energy release remains within limits without becoming explosive. In view of these numerous factors some of which counterfunction, the designing of a nuclear reactor in which self-propagating fission chains yield energy at a steady rate within preset levels, is a highly technical operation. We shall present here only some basic principles involved.

The first nuclear reactor was designed and worked by Enrico Fermi in the University of Chicago, using natural uranium as fuel and graphite as moderator. It went critical and started functioning at a low energy level of 100 W with a thermal neutron flux of 4×10^6 n cm^{-2} s^{-1}. Since then ever so many reactors have been functioning in many countries at very many times higher power levels, extending up to 10^9 W.

7.3 The Four Factor Formula: The Reproduction Factor k

At this stage it is necessary to introduce certain terms and symbols more or less commonly used in reactor technology.

(i) The Average Number of Fission Neutrons ν

This term was described earlier in Sec. 6.8.1 and it refers to the *average number of neutrons thrown out in each act* of fission by thermal neutrons. This number is 2.44 for ^{235}U and 2.5 for natural uranium as listed in Table 6.2. Actually it is ^{235}U in natural uranium (0.72 %) which undergoes fission by thermal neutrons. So ν should be same as for ^{235}U, but the effective value is 2.5 in natural uranium due to the fast fission factor ε which is around 1.03 $(2.44 \times 1.03 = 2.5)$, (see (ii) below).

(ii) The Fast Fission Factor ε

Such of the ν fission neutrons, which are all fast, which meet ^{238}U nuclei, before reaching the moderator, effect fissions in ^{238}U and thus additional fast neutrons are generated. The total number of fast neutrons is thereby increased from ν to $\nu\varepsilon$ where ε *is the fast fission factor*; ε for ^{238}U is 1.03. The 3% increase in the number of fast neutrons has an important effect in the conservation of total neutrons in a reactor.

(iii) The Fast Neutron Loss Factor l_f

Some allowance must be made for the loss of a fraction l_f of the fast neutrons which neither meet ^{238}U nor the moderator but leak out of the reactor. The fraction of fast neutrons remaining in the reactor is therefore $\nu\varepsilon(1 - l_f)$. No doubt the loss can be minimized by making the size of the reactor large.

(iv) The Resonance Capture Loss $(1 - p)$: The Resonance Escape Probability p

As the $\nu\varepsilon(1 - l_f)$ fast neutrons pass through the moderator, the process of thermalization starts through successive collisions of neutrons with the atoms of the moderator substance. The neutrons must necessarily pass through all intermediate energies and in this process neutrons of specific energies, called *resonance* energies, as 6.6, 20 and 38 eV and a few other values*, are captured by ^{238}U with a large

---

*These correspond to the peaks in the curve of capture cross section *versus* neutron energy.

cross section leading to the formation of the compound nucleus $^{239}U^*$ which by successive β^- decays yields ^{239}Np and ^{239}Pu (Fig. 7.2).[3] If the fraction lost through resonance capture is $(1 - p)$, the number of slow neutrons escaping resonance capture is $v\varepsilon\,(1 - l_f)p$.

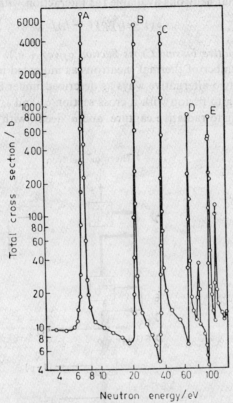

Fig. 7.2 Total neutron capture cross section for ^{238}U as a function of neutron energy[4].

(from *Brookhaven National Laboratory Report*, BNL 325, reproduced with permission).

(v) *The Thermal Neutron Loss Factor l_t*

Once again allowance must be made for the leaking out of the reactor assembly a fraction of thermal neutrons l_t. This leaves behind in the reactor a total number of $v\varepsilon\,(1 - l_f)p\,(1 - l_t)$ thermal neutrons. Here also the loss l_t can be reduced by enlarging the size of the reactor, as well as by surrounding the reactor with a material such as graphite or beryllium which, without absorbing, reflects the slow neutrons back into the reactor.

(vi) *The Thermal Utilization Factor f*

Cognizance must be also taken of the fact that a fraction of thermal neutrons are lost by capture by *other materials* present in the reactor as impurities, container walls, other structural materials, and by accumulating fission fragments, particularly those with large neutron capture cross section, as ^{135}Xe ($\sigma = 3.6$ Mb), ^{149}Sm ($\sigma = 4.1$ kb). If the loss factor due to these materials is $(1 - f)$, the *thermal utilization factor f* of total thermal neutrons available for interaction with ^{235}U is

$$\nu \varepsilon (1 - l_f)\, p\, (1 - l_i) f.$$

(vii)   *The Relative Fission Cross Section $\sigma_f/(\sigma_f + \sigma_r)$*

The net number of thermal neutrons as indicated in (vi) above, react with ^{235}U in two alternative ways as described under Sec. 6.7:

(a)   leading to fission with a cross section σ_f and

(b)   leading to radiative capture and α decay with a cross section σ_r.

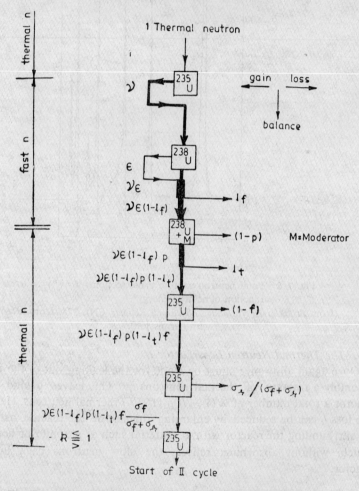

Fig. 7.3   The neutron balance in a reactor: the multiplication factor k. The ^{235}U and ^{238}U shown represent these components as present in natural uranium.

The *relative* fission cross section is given by the fraction $\sigma_f/(\sigma_f + \sigma_r)$. Using the values for natural uranium given in Table 6.2, *viz.* $\sigma_f = 4.18$ b, $\sigma_r = 3.5$ b, the ratio $\sigma_f/(\sigma_f + \sigma_r)$ comes to 0.544. Thus we arrive at the number of fissions in ^{235}U in natural uranium in the second generation to be $k = \nu\varepsilon(1 - l_f)\,p\,(1 - l_t)\,f\,\dfrac{\sigma_f}{\sigma_f + \sigma_r}$ per fission in the first generation (see Fig. 7.3).

(viii) *The Four Factor Formula and the Reproduction Factor k*

The ultimate factor of importance is the *reproduction or multiplication factor k* which is the *ratio of the number of neutrons available for fission in a generation to that available in the preceding generation*, thus from above

$$k = \frac{\nu\sigma_f}{\sigma_f + \sigma_r}\,\varepsilon\,pf(1 - l_f)\,(1 - l_t) \qquad (7.1)$$

Replacing the product $\dfrac{\nu\sigma_f}{\sigma_f + \sigma_r}$ by η which represents the number of *fast neutrons* per thermal neutron used up, we have for a reactor of finite dimensions

$$k = \eta\,\varepsilon\,pf(1 - l_f)\,(1 - l_t) \qquad (7.2)$$

and for a reactor of dimensions greater than a critical one, the loss of thermal as well as fast neutrons is nearly zero. Hence,

$$k_\infty = \eta\,\varepsilon\,pf \qquad (7.3)$$

This is frequently referred to as the *four factor formula*.

Here the subscript ∞ only means that the size of the reactor is sufficiently large to prevent escape of neutrons both fast and thermal, *i.e.*

$$l_f = l_t = 0.$$

The value of k is very important as it determines the functioning of the reactor; the three cases being:

(a) $k = 1$ signifying a *steady state* where the number of neutrons and fissions is constant from cycle to cycle, and the amount of energy output in unit time is constant.

(b) $k > 1$ signifying a *divergent state* where the number of neutrons, fissions and energy output rapidly increase from cycle to cycle, ending up in an explosion.

(c) $k < 1$ signifying a *convergent state* where the number of neutrons, fissions and energy output diminish from one cycle to next and soon the reactor is quenched; this is of no interest.

Extremely delicate controls are needed to keep k slightly greater than unity for a steady state operation of the reactor, as the values of the four factors, in the case of U-graphite reactor are around $\eta = 1.3$, $\varepsilon = 1.03$ and $p \simeq f \simeq 0.88$.[2]

If the reactor fuel consists ⌈of pure ^{233}U, ^{235}U or ^{239}Pu, $i.e.$ unmixed with any material which is not fissile by thermal neutrons, $\varepsilon = p = 1$

$$k_\infty = \eta f = \nu f \frac{\sigma_f}{\sigma_f + \sigma_r} \qquad (7.4)$$

Thus η is a characteristic of only the fissile material used as the fuel, while ε depends both on the fuel element and size and shape of the assembly making up the reactor, and the other two terms p and f depend on the nature of fuel element, the moderator substance and other materials present, as well as on the geometry of the structure of the reactor, or on its lattice characteristics. The principal problem in reactor designing is to find the best lattice structure of distributing the fuel and the moderator to lead to the maximum pf.

7.4   The Classification of Reactors

Nuclear reactors are referred to in several alternative ways depending on the characteristic(s) to be emphasized, such as:

(i)   *The fuel:*   The natural uranium reactor with 0.72% ^{235}U, or the enriched uranium reactor with ^{235}U content $> 0.72\%$, or the ^{239}Pu, or the ^{233}U reactor.   The last isotope results from ^{232}Th following resonance capture of a neutron and two β^- decays, similar to the process of obtaining ^{239}Pu from ^{238}U.

$$^{232}\text{Th} + n \xrightarrow[\text{capture}]{\text{resonance}} {}^{233}\text{Th}^* \xrightarrow[\text{22.3 min}]{\beta^-} {}^{233}\text{Pa} \xrightarrow[\text{27.0 d}]{\beta^-} {}^{233}\text{U}$$

(ii)   *The neutron energy:*   As fast, intermediate, or slow neutron reactors.

(iii)   *The moderator used:*   As graphite, heavy water, or ordinary water (swimming pool), and less often beryllium, moderated reactors.

(iv)   *The coolant used:*   As air, water or liquid metal (sodium) cooled reactors.

(v)   *The purpose of the reactor:*   As power generation, plutonium extraction, isotope production, or purely research reactors.

(vi)   *Homogeneous or heterogenous:*   Depending on whether the fuel and moderator are in one phase as solution or two different phases.

Often it becomes necessary to combine more than one characteristic to convey the full nature and scope of a reactor, $e.g.$ 'thermal, natural uranium, heavy water, heterogenous water-cooled research reactor'.

7.4.1   TYPICAL REACTORS

We shall discuss here some relevant issues in designing a nuclear reactor

---

*As mentioned earlier, ^{233}U has fissile characteristics similar to ^{235}U or ^{239}Pu. Hence this fuel would be of particular interest to India with ^{232}Th available in abundance.

using different fuel-moderator combinations. A quantity referred to as the *design parameter F* defined as

$$F = \frac{\text{Number of moderator atoms}}{\text{Number of fuel atoms}}$$

is extremely important in designing a nuclear reactor with $k \geqslant 1$. Most of the ensuing discussion will centre around the value of F.

(i) Natural Uranium, Ordinary Water or Graphite Reactor

It has been found that with natural uranium (with 0.72 per cent of ^{235}U) there can be no self-sustaining fission chain reaction with either ordinary water or graphite as the moderator. The maximum value of the reproduction factor k obtainable is 0.8 at $F = 5$ with ordinary water as the moderator and at $F = 400$ with graphite moderator. This situation is mainly due to the small value of the resonance escape factor p in this type of reactor.

(ii) Natural Uranium, Heavy Water Homogeneous Reactor

With heavy water (D_2O) as the moderator, it is possible to realize with natural uranium a reproduction factor $k > 1$. As the parameter F is varied, k rises from 0.02 for $F = 1$ to a maximum of 1.17 at $F = 300$-400 and thereafter diminishes again to 1.10 at $F = 1000$.

(iii) Enriched Uranium Graphite Reactor

Employing uranium adequately enriched in the isotope ^{235}U, it is possible to make a reactor go critical, *i.e.* $k \geqslant 1$. Maintaining a constant value for the parameter F at 400 in the case of a graphite moderated reactor, it is found that k rises significantly with the degree of enrichment in ^{235}U in the fuel. Expressing the enrichment in terms of α the per cent of ^{235}U in the uranium, it is found that k rises from a subcritical value of 0.8 for $\alpha = 0.72$ (natural uranium) to 1.01 for $\alpha = 1.23$. Further enrichment results in continuous increase in k as shown in Table 7.1 below.

This shows that under the above conditions, the minimum enrichment

TABLE 7.1: Variation of k with the degree of enrichment α of ^{235}U in the
fuel with graphite moderator at $F = 400$[5]

(from *Nuclear Physics*, by I. Kaplan, © 1955, 1963. Addison-Wesley Publishing Co., Inc., reproduced with permission)

α	0.72*	0.83	0.99	1.10	1.23	1.41	1.64	1.96
k	0.8	0.86	0.93	0.97	1.01	1.05	1.10	1.16

*Natural uranium.

of ^{235}U has to be 1.23. Similar conditions have been worked out for enriched uranium—ordinary water (swimming pool type) reactor like the *Apsara*, developed under the direction of H.J. Bhabha. This was India's and Asia's first reactor which went critical in August 1956. Other reactors functioning in the country are described in Sec. 7.9.

(iv) *Natural Uranium Heterogenous Reactors*

The main difficulty with natural uranium homogeneous reactors, except with heavy water, is the high resonance capture loss. Fermi and Szilard argued that if instead of homogeneous solution or dispersion, the uranium is placed in the form of well separated rods in a matrix of the moderator, the ratio of the surface area to volume of the fuel element would be greatly reduced and hence the loss of neutrons by ,resonance capture, as the latter takes place mainly at the surface. This involves two parameters (i) Optimum fuel-rod diameter d and (ii) Optimum inter-fuel separation or the slowing down length l.

(i) *Optimum fuel rod diameter:* Increasing the rod diameter reduces the surface and therefore the resonance capture loss, and hence an increase of factor p, which is desirable. However, increasing the rod diameter reduces the thermal utilization factor f. On the other hand, reducing the rod diameter is equivalent to moving towards homogenization, *i.e.*, increasing the surface, with opposite effects on p and f. In other words, an optimum fuel rod diameter has to be ascertained. This should be such that a neutron born out of a ^{235}U fission shall make no more than one or two collisions with the fuel element atoms (^{238}U) before leaving the surface. In other words, the rod diameter should roughly correspond to one mean free path of a thermal neutron in uranium. The mean free path of a thermal neutron is given by

$$\lambda = (N \sigma_t)^{-1} \qquad (7.5)$$

where N is the concentration of the fuel atoms ($= 0.048 \times 10^{24}$ atoms of ^{238}U per cm^3) and σ_t is the *total* absorption cross section for fast neutrons by ordinary uranium ($= 7.2 \times 10^{-24}$ cm^2).

$$\lambda = \frac{1}{0.048 \times 7.2} = 2.89 \text{ cm}$$

Usually, the uranium rods of diameter slightly less than this value, *viz.* between 2.3 and 2.6 cm clad in aluminium (or Zr + Al alloy) are used both with graphite and heavy water moderator.

(ii) *Optimum inter-fuel rod separation or the slowing down length:* The inter-fuel rod separation should be such that a fast or slightly slowed neutron leaving the surface of one fuel rod gets fully thermalized before reaching the surface of the next fuel rod. This slowing down length has been found to be 5.3, 11.2 and 19.1 cm in H_2O, D_2O and C (graphite) respectively.[5] The lattice spacing of the fuel rods is made about equal to the slowing-down length.

By carefully controlling the rod diameter and the inter-fuel rod separation at the optimum values it has been possible to register a multiplication factor of 1.075 and 1.21 with natural uranium with graphite and heavy water as the moderator respectively.

(iii) *Approximate balance sheet of reactor neutrons:* In a natural uranium-graphite heterogenous reactor, the production of neutrons is 2.52 per ^{235}U fission, (2.46 from ^{235}U thermal fission + 0.06 from ^{238}U fast fission).

These are used up approximately as follows:[5a]

(a)	Resonance capture by ^{238}U	0.8
(b)	Radiative capture by ^{238}U	0.2
(c)	Absorption by graphite	0.3
(d)	Absorption by other materials	0.05
(e)	Loss by leakage	0.09
(f)	Chain propagation (k)	1.08
	Total	2.52

7.5 Reactor Power

Reactors designed to generate electricity are referred to by their capacity for power generation. Each fission releases about 200 MeV or 3.2×10^{-17} MJ (Secs. 6.6 and 7.1). Hence 3.1×10^{13} fissions per second is equivalent to a power of 1 kW*. The total power of a reactor is known if the number of fissions occurring per second is known. This latter is given by

$$A = \sigma N \phi V \qquad (7.6)$$

where σ is fission cross section, N the number of uranium atoms per cm^3, ϕ the neutron flux (number $cm^{-2} s^{-1}$), and V the volume of the reactor. The power of a reactor is given by

$$P = \sigma N \phi V / 3.1 \times 10^{13} = 3.2 \, N \phi V \times 10^{-14} \, kW \qquad (7.7)$$

7.6 Critical Size of a Thermal Reactor

The condition $k_\infty \geqslant 1$ ensures the reactor functions with self-maintaining fission chains under the condition that the reactor is of infinite dimensions (very large) such that no neutron escapes. It is relevant to examine whether it is possible to realize the steady state conditions such that the loss of neutrons is balanced by the rate of production even in a reactor of finite dimensions.[5-7]

Let us consider a rectangular slab reactor of sides a_∞, b_∞ and c

---

*1 fission = 200 MeV = 3.2×10^{-17} MJ (see p. 210)
∴ 1 kW = $10^3/(3.2 \times 10^{-11}) = 3.1 \times 10^{13}$ fissions

parallel to the X, Y, Z coordinates with the origin at the centre of the stack. Two of the sides a_∞ and b_∞ are sufficiently long to ensure no escape of neutrons from planes perpendicular to the X and Y axes. It is proposed to calculate the critical height c of the reactor which enables the reactor to function (Fig. 7.4). This means that the following equilibrium exists in respect of neutron distribution in planes normal to the Z axis

$$n_{es} + n_{ab} = n_{pr} \qquad (7.8)$$

where the rates of neutron escape, absorption and production are shown by n_{es}, n_{ab} and n_{pr} respectively.

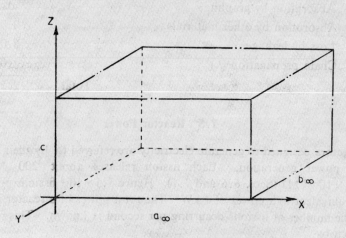

Fig. 7.4   Critical size of a thermal reactor.

It is necessary to make two assumptions to simplify the treatment: *First*, that the distribution of neutrons, *i.e.* the processes of escape, absorption and production occur in a homogeneous manner in all the planes perpendicular to the Z and *secondly*, that all the neutrons are thermalized and are monoergic.

If the critical height c of the reactor to ensure steady state functioning is c_{crit} (to be determined), it implies for all planes normal to the Z axis at heights $c \geqslant c_{crit}$ the neutron density is zero, *i.e.*

$$n(z) = (n_{pr} - n_{es} - n_{ab}) = 0 \quad \text{for } z = \pm c/2 \qquad (7.9)$$

The relevant height is $c/2$ as the origin of the coordinates is assumed to be in the centre of the stack.

The general expression for $n(z) = 0$ is given by

$$n(z) = A \cos Bz + C \sin z \qquad (7.10)$$

where A, B and C are constants, with

$$B = \frac{(k-1)^{1/2}}{M} \qquad (7.11)$$

Here M^2 stands for *migration area* given by

$$M^2 = L^2 + l^2 \tag{7.12}$$

where L is the diffusion length and l is the slowing down length described under Sec. 7.4.2. Since the neutron distribution is assumed to be symmetric about the origin, the constant C must vanish, which leaves behind only

$$n(z) = A \cos Bz$$

In order that this quantity may reduce to zero (Eq. 7.9)

$$B\,c/2 = \pi/2$$

or

$$c = \pi/B \tag{7.13}$$

Finally substituting the value of B from Eq. 7.11 we have

$$c = \frac{\pi M}{(k_\infty - 1)^{1/2}} \tag{7.14}$$

Eq. 7.14 shows that c can have a real *finite* value only for $k_\infty > 1$. The above is a simplified one-group model treatment and the critical thickness arrived at is for symmetrical neutron distribution, *i.e.* c may be taken as the *critical radius* of a spherical reactor, whereas the critical side of a cubical reactor would be $\sqrt{3}\,c$.[5]

Thus we arrive at the following critical dimensions which permit the functioning of a thermal neutron reactor in terms of the nuclear properties of the reactor

$$\left.\begin{array}{l}\text{(i)} \quad \text{Cubic shape: side } a = b = c = \dfrac{\sqrt{3}\,\pi M}{(k_\infty - 1)^{1/2}} \\[2mm] \text{(ii)} \quad \text{Spherical shape: radius } R_c = c = \dfrac{\pi M}{(k_\infty - 1)^{1/2}}\end{array}\right\} \tag{7.15}$$

From these data the critical volume V_c and hence the critical mass of the uranium needed (density $= 18.95$ g cm^{-3}) are readily calculated. [V_c (cube) $= a^3 = 161$ W and V_c (sphere) $= 4/3\,\pi R_c^3 = 130$ W, where $W = (M^2/k_\infty - 1)^{3/2}$].

There are numerous other technological details in designing a nuclear reactor including shieldings which are beyond the scope of this book.

7.7 Excess Reactivity and Control

More often reactors are worked not only just under steady state conditions for power generation, but as a source of fast and thermal neutrons in high flux for various studies, such as:
(a) Study of the properties of neutrons,
(b) Study of properties of materials subjected to neutron irradiation,
(c) Study of nuclear reactions induced by neutrons,
(d) Neutron activation analysis of materials,

(e) Production of radioisotopes for use in research, medicine, agriculture and industry.

To meet these additional neutron requirements, some *excess reactivity*
should be available. For this the reactors are designed to function
with $k = 1 + \delta$ where δ is the excess reactivity, which is around 0.02.
This necessitates the installation of an *automatic control system* which
consists of boron steel or cadmium rods, which have a very high capture
cross section for thermal neutrons (^{10}B: $\sigma = 3\,836$ b and ^{113}Cd: $\sigma =
19\,910$ b).* These control rods are held in position by an electromagnet
the current to which is controlled through relays actuated by the
ionization current from the reactor. As the latter rises beyond a pre-set
limit, the control rods are made to descend deeper into the reactor
which act automatically reduces the ionization current due to lowered
neutron flux and, if this falls below another pre-set limit, the current to
the electromagnet increases and the control rods are lifted out propor-
tionately. In this way the reactor multiplication factor is maintained
close to unity $\pm \delta$. The role of the less than 1% delayed neutrons
(Sec. 6.8.2) is important in the functioning of the reactor, both in
preventing a rapid build up of the neutron concentration before the
control rods come down and in providing the minimum neutrons
immediately the rods go up.

7.8 The Breeder Reactor

We shall conclude this chapter with a short reference to the *breeder
reactor*. As the name suggests in this type of reactor, more fuel element
is produced than what is consumed during the generation of energy.

Consider uranium enriched with the fissile isotope ^{235}U or ^{239}Pu.
It is possible to control the conditions such that of the 3 neutrons
emitted in each fission, one is used up in propagating fission chains
reacting with ^{235}U, while the rest of the neutrons (two) are used in
resonance capture by ^{238}U resulting in the production of two atoms of
^{239}Pu each of which is fissile and constitutes therefore *new fuel bred* in
the reactor. Thus, *two* fissile atoms of ^{239}Pu are created for one of ^{235}U
consumed. As the process goes on, more and more fuel element is
generated than what is consumed in producing energy and power.
The newly created fuel can in its turn be used to set up further reactors
for power. This is the principle of the *breeder reactor* which is receiving
great attention, specially in view of the limited availability of fissile
materials in nature.

The operation conditions for effecting *breeding* have to be very
carefully chosen, such that there is no loss of neutrons, only one neutron
is thermalized and used with total efficiency in maintaining ^{235}U thermal

*Values for natural boron (20 % ^{10}B) and cadmium (12 % ^{113}Cd) are 755 and 2550 neutron fission chains, while the other first generation fast neutrons are moderated to the right *resonance* energy value, in the region 6–38 eV and made available to ^{238}U for producing two atoms of ^{239}Pu. The first Russian breeder reactor of capacity 120 MW was set up in 1973 at Shevchenko on the shores of the Caspian Sea.

In natural uranium, under normal conditions of reactor functioning, each ^{235}U releasing 2–3 neutrons, succeeds in producing on the average through resonance capture 0.8 atom of ^{239}U, which in its turn generates $(0.8)^2$ Pu atoms, and in this way we shall have a total of five atoms of ^{239}Pu per ^{235}U atom used up due to inherent self-breeding

$$1 + (0.8) + (0.8)^2 + \ldots + (0.8)^n = \frac{1}{1 - 0.8} = 5 \qquad (7.16)$$

This amounts to only 3.6% of the total as the ^{235}U content is only 0.72%, whereas in a *breeder* reactor the multiplication of fissile fuel atoms is 200% of what is consumed.

It is the low value of η (the number of fast neutrons produced per thermal neutron used up), (*e.g.* 2.08 for ^{239}Pu), which makes the functioning of the reactor as a breeder impracticable. However, in a *fast neutron reactor* η for ^{239}Pu is much higher and breeder reactors have been set up with fast neutrons in a mixture of ^{239}Pu and natural uranium. Similarly, a mixture of ^{233}U and natural thorium also can be used in a breeder reactor.

7.9 Nuclear Reactors in India

Listed below are the different nuclear reactors developed in the country, together with their chief characteristics.[8]

TABLE 7.2: Nuclear reactors in India

Reactor	Power/ MW	Fuel	Cladding	Modera- tor	Coolant	Purpose	Year
1	2	3	4	5	6	7	8
Apsara (swimming pool)	1	en–U*	Al	o–w	o–w	research and isotope pro- duction	1956
Cirus	40	n–U*	Al	h–w	h–w* /o–w	,, ,,	1960
Zerlina	0	n–U	Al	h–w	h–w /o–w	research	1961
Purnima (fast reactor)	0	n–U/Pu oxide	stainless steel		o–w	research	1972
Tarapur (boiling water)	2 × 200	en–U	Zr–Al	o–w	o–w	power gene- ration	1969

(*Contd.*)

(*Contd*).

1	2	3	4	5	6	7	8
Kota	2 × 220	n–U	Zr–Al	h–w	h–w/ o–w	power generation	1973
Kalpakkam	2 × 235	n–U	Zr–Al	h–w	h–w/ o–w	,, ,,	1980 s
Narora	2 × 235	n–U	Zr–Al	h–w	h–w/ o–w	,, ,,	1980 s
Fast test breeder	40	mixed oxides of U, Th, Pu	stainless steel		liquid sodium	research	1980 s
R–5	100	n–U	Al	h–w	h–w/ o–w	research	1980 s

*o–w: ordinary water; h–w: heavy water; en: enriched; n: natural.

The heavy water used as the moderator also serves as a primary coolant, the secondary cooling being done by ordinary water.

7.10 Reprocessing of Spent Fuels: Recovery of Uranium and Plutonium

Obviously it is necessary to reprocess the spent fuels to recover therefrom the fuel elements uranium and plutonium for their further applications.

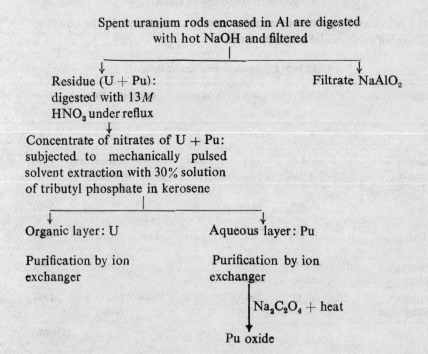

Spent uranium rods encased in Al are digested
with hot NaOH and filtered

Residue (U + Pu):
digested with 13M
HNO$_3$ under reflux

Filtrate NaAlO$_2$

Concentrate of nitrates of U + Pu:
subjected to mechanically pulsed
solvent extraction with 30% solution
of tributyl phosphate in kerosene

Organic layer: U

Aqueous layer: Pu

Purification by ion
exchanger

Purification by ion
exchanger

Na$_2$C$_2$O$_4$ + heat

Pu oxide

Though the chemistry involved in the separation of uranium and plutonium from each other and from the cladding material, usually aluminium,
or zircaloy (Zr + Al alloy) is simple, because of the intense radioactivity
and their highly toxic nature, very sophisticated techniques employing
electromechanical devices, all remotely controlled, have to be used, all the
operations being behind thick shielding walls, with lead glass windows
for viewing. The broad stages involved in the reprocessing of the spent
fuels are shown above.[9-11]

References

(Where marked*, see Bibliography)

1. F. Joliot and I. Joliot-Curie, "Nobel Lectures-Chemistry, 1935" Nobel Foundation, Elsevier Publishing Co., 1966.
2. W.E. Burcham*
3. H.D. Smyth, 'Atomic Energy for Military Purposes' Princeton University Press,
   Princeton, N.J., 1945, *Revs. Mod. Phys.*, 1945, 17, 351.
4. *Brookhaven National Laboratory Report*, 325, 2nd Ed., 1958.
5. I. Kaplan*
5.(a) J. D. Cockroft, "*Instrumentation of Nuclear Reactors*", *Nature*, 1973, 171,
   411.
6. S.E. Liverhant*
7. A. Salmon*
8. *India's Atomic Energy Programme* (Minestry of Information & Publicity,
   New Delhi).
9. F.S. Martin and G.L. Miles*
10. J.J. Flagg*
11. C.B. Amphlett*

Problems

7.1 Assuming no loss of thermal or fast neutrons occurs, calculate the reproduction
factor for a reactor for which the fast fission factor is 1.03, the number of fast
neutrons generated per thermal neutron used up is 1.32, the resonance escape
factor is 0.89 and the thermal utilization factor is 0.87.   [1.053]

7.2 Calculate the approximate critical dimensions of a ^{239}Pu reactor to function
in a steady state ($k = 1.04$) given the migration area for this reactor is 0.032
m^2, in the case where the reactor is (a) of a cubical shape and (b) spherical
shape.

   [(a) side = 4.87 m;   (b) radius = 2.81 m]

7.3 Determine the design parameter (F = ratio of moderator to fuel atoms) for
a ^{235}U + thermal neutron reactor to function at $k = 1$, using (a) ordinary
water (b) heavy water and (c) graphite as the moderator given the neutron
absorption cross sections for ^{235}U, H_2O, D_2O and C to be 687; 0.66; 0.0093;
and 0.0045 b respectively. [*Hint*: use the relation

$$F = \frac{\eta - 1}{1} \cdot \frac{\sigma_U}{\sigma_M} \text{ with } \eta = 2.07).$$

   [(a) 1.6×10^5; (b) 2.2×10^3; (c) 1.6×10^6]

Chapter 8

Applications of Radioactivity

8.1 Probing by Isotopes

If we could know the precise mechanism of a chemical, physical or biochemical reaction, how exactly a drug functions in the human system, how the plants draw the nutrients from the soil, where are micro defects in large castings of machine bodies located, and when does critical wear-out occur in their moving parts, *etc.* we would be able to utilize more efficiently the materials available and obtain the optimum output from them. However, as it is impossible to know what goes on from moment to moment in the submicro-world of atoms and molecules, we have to depend on our best guesses based on indirect gross observations and empirical deductions. Some of these could be far away from the reality and can be even wrong sometimes. With the discovery of artificial radio-activity by Frédéric and Irène Joliot-Curie in 1934 and the present-day availability of radioisotopes of most of the chemical elements, accompanied by the high degree of perfection of instrumentation which helps the detection of trace amounts of the order of 100 Bq of radioactivity, ($\sim 10^{-9}$ Ci)*, a new and powerful tool is made available to probe into the problems of the type referred to in the beginning.

Isotopes of the same element are practically indistinguishable from one another. If to a substance participating in a reaction a very small amount of a radioisotope of the element in the same chemical form as the substance is added, the two isotopic molecules function identically, participating in every stage of the reaction in exactly the same way and in proportion to their initial amounts in the labelled reactant. The only difference which the radioisotope makes is in the emission of signals which can be measured with a great precision. Thus, one can monitor the movements of the reactant atom along the different intermediate stages to the end-product. A deeper insight into complex reactions which otherwise would have been missed, has thus become possible by the use of *radioisotopes as tracers.*

*1 Bq $= 2.7 \times 10^{-11}$ Ci.

Innumerable applications of radioisotopes in research, industry, medicine and agriculture have been developed and these are ever on the increase as borne out by the annual statistics of production and sale of isotopes in different countries. We shall present here only some selected applications in each area to give an idea of the immense scope of the subject.

8.1.1 THE MORE WIDELY USED RADIOISOTOPES

While over 200 different radioisotopes are being prepared and used in innumerable types of investigations, we list in Table 8.1 about 50 of the more widely used ones, the more convenient modes of their preparation, their half-lives and the nature and energy of the particles and photons they emit. The symbols in the column of half-life, *viz.* y, d, m and s stand for years, days, minutes and seconds respectively. The other symbols in the column on the facility are:

A : Accelerator product, *i.e.* the isotope is obtained by bombarding the appropriate target with a beam of particles accelerated to high energy as from a cyclotron, or any other type of accelerator.

F : Fission product, *i.e.* the isotope is present amongst the products of nuclear fission of (generally) uranium in a reactor.

N : Naturally occurring isotope, and/or is being formed in nature by neutrons of cosmic origin.

(n, γ): A product of (n, γ) reaction on a target of the stable isotope of the element of one mass number less.

R : Nuclear reactor product, *i.e.* employing the high neutron flux of the reactor.

The β emission is to be understood as always β^- except where shown as β^+. Also in the case of β^+ there will be two γ photons of energy 0.51 MeV (the annihilation photons). X indicates X-radiation.

TABLE 8.1:   Characteristics of some of the more commonly used radioisotopes

Radio-isotope	Facility	Mode of formation	Half-life[1]	Principal radiation energy /MeV		Usual chemical form
				β	γ	
1	2	3	4	5	6	7
^{3}H	N	^{14}N$(n, t)^{12}$C	12.33 y	0.018		various
	R	^{6}Li$(n, \alpha)^3$H,				
^{14}C	N	^{14}N$(n, p)^{14}$C	5730 y	0.155		various
	R					
^{22}Na	A	^{24}Mg$(d, \alpha)^{22}$Na	2.6 y	β^+0.54–1.83	0.51	
^{24}Na	R	(n, γ)	15.02 h	1.39	1.38–2.76	NaCl aq.
^{31}Si	R	(n, γ)	2.62 h	1.47		
^{32}P	R	(n, γ)	14.28 d	1.71		H_3PO_4 in
		^{32}S$(n, p)^{32}$P				HCl soln.
^{35}S	R	(n, γ)	87.4 d	0.167		H_2SO_4 aq
		^{35}Cl$(n, p)^{35}$S				

(Contd)

(*Contd.*)

1	2	3	4	5	6	7
^{36}Cl	R	(n, γ)	3.0×10^5 y	0.714		HCl aq.
^{38}Cl	R	(n, γ)	37.3 m	4.9	2.17	
^{40}K	N	0.012%	1.28×10^9 y	1.3		
^{42}K	R	(n, γ)	12.36 h	3.5	1.53	KCl aq.
^{45}Ca	R	(n, γ)	165 d	0.25		CaCl$_2$ in HCl
^{46}Sc	R	(n, γ)	83.8 d	0.36	0 89 −1.12	ScCl$_3$ in HCl
^{49}V	A	^{48}Ti$(d, n)^{49}$V	330 d		X	
^{51}Cr	R	(n, γ)	27.7 d		X 0.005	CrCl$_3$ in HCl
^{56}Mn	R	(n, γ)	2.58 h	2.9	0.85 X 0.0059	
^{55}Fe	A R	^{55}Mn$(p\ n)^{55}$Fe (n, γ)	2.7 y			FeCl$_3$ in HCl
^{59}Fe	R	(n, γ)	44.6 d	0.46	1.1	FeCl$_3$ in HCl
^{58}Co	R	^{58}Ni$(n, p)^{58}$Co	70.8 d	β^+0.49	0.51	CoCl$_2$ in HCl
^{60}Co	R	(n, γ)	5.27 y	0.366	1.17, 1.33	metal or CoCl$_2$ in HCl
^{63}Ni	R	(n, γ)	100 y	0.067		NiCl$_2$ in HCl
^{64}Cu	R	(n, γ)	12.7 h	β^+0.66	0.51, 1.34 X 0.0075	CuSO$_4$ aq.
^{65}Zn	R	(n, γ)	244.1 d	β^+0.325	0.51, 1 11 X 0.008	ZnCl$_2$ aq.
	A	^{65}Cu$(p, n)^{65}$Zn				
^{76}As	R	(n, γ)	26.3 h	2.97	0.55	HAsO$_2$ in HCl
^{75}Se	R	(n, γ)	118.5 d		0.024– 0 402 X 0.0105	Na$_2$SeO$_4$ in Na$_2$SO$_4$ aq.
^{80m}Br	R	(n, γ)	4.42 h		0.04	NaBr aq.
^{80}Br		from ^{80m}Br	17.6 m			
^{82}Br	R	(n, γ)	35.34 h	0.44	0.78	
^{85}Kr	F		10.7 y	0.67	0.52	

1	2	3	4	5	6	7
^{86}Rb	R	(n, γ)	18.8 d	1.77	1.08	RbCl in HCl
^{89}Sr	R	(n, γ)	50.5 d	1.46	0.39	Sr(NO$_3$)$_2$ in HNO$_3$
^{90}Sr	F		28.8 y	0.54		Sr(NO$_3$)$_3$ in HNO$_3$
^{90}Y	F	also from ^{90}Sr	64.1 h	2.26		YCl$_3$ aq.
^{99}Mo	R,F	(n, γ)	66 h	1.23	0.14 impurity	(NH$_4$)$_2$MoO$_4$ in NH$_4$OH
^{108}Ag	R	(n, γ)	2.4 m	1.7		
^{111}Ag	R	^{110}Pd $(n, \gamma\beta^-)^{111}$Ag	7.45 h	1.05	0.34	AgNO$_3$ in HNO$_3$
^{115m}Cd	R	(n, γ)	44.8 d	1.61	0.94	Cd(NO$_3$)$_2$ in HNO$_3$
^{116}In	R	(n, γ)	54.1 m	1.0	1.27	
^{113}Sn	R	(n, γ)	115.1 d		0.26, 0.39	SnCl$_2$ in HCl
^{124}Sb	R	(n, γ)	60.3 d	0.61	0.60	SbCl$_3$ + SbOCl in HCl
^{125}I	A	^{124}Te$(d, n)^{125}$I	60.14 d		0.035	
^{128}I	R	(n, γ)	24.99 m	2.12	0.45	
^{131}I	F		8.04 d	0.61	0.36	NaI in Na$_2$SO$_3$ sol.
^{133m}Xe	F		2.19 d		0.23	
^{131}Cs	F		9.688 d		X 0.36	
^{137}Cs	F		30.17 y	0.52	0.662 from ^{137}Ba	CsCl in HCl
^{131}Ba	R	(n, γ)	12.0 d		0.5 X 0.031	BaCl$_2$ in HCl
^{140}Ba	F		12.79 d	1.02	0.03–0.54	BaCl$_2$ in HCl
^{144}Ce	F		284 d	0.31	0.134	CeCl$_3$ in HCl
^{147}Pm	F		2.62 y	0.223		
^{170}Tm	R	(n, γ)	128.6 d	1.0	0.084	
^{192}Ir	R	(n, γ)	74.2 d	0.7	0.316	
^{198}Au	R	(n, γ)	2.696 d	1.0	0.41	HAuCl$_4$ aq.
^{203}Hg	R	(n, γ)	46.8 d	0.21	0.279 X 0.011–0.073	Hg(NO$_3$)$_2$ in HNO$_3$
^{204}Tl	R	(n, γ)	3.77 y	0.77		Tl$_2$SO$_4$ aq.
^{210}Pb (Ra–D)	N		22.3 y	0.017	0.047 X 0.01	

8.1.2 PURITY AND STRENGTH OF RADIOISOTOPES

The methods of preparation listed in Table 8.1 are not the only ones possible, but are the ones more frequently and conveniently used. It should further be noted that the radioisotopes formed are not always *radiochemically pure*, i.e. they are not likely to be free from the presence of one or more other radioisotopes formed at the same time due to impurities in the target substance and/or due to alternative nuclear reactions possible with the same substance. This is specially so in the case of products of fission origin. Sometimes it is possible to obtain certain radioisotopes in a *carrier-free state* which only means that they are free from the presence of traces of *stable* isotope(s) of the same element. However, it does not follow that a carrier-free radioisotope is necessarily radiochemically pure, or is free from other chemical impurities. It is almost impossible to avoid the presence of some other salts, acids or bases used in the chemical process of preparation. For instance sodium sulphite is present at a pH of 8 in samples of carrier-free ^{131}I in the form of NaI. Similarly carrier-free ^{32}P is in the form of H_3PO_4 in dilute hydrochloric acid. Finally, every radioactive preparation is valued in terms of its *specific* activity, i.e. the strength of the preparation in units of milli or microcuries per mg or millilitre of the preparation. The specific activity is indicated by the supplier as on the date of despatch, and/or is determined by the user. This information is necessary for correct dilution of the sample for labelling preparations in the desired way.

8.2 Typical Reactions Involved in the Preparation of Radioisotopes

We shall describe now some typical reactions involved in the formation of a few selected radioisotopes and some simple methods of their preparation.

(a) *Tritium or hydrogen-3*   ($\tau = 12.33$ y; decay: $^3H \rightarrow {}^3He + \beta^- + \bar{\nu}$)
Significant amounts of ^3H are formed continually in nature by the interaction of fast neutrons of cosmic origin (flux $2.6n$ cm^{-2} s^{-1}) with the nitrogen of the atmosphere

$$^{14}N + n \rightarrow {}^3H + {}^{12}C$$

In due course the T (^3H) forms HT and gets oxidized into tritiated water HTO and through rains reaches the seas, rivers, lakes and such other large surfaces of water open to the atmosphere. The equilibrium ratio of T/H in such *open* waters is computed to be $\sim 10^{-18}$. Once a finite amount of the water, large or small, is withdrawn, or its contact with the atmosphere is cut off, the T content of it decreases with its characteristic half-life. The actual T/H ratio in a *given* sample of water can be used to determine its 'age', *i.e.* the period it had been drawn out from its natural source (Sec. 8.6.4).

For large-scale needs of ^3H, for research and nuclear fusion reactions, it is obtained by the reaction $^6Li(n, \alpha)^3H$. A lithium-magnesium alloy is irradiated and the tritium is recovered by heating the alloy subsequently.

(ii)   *Carbon-14* (τ: 5730 y; decay: $^{14}C \rightarrow {}^{14}N + \beta^- + \bar{\nu}$)

Large amounts of ^{14}C are formed continually in nature by an alternative interaction of fast neutrons of cosmic origin with the atmospheric nitrogen.

$$^{14}N + n \rightarrow {}^{14}C + p$$

In due course the ^{14}C changes into $^{14}CO_2$ which together with the ordinary CO_2 of the atmosphere is taken up by living plants to provide the food for their growth by a photosynthetic process. The $^{14}C/^{12}C$ ratio in any part of a *living* plant or animal is the equilibrium mass ratio corresponding to 1.6×10^{-12}, yielding 16.1 ± 0.3 disintegrations min^{-1} g^{-1} (total C)*.[2] However, once the plant or animal is dead, the ^{14}C in it decays with its characteristic half-life. Thus the actual $^{14}C/^{12}C$ ratio in a sample of plant or animal origin can be used to determine its 'age', *i.e.* the period it had been dead (Sec. 8.6.4). For large-scale needs of ^{14}C used in the preparation of different organic substances labelled with this isotope, a substance rich in nitrogen, but containing no other element which interacts with neutrons, as beryllium or aluminium nitride, is irradiated by high flux slow neutrons in a reactor when the reaction $^{14}N(n, p)^{14}C$ takes place, the cross section being $1.81 b$. The first resonance for the reaction is with neutrons of energy 495 keV. The irradiated sample is dissolved in 65% sulphuric acid and hydrogen peroxide added when the radiocarbon is released as $^{14}CO_2$ The gas is passed over copper oxide heated to 750°C, when CO, CH_4 and HCN, produced in less amounts, are all oxidized to CO_2. Finally the $^{14}CO_2$ is absorbed in sodium hydroxide and precipitated as $Ba^{14}CO_3$. The desired organic substance labelled with ^{14}C can be synthesized by releasing the $^{14}CO_2$ from the barium carbonate.[3]

---

*Since the number N of ^{14}C atoms in 1.6×10^{-12} g $= 6.883 \times 10^{10}$ and λ the decay constant of ^{14}C

$$= \frac{0.693 \times 60}{5.730 \times 3.16 \times 10^{10}} \text{ min}^{-1} = 2.296 \times 10^{-10} \text{ min}^{-1}$$

the ^{14}C activity $= (N\lambda) = 6.883 \times 10^{10} \times 2.296 \times 10^{-10}$

$$= 15.80 \text{ dis. min}^{-1} \text{ g}^{-1}$$

The currently accepted figure $= 16.1 \pm 0.3$ dis. min^{-1} g^{-1}.

(see also note on p. 262)

(iii) *Sodium-22* ($\tau: 2.6$ y; decay: $^{22}Na \rightarrow {}^{22}Ne + \beta^+ + \nu$)

^{22}Na is a cyclotron or similar accelerator product obtained by bombarding magnesium with 8.5 MeV deuterons by the reaction $^{24}Mg(d, \alpha)^{22}Na$. The irradiated magnesium is dissolved in dilute hydrochloric acid and the solution electrolysed at 12 V between a platinum anode and revolving mercury cathode as shown in Fig. 8.1. The ^{22}Na goes to the mercury and the amalgam formed can be subsequently decomposed to yield $^{22}NaOH$ solution.[4]

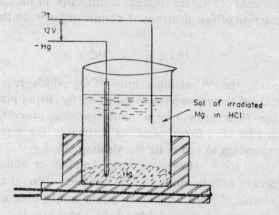

Fig. 8.1 Separation of ^{22}Na by the electrolysis of a solution in hydrochloric acid of magnesium subjected to (d, α) reaction.

(iv) *Phosphorus-32* ($\tau = 14.28$ d, decay: $^{32}P \rightarrow {}^{32}S + \beta^- + \bar{\nu}$)

Two modes are in vogue for obtaining radiophosphorus.

(i) By (n, γ) reaction on ordinary red phosphorus (^{31}P isotopic abundance; 100%). This is less expensive but the product would be of a low specific activity. The radiophosphorus is converted into any of the several reactive species as P_2O_5, PCl_3, PCl_5, $POCl_3$ and $PSCl_3$.

(ii) By (n, p) reaction on ^{32}S (isotopic abundance: 95%). The product though carrier-free is mixed with ^{33}P ($\tau = 25$ d) formed from ^{33}S (isotopic abundance: 0.75%). Where high specific activity is needed this procedure is adopted. The unreacted sulphur is sublimed off at 600°C and the residue extracted in an acidic medium. On the addition of hydrogen peroxide the ^{32}P is oxidized to the orthophosphate form.[3]

(v) *Sulphur-35* ($\tau: 87.5$ d; decay: $^{35}S \rightarrow {}^{35}Cl + \beta^- + \bar{\nu}$)

^{35}S is formed when sodium chloride is irradiated by high flux neutrons, as in a reactor, when the reaction $^{35}Cl(n, p)^{35}S$ occurs. Following other reactions also occur at the same time resulting in the formation of corresponding radioisotopes:

$^{23}Na(n, \gamma)^{24}Na$; $^{37}Cl(n, \gamma)^{38}Cl$; $^{35}Cl(n, \alpha)^{32}P$ and to a negligible extent $^{35}Cl(n, \gamma)^{36}Cl$.

The ^{35}S is readily extracted in the form of carrier-free $H_2^{35}SO_4$ as follows. The irradiated sodium chloride is allowed to stand for about a week when the ^{24}Na$(\tau: 15\ h)$ and ^{38}Cl$(\tau: 37\ min)$ decay completely (the yields of the long-lived ^{36}Cl and ^{32}P being negligible). It is then heated in a platinum boat in a slow current of pure dry hydrogen and the exit gas is made to bubble through some bromine water (Fig. 8.2) when the following reactions occur.[5,6]

$$^{35}S \xrightarrow{\ H_2\ } H_2^{35}S \xrightarrow{\ Br_2\ } H_2^{35}SO_4$$

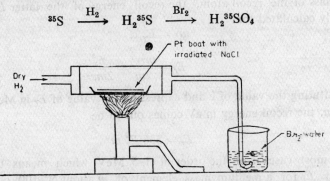

Fig. 8.2   Separation of ^{35}S from neutron irradiated sodium chloride.

Alternatively, the $H_2^{35}S$ is fixed as thiourea by making it react with cynamide

$$H_2^{35}S + NH_2CN \rightarrow C^{35}S(NH_2)_2$$

(vi) *Iodine-131* $(\tau = 8.04\ d$, decay: $^{131}I \rightarrow {}^{131}Xe + \beta^- + \bar{\nu})$

Radioiodine (^{131}I) is generally obtained either from fission products or by the (n, γ) reaction on ^{130}Te (isotopic abundance: 34.5%). The ^{131}Te formed decays with a half-life of 25 min into ^{131}I. Being short-lived, radioiodine is generally prepared only when needed. It is marketed as a carrier-free solution of NaI in sodium sulphite at a pH of 8. The radioiodine is easily converted into iodine monochloride by treatment with potassium iodate and hydrochloric acid.

$$2\ ^{131}I^- + IO_3^- + 6\ HCl \rightarrow 3\ ^{131}ICl + 3\ Cl^- + 3\ H_2O$$

A carbon tetrachloride extract of ^{131}ICl is a convenient labelled iodinating agent.

8.3   The Szilard-Chalmers' Reaction

The most common nuclear reaction occurring with most elements is of the (n, γ) type. When the nucleus of a target atom, like ^{127}I, captures a slow neutron it forms an isotope of one mass number higher

$$^{127}I + n \rightarrow {}^{128}I^*$$

The product nucleus is in an excited state, indicated by the asterisk. In most cases the excited nucleus returns to the ground state, almost immediately, the excitation energy being emitted as one or more γ photons.

$$^{128}I^* \rightarrow {}^{128}I + \gamma$$

Conservation of momentum requires that the momentum (mv) of the recoil atom ^{128}I be equal but opposite in sign to the momentum of the photon released which is E_γ/c, where E_γ is the energy of the photon and c the velocity of light. Knowing the energy of the photon released and the mass of the recoil atom, the recoil energy of the latter E_r can be readily calculated for

$$mv = E_\gamma/c$$

and

$$E_r = \frac{m^2 v^2}{2m} = \frac{E_\gamma^2}{2mc^2} \tag{8.1}$$

Substituting the value of c and expressing the value of E_γ in MeV and of m in u, the recoil energy in eV comes out to be

$$E_r = 536\, E_\gamma^2/m \tag{8.2}$$

E_γ in most cases is of the order of 1–5 MeV which means the recoil energy E_r for a medium mass element of m about 50–100, comes out to be 5–250 eV. This value, it may be noted, is generally much greater than the chemical bond energy holding the atom in the molecule, which rarely exceeds 5 eV. Hence the bond generally breaks. This is the basis of the Szilard-Chalmers' reaction, described below.

Table 8.2 gives the maximum energies of γ photons accompanying (n, γ) reactions with halogen atoms together with the resulting recoil energies, and the carbon-halogen bond energies.[7]

TABLE 8.2:   Data relevant to some Szilard-Chalmers' reactions

Halogen atom	$E_{\gamma\ max}$/MeV	$E_{recoil\ max}$/eV	C-halogen bond energy/eV[7a]
Cl	6.2	543	3.4
Br	5.1	174	2.16
I	4.8	96	2.26

It should however be remembered that the actual recoil energy is less than the maximum value calculated by Eq. 8.2 if more than one photon is emitted during the (n, γ) reaction. Following the bond rupture, the radioactive atom finds itself in a 'free' state which makes it extremely reactive leading to a variety of interactions between it and other species present in the system, as other free radicals, broken molecular fragments, impurity atoms, and the solvent, the chemistry of the recoil atom being often complex.

Szilard and Chalmers discovered in 1934 a new and simple way of separating the radioisotope product of (n, γ) reactions.[7] They found that when ethyl iodide is irradiated by slow neutrons in the presence of water, most of the recoil ^{128}I atoms following bond rupture readily pass into the aqueous phase as ^{128}I$^-$ ions, thus separating the radioisotope ^{128}I from the bulk of the inactive isotope ^{127}I which remains in the organic phase bound to the carbon atoms in the parent molecule. The inorganic yield can be greatly increased if some I$^-$ ions in the form of KI are initially added as a carrier. Thus a large fraction of the radioisotope formed is separated into the water layer in a state of high specific activity. If no KI is added the resulting product is carrier-free. This reaction is commonly referred to as the *Szilard-Chalmers' reaction*. Substances best suited for this mode of radioisotope separation are organic chloro-, bromo- and iodo-compounds, stable complex ions and some oxyanions and such organo-metallic compounds as $As(C_6H_5)_3$, $Bi(C_6H_5)_3$, $Pb(C_6H_5)_4$, $Sn(C_6H_5)_4$, ferrocyanides and cobalt and platinum amino complexes.

8.4 Use of Charged Plates in the Collection of Radioisotopes

Because of the large net charge on radioactive atoms at the *moment of their formation* they can be separated to some extent from their parent atoms in an external electric field. This technique had been used by pioneer workers from the earliest days of the study of natural radioactivity for isolating certain radioelements. Irradiating the vapour of methyl iodide contained in a wire-in-cylinder type of vessel with neutrons, Fermi, Rassetti and coworkers,[8] Paneth[9] and several others[10–12] later showed that ^{128}I can be collected in appreciable amounts on the wire if it is given a negative potential with respect to the outer cylinder. It is so

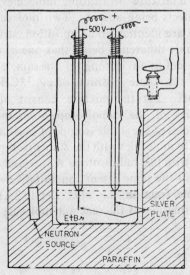

Fig. 8.3 Collection on charged plates of radiobromine (or iodine) formed in (n, γ) reaction on organic halogen compounds.

because the ^{128}I acquires a large positive charge during the internal conversion accompanying its formation (Sec. 4.8.4). Some studies on the use of charged plates for collecting the radioisotope products of (n, γ) reaction in the liquid state are described here. Two silver plates immersed in an organic halogen compound, such as ethyl bromide, iodobenzene, *etc.* are connected to a dc potential of 100–500 V while the system is being irradiated by thermal neutrons from an $^{124}Sb + Be$ neutron source (Fig. 8.3)[12]. In the end the plates are washed with dilute solution of sodium thiosulphate and the radiohalogen recovered in a state of high specific activity. A similar arrangement had been used earlier for recovering ^{32}P formed in carbon disulphide by $^{32}S(n, p)^{32}P$ reaction by Saha[13].

8.5 Radiochemical Principles in the Use of Tracers

The use of stable or radioisotopes as tracers to follow the course of a reaction, physical, chemical, biological or any other, is based on the important assumption that two isotopes of the same element behave in an absolutely identical manner throughout; in other words, that *isotope effects are absent*. Such an assumption is not strictly correct, as shown by the kinetic and thermodynamic isotope effects revealed respectively by the differences in the rates of reaction and in equilibrium constants, due to the difference in the masses of the isotopes. However, such effects are too small to be of significance, except only in the case of very light elements hardly extending up to oxygen. The isotope effects are difficultly noticeable with heavier elements.

Let us look into a mixture of isotopic molecules, participating in a reaction, isotope effects being absent. Two molecules are isotopic with one another if they are identical in composition, structure and in every other respect, the only difference being that one of the atoms of one of the elements is present as an isotope of the same element in one of the molecules and in the same position, *e.g.* $^{12}CH_3^{12}CH_2^{12}COOH$ and $^{12}CH_3^{12}CH_2^{14}COOH$. Let the mixture consist of a very small trace amount of a moles of the radioisotope atom, mass number A and a large excess of b moles of the stable isotope of mass number B (*i.e.* $a \ll b$). Whatever happens to molecules with the stable isotope B also happens to molecules labelled with the radioisotope A, precisely at every stage of the reaction, and to the same extent quantitatively, *i.e.* in strict proportion to the mole fraction, *i.e.* a/b. Let 1, 2..i..t be the different steps in the transformation of the reactant molecule to the final product.

State	1	2	3	...i	...t
Amount of stable isotope molecule	b_1	b_2	b_3	...b_i	...b_t
Amount of radioisotope molecule	a_1	a_2	a_3	...a_i	...a_t

The change in the stable molecule at the ith stage is $\Delta b_i = (b_1 - b_i)$, while the corresponding change in the radioisotope molecule is $\Delta a_i = (a_1 - a_i)$. In the absence of isotope effects,

$$\frac{\Delta a_i}{\Delta b_i} = \frac{a}{b} = \text{constant} \tag{8·3}$$

Often it is extremely difficult to determine the slight change in the amount of the stable isotopic molecules Δb_i at a given stage of the reaction but the corresponding amount of change in the labelled molecules Δa_i can be measured with precision, even up to changes of the order of 10^{-12} to 10^{-16} M. By measuring Δa_i the quantity Δb_i is readily assessed, by Eq. 8.3.

The following points should be taken care of in using radioisotopes as tracers.

(1) The tracer isotopic molecule and the stable one should be in the same chemical form, as sometimes isotopes in molecules of different chemical form may not exchange rapidly.

(2) In case more than one radioisotope is available, the one to be chosen for labelling should have a convenient half-life and the energy of the radiations emitted should be such that it permits easy measurement: e.g. ^{24}Na ($\tau = 15$ h) is recommended for biological experiments, as it would be completely eliminated by decay in about 4 days, while ^{22}Na (τ: 2.6 y) would be preferable for investigations of physico-chemical problems.

(3) The total amount of the radioisotope should be just enough to provide measurable signals. Large excess should be avoided as otherwise the system under study may get chemically damaged by self-irradiation, besides increasing the health hazard to the worker.

8.6 Typical Applications of Radioisotopes as Tracers

We shall now present briefly some of the more important applications of isotopes as research tools. Besides radioisotopes, sometimes the less abundantly occurring stable isotopes also are used for labelling, as ^{2}H and ^{18}O. In such cases the monitoring is done by mass spectrometry. With the ready availability of radioisotopes, innumerable applications are known and the number is on the increase; only some typical examples would be included here to give an idea of the vast scope of the technique. It may be emphasized here that the use of isotopes as labels is the *only* method of understanding some of the problems. The applications selected are grouped under the following heads:

1. Chemical investigations.
2. Physico-chemical applications.
3. Analytical applications.
4. Age determinations.

5. Medical applications.
6. Agricultural applications.
7. Prospecting of natural resources.
8. Industrial applications.

Uses of nuclear radiations and radioisotopes as a source of electricity are considered in subsequent sections.

8.6.1 CHEMICAL INVESTIGATIONS

Some typical applications of isotopes in elucidating (A) Reaction mechanisms, (B) Structure determinations and (C) Isotope exchange reactions are described here.

(A) Reaction Mechanisms

(i) *Esterification:* It could never be shown experimentally whether the water eliminated in an esterification reaction is formed from the OH of the alcohol and H of the acid or it is the other way, corresponding to the upper or the lower bracketing in Eq. 8.4 a

$$RCH_2CO\ O\ H + H\ O\ CH_3 \rightarrow RCH_2COOCH_3 + H_2O \qquad (8.4a)$$

By using $CH_3\ ^{18}OH$. it was found that the ^{18}O goes into the ester showing thereby that it is the alcohol which contributes H and the acid the OH, corresponding to the lower bracketing in Eq. 8.4 a. This demonstration, that the cleavages are C—OH bond in the acid and H—O bond in alcohol, could never have been possible except by the method of isotopic labelling as otherwise all O atoms are alike, as are the H atoms.

(ii) *Hydrolysis:* In the reverse process of hydrolysis of an ester a similar technique of using water enriched in ^{18}O for causing the hydrolysis showed that the ^{18}O is found in the acid, confirming the previous mechanism of bond ruptures. Usually the labelled atom is shown with an asterisk

$$RCH_2CO\ OCH_3 + H^*O - H \rightarrow RCH_2CO^*OH + CH_3OH \qquad (8\ 4b)$$

(iii) *Decomposition of H_2O_2 by PbO_2:* The net reaction here is

$$PbO_2 + H_2O_2 \rightarrow PbO + H_2O + O_2 \qquad (8.5)$$

The earlier idea was that each of the reactants provides an atom of oxygen to yield the molecular oxygen in Eq. 8.5. However, when ^{18}O-labelled H_2O_2 was used, the resulting oxygen had all the ^{18}O, none remaining with the water. This shows conclusively that the molecular oxygen formed comes wholly from the H_2O_2 as shown below

$$O = Pb \doteq O + H \doteq {}^*O - O \doteq H \rightarrow PbO + H_2O + {}^*O_2 \quad (8.5a)$$

The same was also found to be the case in the catalytic decomposition of H_2O_2 by MnO_2, sevaral metals, Br_2, I_2, Fe^{+++} and catalase[14].

(iv) *Oxidation of CO by air in the presence of catalyst MnO_2:* The earlier idea of this reaction was

$$\left.\begin{array}{l} CO + MnO_2 \rightarrow CO_2 + MnO \\ MnO + O \text{ (air)} \rightarrow MnO_2 \end{array}\right\} \qquad (8.6a)$$

Labelling MnO_2 with ^{18}O showed that the resulting CO_2 had none of the enrichment in ^{18}O which remained wholly with the catalyst, suggesting that the oxidation is directly between the reactants, the catalyst remaining undissociated, thus

$$CO + O \text{ (air)} + [Mn^*O_2] \rightarrow CO_2 + [Mn^*O_2] \qquad (8.6b)$$

(v) *Oxidation of fumaric acid by $KMnO_4$:* It is known that a molecule of fumaric acid on oxidation by acidified permanganate yields carbondioxide, water and formic acid as per the reaction

$$\begin{array}{l} COOH \\ | \\ CH \\ \| \qquad\qquad + 5 \quad O \rightarrow 3CO_2 + H_2O + HCOOH \qquad (8.7\,a) \\ CH \\ | \\ COOH \end{array}$$

It cannot, however, be known which of the four C atoms (two carboxylic and two methylinic) end up as CO_2 and which as the formic acid. This was investigated by labelling the end carboxylic carbons with the radioisotope ^{11}C of 20 minutes' period. By this technique Ruben and Allen[15] found that the activity is wholly associated with the CO_2 and none with the formic acid, showing thereby that the acid results from one of the methylinic carbons, the mechanism being:

$$\begin{array}{l} *COOH \qquad\qquad *COOH \qquad\qquad *CO_2 \\ | \qquad\qquad\qquad\quad \cdots|\cdots \qquad\qquad\quad + \\ CH \quad +O \qquad COH \quad +2\,O \qquad COOH \quad +10 \\ \| \quad \longrightarrow \qquad \| \quad \longrightarrow \qquad \cdots|\cdots \quad \longrightarrow \\ CH \qquad\qquad\quad CH \qquad\qquad\quad CHOH \\ | \qquad\qquad\qquad\quad | \qquad\qquad\qquad\quad | \\ *COOH \qquad\qquad *COOH \qquad\qquad *COOH \end{array}$$

$$\begin{array}{l} CO_2 + H_2O \\ CH = O \quad +O \qquad HCOOH \\ + \cdots|\cdots \quad \longrightarrow \qquad + \\ *COOH \qquad\qquad *CO_2 \qquad\qquad (8.7b) \end{array}$$

(vi) *Mechanism of the Friedel-Crafts' reaction:* Anhydrous aluminium chloride is a useful reagent for bringing about a large number of reactions known as the Friedel-Crafts' reactions. Consider the reaction

$$C_6H_6 + ClCOCH_3 \xrightarrow{\quad AlCl_3 \quad} C_6H_5COCH_3 + HCl \qquad (8.8a)$$

Theoretically the following three alternative mechanisms are possible for the role of the catalyst. It was only by using $AlCl_3$ labelled with ^{36}Cl that the true mechanism was revealed.[20] The three mechanisms are:

(a) The reaction occurs directly between the reactants, the catalyst not participating at all. In that case the total activity of $AlCl_3$ should remain with it at the end of the experiment and HCl should be totally inactive. This is not what happens and hence this mechanism is invalid.

(b) The catalyst first reacts with benzene forming

$$C_6H_6 + Al^*Cl_3 \rightarrow C_6H_5Al^*Cl_2 + H^*Cl$$

followed by

$$C_6H_5Al^*Cl_2 + ClCOCH_3 \rightarrow C_6H_5COCH_3 + Al^*Cl_3$$

$$\left.\right\} \quad (8.8b)$$

(An asterisk used as in Al^*Cl_3 means one of the Cl atoms is radioactive, without mentioning which one and without mentioning the specific radioisotope, ^{36}Cl or ^{38}Cl).

If this mechanism were valid the catalyst has lost 1/3 of its total activity to HCl. Hence the ratio of activity on HCl to that on the residual catalyst is 1/2. This does not happen either and hence this mechanism also has to be ruled out.

(c) First the acetyl chloride and benzene dissociate into charged fragments:

(i) $CH_3COCl \rightarrow CH_3CO^+ + Cl^-$

(ii) $C_6H_6 \rightarrow C_6H_2^- + H^+$

followed by

(iii) $Al^*Cl_3 + Cl^- \rightarrow Al^*Cl_4^-$

Finally, the appropriate fragments recombine

(iv) $C_6H_5^- + COCH_3^+ \rightarrow C_6H_5COCH_3$

(v) $Al^*Cl_4^- + H^+ \rightarrow Al^*Cl_3 + H^*Cl$ (8.8c)

On this mechanism the HCl should carry 1/4 of the total activity and the catalyst the rest. Hence the ratio of activity of HCl to that of the residual catalyst should be 1/3. This is precisely what is observed experimentally; hence this third mechanism is accepted as the valid one.

There are a large number of other instances where reaction mechanisms have been unequivocally established by the technique of using radioactive isotopes as tracers.

(vii) *Evidence for the formation of an intermediate precursor:* When a reaction is postulated to proceed in two or more stages as in

$$M \rightarrow N \rightarrow P$$

there may be some uncertainty regarding the formation of the intermediates. Isotopic labelling of the reactant(s) and subsequent analysis of the products would, in general, provide evidence in favour or otherwise of the intermediate. A few examples are cited here.

(a) Cholesterol formation: The hydrocarbon squalene ($C_{30}H_{50}$) is postulated as an intermediate in the transformation of pyruvic acid into cholesterol.

Pyruvic acid	$\rightarrow$	Isoprene	$\rightarrow$	Squalene	$\rightarrow$	Cholesterol
$CH_3COCOOH$		C_5H_8		$C_{30}H_{50}$		$C_{27}H_{45}OH$

To verify this, two groups of rats were experimented upon: one fed with ^{14}C labelled pyruvic acid and unlabelled squalene and the other fed with unlabelled pyruvic acid and labelled squalene. The observation of active squalene in the first group and active cholesterol in the second group demonstrated the formation of squalene as an intermediate precursor to cholesterol formation.[16]   It is to be noted that the formation of the precursor hydrocarbon could not have been detected by known biochemical methods, without recourse to radioactive labelling.

(b) Preparation of purine rhibotide: an anticancer drug: To synthesize purine rhibotide beginning with purine incomplete in the second carbon position, two pathways are open: (i) to complete the purine base first and then to bring in the sugar moiety, (ii) or the reverse.   All earlier attempts following the pathway (i) were futile,   It was only when the sugar phosphate was first incorporated and then the base part completed that the purine rhibotide resulted having anticancer properties.[17]   These studies would not have been possible except by the use of radioisotopes ^{14}C and ^{32}P for labelling.

(c) Electrodeposition of chromium: A solution of chromate Cr(VI) is used as the electrolyte bath in the electroplating of metals by chromium.   The problem is to know if Cr(III) is an intermediate in the electro-reduction process

$$Cr(VI) \rightarrow Cr(III) \rightarrow Cr(0)$$

Labelling by ^{51}Cr has provided the answer.   A mixed electrolyte solution of CrO_4^{--} and Cr^{+++} ions was employed of which either alone was labelled with ^{51}Cr in a given experiment.   This is possible as isotopic exchange between CrO_4^{--} and Cr^{+++} is known to be virtually absent at room temperature.   The study revealed that the resulting metal deposit was active only when CrO_4^{--} was labelled and not when Cr^{+++} was labelled, establishing thereby that Cr (III) is not an intermediate in the electro-reduction of the chromate.

(B) *Structure Determinations*

    When two or more atoms of the same element are present in a molecule, the question of their structural equivalence or otherwise arises which can be elegantly settled by the labelling technique.   This is illustrated here with reference to two substances (1) phosphorus pentachloride and (2) the thiosulphate ion.

(i) *Phosphorus pentachloride*: To know whether all the five chlorine atoms in PCl_5 occupy structurally equivalent positions or not, the substance is synthesized using PCl_3 and Cl_2 labelled with its radioisotope, ^{36}Cl.

$$PCl_3 + {}^*Cl_2 \rightarrow P{}^*Cl_5 \qquad (8.9)$$

Subsequently, the product is hydrolyzed when the following reaction takes place.

$$P{}^*Cl_5 + H_2O \rightarrow POCl_3 + 2H{}^*Cl \qquad (8.10)$$

Experimentally it was found that all the radioactivity remained with the HCl and none with $POCl_3$. It is obvious that two Cl atoms in PCl_5 occupy positions different from the rest of the three Cl atoms. This agrees with the trigonal bipyramidal structure accepted for PCl_5, with three Cl atoms in the equitorial plane and two along the vertices. Further, the equitorial P — Cl distance is known to be shorter than the apical P — Cl distance (discussed later in this Section, p. 244).

(ii) *Thiosulphate ion:* Two structures for the thiosulphate ion can be envisaged

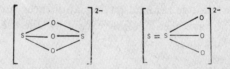

(a) Equivalent positions.   (b) Non-equivalent positions.

The problem is to know which of the structures (*a*) or (*b*) is correct. This has been solved by synthesizing sodium thiosulphate by boiling a solution of sodium sulphite with sulphur labelled with ^{35}S.

$$Na_2SO_3 + {}^*S \rightarrow Na_2{}^*S_2O_3 \qquad (8.11)$$

The product is decomposed subsequently by adding to it a solution of silver nitrate in the presence of nitric acid. An examination of the final products, silver sulphide and sodium sulphate, show the activity is exclusively on the former.

$$Na_2{}^*S_2O_3 + 2AgNO_3 + HNO_3 \rightarrow Ag_2{}^*S + Na_2SO_4 + \text{products} \qquad (8.12)$$

This points to non-equivalent structures for the two sulphur atoms in the thiosulphate ion.

(C) *Isotope Exchange Reactions*
    When two substances, molecules or ions or a precipitate, having an

atom or ion in common, come together in a uniform solution (homogeneous system), or along a surface (heterogeneous system), *a constant exchange* of the common atom or ion between the two substances takes place *all the time, though the system may be in chemical equilibrium* all the time: some examples being:

(a) $I^- + IO_3^-$;   (b) $SO_3^{2-} + S_2O_3^{2-}$;

(c) As (III) + As (V);   (d) EtI + I^- ;

(e) Ba (SO_4) (solid) + (SO_4^{2-}) (solution)

Such exchanges cannot be detected nor can their rates be measured as the system before and after exchange is chemically indistinguishable. However, if one of the species, say I^- in (a) or (d) be labelled with ^{131}I, the exchange rate can be followed by separating the two samples from time to time. Once the isotopic equilibrium is reached, the exchange rates in the two directions will be equal. Such an exchange of atoms of the same kind between two components or phases can never be detected otherwise.

An expression for the rate constant of a homogeneous isotope exchange reaction of the type

$$AX + B^* X \rightleftharpoons A^*X + BX$$

was first derived by H.A.C. McKay[18,19] in the following form. Here *X is a radioisotope of X. Let the concentrations of the different species be represented as follows:

The total species (active + inactive): $[A^*X] + [AX] = a$

$$[B^*X] + [BX] = b$$

The active species: $[A^*X] = x, [B^*X] = y$

The inactive species, it follows, $[AX] = a - x; [BX] = b - y$.

Assuming that there is no isotope effect, the rate of exchange in the forward direction will be proportional to the fraction B^*X/b and AX/a. Similarly, the rate of the exchange in the reverse direction will be proportional to the fractions A^*X/a and BX/b, the net rate of the exchange being given by

$$\frac{dx}{dt} = -\frac{dy}{dt} = R\frac{y}{b}\frac{(a-x)}{a} - R\frac{x}{a}\frac{(b-y)}{b}$$

$$= \frac{R}{ab}(ay - bx) \qquad (8.13)$$

where R is the rate of gross exchange.

The conservation of the total active species demands

$$y - y_\infty = x_\infty - x \qquad (8.14)$$

and

$$x_\infty / y_\infty = a/b \qquad (8.15)$$

where x_∞ and y_∞ represent the final amounts of active species after equilibrium is reached.

Substituting for y and x in the right hand side of Eq. 8.13 by their values given by Eq. 8.14, $viz.$ $y = (x_\infty - x + y_\infty)$ and $x = (x_\infty - y + y_\infty)$, and noting that $ay_\infty = bx_\infty$ (from Eq. 8.15) one arrives at

$$\frac{dx}{dt} = \frac{R}{ab}(a + b)(x_\infty - x) \qquad (8.16)$$

Integration of Eq. 8.16 leads to

$$\frac{(a + b)}{ab} Rt = -\ln \frac{x_\infty - x}{x_\infty} = -\ln(1 - F) \qquad (8.17)$$

where F is the fraction exchanged in time t. A plot of $\ln(1 - F)$ vs t gives a straight line passing through the origin with a slope of $-\dfrac{(a + b)}{ab} R$.

Eq. 8.17 shows that the over-all exchange follows first order kinetics, irrespective of the actual mechanism of the isotopic exchange. One feature of these studies is that the *reaction rate is determined under conditions of equilibrium*, unlike in the usual kinetic studies where the rates are necessarily measured under conditions far removed from equilibrium. A very large number of isotope exchange studies have been made and the rates are found to vary over very wide limits, from immeasurably slow ones to instantaneously fast ones.[20]

As mentioned earlier, the linear plot of $\ln(1-F)$ versus time, generally passes through the origin, in accord with Eq. 8 17. However, it is known to intercept the ordinate above the zero, in some cases. This indicates that the exchange is either catalysed or that it follows two mechanisms, one of which is very fast. An example of this is the exchange between PCl_5 and Cl_2 dissolved in carbon tetrachloride, studied by Moureux, Magat and Vetroff.[21] The three planar chlorine atoms in the trigonal bipyramid of PCl_5 exchange with the dissolved chlorine almost instantaneously, while the two chlorine atoms at the vertices exchange slowly. This is revealed in the log $(1-F)$ vs t plot by the straight line intercepting the ordinate.

Sometimes, the curve is known to meet the Y-axis below the zero which indicates the existence of a period of induction, preceeding the start of the exchange. An example of this is the radiation induced exchange between the bromide and bromate ions in solution studied by Arnikar et al.[22] It is well-known that this halide-halate exchange is immeasurably slow even up to 200°C.[23] It was, however, found that on exposure of aqueous solutions of $^{82}Br^-$ (0.2—1 mM) and BrO_3^-

(0.5-1.5 M) to γ-radiation from a ^{60}Co source, at dose rates of 20–80 rads/s, the exchange proceeds nearly to completion in times of the order of 50 to 100 min, at room temperature. There is in every case, a clear period of induction, varying from 6 to 36 min. The following rate expression was obtained,

$$R = k [BrO_3^-] D$$

where D is the *dose rate*. This shows the independence of the exchange rate on the bromide ion concentration. The mechanism of exchange proposed envisages the formation of a complex between the Br$^-$ and the BrO$_2^-$, the latter being a product of radiolysis

$$BrO_2^- + {}^{82}Br^- \rightleftharpoons [BrO_2 {}^{82}Br]^{2-} \rightleftharpoons Br^- + {}^{82}BrO_2^-$$

The ^{82}BrO$_2^-$ readily gets oxidized to ^{82}BrO$_3^-$ by interaction with the ·OH, another product of radiolysis:

$$^{82}BrO_2^- + \cdot OH \rightarrow {}^{82}BrO_3^- + H \text{ (dimerizes)}.$$

The formation of BrO$_2^-$ and its accumulation in sufficient concentration explain the induction period observed. Some other isotope exchange reactions of interest studied recently by us are:

$$I^- - IO_3^- {}^{24}; Sb(V) - Sb(III)^{25}; \text{ and As}(V) - As(III)^{26}.$$

8.6.2 Physico-Chemical Research

The application of radioisotopes to some physico-chemical problems as the determination of (A) the solubility of a sparingly soluble substance, (B) the surface area of a powder or precipitate, and (C) rates of diffusion, including self-diffusion and surface migration, are described here.

(A) *The Solubility of a Sparingly Soluble Substance*

The principle of solubility determination by the tracer technique consists in comparing the activity of an aliquot of a saturated solution of the labelled substance with that of a known amount of the labelled substance. We illustrate this with reference to lead iodide.[27]

A stock solution of potassium iodide labelled with ^{131}I is diluted such that it gives about 10 000 to 50 000 counts ml^{-1} min^{-1}. To this is added an excess of lead acetate solution. When the Pb*I$_2$ settles down to the bottom, the same is centrifuged to remove the decantate. Distilled water is added to the precipitate and recentrifuged. This operation is repeated two or three times to ensure the complete removal of all excess KI. Finally, the precipitate is dried under an infra-red lamp, and the specific activity of the Pb^{131}I sample is determined ($=s_1$ counts mg^{-1} min^{-1}).

Next a finite amount of the precipitate is shaken with distilled water at a temperature of about 50°C and then cooled to the temperature at which the solubility is to be determined. 0.1 ml of the saturated solution is removed by centrifugation to a cupped planchette and the contents carefully dried under an infra-red lamp. When dry it is covered with a film of collodion and the activity measured ($=s_2$ counts min^{-1}).

The solubility of $PbI_2 = s_2/s_1 \times 10^4$ mg PbI_2 per litre or $s_2/s_1 \times 10/M$ moles of PbI_2 per litre, where M is the formula weight of PbI_2.

In the same way, if the solubilities S_1 and S_2 be determined at two temperatures T_1 and T_2, one obtains the enthalpy of solution, ΔH, from the relation

$$\log \frac{S_2}{S_1} = \frac{\Delta H}{2.303 \, R} \left(\frac{1}{T_1} - \frac{1}{T_2} \right) \qquad (8.18)$$

where R is the gas constant.

Other examples would be the determination of the solubilities of AgI labelled with ^{131}I, of $BaSO_4$ labelled with ^{35}S, $MgNH_4PO_4.6H_2O$ labelled with ^{32}P, etc.

(B) Surface Area of a Powder or Precipitate

Information regarding the surface area of a powder or a precipitate is of great importance in surface chemistry, in the study of the processes of adsorption and catalysis. Isotopic labelling provides a convenient method for computing surface area of powders. This is based on the principle that when a precipitate is in contact with its saturated solution, there is a rapid exchange of ions between the surface of the solid phase and the solutions. The extent of exchange depends on the surface area of the powder and this is readily measured if the solution is initially labelled with a radioactive isotope. On attainment of equilibrium, we have

$$\frac{\text{Total active atoms on surface}}{\text{Total active atoms in solution}} = \frac{\text{Total amount of substance on surface}}{\text{Total amount of substance in solution}}$$

$$(8.19)$$

The technique of this method will be described with reference to the determination of the surface area of a given preparation of barium sulphate.[27]

A clear saturated solution of sodium sulphate free from solid particles is prepared and to this is added between 0.1 and 0.5 ml of tracer $Na_2{}^{35}SO_4$ of high specific activity. Let the solution thus prepared possess a specific activity of s_1 counts ml^{-1} min^{-1}. 1 g of the given $BaSO_4$ precipitate sample is taken and to it are added say V ml of the labelled Na_2SO_4 solution. A rapid isotopic exchange occurs between the $SO_4{}^{--}$ ions on the surface of the precipitate with the $^{35}SO_4{}^{--}$ ions in solution till an equilibrium is reached.

$$SO_{4(solid)}^{--} + {}^*SO_{4(solution)}^{--} \rightleftharpoons {}^*SO_{4(solid)}^{--} + SO_{4(solution)}^{--} \qquad (8.20)$$

We now have

$$\frac{\text{Total } SO_4^{--} \text{ on surface}}{\text{Total } SO_4^{--} \text{ in solution}} = \frac{\text{Active } *SO_4^{--} \text{ on surface}}{\text{Active } *SO_4^{--} \text{ in solution}}$$

Here the total SO_4^{--} stands for active + inactive SO_4^{--}. The precipitate is centrifuged and the reduced specific activity of the solution is determined $(= s_2$ counts ml^{-1} $min^{-1})$.

The activity transferred from the solution to the surface of the precipitate is $V(s_1 - s_2)$ and that remaining in the solution is Vs_2. Since each SO_4^{--} ion corresponds to one $BaSO_4$ entity in precipitate and one Na_2SO_4 in solution,

$$\frac{\text{Total } BaSO_4 \text{ entities on surface}}{\text{Total } Na_2SO_4 \text{ entities in solution}} = \frac{s_1 - s_2}{s_2} \qquad (8.21)$$

In Eq. 8.21, all the quantities except the numerator of the left hand side are known. This is readily calculated and let this be $= a$.

On dividing the formula weight of the $BaSO_4$ $(= 233)$ by its density $(d$ g $cm^{-3})$ and by the Avogadro constant (L), one obtains the *surface area b* of one $BaSO_4$ entity

$$b = \left(\frac{M}{dL}\right)^{2/3} \qquad (8.22)$$

The surface area of the $BaSO_4$ precipitate sample is simply ab cm^2 g^{-1}.

(C) *Rates of Diffusion*

(i) *Diffusion:* Diffusion is an irreversible process by which a difference in concentration, if present between different regions of a medium or across two phases, is reduced by the spontaneous flow of matter from the region of higher to that of lower concentration. This is a direct consequence of Brownian motion present in all matter at all temperatures above 0 K. The rate of net flow of matter is approximately proportional to the difference in concentration between the two volume elements in contact. We shall consider here a one-dimentional diffusion, for simplicity, while similar processes go on in all the dimensions.

Let J be the flux of matter in moles crossing unit area of a plane perpendicular to the direction of flow in unit time. According to *Fick's first law* of diffusion (1855), J is proportional to the concentration gradient, *viz.* $\partial c/\partial x$, and this provides a definition for the *diffusion coefficient D*, as the constant of proportionality. Thus

$$J = - D \frac{\partial c}{\partial x} \qquad (8.23)$$

Since the concentration falls in the direction of flow of matter, $-\partial c/\partial x$ is used in Eq. 8.23 to make D positive. Inserting the units for the quantities involved in Eq. 8.23, it can be readily shown that D has the dimensions of cm^2 s^{-1}.

$$J \text{ moles } cm^{-2} s^{-1} = - D \frac{\text{moles } cm^{-3}}{cm}$$

Unless so maintained, the concentration gradient itself changes with time as diffusion proceeds, which limits the applicability of Fick's first law in practice. Hence, a second order partial differential equation relating concentration with distance and time, known as *Fick's second law* in the form

$$\frac{\partial c}{\partial t} = D \frac{\partial^2 c}{\partial x^2} \tag{8.24}$$

is found more useful. Here it is assumed that the rate of diffusion is independent of concentration change. This is, however, not strictly true especially where large concentration changes occur. The more general expression of Eq. 8.25 has to be used in all cases except when the net concentration change is small

$$\frac{\partial c}{\partial t} = \frac{\partial}{\partial x} \left[D \frac{\partial c}{\partial x} \right] \tag{8.25}$$

The corresponding form for a three dimensional diffusion is

$$\frac{\partial c}{\partial t} = \text{div} (D \text{ grad } C) \tag{8.26}$$

One of the methods commonly used for determining the diffusion coefficient of a substance A in a uniform medium B, crystal or gel, is to locate A in the form of a narrow zone of negligible thickness in the midst of semi-infinite column of B, of length $2a$, as in Fig. 8.4 (a) and maintaining the system at a constant temperature for a given period of time.

The boundary conditions for the concentration C at distance x and time t, valid for the zone diffusion, are

$$C = C_0 \quad \text{for } x = t = 0$$
$$C = 0 \quad \text{for } x \gtrless 0 \quad \text{at } t = 0$$
$$C = 0 \quad \text{for } x = \pm a \quad \text{for } t > 0.$$

The quantity to be experimentally determined is $C_{(x, t)}$, the concentration at different values of x after a given time t of diffusion. Theoretically, $C_{(x, t)}$ is given by an integral form of Fick's second law, *viz.*

$$C_{(x, t)} = \frac{C_0}{\sqrt{4\pi D t}} e^{-x^2/4Dt} \tag{8.27}$$

The changes in C for small changes in x are too small for precise determination by chemical analysis of successive segments of the column. It is just in this context that radioactive labelling of the initial zone is found very convenient. At the end of the experiment the column is cut into a series of segments each of known length and the radioactivity in each is determined under conditions of constant geometry and the measured activity $a_{(x, t)}$ is taken as proportional to the corresponding concentration. A plot of activity a as a function of x is gaussian, while a plot of log a vs x^2 is linear, the slope of which ($=1/2.303 \times 4Dt$) gives the diffusion coefficient D.   Fig. 8.4(b) and (c) show the results for the diffusion of $^{22}Na^+$ ions in a single crystal of KCl at 710°C, time 4 h 20 min.   Fig. 8.4(d) shows the results obtained by this method for the tracer diffusion of $^{22}Na^+$, and $^{137}Cs^+$ ions and self-diffusion of $^{42}K^+$ ions in single crystals of KCl over the temperature range 570–750°C. The corresponding energies of activation calculated from the slopes of the linear plots of log D vs $1/T$ were 1.75, 1.74 and 1.74 eV respectively.[28]

(ii)   *Tracer diffusion:* This method is available even when the concentration of the labelled diffusing substance is extremely low and the medium consists of another substance at high concentration.   It is then referred to as *tracer diffusion, e.g.* diffusion of $^{22}Na^+$ ion at very low concentration into a solution of KCl or of $^{42}K^+$ or $^{36}Cl^-$ ion at tracer concentration into a solution of NaCl, or the diffusion of a thin film of ^{64}Cu into silver, *etc.*

(iii)   *Self-diffusion:* The diffusion of one species of matter (molecules, atoms or ions) into the *same* matter and at the same concentration and hence chemically homogeneous system, constitutes *self-diffusion, e.g.* the diffusion of K^+ or Cl^- ions into a crystal of KCl or into KCl solution of the same concentration, or of individual water molecules in a medium of water.   Self-diffusion is a direct consequence of Brownian motion and it cannot be ordinarily measured due to the indistinguishibility of molecules or atoms of the same kind.   However, by isotopic labelling, self-diffusion can be studied, as this is the only way of distinguishing the movement of one species in a medium of the chemically same species. A mixture of isotopic species is thermodynamically ideal and the driving force for the inter-diffusion of the isotopic species is the free energy change arising wholly from the entropy of mixing, the enthalpy term being zero.   The entropy of mixing obeys the ideal mixture relation

$$S_{(mixing)} = -R(N_1 \ln N_1 + N_2 \ln N_2) \tag{8.28}$$

N_1 and N_2 being the mole fractions of the two isotopes.

A precise measurement of self-diffusion coefficient is of importance as it is involved in several phenomena, *e.g.*

(a)   in the mass transport of gases, the self-diffusion coefficient D^* relates the mean free path λ with the mean velocity $\bar{c}$, thus:

$$D^* = 1/3 \, \lambda \, \bar{c} \tag{8.29}$$

(b)   in isotope exchanges in heterogeneous systems, and
(c)   in polarography where the limiting current at the dropping mercury cathode is related to the self-diffusion coefficient of the ion discharged.

Self-diffusion has been studied in a large number of metals, crystals, liquids and solutions.   A result of interest revealed by these studies is in regard to very great asymmetry in the diffusion rates along different directions in certain metals, *e.g.* the D^* in bismuth along directions

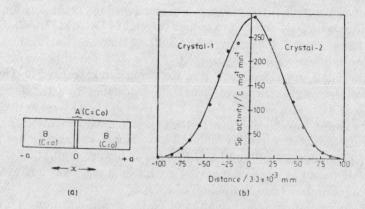

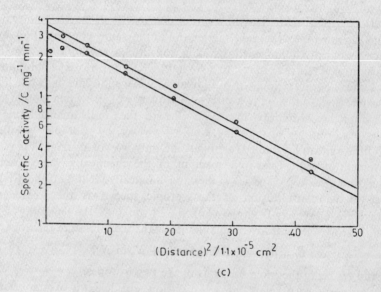

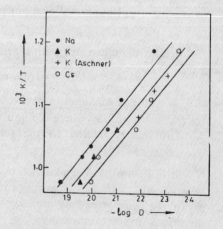

Fig. 8.4 Study of tracer and self-diffusion in single crystals[28]

(a) Initial boundary conditions in zone diffusion. (b) *Répartition* of the activity due to ^{22}Na+ in KCl crystalfollowing diffusion at 710°C for 4 h 20 min. (c) Plot of log activity vs (distance)^2. (d) Tracer diffusion of ^{22}Na+, and ^{137}Cs+ ions and self diffusion of ^{42}K+ in single crystals of KCl as a function of temperature: plots of log D vs $1/T$.

parallel and perpendicular to the c-axis are 10^{-15} and 10^{-10} cm^2 s^{-1} respectively.

(iv) *Surface migration:* Migration of atoms and ions on the surface of metals and crystals and in adsorbed layers has been known and studied by different techniques. Surface migration in adsorbed layers of iodide ions on copper and silver was studied by Arnikar[29],[30] by adsorbing the ions on a strip of the metal to a definite layer thickness, one half of which had been labelled with ^{131}I with a sharp boundary. The surface self-diffusion coefficient was determined by a modified form of Fick's law applicable to the present case:

$$D^* = \frac{S^2\pi}{b^2 C_0^2 t} \tag{8.30}$$

where S is the activity crossing the boundary in time t, C_0 the total activity deposited and b the width of the boundary. Fig. 8.5 shows autoradiographs of mono- and multi-layer thick I$^-$ ($+$ ^{131}I) ions on copper and silver before and after surface self-diffusion at different temperatures.

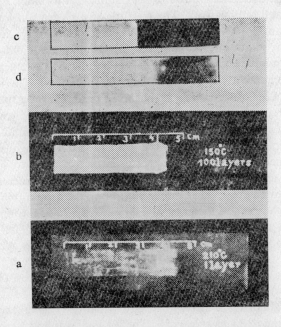

Fig. 8.5 Autoradiographs representing the surface self-diffusion of I$^-$ ions : in (a) its mono- and (b) multi-layers adsorbed on copper. The initial boundary line between the labelled and unlabelled halves was at 4 cm from the left. (c) Autoradiographs of a 10 layer thick I$^-$ ions on silver before and (d) after surface self-diffusion for 4 h at 440 °C.

8.6.3 ANALYTICAL APPLICATIONS

We shall consider here some of the widely used techniques based on radioactivity in analytical chemistry, *viz.*
  (a) Radiochromatography,
  (b) Isotope dilution analysis,
  (c) Neutron activation analysis,
  (d) Neutron absorptiometry and
  (e) Radiometric titrations.

(a) *Radiochromatography*

There are innumerable applications of radioisotopes in all forms of chromatography, paper, column, or gas, as well as in electrophoresis. Almost any chromatographic separation can be carried out using labelled samples. No other developer is needed to reveal the movement of the initial spot and its resolution in the final chromatogram; as the activity distribution is easily scanned.

The most spectacular use of radiochromatography has been in the detection and discovery of some trans-plutonium elements by Seaborg and collaborators (1950–54).[31] They were able to separate from a mixture, six $5f$ elements: americium, curium, berkelium, californium, einsteinium and fermium, all radioactive. The mixture was placed on a column of a cation exchanger Dowex-50 of 2 mm diameter and 5–6 cm length and eluted with a solution of ammonium citrate or ammonium acetate, at 87 °C. An automatic drop fraction collector received the eluent and the α and/or fission activity was recorded for each fraction. The identity of each element of the $5f$ series was established unmistakably by the sequence of their appearance, absolutely analogous to the sequence of the corresponding six $4f$ elements, the rare earths, europeum, gadolinium, terbium, dysprosium, holmium and erbium. Fig. 8.6 shows the analogous positions of the six elements of the $4f$ series (rare earths) $Z = 63$ to 68 and of the $5f$ series (actinides) $Z = 95$ to 100 all in decreasing order of atomic numbers with increase in the time of elution or the drop number.

There are many other instances of the use of radiochromatography in analytical work. A complete separation of the alkali metal ions Li^+, Na^+, K^+, Rb^+ and Cs^+ was shown to be possible by Arnikar and Chemla[32, 33] using an acid washed asbestos paper and dilute hydrochloric acid as solvent, by labelling the ions with their radioisotopes (^{22}Na, ^{42}K, ^{86}Rb and ^{137}Cs)* (Fig. 8.7; Table 8.3).
Similarly, the alkali earth metal ions were separated using their radioisotopes ^{90}Sr and ^{131}Ba as tracers.[34] The R_f values found were

Y^{+++}	Sr^{++}	Ba^{++}
0.18	0.76	0.90

*As Li has no radioisotope, its movements were studied by flame photometry.

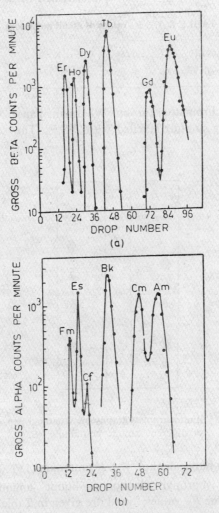

Fig. 8.6 Radiochromatography of (a) lanthanides: Eu to Er, (b) actinides: Am to Fm[31] (from S.G. Thomson, B.G. Harvey, G.R. Chopin and G.T. Seaborg[31] reproduced with authors' permission).

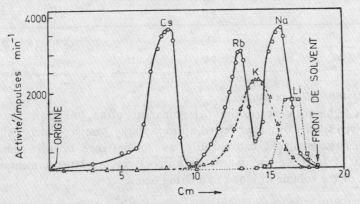

Fig. 8.7 Radiochromatography of alkali ions on asbestos paper.[32]

TABLE 8.3: R_f values of alkali metal ions

Ion	Li+	Na+	K+	Rb+	Cs+
R_f	0.99	0.86	0.77	0.72	0.45

Figure 8.8 is a chromatogram on Whatman paper No. 1 of different anions containing sulphur labelled with ^{35}S.[35] The solvents employed were

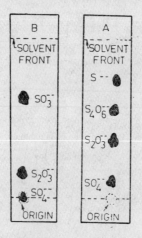

Fig. 8.8 Radiochromatography on Whatman paper No. 1 of different anions containing ^{35}S.

(A) dioxan + n-butyl alcohol + 1 N ammonia (1:1:1)

(B) acetone + isopropyl alcohol + liquor ammonia ($d = 0.888$) (2:1:1). The R_f values found are given in Table 8.4.

TABLE 8.4: R_f values of oxyanions containing sulphur

Solvent	SO_4^{--}	$S_2O_3^{--}$	SO_3^{--}	$S_4O_6^{--}$	S^{--}
(A)	0.12	0.43	—	0.54	0.77
(B)	0.00	0.14	0.61	—	—

(b) Isotope Dilution Analysis

This technique concerns the determination of an unknown amount of a given species of matter mixed up in a large sample which cannot be otherwise analysed conveniently, as for instance in assessing the amount of an active component as aureomycin in a large fermentation broth, or the volume of blood in a living being.

The principle of isotope dilution analysis: The technique consists in adding to the sample containing say x g (unknown) of the species, y g of a radioisotopic form of the species of intlial specific activity s_i counts mg^{-1} min^{-1}. After thoroughly mixing, a small amount of the species is isolated from the mixture and its final specific activity s_f is determined. Obviously s_f would be less than s_i. Just with these two measurements, the unknown amount x is calculated on the principle of the conservation of total activity, *i.e.* initial total activity should equal the final total activity, *i.e.*

$$(x + y)\, s_f = y\, s_i \qquad\qquad (8.31)$$

Hence

$$x = y\, \frac{(s_i - s_f)}{s_f}$$

Some applications of isotope dilution analysis: This method of analysis may be illustrated by a problem faced by the manufacturer of antibiotics. A given fermentation broth contains an unknown amount of aureomycin which is to be determined. Isotope dilution analysis constitutes a simple way of solving this. Suppose to a kg of the broth containing x mg (unknown) of aureomycin, one adds a mg of aureomycin labelled with ^{14}C whose initial specific activity is s_i (= say 150 counts mg^{-1} min^{-1}). After a thorough mixing, one mg of aureomycin is isolated and suppose the sample registers 400 counts in 20 minutes. This makes the final specific activity $s_f = 20$ counts mg^{-1} min^{-1}. Where the count rate is small it is necessary to extend the counting over a sufficiently long period, to minimize counting errors. By Eq. 8.31,

$$(x + 1)\, 20 = 150.$$

Hence $x = 6.5$ mg of aureomycin per kg of broth.

An instance where the technique was used by the author was in computing the trace amount of potassium impurity in filaments of tungsten used as supports for the solid ion source in mass spectrometry, as this was interferring with the analysis of isotopically enriched samples of potassium. By diluting the impurity with potassium enriched in ^{40}K (0.57%)*, the impurity potassium was found to be 3×10^{-6} per cent of tungsten.[36]

The application of this technique to the estimation of the volume of blood in a living being is described under medical applications (Sec. 8.6.5).

(c) *Neutron activation analysis*

In this technique the element whose amount in a sample is to be determined is transformed by (n, γ) reaction into its radioactive isotope

---

*In naturally occurring potassium^{40} K constitutes 0.012%.

and from the activity of the product, the amount of the target element is computed. Since the amounts of radioactive isotopes of half-lives, between hours and years, can be determined with precision of the order of 10^{-12} g, the technique is well-suited and extremely efficient for a large number of elements, specially those with large neutron capture cross sections. The analysis of trace elements in minerals and ores, in soils and special preparations has been possible by neutron activation. Another great advantage of this technique is that it is non-destructive, *i.e.* the sample remains unchanged at the end of the analysis, except for the nuclear transformation of atoms in tracer concentration, and hence it is well adapted for the analysis of rare and precious samples as jewels, precious stones, ancient coins and other archaelogical specimens, as pottery sherds, *etc.* Elements which permit neutron activation analysis include: Na, P, Ca, Sc, Cr, Mn, Cu, Cu, Zn, Ge, As, Se, Ag, In, W, Ir, Pt, Au and many others. Some of the rare earth elements as Sm, Eu, Dy, Ho, Yb, Gd having high neutron capture cross sections are well-adapted for neutron activation analysis.

The principle of neutron activation analysis: Suppose the problem is to determine the amount of a given element X in a particular sample. Let x g of the sample containing N atoms of the element (considered to be mono-isotopic in the first case), be placed in a uniform flux of thermal neutrons for a sufficiently long period of time t seconds to produce measurable activity, say A_t. It is presumed that the activity A_t is solely due to the isotope under study. If any other nuclide present in the sample also becomes radioactive, the activity of the former should be distinguished from the rest by its characteristic radiation, half-life, *etc.* The activity A_t produced is given by

$$A_t = N \phi \sigma \, (1 - e^{-\lambda t}) \qquad (8.32)$$

where ϕ is the neutron flux (*i.e.* number of neutrons cm^{-2} s^{-1}), σ, the neutron capture cross section in cm^2 for the given target nuclide, to be obtained from tables and λ is the decay constant in s^{-1} of the radioactive product. The number of the product nuclei produced, N', is given by A_t/λ, which it is not necessary to know. In the above Eq. 8.32. A_t is the activity of the product if measured *immediately at the end of irradiation* (time t). Often this is not possible and a finite time t' lapses between the end of irradiation and the start of counting, during which time some of the activity would have decayed. The activity one actually measures after an interval t' after irradiation is given by

$$A_t' = A_t \, e^{-\lambda t'} = N \phi \sigma (1 - e^{-\lambda t}) \, e^{-\lambda t'} \qquad (8.33)$$

From Eq. 8.33, the weight W g of the particular element present in the x g of the sample is known from

$$W = \frac{NM}{L} = \frac{M}{L} \frac{A_t'}{\phi \sigma (1 - e^{-\lambda t}) \, e^{-\lambda t'}} \qquad (8.34)$$

where M is the atomic weight of the element and L the Avogadro constant $(=6.022 \times 10^{23})$.

In the case of products of short half-lives the period of irradiation t can be prolonged to equal about six half-lives, when the factor $e^{-\lambda t} = e^{-0.693t/\tau} \simeq 0$, as $t \gg \tau$ and the expression simplifies. The (n, γ) reaction in such a case goes to saturation. Where τ is long it would not be possible to irradiate to saturation.

The above treatment needs only a small modification in case the target element is not monoisotopic, but consists of two or more stable isotopes. If the proportion of the particular isotope in the target element whose (n, γ) radioactive product is being measured is f parts per 100 of the element, the resulting N in Eqs. 8.32 and 8.33 and hence W in Eq. 8.34 must be multiplied $100/f$, to obtain the total amount of the element X in x g of the target sample.

In actual practice the use of the complicated Eq. 8.34 is avoided, by irradiating simultaneously and under identical conditions two samples, one standard containing a known amount of the element W^0 and the other the unknown W. If the resulting activities are A_t^0 (known) and A_t (unknown)

$$\frac{W}{W^0} = \frac{A_t}{A_t^0} \qquad (8.35)$$

Alternatively, a series of known samples containing W_1, W_2, ..., g of the element and the unknown are irradiated together and from the linear plot of W versus A_t the content of the unknown is determined.

Generally, the target sample contains several elements some or all of which may be neutron activated but their yields would depend on their amounts in the sample, their cross sections and half-lives. Thus, more than one activity results often, and the activity of the particular isotope in question has to be distinguished. Usually a large difference in the energy of the principal γ and/or β component, and/or the difference in half-lives help in differentiating the relevant product isotope from the others. With the availability of high resolution γ-ray spectrometers, using solid state detectors (as Ge-Li or Si-Li) analysis by neutron activation has today become a highly perfected technique for detecting and estimating a very large number of elements present in trace amounts in a variety of samples. Mentioned here are only a few applications of neutron activation analysis from out of a large number on record and in continuous use.

(i)   Chromium Content of a Ruby

The ^{50}Cr in natural chromium becomes by (n, γ) reaction the 27.7 day ^{51}Cr. By irradiating with slow neutrons under identical conditions a chromium bearing ruby with a series of $Al_2O_3 + Cr_2O_3$ mixtures of varying, but known Cr-content, it was found that the rubies have 0.1 to 0.4% Cr. The precision and the fact that the precious ruby remains undamaged at the end of the analysis highlight the value of this method of analysis.

(ii) Manganese content of tea leaves

The monoisotope ^{55}Mn becomes by (n, γ) reaction 2.58 h ^{56}Mn. Neutron irradiation of a known weight of dry tea leaves, or better its calcined ash, along with a series of samples of known Mn content reveal that tea leaves contain around 0.13% of Mn about half of which passes into the brew and the rest goes to waste.

(iii) Archaeological specimens

Neutron activation analysis has helped in determining the precise composition of some ancient coins non-destructively and the results have thrown light on their historical and geographic origin. Similarly the analysis of coloured pottery sherds of archaeological discoveries go to establish the possible age, geographic proximity to available minerals, and trade routes in vogue, besides throwing light on the development of ceramics in that region and of that epoch. All this is achieved without destroying the valuable specimens.

(iv) Arsenic in hair: slow arsenic poisoning

The monoisotope ^{75}As becomes by (n, γ) reaction 26.3 h ^{76}As.

If arsenic is administered in small doses over a period of time, a definite fraction of the element tends to accumulate at the root of hairs and nails. As the hair grows on the average about 0.5 mm per day, the arsenic also moves forward along the length of the hair at the same rate. If now some of the hair (in case they have not been destroyed), of a person suspected of death by slow arsenic poisoning, be neutron irradiated, along with some hair of a normal person, and the distributions of ^{76}As along the length compared, the pattern and the schedule of arsenic poisoning would be revealed. In the case of hair from a normal person, the ^{76}As content is much lower and remains nearly constant all along the length except towards the tip, while the pattern in the case of arsenic poisoning reveals distinct peaks corresponding to days of poisoning, each day corresponding to about 0.5 mm length of hair.[57]

It is true that the interpretation of the results is delicate and difficult. The technique has obviously a great importance in criminology and medical jurisprudence. An examination of Napolean's hair by this technique in 1962 revealed an abnormal amount of arsenic, however, the evidence was not considered conclusive.

(d) Neutron Absorptiometry

Neutron absorptiometry is an alternative method of analysis applicable to elements of high neutron capture cross section, as boron and cadmium (used for this property as control rods in nuclear reactors) (Sec. 7.7), and some of the rare earth elements as, Sm, Eu, Gd, Dy, Yb and Lu. A known weight of a sample of the element or one of its compounds is placed in a definite position between a source of thermal neutrons and the detector. The neutron flux reaching the detector falls in proportion to the amount absorbed by the element in the sample. The method can be standardized to determine the amount of the element in the sample, provided the thickness of the sample and its positioning with respect to the neutron source and the detector are controlled with precision. The extent of neutron absorption can be readily measured by the fall in the activity induced in a silver or an indium foil embedded in the sample itself, the nuclear reactions involved being:

$$^{107}\text{Ag}\,(n, \gamma)\,^{108}\text{Ag}\xrightarrow[2.4\ \text{min}]{\beta^-\,(1.65\ \text{MeV})}\,^{108}\text{Cd (stable)}$$

$$\sigma = 35\ \text{b};\, f = 51.4\%;$$

$$^{115}\text{In}\,(n, \gamma)\,^{116}\text{In}\xrightarrow[54.1\ \text{min}]{\gamma\,(1.27\ \text{MeV})\,\beta^-\,(1\ \text{MeV})}\,^{116}\text{Sn (stable)}$$

$$\sigma = 155\ \text{b};\, f = 95.8\%*$$

where f is the abundance of the isotope in the naturally occurring element.

In the case of silver, a 15-minute irradiation is adequate to lead to saturation yield of the product ^{108}Ag which being short-lived, the counting of the activity should be started as soon after the end of irradiation, but after a *definite interval* of time in every case. A method developed by the author[38] is described here to determine boron and cadmium in their compounds, either in dissolved state, or in solid state dispersed in paraffin, over the concentration range 10^{-4} to $10^{-2}\ \text{M}$. A quickly demountable circular silver foil $(d = 30\ \text{mm})$ suspended in the aqueous solution, or between a pair of compressed paraffin pellets, containing a known amount of the boron or cadmium compound, was placed in a fixed position of constant geometry with respect to a Pu-Be neutron source of constant flux $(= 10^5\ n\ \text{cm}^{-2}\ \text{s}^{-1})$. The irradiation was stopped after 15 min, and exactly 35 s thereafter the silver foil was cleaned, dried and its activity measured with an end-window GM counter. A plot of log activity A *versus* the number of moles of the substance (B or Cd atoms) intercepting the neutrons in the path before the sensor element of unit area, x, is found to be linear for x below 15 millimoles, in accord with the expression

$$A_{(x)} = A_0\,e^{-Kx} \tag{8.36}$$

where A_0 is the activity in the absence of B or Cd (*i.e.* $x = 0$), and K is the molar neutron absorption coefficient for the element. Fig. 8.9 shows the results.

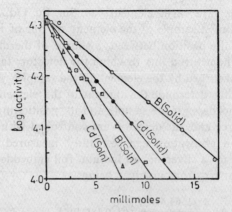

Fig. 8.9 Determination of boron and cadmium by
neutron absorptiometry.

(e) Radiometric Titrations

Radiometric titrations employ radioisotopes to indicate the end point
by a sudden release to, or absorption from, the solution of activity.[19] For
instance, in the titration of silver by chloride ions labelled with ^{36}Cl,
the solution remains inactive till the end point is reached, as all the
activity is removed as AgCl precipitate. The end point is indicated by
a sudden release of activity into the solution which keeps increasing
thereafter. On the contrary, if the silver ion had been labelled with
^{110}Ag, the solution remains active, though decreasingly so, and the end
point corresponds to a constant minimum of activity. In either case,
the end point corresponds to a sharp inflection in the activity vs titre
curve. It is necessary in every case that the silver chloride formed precipitates out without remaining colloidally suspended.

In another type of radiometric titration, the indicator remains an
insoluble solid till the end point is reached when it starts dissolving and
releasing activity into the solution. As an example may be cited the
complexometric titration of calcium by EDTA with solid $^{110}AgIO_3$ as the
indicator. The added EDTA is all removed by Ca^{++} and it is only after
the end point that the EDTA reacts with Ag^+ to form a soluble Ag-EDTA
complex, thereby releasing activity into the solution.

8.6.4 AGE DETERMINATIONS

Each radioactive isotope decays with a characteristic rate which is
invariable under all conditions of temperature, pressure and chemical
environment. However, radioactivity being a statistical phenomenon,
the invariability of the decay constant is assured only as long as a large
number of the atoms is present; with this provision, radioisotopes can
be looked upon as nature's atomic clocks recording the passage of time
since the birth of the universe in terms of the number of atoms decayed.

Measurement of residual radioactivity has been one of the most reliable methods of dating samples.

The basis of age determination by a radioactive method depends on the sample containing a radioisotope in equilibrium with its stable product and of an age commensurate with the half-life period of the isotope, *i.e.* within about 3–4 spans of the half-life. Thus, the ratio of $^3H/H$ in aqueous samples could be depended upon for samples of 0–40 years age, the half-life of ^3H being 12.33 years. For historic and archaelogical ages up to about 20 000 years one resorts to ^{14}C with a half-life of 5730 y in the form of $^{14}C/C$ ratio of the sample, while for computing the age of minerals and rocks, or of the earth, the very long lived radioelements of U and Th are depended upon, in a variety of combinations. Some of these are considered here.

(a) *Dating by Tritium Content*

Since the HTO (tritiated water) continuously forming in the atmosphere (Sec. 8.2) mixes with the ordinary water of large surfaces open to the atmosphere as seas, rivers and lakes, the $^3H/H$ in these 'open' waters is constant at the equilibrium value of about 10^{-18}. However, once a sample of the water is withdrawn for any purpose, or gets isolated, the $^3H/H$ ratio in the sample will keep decreasing with a half-life of 12.33 years. The residual amount of ^3H or the decrease in the ratio from 10^{-18} is a measure of the 'age' of the sample, *i.e.* the period it had been isolated from open waters. As the radiation from ^3H is very soft ($E_\beta = 0.018$ MeV), special counting devices, as the liquid scintillation counter with a low background, would be needed to measure the activity of ^3H.

Suppose a fresh sample of water (age $= 0$ y), gives n counts per gram of water per minute. Theoretically, other samples of ages 1, 2, 3,... half-lives (*i.e.* 12.33, 24.66, 36.99,... years) would register under identical conditions of counting geometry and efficiency, $n/2$, $n/4$, $n/8$,... counts g^{-1} min^{-1}. A standard reference curve as Fig. 8.10 can thus be readily drawn. The age of any sample can then be read off this curve, once the activity of this sample has been determined and normalized to the activity of a fresh sample to n. Measurements with samples older than 3 half-lives involve uncertainty which increases with age, hence this method would not be available for aqueous samples older than about 40 years. The time to time explosion of thermonuclear devices these days has rendered this method of dating uncertain due to varying amounts of tritium released into the atmosphere in each explosion.

(b) *Dating by Carbon-14*

The technique of dating of historic and archaeological organic samples by their ^{14}C content was first developed by W.F. Libby for which he was awarded the Nobel Prize in 1960. Living plants provide food for themselves by photosynthesis of sugars from water and carbon dioxide of the atmosphere. Since the mass ratio of $^{14}CO_2/CO_2$ of the atmosphere ap-

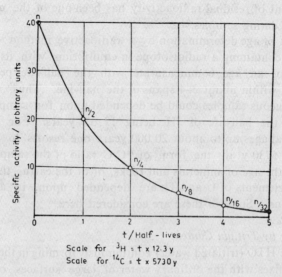

Fig. 8.10 Standard decay curves for age determination by ^3H and ^{14}C

pears to have remained sensibly constant over the ages (around 1.6×10^{-12}) all *living* beings, plants and animals, if analysed would give a constant value for ^{14}C, which on the average is found to be 16.1 ± 0.3 disintegrations $min^{-1} g^{-1}$ of total carbon*.[43] However, once a plant dies, it cannot photosynthesize any more, *i.e.* no further CO_2 of the atmosphere is absorbed. This results in a continuous decay of whatever ^{14}C it possessed at the time of death, at an exponential rate corresponding to the half-life of ^{14}C, *viz.* 5730 years. Hence, a determination of the actual count rate due to ^{14}C in a given sample of once living, but now dead matter would permit a computation of the 'age' of the sample, rather the period it has remained dead. The method is quite similar to that described under tritium dating, only the time scale would be in half-lives of ^{14}C which is 5730 years (Fig. 8.10). The radiation from ^{14}C being soft ($E_\beta = 0.155$ MeV) and the specific activity even in fresh living samples being very low, special counters with very low background are needed for measuring ^{14}C activity, in addition to great care in normalizing the results before interpreting them. The ^{14}C in a sample is counted either as pure $*CO_2$ in a proportional counter, or after its transformation into benzene in a liquid scintillation counter, the steps involved being:

---

*The precise value of the specific disintegration rate of ^{14}C in use has varied from 14 to 16 d $min^{-1} g^{-1}$. The more recent value according to Swedish workers[39] is closer to 13.6. This represents the actual *number of ^{14}C atoms disintegrating* per minute (dpm) in a gram of total carbon. The net *counts per minute* (cpm) of course would be less than this number, depending on the geometry of positioning of the sample in the counter and the latter's efficiency of counting.

$$\text{Sample} \xrightarrow{+O_2} *CO_2 \xrightarrow{Ba(OH)_2} Ba* CO_3 \xrightarrow{H_2SO_4} *CO_2 \xrightarrow{Li} Li_2*C_2$$

$$\xrightarrow{\text{water}} *C_2H_2 \xrightarrow{\text{polymerization}} *C_6H_6$$

In practice the way of calculating the age of a dead organic sample is as follows. First, its ^{14}C activity in absolute units of disintegration g^{-1} min^{-1} is determined using a calibrated counter which permits the conversion of counts per minute observed to disintegrations per minute. Let the dpm be s. The period the sample has been dead is given, in units of the half-life period n of ^{14}C, by the relation

$$s = 16 \cdot 1 (0.5)^n \tag{8.37}$$

This is a particular form of the more general expression applicable to residual activity of any radionuclide

$$s = s_0 (0.5)^n \tag{4.15}$$

where s is the activity of the sample after n half-lives are over, s_0 being its activity at time zero.

This is based on the assumption that a live sample (age zero) gives 16.1 dpm per gram of total carbon. The actual age of the sample is simply n times 5730 years. This is illustrated by the following example. A piece of sack cloth found in an ancient cave, when analysed in the year 1976 gave 11.3 dpm. Substituting this value for s in Eq. 8.37 leads to a value of 0.511 for n. Hence the sample has remained dead for 2930 years in 1976. In other words, the sample can be dated to 950 BC approximately.

Numerous historic and archaelogical samples have been dated by the radiocarbon technique. The famous Dead Sea Manuscripts have been dated to be of 20 BC on the basis of their ^{14}C content. Beyond about 15 000 years increasing uncertainty sets-in in the age computed by this method.

In recent times, however, the upper limit of ^{14}C dating has been greatly extended by subjecting the sample to isotopic enrichment. The degree of enrichment is monitored by a mass spectrometric analysis of the $^{13}C/^{12}C$ ratio, which in natural carbon is 0.011 2. An enrichment of 2% in ^{13}C involves its square, i.e., 4% in the ^{14}C enrichment, leading to a corresponding increase in its specific activity from 16 to about 64 d min^{-1} g^{-1}, Hence the dating of samples as old as about 60 000 to 70 000 years beccomes possible. It should, however, be remembered that all isotopic enrichments are difficult and after the first stage the efficiency goes down progressively.

(c) *Age of Minerals and Rocks*

The naturally occurring radionuclides ^{238}U, ^{235}U and ^{232}Th decay finally to yield the stable products, the isotopes of lead ^{206}Pb, ^{207}Pb and

^{208}Pb respectively through a series of α and β decays (Appendix I). ^{234}U (earlier known as uranium-II) being the longest-lived ($\tau = 2.52 \times 10^5$ y) amongst the daughter elements of all the three series, a secular equilibrium (see Sec. 4.5.7) gets established for all the intermediate products in all the three series, within about a million years of the creation of the parent elements. Hence, a measurement of the ratio of the amount of the *radiogenic* lead* to uranium and thorium in a given mineral or rock would enable us to compute the age of the specimen, t years, employing a relation first arrived at by Keevil[40] in 1939, *viz.*

$$M = n_1 N_1 (e^{\lambda_1 t} - 1) + n_2 N_2 (e^{\lambda_2 t} - 1) + n_3 N_3 (e^{\lambda_3 t} - 1) \qquad (8.38)$$

where M is the *total* number of lead atoms formed in time t ($\gg 10^6$ years, the time for equilibrium); n stands for the number of Pb atoms *per atom* of the parent decayed: N is the number of parent atoms surviving at the present time, *i.e.* after t years; and λ is the decay constant of the parent nuclide; the subscripts 1, 2 and 3 refer to ^{238}U, ^{232}Th and ^{235}U.

Since $n_1 = n_2 = n_3 = 1$, the equation gets partly simplified. Even so, the solution of the equation is complicated. However, on the basis of the fact that the ^{235}U content of natural uranium is only 0.72%, the contribution of ^{207}Pb from this parent may be neglected without a grave error. This then leaves only the first two terms of the Eq. 8.38 on the right side. Retaining only the terms $1 + x$ in the expansion of the series e^x, we arrive at

$$M = (N_1 \lambda_1 + N_2 \lambda_2) t \qquad (8.39)$$

Inserting the value of $\lambda_1 = 1.54 \times 10^{-10}$ y^{-1} and $\lambda_2 = 4.99 \times 10^{-11}$ y^{-1} we finally get t in years as

$$t = \frac{M}{1.54 \times 10^{-10} N_1 + 4.99 \times 10^{-11} N_2} \qquad (8.40)$$

for the age of the specimen. This reduces to a precise measurement of M the total number of radiogenic lead atoms ^{206}Pb and ^{208}Pb, and of N_1 and N_2 the numbers of ^{238}U and ^{232}Th in the given specimen. Wickman[41] has constructed a family of graphs from which the age of the rock or mineral, between 10 and 100 million years can be read off with an error $\pm 10^6$ years, once the Pb/(U + Th) and U/(U + Th) ratios of the specimen have been determined by analysis.

Alternative equations for assessing the age of the minerals and rocks applicable to samples containing only pure U and ^{206}Pb, or pure Th and ^{208}Pb have been also developed, *viz.*

$$t = 15.15 \times 10^9 \log \left[1 + \frac{1.158 \, ^{206}\text{Pb}}{^{238}\text{U}} \right] \text{ years}$$

and
$$\qquad (8.41)$$

$$t = 46.2 \times 10^9 \log \left[1 + \frac{1.116 \, ^{208}\text{Pb}}{^{232}\text{Th}} \right] \text{ years.}$$

*As distinct from lead directly found in nature unassociated with uranium or thorium.

Other methods based on the ratios of other radionuclides and their stable products also exist, as for example, the ratio of ^{40}Ar to ^{40}K in potassium bearing rocks (as felspars, felspathoids, *etc.*) by the relation

$$M = N\frac{\lambda(e)}{\lambda}(e^{\lambda t} - 1) \tag{8.42}$$

where M is the number of ^{40}Ar atoms (formed by electron capture by ^{40}K atom) with *partial decay constant* $\lambda(e)$ and *total decay constant* λ of ^{40}K, and N is the number of ^{40}K atoms surviving at time t.*

Helium being another stable product of natural radioactivity, in the form of α particles, it is also possible to compute the age of a rock or mineral from the ratio of the amount of helium occluded in it per gram of U or Th, assuming that none of the gas had escaped from the mineral over the ages. As a lower limit of the age this method is permissible, as it is relatively simple to collect all the helium occluded.

(d) *The Age of the Earth*

It would be natural to expect that the age of the most ancient minerals and rocks, represents the *minimum* age of the earth. Amongst the oldest minerals of the world are stated to be uraninites of the Huron Claim pegmatites in south eastern Manitoba in Canada. These have been computed by Holmes[42] to be 2.3×10^9 years. The accepted figure for the age of the earth appears to be $5.0 \pm 0.5 \times 10^9$ years.

8.6.5 MEDICAL APPLICATIONS

Probably it was in medicine and biochemistry that some of the earliest applications of radioisotopes have been made, as these promised to be a new powerful tool in an area of vital importance as the understanding of metabolic reactions, the mechanisms of the action of drugs, the location of cancerous growths and obstructions in the flow of blood, *etc.* The scope of the subject would appear to be almost unlimited in the hands of specially trained experts. Besides the use as radioactive tracers in microcurie doses in monitoring certain processes in the body, larger doses have been successfully used for therapeutic purposes for destroying cancerous tissues. We present here only a few applications without details. For more information specialized publications have to be consulted.[43-45]

(a) *Thyroidisis (Goitre)*

Most of the iodine we obtain from food is known to accumulate in the thyroid gland which plays a vital role in our well being as it controls the growth and proper metabolism. As against a normal thyroid, the gland in some people becomes over-active (*hyperthyroidisis*) while in

---

*^{40}K decays partly by electron capture to form ^{40}Ar and partly by β^- decay to yield ^{40}Ca.

some others it becomes sluggish or underactive (*hypothyroidisis*), both conditions being unhealthy and may lead to serious consequences. if not detected and treated in time.

(i) *Diagnosis:* The condition of the thyroid is clearly revealed by administering a light dose of radioiodine to the patient. Usually, a glass of orange juice containing about 10 μCi of ^{131}I in the form of NaI is given to the patient and it has no unpleasant taste and the patient is hardly aware of it. The counting of the γ activity emitted by the patient's thyroid is started immediately with a scintillation counter fixed at a distance of 20 cm from the thyroid. The counts are compared with those from a dummy plastic thyroid injected with the same amount of ^{131}I and counted at the same distance. The counts are continued every hour for the first six hours and at larger intervals thereafter. The ratio of the counts D/P (dummy/patient) are plotted as a function of time and compared with the curve for a normal. Fig. 8.11 shows the characteristic patterns of D/P for a hyperthyroidisis, a hypothyroidisis and a normal person. Throughout the period of diagnosis, the patient feels no adverse effect.

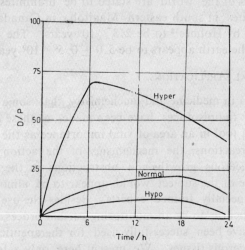

Fig. 8.11 Diagnosis of a normal thyroidisis.

(ii) *Therapy:* Once a case is diagnosed to be of hyperthyroidisis, the treatment is possible by radioiodine ^{131}I ($\tau = 8$ d) or better still ^{126}I ($\tau = 13$ d). The dose has to be much higher, usually around 200 μCi. The high energy radiations (0.36 MeV γ and 0.61 MeV β^- from ^{131}I, or 1.11 MeV β^+ and 0.39 MeV γ from ^{126}I) destroy the excess growth causing the hyperthyroidisis. The progress is followed by the autoradiography of the gland and by point collimated scintillation counter.*

*The Institute of Medical Sciences, Banaras Hindu University, was one of the earliest t o in stal a radioiodine therapy unit for thyroidisis in our country, in 1960.

(b) *Brain Tumour Location*

Brain tumours are difficult to locate. It is known that certain dyes as fluorescein, rose bengal are preferentially adsorbed by cancerous cells. The technique is to label the dye with ^{131}I as diiodofluorescein or rose bengal and scan the entire space around the skull by special counters. By this it may be possible to locate the tumour fairly closely. Sometimes, a solution of albuminate of iodine, labelled with ^{131}I is administered to the patient and the region of the brain where ^{131}I accumulates is located.

(c) *Assessing the Volume of Blood in a Patient*

Sometimes it becomes necessary for a surgeon to know the amount of blood in a patient of anemia, or one who has had severe haemorrhage in an accident. The simplest way of assessing the volume of blood in a person is by the technique of isotope dilution, described earlier (Sec. 8.6.3). One cm^3 of the patient's blood is withdrawn and it is labelled with a solution of ^{24}Na as NaCl (or less often with ^{128}I or ^{51}Cr or ^{32}P). The initial specific activity of the labelled blood is measured in 0.1 cm^3 of it. Let this be s_i cm^{-3}. The rest of the labelled sample containing 0.9 cm^3 of blood $(= y)$ is reinjected intraveinously. After about 15 min, needed for the circulation and homogenization of the blood, once again 1 cm^3 of the blood is withdrawn and its specific activity s_f determined. The unknown volume of the blood in the patient's body x cm^3 is calculated from

$$ys_i = (x + y)\, s_f = xs_f \qquad (\because \quad y \ll x)$$

$$x = y\, \frac{s_i}{s_f}\ \text{cm}^3 \qquad\qquad (8.31)$$

A normal adult human being may have between 5 to 6 litres of blood.

(d) *Defects in Blood Circulation: Effect of Drugs*

A small known amount of ^{24}Na as NaCl solution is injected intraveinously into the left forearm of the patient and the time needed for its arrival at various other parts of the body, as detected by a GM counter, is an indication of the normal or defective circulation of blood. Timings observed are compared with standard data for a normal person. Any local obstruction as a clot (thrombosis) in a given part will be indicated by a slowing down of circulation over that part. The efficacy of a given anti-hypertension drug is measurable by the improvement in circulation.

(e) *Mechanism of Bone Fracture Healing*

There has been some uncertainty regarding the precise mechanism of the healing of bone fracture, especially of the chemical processes and their sequence in the pre-calci. This was studied to a certain extent by

Udupa, Singh and Arnikar,[46] by injecting a solution of Na_2SO_4 and Na_2HPO_4 labelled with ^{35}S and ^{32}P respectively, into a series of albino rats one of whose forelegs was fractured. Besides normal X-ray and histological studies, batches of the animals were sacrificed at the end of each week and the region around the fractured bone was analysed for the activity of sulphur and phosphorus, till complete healing was observed (in the rest of the rats). The study revealed that sulphated mucopolysaccharides must first accumulate around the fracture site (during the second week) and these saccharides must begin disappearing before calcification can commence (end of the third or early fourth week).

The study was extended to verify the efficacy of the extract of a commonly growing plant *Cissus quadrangularis* (Sanskrit: *Asthisanhar*: Hindi: *Hadjod*) (Fig. 8.12) in accelerating fracture healing, as believed locally. This was done by administering a definite amount of the milky extract of the plant to a batch of rats and studying the ^{35}S and ^{32}P concentrations as a ratio F/I in the fractured and in the intact bone week by week as before, and comparing the results with two other batches of rats, one as control and the other given a heavy vitamin-C dose. Results clearly showed that the extract of the plant was helpful in

Fig. 8.12 *Cissus quadrangularis* (*Hadjod*).

effecting an early healing more efficiently than vitamin-C alone (Fig. 8.13).

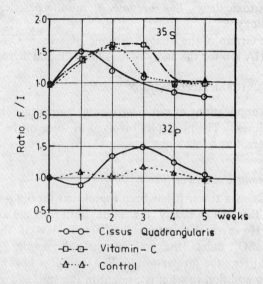

Fig. 8.13   Rate of bone fracture healing studied by ^{35}S and ^{32}P.

(f) Radioimmunoassay

The technique of *radioimmunoassay* (RIA) was first developed by Miles and Hales[47] in 1968. This has since then proved to be a versatile technique for assessing the concentration levels of vitally important biological ingredients in the body fluids, such as, harmones, vitamins, steroids, drugs and antigens of extraneous origin. As an example is considered here the determination of the concentration of the antigen Harmone-insulin in a sample of a blood serum. An axcess of the labelled antigen is added to the sample and it is incubated with a known amount of the corresponding antibody (in this case anti-insulin serum). Because of the highly specific reaction of an antigen with its antibody the two get bound as an antigen-antibody complex which precipitates out. The excess of the antigen not bound to the antibody is removed by centrifuging in the presence of an immuno adsorbent as dextran-coated charcoal. The radioactivities of the supernatant (free antigen) (F) and of the precipitate (bound) (B) are determined. The concentration of the antigen in the original sample is obtained by interpolating the observed B/F value against a standard curve of B/F *vs* antigen concentration.

The RIA technique is being used increasingly in the estimation of the human placentol lactogen (HPL) in the early stages of pregnancy, the information being of vital importance to the gynaecologist, as it enables a clear differentiation of normal pregnancies from abnormal ones involving risks.

The use of radioisotopes in the study of absorption, metabolism and secretion of steroid harmones and vitamins, as well as in ascertaining the safety limits of toxic drugs, has become a routine practice in modern clinical physiology.[48]*

The Isotope Group of the Bhabha Atomic Research Center provides ready to use RIA kits for the assay of insulin, HPL and thyroid harmones.

8.6.6 AGRICULTURAL APPLICATIONS**

Ever so many applications of radioisotopes in agriculture have become routine procedures. The principles involved in some of the applications are outlined here.

(a) *The Optimum Use of Fertilizers*

By using ^{45}Ca as a tracer it has been found that the uptake by plants of calcium from the soil is nearly the same both for CaO and $CaCO_3$ in acidic soils. However, the uptake is distinctly less if the calcium is present as $CaSO_4$, unless the soil is markedly acidic. In respect of phosphate fertilizer, the farmer would like to know how much of it he needs to add in addition to what is present in the soil, and at what stage of the growth of the plant would it be optimum to add the same. By adding ammonium phosphate labelled with ^{32}P, of known specific activity the uptake of phosphorus is followed by measuring the radioactivity as the activity reaches first the lower parts of the plant, then the upper parts, branches, leaves, *etc*. The *total* phosphorus uptake by the whole plant is determined by chemical analysis and that of the added fertilizer by the activity measurement. The difference is the natural phosphorus present in the soil. By a series of experiments it has been established that in the case of crops it is best to add the phosphorus fertilizer very early at the time of sowing itself, when over 60% is taken up. On the contrary, if the fertilizer is added at a later stage, the uptake is less than 35%.

(b) *Irradiation of Seeds*

Beneficial effects of exposing seeds to X or γ radiation on their growth has been well known. This is more easily effected with a 1–2 kCi ^{60}Co source arranged to irradiate panoramically all plants in a large area to a

---

*R.S. Yalow was awarded the Nobel prize in Medicine and Physiology in 1977, for her work in this area.

**Some of the material presented here on the applications of radioisotopes and nuclear radiations in agriculture, metallurgy, prospecting of natural resources and as sources of electricity, is drawn from *Radioisotopes and their Industrial Applications*, by H. Piraux (N.V. Philips' Gloeilampenfabrieken, Eindhoven, 1964), with the kind permission of the publishers.

dose of 100–5000 rads*. However doses beyond 10 krads would be lethal.

(c) *Control of Predatory Insects*

It is not always possible to effectively combat predatory insects with pesticides only. It is necessary to know of their migration and breeding habits. It is possible to obtain to some extent data in this regard by labelling the insects themselves with ^{32}P or ^{60}Co. This is done by dipping a collection of the insects in a solution of cobalt chloride labelled with ^{60}Co. Usually each insect absorbs around 0.4 μCi of activity which provides it a dose of about 300 rads over a period of 6–8 months, which is very much less than the lethal dose. With an elaborate system of a number of detectors spread over a large area, it is possible to follow the migration of the labelled insects. Sometimes the insects have been observed to move about a kilometer per day and scatter around 10 km in a season. They have also been observed to prefer old decayed wood to settle down for hybernation. These spots once located, are sprayed with a suitable insecticide and the predators are thus destroyed.

The green-fly is known to be a great menace to groundnuts as they bring about a fatal disease through a virus transmission. This problem is tackled in a novel way. In a selected plot of the field, the roots of the groundnuts are watered with the solution of a phosphate labelled with ^{32}P. The groundnuts growing therefrom are in their turn labelled, and the greenflies are allowed to feed on these nuts. These insects imbibing the activity are able to transmit the same to the next two or three generations. The habitats of these flies are thus easily located and destroyed.

Sometimes, the male of certain insects harmful to fruits are isolated, well fed and exposed to a heavy γ dose and let off. Later, on mating they give rise to eggs which are sterile, thus checking the growth of the species in a given area.

8.6.7 PROSPECTING OF NATURAL RESOURCES

Because a large number of elements can be activated by neutrons and in the process they emit radiation whose energy is characteristic of the element, the technique of identifying some of the elements and their compounds by a neutron probe is well developed. Some examples are presented here.

(a) *Prospecting of Water and Petroleum*

A drilling is made in the terrain to be examined and a neutron probe, usually a (Po + Be) source** of flux around 10^7 n/s is inserted as shown

---

*Radiation doses are measured in units of rads: 1 rad being equivalent to the absorption of radiation energy of 10^{-5} J (= 100 ergs) per gram, or 10^{-2} J kg^{-1}. The SI unit of dose is the gray (Gy), representing the absorption of radiation energy of one joule per kg. Hence, 1 Gy = 100 r.

**The source emits 3.5 MeV neutrons by (α, n) reaction on ^9Be.

in Fig. 8.14. As the probe is lowered to different depths, the neutrons induce radioactivity in the elements present in the various layers of the earth and in the process of activation each element emits its characteristic γ rays. By proper collimation, these γ photons reach a scintillation detector placed in the probe and well shielded by lead to cut off stray radiation. The signals after amplification are analyzed by a γ ray spectrometer and recorded. From the energy of the photons, the nature of the elements present at the given depth is known. This technique is widely used in locating the presence of large amounts of water and petroleum by the 2.2 MeV photons of hydrogen and 6.7 MeV photons of oxygen. Presence of carbon is indicated by 4.4 MeV photons.

(b) Some Other Elements

Some other elements emitting characteristic γ radiation on neutron activation are magnesium: 1.37 MeV; potassium: 1.53 MeV; chlorine: 2.15 MeV and calcium: 3.73 MeV.

(c) Diamonds and Beryl

Generally diamonds are present in pipes or veins of umberlite, a basaltic rock the natural radioactivity of which is very feeble and these

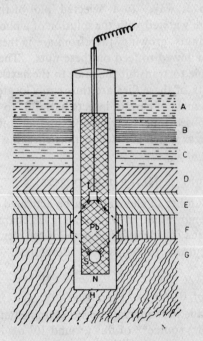

Fig. 8.14   Neutron probe for prospecting natural resources
A,B,... G: different rock formations,
S: neutron source; T: γ detector,
Pb: lead shielding.
H: outer pipe holding the neutron probe N.

pipes are generally surrounded by granites rich in quartz and whose natural radioactivity is considerably higher. Thus while charting rock formations with a probe consisting of a sensitive GM counter, a *sharp decrease* in activity and its rise again generally indicates pipes of basalts and there is a probability of these containing diamonds.*

Beryl is a naturally occurring mineral containing BeO in a pleasantly green transparent hexagonal crystalline form, in large columns sometimes. It is one of the precious stones, and while prospecting one should avoid its breakage. Advantage is taken of the large cross section for the reaction

$$^9Be\,(\gamma, n)\,2\alpha$$

in prospecting for beryl. A high energy γ source as ^{124}Sb or ^{140}La is placed in the probe with a neutron detector as $^{10}BF_3$. By this technique beryllium is uniquely detected. In fact, the common laboratory neutron source of $^{124}Sb + Be$ involves the above reaction.

(d) Uranium and Thorium

Being naturally radioactive, minerals bearing uranium and/or thorium are readily detectable with a sensitive GM counter. The fact that granitic rocks contain usually 4 g of U and about 13 g of Th per tonne of the rock should be borne in mind as constituting the background. It is only when the detector registers an activity far in excess of the background that the material may be considered as a useful source of these elements.

8.6.8 INDUSTRIAL APPLICATIONS

In addition to the applications in different areas discussed above, numerous industrial applications of radioisotopes and of their radiations, β and γ, are known. Some of these are described below.

(a) Thickness Measurement and Control

A non-destructive method of measuring the thickness of coatings or layers, levels of liquids in containers (static), or of moving sheets or layers of textiles, paper, rubber sheets, moving on a conveyor belt and controlling their thickness has been in vogue in many industries, using usually a ^{90}Sr beta source below the sheet or coating and a GM detector above it. The 0.54 MeV betas are well suited for measuring thicknesses over the range of 60 to 500 mg/cm² of matter.**[49]

The strength of the signal from the detector is an inverse measure of

---

*The uranium content of granites is around 4 g per tonne, as against 0 8 g per tonne in basalts.

**To convert thickness in mg/cm² to cm, divide by the density in mg/cm³; *e.g.* a foil of Al of thickness 100 mg/cm² $= \dfrac{100}{2.7 \times 10^3} = 0.037$ cm thick.

the thickness, *i.e.* larger the thickness feebler the signal. Usually the thickness of the moving sheet is determined by the pressure exerted by the rollers between which it is moving. The change in the ionization current after amplification actuates a relay which in its turn controls the pressure between the rollers. Thus it is possible to have an automated unit which measures and controls the thickness. A more sophisticated unit employs a pair of matched source-detector systems a few cm apart (Fig. 8.15a). The signals are in anticoincidence and the meter would read almost zero net current. Any imbalance due to variation of thickness is amplified and this actuates a relay to restore the thickness to within the predetermined limits.

The above *transmission* technique would not be possible unless both sides of the sheet or coating are accessible for placing the source and the detector on opposite sides as in Fig. 8.15a. Sometimes only the outer side is accessible, the inner being solid, or filled with some material, as for instance the paint on a solid body, or lining of the walls of a furnace, or corrosion growth in a reactor vessel, *etc.* In such cases, the *back-scattering* technique is used, the source and the detector are placed on the same side as in Fig. 8.15(b). The signal strength due to radiation

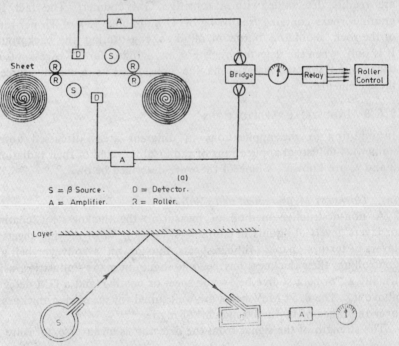

(a)

S = β Source.   D = Detector.
A = Amplifier.   R = Roller.

Fig. 8.15 Thickness control of sheets and layers by β radiation
(a) sheet, (b) layer
(from *Radioisotopes and their Industrial Applications*, by H. Piraux, © 1964,
N.V. Philips' Gloilampenfabrieken, Eindhoven, reproduced with permission).

scattered by the layer can be calibrated against its thickness. In this case the problem is only to know the thickness of the paint, or corrosion layer as it grows.

The radiations get reflected from the coating and the detector is placed at the right position and direction to receive the back scattered radiation. Thicker the coat stronger is the back scattering up to a limit.

Where the thickness to be measured is much larger, a gamma source as ^{137}Cs or ^{60}Co is used whose γ radiation has a larger penetrating power of over 90 and 150 mm of steel respectively.

(b) *Friction and Wearout*

When two surfaces of same or different metals or alloys rub against each other, as during the motion of one relative to the other, friction develops and trace amounts of material are transferred and the surfaces wear out. The presence of a lubricant reduces the friction and wearout. It is difficult by normal chemical analysis to know the trace amounts of matter lost by friction. It is however desirable to know this, so that the period after which the machine parts become unserviceable can be anticipated, besides being able to evaluate the efficiency of a given lubricant in minimizing friction. Radioisotopes find a valuable application in this context. Of the two rubbing surfaces, one is neutron activated so that it becomes radioactive. After a certain period of operation, without a lubricant the other surface is autoradiographed and this indicates the amount of matter transferred from the first surface during that period of time. When worked with a lubricant, the used oil after a given period is counted for radioactivity. Transfer of matter of less than a microgram can be measured by this technique. For example, a wearout of one per cent of a steel component can be determined after working it for just a minute, the part having been neutron activated to produce ^{59}Fe. In this way the rate of wear can be assessed in a matter of an hour and the data would help in assessing the serviceable life of the machine parts right in the beginning. This technique finds routine application in some automobile industries for assessing the wearout of piston rings. The method also is employed in knowing in advance when the holes of a draw plate, (made of hard tungsten carbide) used for drawing out wires of a fixed diameter, enlarge by friction.

Because of the radioactivity of the components involved, adequate shielding and radiation precautions are to be ensured before adopting these techniques.

(c) *Gamma Radiography*

The technique of examining industrial castings and machine parts for microcracks and defects by X-rays is well-known. This, however, is being replaced in some cases by gammagraphy, using γ radiation from certain radioisotopes. The advantage lies in the fact that these γ emitters can be had in compact capsule or pellet form containing sufficient activity

(10^2-10^3 curies), as compared to the elaborate X-ray machines with their bulky high voltage power supplies. Also the γ sources need no cooling arrangement which are necessary for X-ray machines. The γ sources thus permit easy mobility. However, because of the greater energy of the radiation (10^3-10^6 eV), the health hazard is greater with the γ sources but adequate methods of shielding and protecting the personnel are well developed. Some of the γ sources commonly used are listed below in Table 8.5.

TABLE 8.5: Sources for gammaradiography

Source	Half-life	γ Energy/MeV	Half-thickness*/mm steel
^{55}Fe	2.7 y	0.0059	0.01
^{60}Co	5.27 y	1.17, 1.33	34
^{137}Cs	30.17 y	0.662	16.5
^{170}Tm	128.6 d	0.084	1
^{192}Ir	74.2 d	0.3 to 2.0	10–50

*The half-thickness is the thickness which reduces the intensity of the radiation to half the initial value $= 0.693/\mu$, where μ is the linear absorption coefficient.

Suppose a large metallic casting is to be examined for defects. A photographic film sensitive to γ radiation is placed behind it in close contact with it and a gamma source is placed in front of it at different positions. Any denser blackening at certain parts of the film on development corresponds to the presence of a crack or defect in the casting. The Diesel Locomotive Works, Varanasi, have been using about 8 Ci of ^{192}Ir for testing by gammagraphy steel plates of thickness up to 76 mm used in the manufacture of diesel locomotives for the Indian Railways since the mid sixties.

In metallurgy, valuable information has been obtained about inclusions and distribution of small amounts of other elements in alloys by neutron activation followed by autoradiography, or by adding the impurity element labelled with its radioisotope during metallurgy and then autoradiographing the product. The general finding in all cases has been that the impurity elements tend to concentrate along the surface, grain boundaries or interdendritic sites. A part of the antimony added to germanium to obtain semi-conductor crystals is found to be lost in the surface. Similar was the finding in respect of aluminium added to silicon in preparing silicon rectifiers.

8.7   Uses of Nuclear Radiations

8.7.1   RADIATION STERILIZATION

It is found more convenient and effective to sterilize surgical instruments, sutures, gloves, and ampules by exposure to a high gamma dose of a few megarads, than by the conventional way of steaming in an autoclave, or by chemicals. Similarly, the sterilization of drugs and pharmaceuticals has also been attempted with success.

All foodstuffs, vegetables, milk, eggs, and meat have a limited life after which they decay and become inedible. Sometimes large amounts of foodstuffs are lost this way. Usually this happens when the number of microorganisms exceed 10^8 g^{-1} of matter. An exposure to an appropriate dose of γ radiation at room temperature is known to destroy the harmful microorganisms and the shelf-life of the food is thereby considerably increased, without affecting the taste, colour or appearance, so that it remains as acceptable for consumption as a fresh sample.

Water itself can be adequately sterilized at room temperature by a γ-dose of the order 0.2 Mrad. A dose of 5 to 20 krads given to potatoes prevents sprouting for a few months longer than unirradiated samples. Similarly, γ-irradiated onions and meat keep fresh for long periods without any adverse effect. There is always an optimum dose for each material, which if exceeded may lead to destruction of the vitamins in the food and to its ultimate decay even faster. In spite of these facts being well demonstrated, there is public distrust in accepting irradiated foodstuffs so far; however, conditions may change in favour of adopting techniques for controlled irradiation of foodstuffs to prolong their shelf-life. In some countries facilities for fast irradiation on conveyer belts employing megacurie sources of ^{60}Co with remote controls exist.

8.7.2   RADIATION ENERGY FOR CHEMICAL SYNTHESIS

A large number of chemical syntheses employing γ radiation has been shown to be technically feasible and economically viable. It would appear to be an excellent use of the energy of large 10^5-10^6 rad/h γ-sources, and of the spent fuel rods which emit 2–3 Mrad per hour while they are cooling; in any case all this energy would go waste, otherwise. There are other advantages besides, such as the use of metallic reactors on account of the high penetrability of γ radiation and the more uniform irradiation of the bulk of the reaction space. Since radiation-induced reactions take place at room temperature and without a catalyst, the products are likely to be purer. Some of the reactions found to be feasible are mentioned below.

(i)   Ethyl Bromide

Passing a mixture of hydrogen bromide and ethylene at room temperature around a high intensity ^{60}Co source leads to the formation of ethyl bromide (Fig. 8.16) $C_2H_4 + HBr \rightarrow C_2H_5Br$. The purity is around

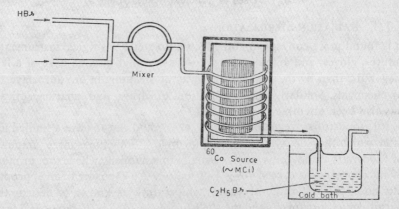

Fig. 8.16 Radiation synthesis of ethyl bromide.

99.5% and the yield corresponds to a low energy absorption of 96 J/mol product, or $G(C_2H_5Br) = 10^5$.*

(ii) Gammexane

Gammexane is one of the six stereoisomers of benzene hexachloride formed by the chlorination of benzene

$$C_6H_6 + 3Cl_2 \rightarrow C_6H_6Cl_6 \ (\sim 12\% \ \gamma \ isomer)$$

It is used mixed with other isomers as a powerful insecticide. The radiation yield $G\,(C_6H_6Cl_6)$ is of the order of 10^5, of which around 12% is the γ isomer. Being a highly exothermic reaction, efficient cooling is necessary and this is more easy with a metallic reactor used with γ radiation than a glass reactor necessary for photochemical synthesis.

(iii) Cyclohexanesulphonyl Chloride

When a mixture of cyclohexane, chlorine and sulphur-dioxide is exposed to γ radiation, the reaction leads to the formation of cyclohexane sulphonylchloride as the main product:

$$C_6H_{12} + SO_2 + Cl_2 \rightarrow C_6H_{11}SO_2Cl + HCl$$

Spent fuel rods have been used with success in this case as the source of γ radiation, providing a dose rate of about 2.5 Mrad/h. The product has to be chemically separated from other by-products as cyclohexane disulphonylchloride and chlorohexane, forming in small amounts.

Several other hydrocarbons have been successfully sulphochlorinated by γ radiation with high yields.

*In radiation chemistry the yields are expressed in terms of the G value of the product, i.e., the number of molecules of the product formed per 100 eV energy absorbed.

(iv) *Some Other* γ *Radiation Induced Reactions*

Various types of other reactions induced by γ radiation have been studied and the G values determined, though none of them appears to have been adopted on a commercial scale, probably mainly due to heavy initial expenses in obtaining large intensity γ sources and in providing elaborate shielding to protect the workers. Preparation of silicone lubricants, egosterol from yiest, ethylene glycol from methanol and the fixation of atmospheric nitrogen are amongst the reactions considered possible using γ radiation. γ irradiation of wood treated with methyl methacrylate (MMA) results in the polymerization of the latter (MMA → PMMA) which imparts to the wood greater strength and resistance to water absorption.

8.8 Radioisotopes as a Source of Electricity

Because of the large amount of energy released in the decay of each radioactive atom, it has been a tempting and challenging proposition from the early times to convert this energy into electricity. However, only small power generators have been possible so far and these have been used mainly for special purposes as in defence and space research, more often to charge batteries.

Moseley, the renowned physicist who provided the experimental evidence for the concept of atomic number,* appears to have been the earliest to build a small cell using 20 mCi of the active *deposit of radium*** placed inside a small quartz sphere and collecting the beta particles on an outer sphere in vacuum. The outer surface of the inner and the inner surface of the outer spheres being silvered, acted as the anode and cathode respectively. It is reported that initially a very high potential of the order of "150 kV" and a current of 0.1 mA were observed. Later workers obtained larger currents by using β emitters of artificial origin as ^{90}Sr of much higher activity.

In the cell developed by Ohmart[49], γ radiation from ^{60}Co is used to ionize a gas between two electrodes of different work functions, as gold and lead, or copper and lead. A specially prepared Ohmart cell is known to give a constant potential of 0.7 volt at a microwatt level. Attempts have also been made to obtain power by bombarding the *p–n* junction of a Ge or Si semiconductor with β particles. With use, however, the crystal gets damaged.

The SNAP (Strontium-Ninety Auxiliary Power) developed in US represents an efficient source of power, rather auxiliary power, as it is used mainly for charging batteries used in submarines, space craft, unmanned Arctic stations and in nuclear devices coupled to high fre-

---

*H.G.J. Moseley, while still at the prime of his scientific achievements, was killed in World War I at a young age.

**The solid radioactive material resulting from the decay of the 3.8 day radon, ^{222}Rn.

quency transmitters for continuous signalling of weather conditions and of sudden large bursts of radiation release as in, otherwise possibly unknown, nuclear explosions. The SNAP is reported to use the 0.54 MeV β emitter ^{90}Sr in the form of strontium titanate of strength around 20 kCi in a highly compact packing which gets heated to temperatures of the order of 500°C which provides the thermoelectric power through a large number of efficient thermojunctions as of Ag-Bi, the cold junctions outside being at a temperature around 50°C (Fig. 8.17). Sometimes the 5.4 MeV α emitter ^{238}Pu (86.4 year period) is stated to be used in place of ^{90}Sr. Two such devices were reported to have been placed in the Himalayan regions (Nanda Devi and elsewhere) in 1965–68. One of them, it has been stated, was lost under a glacier. It is only to be hoped that the encapsulation does not give way, for if any leak develops, the waters of the Ganga would become hazardously radio-active for about 5-6 half-lives of the isotope involved.

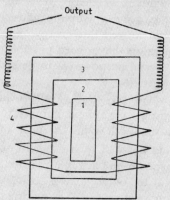

Fig. 8.17   Radioisotope (^{90}SrTiO$_3$) as a source of
              thermoelectricity (SNAP)
              1: Column of ^{90}SrTiO$_3$ ~ 20 kCi,
              2: Insulator,   3: Shielding
              4: Thermocouples

The development of electrical power on a commercial scale by burning nuclear fuels as enriched uranium, has been achieved since the mid-fifties. The first atomic power station of India rated to generate 480 MW has been in successful operation at Tarapur since October 1969. Since then other atomic power stations have been coming up in different parts of India (see Sec. 7.9).

References
(where marked*, see Bibliography)

1. C.M. Lederer and V.M. Shirley*
2. E.C. Anderson and W.F. Libby, 'World-wide Distribution of Natural Radiocarbon', *Phys. Rev.*, 1951, **81**, 64.
3. An. N. Nesmeyanov*
4. M. Chemla et J. Pauly, 'La séparation de ^{22}Na d'une cible de Mg par electrolyse sur cathode de mercure renouvelée', *Bull. Soc. Chim. France*, 1953, 432.
5. M. Chemla et P. Sue, 'Nouvelle méthode de préparation de radioelements artificiels sans entreineur: cas de ^{35}S', *Comptes rendus* (Paris), 1951, **233**, 247.
6. M. Chemla et P. Sue, 'Séparation de ^{35}S sans entreineur a partir de NaCl irradié au néutrons', *Comptes rendus* (Paris), 1954, **238**, 1502.
7. L. Szilard and T.A. Chalmers, 'Chemical Separation of Radioactive Element from its Bombarded Isolope in Fermi Effect', *Nature*, 1934, **134**, 462.
7. (a) R.D. Harrison.*
8. E. Amaldi, O.D' Agostino, E. Fermi, B. Pontecorvo, F. Rasetti and E. Segrè, 'Artificial Radioactivity Produced by Neutron Bombardment, II' *Proc. Roy. Soc.* (London), 1935, **A149**, 522.
9. F. Paneth and J. Fay, 'Concentration of Artificially Produced Radioelement by an Electric Field' *Nature*, 1935, **135**, 820; *J. Chem. Soc.*, 1936, 384.
10. P.C. Capron, G. Stokkink and M. van Meerssche 'Separation of Nuclear Isomers in Electric Field', Isotope is Fermi Effect' *Nature*, 1946, **157**, 806.
11. S. Wexler and T.H. Davies, 'The Dissociation of Ethylbromide and iodide by Neutron Capture' *J. Chem. Phys.*, 1952, **20**, 1688.
12. H. J. Arnikar, 'L' emploi de champ electrique pour séparer des produits de recul (n, γ) en brome et iode—III', *J. Phys. Radium*, 1962, **23**, 578.
13. N.K. Saha and L.K. Rangan, 'Determination of Absolute Cross Section of (n, p) Reaction in ^{32}S' *Ind. J. Phys.*, 1956, **30**, 80.
14. A.E. Cahill and H. Taube, 'The Use of Heavy Oxygen in the Study of Reactions of Hydrogen Peroxide', *J. Amer. Chem. Soc.*, 1952, **74**, 2312.
15. M.B. Allen and S. Ruben, 'Tracer Studies with Radioactive Carbon and Hydrogen: Synthesis and Oxidation of Fumaric Acid', *J. Amer. Chem. Soc.*, 1942, **64**, 948.
16. K. Bloch and F. Lynen, *Nobel Lectures in Medicine and Physiology*, (Nobel Foundation, Stockholm, 1964).
17. J.N. Buchanann, *Advances in Enzymology* (Ed. F.F. Nord, Academic Press, N.Y.).
18. H.A.C. McKay, 'Kinetics of Exchange Reactions', *Nature*, 1938, **142**, 997; *J. Amer. Chem. Soc.*, 1943, **65**, 702.
19. H.A.C. McKay*
20. A.C. Wahl and N.A. Bonner*
21. H. Moureux, M. Magat et G. Vitroff 'Spectres Raman des deux formes moléculaires du pentachlorure de phosphore' *Comptes rendus* (Paris), 1937, **205**, 276.
22. H.J. Arnikar, S.F. Patil, P.P. Joshi and S.D. Prasad 'Radiation Induced Exchange between Bromide and Bromate Ions', *Radiochem. Radioanal. Letters*, 1974, **19**, 303.
23. R. Daudel, P. Daudel et M. Martin, 'Covalaffinité potential d' oxydo-reduction et réactions d' echange', *Comptes rendus* (Paris), 1944, **219**, 129.
24. H.J. Arnikar and R. Tripathi, *J. Chromatography*, 1962, **7**, 362.
25. H.J. Arnikar, S.F. Patil, R. Harnesswala and V.G. Dedgaonkar, *Ind. J. Chem.*, 1975, **13**, 1055.
26. H.J. Arnikar, V.G. Dedgaonkar and M.S. Barve, *Ind. J. Chem.*, 1977, **15A**, 100.
27. R.T. Overman and H.M. Clark*
28. H.J. Arnikar et M. Chemla, 'Diffusion de ^{22}Na+, ^{42}K+ et ^{137}Cs+ dans des mono-

cristaux de KCl' *Comptes rendus* (Paris), 1956, **242**, 2132.

29. H.J. Arnikar and O.P. Mehta, 'Surface Self-diffusion of Iodide Ions in Thin Films', *J. Phys. Chem. Solids*, 1963, **24**, 1633.

30. H.J. Arnikar, E.A. Daniels and S.V. Kulkarni, 'Surface Diffusion of Chloride and Iodide Ions on Silver—Part II', *Ind. J. Chem.*, 1979, **18A**, 13.

31. S.G. Thompson, B.G. Harvey, G.R. Chopin and G.T. Seaborg, 'Chemical Properties of Elements 99 and 100', *J. Amer. Chem. Soc.*, 1954, **76**, 6229.

32. H.J. Arnikar et M. Chemla, 'Chromatographie des Ions Alkalins sur Papier d' Amiante', *Comptes rendus* (Paris), 1957, **244**, 68.

33. H.J. Arnikar, 'Radiochromatography of Alkali Ions', *Nature*, 1958, **182**, 1230.

34. H.J. Arnikar and O.P. Mehta, 'Radiochromatography of Alkali Earth Ions', *Current Science*, 1959, **28** 400.

35. H.J. Arnikar and J.P. Tandon, 'A Chromatographic Study of the Isotope Exchange Reaction between Sulphite and Thiosulphate Ions' *J, Banaras Hindu University*, 1959-60, **10**, 174.

36. H.J. Arnikar, Thèse, Paris, 1958, *Ann. Phys.* (Paris), 1959, **13** (4), 1291.

37. P. Savel, 'Determination of Arsenic in Hair by Activation Analysis', Ann. Pharm. France, 1963, **21**, 303.

38. H.J. Arnikar, V.G. Dedgaonkar and S.J. Bhagat, 'Neutron Activation of Silver in Estimating Boron and Cadmium', *Ind. J. Chem.*, 1972, **19**, 541.

39. T.A. Littlefield and N. Thorley*

40. N.B. Keevil, 'The Calculation of Geological Age', *J. Amer. Chem. Soc.*, 1939, **237**, 195.

41. F.E. Wickman (see K. Rankama*).

42. A. Holmes, 'The Oldest Known Minerals and Rocks' (see K. Rankama*).

43. S. Silver*

44. M.D. Kamen*

45. G. Wolf*

46. H.J. Arnikar, L.M. Singh and K.N. Udupa, 'On the Healing of Fractures and the Use of *Cissus Quadrangularis* thereon, Studied by ^{35}S and ^{32}P', *Ind. J. Medical Sci.*, 1961, **15**, 545 and 551.

47. L.E.M. Miles and C.N. Hales, 'Labelled Antibodies and Immunological Assay Systems', *Nature*, 1968, **219**, 186.

48. *Radioimmunoassay and Related Procedures in Medicine* (I.A.E.A., 1974, 1977).

49. H. Piraux.*

Problems

8.1 Find the energy of recoil of ^{128}I atom following the emission of a 4.8 MeV photon in the (n, γ) reaction on ethyl iodide.   [96.48 eV]

8.2 Determine the energy of recoil of ^{65}Zn following (n, γ) reaction on an organozinc compound in which a photon of 1.1 MeV is emitted.   [9.98 eV]

8.3 A 20 ml sample of a saturated solution containing 4 mg/l of labelled $PbSO_4$ has an activity of 1600 c/min. The solution was shaken with 1 g of precipitated $PbSO_4$ and filtered. The filtrate was found to give 450 c/min. All activities are net and free from background. Given the surface area of one formula weight of $PbSO_4$ to be 18.4×10^{-16} cm^2, find the surface area of 1 g of the precipitate sample.   [775.6 cm^2/g]

8.4 A ruby weighing 0.5 g was irradiated in a neutron flux of 10^{12} n cm^{-2} s^{-1} for exactly 24 h and the ^{51}Cr activity ($\tau = 27.7$ d) counted immediately thereafter.

It was found to give 35 000 c/s. Given that the σ for ^{50}Cr to be 15.9 b, the counting efficiency 10% and the ^{50}Cr content of natural chromium to be 4.35% find the chromium content of the ruby.   [0.85 μ g]

8.5 A sample containing an unknown amount of germanium metal is irradiated in a neutron flux of 10^{12} n cm^{-2} s^{-1} for 1 h when the ^{76}Ge forms ^{77}Ge of half-life 1 min. Suppose the activity measured 1 min after the 1 h irradiation is 2500 dis/s, find the amount of germanium in the same, given the cross section for the reaction is 3.28 mb, and the isotopic abundance of ^{76}Ge to be 7.8%.   [2.47 mg]

8.6 To assess the volume of the blood in a patient, one cm^3 of his blood was withdrawn, labelled with ^{32}P and reinjected into his body. After adequate time for homogenization, one cm^3 of his blood was again withdrawn and the sample showed a total activity of 250 net counts in 10 min. Find the volume of blood in the patient, given that 0.1 cm^3 of the labelled blood before injection corresponded to an activity of 14 000 counts per min.   [5.6 litres]

Chapter 9

Elements of Radiation Chemistry

9.1 Radiation Chemistry

Radiation chemistry deals with physical, chemical and biochemical transformations in matter brought about by the absorption of nuclear radiation. This latter conventionally includes not only high energy electromagnetic radiation as X- and γ-rays, but also high energy charged particles as electrons, protons, deuterons, tritons, alpha particles, other accelerated heavy ions and fission fragments as well as neutrons. Reactions due to low energy photons, as visible and ultra-violet, form the subject matter of Photochemistry and hence are left out here. Interaction of photons and particles of energy 100 eV and above with matter are of special interest as they represent an energy range far in excess of the mean Boltzmann value of kinetic energy at 10^4 K.*

Historically, the fluorescence excited on the container glass wall observed by Röntgen in his X-ray apparatus in 1895 and of the blackening of a photographic film by radiations from a uranium salt, noticed by Becquerel in 1896, may be considered as the first reported examples of radiation effects on matter. That such effects can be dangerous to living beings was not well recognized by pioneer workers, as a result of which, some of them suffered irreparable harm to themselves.

We shall present briefly the major characteristics of different radiations as (a) charged particles, (b) neutrons and (c) γ-radiation and their general interactions with matter. The study will be restricted to low and medium energy radiations (100 eV–2 MeV). If we leave out direct interaction of very high enery radiation with atomic nuclei, the rest of radiation chemistry involves interactions with orbital electrons and these consist mainly in excitation and ionization as the *primary* act. The final products are the result of secondary reactions due to these excited and ionized species. Hence, the precise transformations due to the absorption of radiation depend on the nature of the radiation, its energy and on the atomic number of the target substance. Lastly, the physico-chemical

---

*The mean kinetic energy of particles at room temperature ($\sim$ 300 K) is 0.025 eV.

effects may depend also on the rate at which the energy is absorbed.

We shall consider here some of the more important modes of inter-action of different types of radiation with matter, chemical methods of measuring the amount of radiation energy absorbed and the units in use for expressing the same. In the end, the radiation chemistry of water will be discussed in some detail. The reasons for singling out water in this study are many. Firstly, water, as is well-known, forms the major constituent of all living beings. Therefore, a knowledge of whatever happens to water on exposure to nuclear radiation is of vital importance. Secondly, as very large amounts of water are used either as a primary or a secondary coolant in all nuclear reactors, a detailed knowledge of physical-chemical changes occurring in water under intense irradiation is indispensible to reactor designing. Lastly, as we shall see later, most of the radiation effects on dissolved solutes are the result of their interactions with the *primary radiolytic products* (*prp*) of water, the solvent.

Transformations in a variety of inorganic and organic substances in the solid and in the dissolved state, biomolecules, materials of interest in solid state science, and secondary reactions due to hot atoms, and recoil chemistry in general, are beyond the scope of the present treatment. These aspects of radiation chemistry are well dealt in specialized publi-cations on the subject and in reviews of international conferences on the subject (see Bibliography).

9.2 Interaction of Radiation with Matter

We shall study the more important modes of interaction with matter of electrons, other charged particles, neutrons and γ photons, separately.

9.2.1 PRIMARY EFFECTS DUE TO CHARGED PARTICLES

Most effects due to low and medium energy radiations on matter are the overall result of a series of reactions, the *primary* event being electronic excitation or ionization, or sometimes bond rupture resulting in free radicals. The primary event is generally indicated by a wavy arrow:

$$\left.\begin{array}{l} \gamma + H_2O \rightsquigarrow H_2O^* \\ e^- + H_2O \rightsquigarrow H_2O^* + e^- \end{array}\right\} \quad \text{excitation}$$

$$\left.\begin{array}{l} e^- + H_2O \rightsquigarrow H_2O^+ + 2e^- \\ \gamma + H_2O \rightsquigarrow H_2O^+ + e^- \end{array}\right\} \quad \text{ionization}$$

$$e^- + H_2O \rightsquigarrow \cdot H + \cdot OH + e^- \quad \text{radical formation.}$$

After the primary event, the initial electron, now of reduced energy, continues moving through the matter repeating one or the other process as long as it has enough energy. Primary events with other charged particles are similar.

9.2.2 RADIATION TRACKS, SPURS AND δ-RAYS

All along the track of the primary particle are formed islands or clusters of active species consisting of electron-ion pairs, excited species and radicals. These clusters are referred to as *spurs*. The number of active species in a spur, its mean size and inter-spur distance depend on the nature of the radiation, its energy and the rate at which it loses energy in moving through the medium. Each spur may contain 2 to 5 excited species and ion pairs produced by the primary radiation, as well as those created by some of the secondary electrons. However, if the secondary electron has high enough energy (> 100 eV), it would branch off from the primary track and form its own spurs. The latter is termed a δ-*ray* track.

In the case of γ radiation and electrons passing through water, the calculations of Samuel and Magee[1] indicate the spur diameter to be around 2 nm and these occur at intervals of about 10^{-6} m along the track. With densely ionizing radiation as the α particles, the spurs almost overlap yielding what is described as *columnar ionization*, with more δ-ray tracks branching off.

9.2.3 LINEAR ENERGY TRANSFER: LET

The primary radiolytic products (*prp*) interact in their turn in a variety of ways leading to different final products. The yields of the final products depend on the nature of the radiation and its energy, as well as on the nature of the target substance, its atomic number and mass, or its ability to "stop" the radiation. This *stopping power*, S, is defined as

$$S = -(dE/dx)^*$$
(9.1)

i.e. the rate of energy loss per unit length of the matter. The same is also referred to as the *linear energy transfer* (LET) of the substance for the given radiation.

9.2.4 BETHE'S EQUATION FOR LET FOR CHARGED PARTICLES DUE TO COLLISIONS WITH ELECTRONS

Because of the large number of collisions between the moving charged particle and the electrons of the atoms of the stopping matter, the energy lost by the former per collision or per cm path averages out. The following expression was derived by Bethe for the LET for charged particles.[2]

$$\text{LET} = -\left(\frac{dE}{dX}\right)_{\text{coll}} = \frac{4\pi z^2 e^4}{m_e v^2} NZ \left[\ln \frac{2m_e v^2}{I} - \ln(1 - \beta^2) - \beta^2\right]$$
(9.2)

where z = charge of the moving particle ($z = 1$ for e^-, p, d;

$$= 2 \text{ for } \alpha, \text{ etc.}),$$

---

* The mass stopping power is S/ρ, where ρ is the density.

e = electron charge = 4.8×10^{-10} esu,

m_e = electron mass = 9.1096×10^{-28} g,

v = velocity of moving particle in cm/s,

N = number of stopping atoms/cm^3 = $L\rho/A$,

(where L is Avogadro number, ρ and A are density and atomic weight of the atoms of the stopping matter),

Z = atomic number of the atoms of the stopping matter,

I = mean of excitation and ionization energy of the stopping atom $\simeq 30$ eV for all atoms*,

$\beta = v/c$ the ratio of particle velocity to that of light.

Since $\ln \dfrac{2\,m_e\,v^2}{I}$ varies slowly with v, the Bethe equation gets simplified to

$$\text{LET} = -\left(\frac{dE}{dx}\right)_{\text{coll}} \propto \frac{Mz^2}{E} \qquad (9.3)$$

where M and E are the mass and energy of the moving particle. The above expression shows that LET increases up to a maximum as v decreases along the path, after which the LET decreases along with v.

9.2.5 BREMSSTRAHLUNG

All charged particles as they move through matter lose energy by two modes, (i) by collisions with orbital electrons of the stopping matter, considered in Sec. 9.2.3, and (ii) by emission of radiation (X-rays) as the particles approach atomic nuclei of the stopping matter. As a charged particle comes close to the field of an atomic nucleus, it suffers a change in its acceleration (+ or −) wihch, on the classical electromagnetic theory, must result in the emission of radiation.** This emission due to the "brake" action is termed the *bremsstrahlung*. The energy spectrum of bremsstrahlung is continuous from zero up to the energy of the particle itself. This will be in the X-ray region.

The net LET is the sum of $(dE/dx)_{\text{coll}}$ and $(dE/dx)_{\text{brem}}$. Though the full expression for $(dE/dx)_{\text{brem}}$ is a lengthy one, in essence it implies that

$$-(dE/dx)_{\text{brem}} \propto z^2 Z^2 / M^2 \qquad (9.4)$$

where z and Z are charges of the particle and of the nuclei of stopping matter and M is the mass of the particle. This means loss by bremsstrahlung is important only for particles of low M and of stopping matter of high Z.

*Thus a 1 MeV particle of any type will produce on the average $10^6/30 \cong 30\,000$ electron-ion pairs in any matter. This, however, does not apply to semiconductors.

**In his theory of the atom, Bohr postulated an exception to this by stating that an electron in one of the *permitted orbits* around the nucleus, satisfying certain quantum conditions, does not emit radiation, though under acceleration.

For electrons of energy E MeV, the ratio

$$\frac{(dE/dx)_{\text{brem}}}{(dE/dx)_{\text{coll}}} \simeq \frac{EZ}{1600\, m_e c^2} = \frac{EZ}{800} \qquad (\because \quad m_e c^2 = 0.51 \text{ MeV}) \quad (9.5)$$

In other words, bremsstrahlung becomes important for electrons in a medium of atomic number Z, only if the electron energy $\geqslant 800/Z$ MeV. In general, this mode of energy loss is negligible for electrons of energy below 0.1 MeV, while it becomes all important for electrons of energy above 10 MeV.

Net LET values for water are given for some radiations in Table 9.1.

TABLE 9.1: Some LET values for water[3]

(from *An Introduction to Radiation Chemistry*, by J.W.T. Spinks and R.J. Woods, © 1964, John Wiley & Sons, Inc., reproduced with permission)

Radiation	Energy/MeV	Range in air (15°C, atm)/cm	Range in water/ mm	LET in water/ keV micron⁻¹
Electron	1	405	4.1	0.24
	10	4200	52	0.19
Proton	1	2.3	0.023	43
	10	115	1.2	8.3
Deuteron	10	68	0.72	14
Alpha	10	10.5	0.11	92
γ	1.25	*	*	0.25

*See Sec. 9.4.

The absorption of electrons by matter and their ranges were considered earlier, in Sec. 4.7.2 for electrons both of monoenergy and energy continuum.

9.3   Passage of Neutrons through Matter

Being uncharged, neutrons face no Coulomb barrier and can freely penetrate atomic nuclei. The types of interaction of neutrons with matter depend on the energy of the former and the mass of the target atom. These include scattering, elastic and inelastic, and capture, radiative and non-radiative. Nuclear reactions due to neutrons of different energies with light, medium and heavy atoms were described earlier (Sec. 5.7.1).

9.3.1   ELASTIC SCATTERING OF NEUTRONS

We shall consider here briefly elastic scattering leading to slowing down of fast neutrons, the process involved in the moderation of neutrons in a reactor. The relation between the energy imparted to the recoil atom E_A by a neutron of initial energy E_0 in a single collision is given by

$$E_A = E_0 \frac{4A \cos^2 \theta}{(A+1)^2} \tag{9.6}$$

where A is the atomic mass of the recoil atom and θ is the angle between the initial trajectory of the neutron and of the recoil atom. The fraction of the energy lost by the neutron in each collision (E_A/E_0) is the greatest for $A = 1$, *i.e.* in collisions with hydrogen atoms. (water, paraffin, *etc.*). However, because of the high cross section for the $H(n, \gamma)$ ^2H reaction, ordinary hydrogen (or water) is not the best moderator. Instead, heavy hydrogen (or heavy water) or graphite are found to be the best moderators, with 0.89 and 0.28 as the respective maximum E_A/E_0 factors.

9.4 Interaction of γ Radiation with Matter

Unlike the charged particles which lose a fraction of their energy at every interaction with an orbital electron all along their passage through matter, the γ photons may pass through an indefinite distance through matter without interacting, *i.e.*, without losing any energy. And suddenly in a single encounter with an atomic electron, or in the nuclear field, it may lose all its energy by being captured, or lose a fraction of its energy and get scattered as a photon of longer wavelength. In view of this characteristic behaviour, photons do not have a specific range in matter as the charged particles. Instead, there is an exponential attenuation characterized by a *half-thickness* value for each type of matter, to be described later. First, we shall consider the four principal modes of interaction of γ radiation with matter (1) photoelectric effect, (2) Compton scattering, (3) pair production, and (4) nuclear reaction.

9.4.1 PHOTOELECTRIC EFFECT   10 — 100 MeV

The photoelectric emission is the principal mode of interaction of low energy photons (10–100 keV) with matter. Following are the characteristics of photoelectric emission.

(i) Here the photon of energy E_γ is wholly absorbed by a single electron of the atom and this electron is ejected with an energy E_e given by the difference between E_γ and the energy E_b binding the electron in the atom,

$$E_e = E_\gamma - E_b \tag{9.7}$$

Obviously, for photoelectric emission to be possible, $E_\gamma > E_b$. This implies the concept of a *threshold frequency* ν_0 such that $h\nu_0 = E_b$. Hence photons of energy $> E_b$ *i.e.* photons of frequency $\nu > \nu_0$ alone can cause photoelectric emission; the energy of the photoelectron being given by

$$E_e = h(\nu - \nu_0) \tag{9.8}$$

This mechanism of the photoelectric effect was first developed by Einstein for which he was awarded the Nobel prize in 1921. The importance of Eq. 9.8 is that it provides a method for determining the value of the

Planck constant, being the slope of the linear plot of energy of photoelec-
trons against the frequency of incident radiation.

(ii) As the initial photon is wholly absorbed (*i.e.* it vanishes), the
photoelectric emission is not possible with a free electron. It has to be
with an electron bound in an atom, such that the latter (now an ion)
can recoil to conserve momentum.

(iii) If E_γ is sufficiently high to release K shell electrons, about 80% of
the electrons will be from the K shell and the rest from the L shell.

(iv) The hole created in the K or L shell will be filled by the successive
jumps of outer electrons, emitting corresponding X-rays (the fluorescent
radiation) or by Auger emission (see Sec. 4.8.5).

(v) Absorption of a photon due to photoelectric effect decreases sharply
with increase of photon energy, but increases rapidly with atomic number
Z of the absorber material. The probability of photoelectric absorption
is $\propto Z^5/E_\gamma^{3.5}$.

Hence, it is the dominant mode of radiation absorption for low energy
photons and in heavy elements. The photoelectric absorption falls
smoothly with increasing photon energy but again with a sharp rise as the
energy reaches the photoelectric edge E_K, or E_L, *i.e.* the binding energy
of K or L shell electrons (see Fig. 9.1).

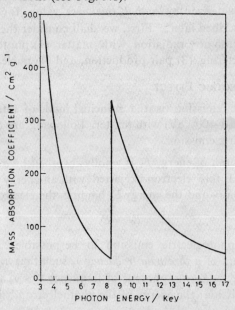

Fig. 9.1 Photoelectric emission in nickel

9.4.2 THE COMPTON SCATTERING

For intermediate energy photons over a wide range (0.1 to 10 MeV), the

dominant interaction is by Compton scattering. Here the photon interacts with a free or loosely bound electron, transfers a part of its energy
to it and itself gets scattered as a photon of correspondingly reduced
energy. The energy and momentum of the incident photon are shared
between the scattered photon and the recoil or Compton electron
(see Fig. 9.2).

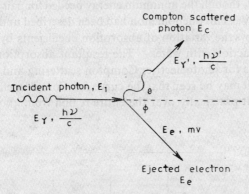

Fig. 9.2 The Compton effect.

$$\text{Energy: } E_\gamma = E_{\gamma}' + E_e \qquad (9.9)$$

$$\text{Momentum: } \frac{h\nu}{c} = \frac{h\nu'}{c} \cos\theta + mv \cos\phi \qquad (9.10)$$

where θ and ϕ are the angles of the scattered photon and the Compton
electron respectively with the initial trajectory. In terms of wavelengths
of the initial and scattered photons

$$\Delta\lambda = \lambda' - \lambda = \frac{h}{m_e c}(1 - \cos\theta) \qquad (9.11)$$

This relation has been experimentally verified for θ 2p to 150°. For $\theta = \pi/2$

$$\Delta\lambda = \frac{h}{m_e c} = 2\,42 \times 10^{-12} \text{ m}$$

which is known as the *Compton wavelength*.

Eqs. 9.8 and 9.11 show that the Compton electrons have a continuously
varying energy from zero to a maximum depending on the angle of the
scattered photon. Further, in terms of energy, Eq. 9 11, becomes

$$\frac{E_\gamma - E_{\gamma}'}{E_{\gamma}'} = \frac{E_\gamma}{m_e c^2}(1 - \cos\theta) \qquad (9.12)$$

If the energies be expressed in MeV and for $\theta = \pi/2$

$$\frac{E_\gamma - E_{\gamma}'}{E_{\gamma}'} = \frac{E_\gamma}{0.51}$$

i.e. the fractional change in energy of the photon is proportional to
the incident photon energy. Since the Compton scattering is the domi-

Some of high E γ ray (photon) $^7Li(p,\gamma)2\,^4He$ $E_\gamma = 17.6\,MeV$

$^3H(p,\gamma)\,^4He$ $E_\gamma = 14.8$

292

ESSENTIALS OF NUCLEAR CHEMISTRY

nant mode of energy loss over the range of 0.1 to 10 MeV, the fractional loss of energy for scattering at 90° is from 20% to total.

9.4.3 PAIR PRODUCTION >10 MeV

Need Read → The phenomenon of photon absorption leading to the creation of an electron-positron pair becomes important with photons of energies, greater than 10 MeV, though the minimum energy needed for pair production is $2m_e c^2 = 1.02\ MeV$. This phenomenon had been described under Sec. 4.9.3.

Figure 9.3 shows the variation of absorption coefficients by the different modes of γ interaction with water. The resultant absorption is the sum of the coefficients for photoelectric, Compton scattering and pair production processes. It may be seen that the curve for Compton effect coincides with the resultant practically over the entire region from about 0.05 to 10 MeV.

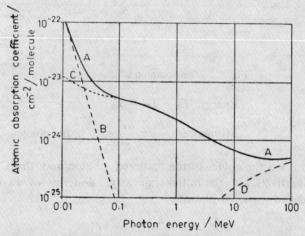

Fig. 9.3   Photoelectric absorption (B), Compton scattering (C) and pair production (D) in water and their resultant (A)[3]

(from *An Introduction to Radiation Chemistry*, by J.W.T. Spinks and R.J. Woods. © 1964, John Wiley & Sons, Inc., reproduced with permission).

9.4.4 NUCLEAR REACTIONS

Photonuclear reactions are the result of direct interaction of photons with atomic nuclei. These are important for photons of very high energy only. Sec. 5.8 gives a brief account of photonuclear reactions.

9.5   Units for Measuring Radiation Absorption

Unlike for the charged particles, the attenuation of X and γ rays through matter follows an exponential law. Several units exist for expressing the absorption coefficient. Some of these are described here.

9.5.1 ABSORPTION COEFFICIENTS

The total absorption of radiation by matter is the sum of mainly absorption due to photoelectric emission, Compton scattering and pair production, though as pointed out earlier, it is the Compton scattering which dominates over a wide range of incident photon energy (0.1-10 MeV). The absorption of energy can be expressed per cm length of matter or per gram, atom, or electron per cm² in the path of the beam. These are related to one another as shown below.

(i) Linear Absorption Coefficient

The simplest expression for the attenuation is given by

$$I = I_0 e^{-\mu x} \qquad \mu = cm^{-1} \tag{9.13}$$

where I_0 is the initial intensity and I the intensity after passing through a thickness x of the matter. μ is *linear absorption coefficient,* and its unit is cm⁻¹. This quantity is less used as it varies widely from substance to substance. Eq. 9.13 provides the concept of "half-thickness" = $0.693/\mu$. This is the thickness which attenuates the beam intensity to half (similar to the concept of half-life period in radioactivity).

(ii) Mass Absorption Coefficient

The linear absorption coefficient divided by the density ρ of the substance gives the *mass absorption coefficient,* μ/ρ. Its units are cm²/g. The mass absorption coefficient is nearly constant for all substances. Eq. 9.13 can be rewritten as

$$I = I_0 e^{-\mu d/\rho} \qquad \mu/\rho = cm^2/g \tag{9.14}$$

where d is the thickness expressed in units of g cm⁻². $=d$

The transmitted energy is given by

$$E = E_0 e^{-\mu d/\rho} \tag{9.15}$$

where E_0 is the initial energy and E the residual energy after passing through a layer of matter of thickness d g cm⁻². Hence, the energy absorbed by this layer of matter is

$$E_{abs} = E_0 - E = E_0 (1 - e^{-\mu d/\rho}) \tag{9.16}$$

Provided d is small, *i.e.* for a thin layer.

$$E_{abs} = E_0 \mu d/\rho \tag{9.17}$$

(iii) Atomic Absorption Coefficient

The absorption of radiation per atom of the stopping matter is related to the number of atoms per unit mass of the matter

$$_a\mu = \frac{\mu}{\rho} \frac{A}{L} = cm^2/atom \tag{9.18}$$

where A is the atomic mass of the atom and L the Avogadro number. The units of $_a\mu$ are cm²/atom.

(iv) *Electron Absorption Coefficient*

The absorption of radiation per electron of the stopping matter in the path is a fundamental quantity as the interaction of radiation is only with electrons of matter, over the range of conditions of interest in radiation chemistry. Since there are LZ electrons per A grams (1 mole) of the substance,

$$_e\mu = \frac{\mu}{\rho} \cdot \frac{A}{LZ} \qquad cm^2/e^- \qquad (9.19)$$

The units of $_e\mu$ are cm²/electron.

Since the mass, atom and electron absorption coefficients have cm² (area) in the numerator, these are expressed in barns per gram (or per atom or per electron) more conveniently; the barn being a unit of area $= 10^{-28}$ m². For this reason, the atom and electron absorption coefficients are also referred to as cross sections.

9.5 2 ABSORPTION IN WATER

Since water is the major constituent of all living beings, and because of its important role in reactor technology, effects of radiation on water form the central theme of radiation chemistry. A precise determination of the absorption coefficients for water has been a convenient starting point for the development of the subject. Careful studies led to a value of 0.0706 cm^{-1} as the linear absorption coefficient of water for photons of 1 MeV energy which interact almost wholly by Compton scattering.[4] Values of other absorption coefficients follow from this, thus

$$(\mu/\rho)_{H_2O} = 0.0706 \text{ cm}^2/\text{g} \qquad (\because \quad \rho_{H_2O} = 1)$$

$$_a\mu = 0.0706\frac{A}{L} = \frac{0\,0706 \times 18}{6.022 \times 10^{23} \times 10^{-24}} = 2.11 \text{ b/atom}$$

$$_e\mu = {_a\mu}/Z = \frac{2.11}{10} = 0\,211 \text{ b/electron*}$$

This result is a fruitful starting point, as this value for the electron absorption coefficient must be same for all electrons of *any* substance, as long as Compton scattering is the dominant mode of interaction, hence:

$$_e\mu_{H_2O} = {_e\mu} \text{ any substance} = \text{constant} = 0.211 \text{ b/electron.}$$

The way atomic and mass absorption coefficients of other substances are calculated from this result is illustrated below.

Hydrogen

$$_e\mu_H = 0.211 \text{ b/electron,}$$

$$_a\mu_H = Z_e\mu_H = 1 \times 0.211 = 0.211 \text{ b/atom,}$$

*As there are 10 electrons in a molecule of water; $Z = 10$.

$$(\mu/\rho)_H = \frac{L}{A}\ _a\mu_H = \frac{6.022 \times 10^{23}}{1} \times 0.211 \times 10^{-24}$$

$$= 0.1266 \text{ cm}^2/\text{g}.$$

Oxygen

$$_a\mu_O = Z_e\mu_O = 8 \times 0.211 = 1.688 \text{ b/atom}.$$

$$(\mu/\rho)_O = \frac{L}{A}\ _a\mu_O = \frac{6.022 \times 10^{23}}{16} \times 1.688 \times 10^{-24}$$

$$= 0.0636 \text{ cm}^2/\text{g}.$$

Carbon

$$_a\mu_C = 6 \times 0.211 = 1.266 \text{ b/atom},$$

$$(\mu/\rho)_C = 0.0633 \text{ cm}^2/\text{g}.$$

Similarly, the atomic and mass absorption coefficients of any element may be evaluated.

9.5.3 MOLECULAR ABSORPTION COEFFICIENT OF COMPOUNDS

Molecular absorption coefficients of compound substances are obtained merely by adding the different atomic absorption coefficients, each in proportion to the number of its atoms, thus:

$$_{mol}\mu_{H_2O} = 2\ _a\mu_H + 1\ _a\mu_O = (2 \times 0.211) + (1 \times 1.688)$$

$$= 2.110 \text{ b/molecule},$$

$$_{mol}\mu_{C_2H_5OH} = 2\ _a\mu_C + 6\ _a\mu_H + 1\ _a\mu_O = 5.486 \text{ b/molecule}.$$

9.5.4 MASS ABSORPTION COEFFICIENT OF COMPOUNDS

Mass absorption coefficients of compound substances are calculated by combining mass absorption coefficients after weighting each atom in proportion of its mass in the molecule.

$$(\mu/\rho)_{H_2O} = \left(\frac{2}{18} \times 0.1266\right) + \left(\frac{16}{18} \times 0.0636\right) = 0.0706 \text{ cm}^2/\text{g},$$

$$(\mu/\rho)_{C_2H_5OH} = \frac{(24 \times 0.0633) + (6 \times 0.1266) + (16 \times 0.0636)}{46}$$

$$= 0.07166 \text{ cm}^2/\text{g}.$$

9.6 Radiation Dosimetry

For a complete understanding of a reaction induced by radiation, one must know the amount of the energy consumed and the yield of the products. These data are essential for formulating a mechanism of the reaction. To begin with we shall consider the units employed for expressing the amount of radiation energy absorbed by the reactants and later a method for measuring the same.

9.6.1 UNITS OF RADIATION ENERGY

Because of the wide application of nuclear radiation in different sciences, pure and applied, several units have been proposed for expressing the dose or the amount of energy absorbed, while the basic unit of a joule of energy absorbed by unit mass of the substance should have sufficed. Since alternative units for the dose are in vogue, these are described below together with their conversion equivalents.

(a) *The Rad*

The *rad* is the most commonly employed unit being defined as:

$$1 \text{ rad } (r) = \text{absorption of 100 ergs per gram of the substance,}$$
$$= 10^{-5} \text{ J/g}$$
$$= 6.24 \times 10^{13} \text{ eV/g.} \tag{9.20}$$

If the target substance is a liquid of density ρ,

$$1r = 6.24 \times 10^{13} \text{ eV}\rho/\text{cm}^3,$$

(b) *The Gray*

The gray is the SI unit of dose defined as

$$1 \text{ gray (Gy)} = 1 \text{ J kg}^{-1} = 100 \text{ rads.} \tag{9.21}$$

It is necessary to include a unit for the *rate* of the energy absorption. This is the dose rate, *i.e.*, dose absorbed/s, in units of rads/s or Gy/s.

(c) *The Röntgen*

The röntgen (R) is the physicist's unit of exposure dose, and this is based on the ability of the radiation to ionize air. This is defined as exposure to such a dose that would produce in 1 cm³ of dry air at STP $(= 0.001\ 293 \text{ g})$ ions carrying 1 esu of electricity of either sign (not both).* Generally,

$$1 \text{ R (air)} \simeq 0.87 \text{ rad} = 8.7 \text{ mGy} \tag{9.22}$$

(d) *The RBE*

RBE stands for the relative biological effectiveness of a given type of radiation. The biologists recognize the differences in the effectiveness of different types of radiations in their action on live tissues and they have graded them as:

$$\text{RBE} = 1, \text{ for } X\text{-rays, } \gamma\text{-rays and } \beta\text{-particles,}$$
$$= 2.5, \text{ for thermal neutrons,}$$
$$= 10, \text{ for } \alpha\text{-particles, fast neutrons and protons.}$$

(e) *The Rem*

Rem stands for *r*öntgen *e*quivalent *m*ammal (or man). This is given by the product of RBE × rads.

---

*This corresponds to the Creation of $1/(4.8 \times 10^{-10}) = 2.08 \times 10^9$ ion pairs in air.

(f) *The Sievert*

The sievert is the SI unit of rem:

$$1 \text{ sievert (Sv)} = \text{RBE} \times \text{grays}$$
$$= 100 \text{ rem.} \tag{9.23}$$

9.6.2 CHEMICAL DOSIMETRY

It should be possible to use any change, physical or chemical, induced by radiation in a substance, as a measure of the energy transferred to the latter, provided, the magnitude of the change is directly proportional to the dose and independent of the dose rate and the nature of the radiation. Some of the physical methods employed consist of measuring the ionization produced in a gas, or photographic blackening, or direct calorimetry, or the intensity of coloration of glasses, specially silver activated phosphate glass.[3] We confine our interest here to chemical dosimetry, *i.e.* the yield in selected chemical reactions induced by radiation, *viz.* $Fe^{2+} \rightarrow Fe^{3+}$ and $Ce^{4+} \rightarrow Ce^{3+}$.

(i) *The Fricke Dosimeter*

This consists in measuring the extent of oxidation of Fe^{2+} to Fe^{3+} under specified conditions.[3,5] The Fricke solution is obtained by dissolving 0.4 g of $FeSO_4 (NH_4)_2 SO_4 6H_2O$, 0.06 g of NaCl* and 22 ml of 95–98% H_2SO_4 and making up the solution in distilled water to a litre, dissolved air being present. A sample of the solution in a thick enough container is exposed to the radiation at the desired spot for a definite period of time. Immediately thereafter, the amount of Fe^{3+} produced is determined spectrophotometrically at the wavelength of 304 nm. The relevant extinction coefficient may be taken as 2174 M^{-1} cm^{-1}, or the resulting concentration of Fe^{3+} may be determined from an experimental plot of optical density against concentration of Fe^{3+}. Knowing the standard yield of Fe^{3+} is 15.5 "molecules" (rather ions) per 100 eV energy absorbed, the unknown dose is readily calculated from the measured yield of Fe^{3+}**. The method gives very reproducible values over a wide range of dose, up to about 0.5 kGy ($= 50$ kr).

The radiation chemistry of the oxidation of Fe^{2+} to Fe^{3+} under conditions of Fricke dosimetry is discussed in Sec. 9.7.

(ii) *The Ceric Sulphate Dosimeter*

Here a 1–10 mM solution of acidified ceric sulphate is exposed to the radiation when Ce^{4+} is reduced to Ce^{3+} and the fall in the concentration of Ce^{4+} is determined spectrophotometrically at 320 nm, the extinction

---

*The NaCl inhibits oxidation of Fe^{2+} by trace organic impurities.

**In radiation chemistry the yield of a substance (X) produced is expressed as $G(X)$ in terms of number of molecules of X produced per 100 eV energy absorbed. Here $G(Fe^{3+}) = 15.5$.

coefficient at this wavelength being 5565 l mole^{-1} cm^{-1}. The G (Ce^{3+}) is 2.44.[6] The ceric sulphate dosimeter is particularly useful for measuring high doses of the order of a MGy ($= 10^8$ r). It should however be noted that it is extremely sensitive to the presence of organic impurities. Usually the dosimeter is calibrated against the Fricke dosimeter.

(iii)   Other Chemical Dosimeters

A large number of other chemical reactions are reported in literature as suitable for chemical dosimetry, as aqueous solutions of $FeSO_4 + CuSO_4$, acidified and aerated;[7] sodium formate (deaerated);[8] calcium benzoate (aerated)[9]; quinine sulphate (acidified)[10]; aqueous chlorform[11]; etc. These are described in the literature cited.

9.6.3   CONVERSION OF MEASURED DOSE VALUES

A dosimetric measurement gives only the dose absorbed by the dosimeter substance (say Fricke solution) at a given position due to a given radiation source.   This information is necessary but not adequate if we intend studying the radiation effects on other substances.   It is, however possible to convert the known value of the dose absorbed by a substance A to that which would be absorbed by substance B when placed in the same position.   This dose conversion is considered below.

Over the region of Compton absorption, we have for the energy absorbed by a thin layer

$$E_{abs} = \text{Dose} = E_0 d\mu/\rho \tag{9.17}$$

Again from Eq. 9.19

$$\mu/\rho = {}_e\mu LZ/A \propto Z/A \tag{9.24}$$

Hence $D \propto Z/A$, i.e. dose absorbed by a substance is proportional to the electron density of the substance.   While Z/A is readily known for elements, its equivalent for compound substances is given by the mean value

$$(\overline{Z/A}) = \Sigma W_i (Z/A)_i \tag{9.25}$$

where W_i is the fraction by weight of element i.   In other words,

$$(\overline{Z/A})_{compound} = \frac{\text{sum of } Z \text{ of all atoms present}}{Molecular\ weight}$$

Examples:

$$(\overline{Z/A})_{H_2O} = \frac{(2 \times 1) + (1 \times 8)}{18} = \frac{10}{18} = 0.556,$$

$$(\overline{Z/A})_{CHCl_3} = \frac{(1 \times 6) + (1 \times 1) + (3 \times 17)}{119.5} = \frac{58}{119.5} = 0.485,$$

$(\overline{Z/A})_{air}$ (considered approximately as N_4O) $= 0.499,$

$(\overline{Z/A})$ Fricke solution (considered mainly as 0.4 M H_2SO_4) $= 0.553.$

These relations help in calculating the dose expected to be absorbed D_2

by a substance S_2 knowing the dose absorbed D_1 by another substance S_1 placed in the same position, by Eq. 9.24

$$\frac{D_2}{D_1} = \frac{(\overline{Z/A})_2}{(\overline{Z/A})_1} \tag{9.26}$$

provided we are within the region where Compton absorption dominates.

For instance if the Fricke dosimeter placed near a ^{60}Co γ-source registers a dose of 48 Gy g^{-1} min$_-^{-1}$, the dose that chloroform placed in the same position, is given by

$$D_{CHCl_3} = D_{Fricke} \frac{(\overline{Z/A})_{CHCl_3}}{(\overline{Z/A})_{Fricke}}$$

$$= 48 \times \frac{0.485}{0.553} = 42.2 \text{ Gy g}^{-1} \text{ min}^{-1}$$

9.7 Radiolysis of Water

In the end, a brief account of the radiolysis of water is presented which illustrates the concepts and methods of radiation chemistry. The supreme importance of water in the study of radiation effects on living beings and on reactor technology was explained earlier (Sec. 9.1.1). The major products of water radiolysis are free radicals $\cdot$H, e_{eq}^- (hydrated electron), $\cdot$OH, $\cdot$HO$_2$, positive ions H$_2$O$^+$ and (in vapour phase to a less extent H$_3$O$^+$, H$^+$ and OH$^+$) and molecular products H$_2$ and H$_2$O$_2$. Some of these are initially formed precursors which lead to the other products by secondary reactions, though the precise sequence of reactions may not be the same for all types of radiation and values of LET. The presence or otherwise of dissolved oxygen or air in the water also affects the final yields of the products; similarly dissolved solutes also alter the yields. Some of these aspects are considered here.

9.7.1 MEAN LET IN WATER RADIOLYSIS

The mean value of the LET in water varies with the nature of the radiation and its energy. LET in water is low for γ photons and high energy electrons; it increases with the mass in the case of particle radiation, in the order:

LET $\gamma <$ high energy electrons $<$ low energy electrons $<$ p $<$ d $<$
$\alpha <$ heavy ions $<$ fission fragments.

The log LET drops roughly linearly with log energy of electrons. Thus, an LET of 100 keV/micron for electrons of energy 0.1 MeV drops to 0.1 keV/micron for electrons of energy 1 MeV.

9.7.2 IONIC PRODUCTS

Following are considered as the initial reactants, not necessarily in the same order.

$$\gamma + H_2O \rightsquigarrow H_2O^* \rightarrow H_2O^+ + e^- \qquad (a)$$

$$e^- + H_2O \rightsquigarrow H_2O^* + e^- \rightarrow H_2O^+ + 2e^- \qquad (b)$$

$$e^- + H_2O \rightarrow H^+ + OH + 2e^- \rightarrow H_2O^+ + 2e^- \qquad (c)$$

$$e^- + H_2O \rightarrow OH^+ + H + 2e^- \rightarrow H_2O^+ + 2e^- \qquad (d)$$

$$e^- + H_2O \rightarrow O^+ + H_2 + 2e^- \qquad (e)$$

$$H_2O^+ + H_2O \rightarrow H_3O^+ + OH. \qquad (f)$$

The formation of negative ions by electron attachment is negligible; the electrons prefer to recombine with positive ions, or to get solvated during the relaxation time of water dipoles, *viz.* 10^{-11} s,

$$e^- + water \rightarrow e_{aq}^- \qquad (g)$$

The ionic products listed above are detected by a mass spectrometer in the radiolysis of water vapour; their relative yields and appearance potentials are given below.

TABLE 9.2:   Yields of ionic products

Ion	Appearance potential/V[12]	Relative abundance	Formation reaction
H_2O^+	12.61	100	a, b, c, d
H_3O^+	12.67	20	f
OH^+	18.1	20	d
H^+	19.6	20	c
O^+	29.2	2	e

The above data show that H_2O^+ is the only important ionic product of water radiolysis.

9.7.3 FREE RADICAL PRODUCTS

The ionic products have all short lives, specially in an excited state. They recombine to yield free radicals.

$$H_2O^+ + e^- \rightarrow \cdot H + \cdot OH \qquad (h)$$

$$H^+ + H_2O + e^- \rightarrow H_3O^+ + e^- \rightarrow 2H\cdot + \cdot OH \qquad (i)$$

$$OH^+ + H_2O + e^- \rightarrow \cdot H + 2\cdot OH \qquad (j)$$

In the presence of dissolved air or oxygen, the perhydroxyl radical $\cdot HO_2$ is formed

$$\cdot H + O_2 \rightarrow \cdot HO_2 \qquad (k)$$

9.7.4 MOLECULAR PRODUCTS DUE TO RADICAL–RADICAL INTERACTIONS

All these radicals being highly reactive, initiate a series of reactions with dissolved solutes, or they recombine amongst themselves, resulting in stable molecular products.

$$\cdot H + \cdot OH \rightarrow H_2O \tag{l}$$
$$\cdot H + \cdot H \rightarrow H_2 \tag{m}$$
$$\cdot OH + \cdot OH \rightarrow H_2O_2 \tag{n}$$
$$\cdot OH + \cdot HO_2 \rightarrow H_2O + O_2 \tag{o}$$
$$\cdot HO_2 + \cdot HO_2 \rightarrow H_2O_2 + O_2 \tag{p}$$

The actual yields of molecular products vary with the nature of the ionizing radiation, the LET and the presence of dissolved solutes.

9.7.5 CHAIN REACTIONS: MOLECULE–RADICAL INTERACTIONS

Under favourable conditions molecule–radical interactions occur involving chain reactions.

$$\cdot H + H_2O_2 \rightarrow \cdot OH + H_2O \tag{q}$$
$$\cdot OH + H_2 \rightarrow \cdot H + H_2O \tag{r}$$

Chain reactions are postulated specially in explaining abnormally high yields of certain radiolytic products, e.g. radiolysis of aqueous benzene–oxygen; aqueous chloroform–oxygen; organic halogen compounds, etc.[3]

9.7.6 DISTRIBUTION OF prp OF WATER

Because of the 1000 fold higher LET in liquid water compared to water vapour, the spurs will be closer along the radiation track permitting a greater interaction amongst the primary radiolytic products (prp). Hydration also will be more pronounced.

Considering reaction (a)

$$H_2O \rightsquigarrow H_2O^+ + e^-$$

as the only important radiation effect in water, the nature of the final products depend on how far the electron moves out from the H_2O^+ ion which remains at the site of the primary event. Two models in this context are relevant. These are commonly referred to as the (a) Samuel and Magee, and (b) Lea, Gray and Platzman models. Theoretical calculations on these models in respect of the separation between the H_2O^+ and e^- species and the consequences thereof are considered below.

(a) *The Samuel–Magee Model*

Calculations on this model[1] indicate that the secondary electron of 10 eV energy would have moved out by a distance of the order of 2 nm from the H_2O^+ ion and hence is well within the electrostatic field between them. This results in a recombination of the two species.

$$H_2O \rightsquigarrow H_2O^+ + e^- \rightarrow H_2O^{**} \rightarrow \cdot H + \cdot OH$$
$$\text{at site} \quad \text{2 nm}$$
$$\text{away}$$
$$\text{from site}$$

Only a fraction of the radicals formed escape recombination and hence the net radiolytic decomposition of water is only slight.

(b)　The Lea-Gray-Platzman Model

Calculations on this model[13] show the secondary electron before thermalization would have moved out by a distance of the order of 15 nm which is well beyond the electrostatic range of attraction between the species, and hence the two species decay independently as shown below:

$$H_2O \rightsquigarrow \underset{\text{at site}}{H_2O^+} + \underset{\substack{\text{15 nm away} \\ \text{from site}}}{e^-}$$

$$\downarrow H_2O \qquad\qquad \downarrow H_2O^*$$

$$\cdot OH + H_3O^+ \qquad \cdot H + \cdot OH_{aq}^-$$

$$\downarrow \qquad\qquad\qquad \downarrow$$

$$0.5 H_2O_2 \qquad\quad 0.5 H_2$$

In reality, neither model may be operative exclusively, but it may be some intermediate one, or a combination of the two.

9.7.7　THE YIELDS OF RADICAL AND MOLECULAR PRODUCTS

Since in the radiolysis of water, not only water molecules are dissociated (reactions a to f), but some of these molecules are reformed (reaction l), one distinguishes G_{-H_2O}, representing the water molecules converted into radicals and molecular products, from $G_{-H_2O\,(initial)}$ which is the number of molecules initially dissociated. The two are related by the expression

$$G_{-H_2O\,(initial)} = G_{-H_2O} + G_{H_2} + G_{H_2O_2} \qquad (9.27)$$

The value of G_{-H_2O} is sensibly independent of the nature of the radiation employed. The radical yields are highest for low LET radiation (as γ and electrons), while the molecular yields are greatest for high LET radiation (as α, heavy ions and fission fragments). The yields of radical and molecular products for radiolysis of water by low LET radiation (as γ or electrons) are given below[14,15].

TABLE 9.3:　Yields of molecular and radical products at low LET

(from *An Introduction to Radiation Chemistry*, by J.W.T. Spinks and R.J. Woods. © 1964, John Wiley & Sons, reproduced with permission)

pH	G_{-H_2O}	G_{H_2}	$G_{H_2O_2}$	$G_{(H+e_{aq}^-)}$	G_{OH}	G_{HO_2}
7	3.64	0.42	0.71	2.80	2.22	0.02
0.5	4.5	0.40	0.80	3.70	2.9	

*Endothermic reaction, made possible by the energy released in the hydration of the resulting OH^- ion.

9.7.8 MATERIAL BALANCE: ALLEN'S EQUATION

While $\cdot H$, e_{aq}^- and H_2 are reducing species, $\cdot OH$, $\cdot HO_2$ and H_2O_2 are oxidizing species. Allen had suggested for the material balance[16,16a]

$$G_H + 2G_{H_2} = G_{OH} + 2G_{H_2O_2} \qquad (9.28)$$

If the respective yields are represented as $a\,H_2$, $b\,H_2O_2$, $c\,H$ and $d\,OH$ a convenient expression results

$$[(2a + c) \text{ or } (2b + d)]\,H_2O \;\rightsquigarrow\; a\,H_2 + b\,H_2O_2 + c\,H + d\,OH \quad (9.29)$$

9.8 Free Radicals in Water Radiolysis

Since ionic products are short lived and molecular products are generally inert, all secondary reactions in water radiolysis are mostly due to free radicals. The reactions leading to the formation of radicals having already been presented in Sec. 9.7.3, we shall consider other aspects as, their removal by scavengers, their constitution and concentration under a steady state.

9.8.1 SCAVENGING OF FREE RADICALS

The technique of using scavengers, $i\,e.$ certain substances in trace amounts which interact with and destroy specific free radicals, is well known. For instance, it was shown by Firestone[17] that deuterium scavenges quantitatively both $\cdot H$ and $\cdot OH$ radicals, thus:

$$\cdot H + D_2 \;\rightarrow\; \cdot D + HD \qquad (s)$$
$$\cdot OH + D_2 \;\rightarrow\; \cdot D + HOD \qquad (t)$$
$$\cdot D + \cdot D \;\rightarrow\; D_2 \quad \text{(at the wall} \qquad (u)$$
$$\text{or a third body)}$$

It follows

$$G(HD) = G(-D_2) = G_H = G_{OH} = G_{-H_2O} \qquad (9.30)$$

Firestone's results on the measurement of $G(HD)$ in the radiolysis of water vapour, showed

$$G_H = G_{OH} = 11.7.$$

However, the sum of reactions $(h) + (i) + (j)$ gives for

$$G_H + G_{OH} = 4$$

which is very much lower than Firestone's results employing the scavenger technique. Also, the accepted value of 30 eV for the mean energy needed to excite/ionize a water molecule indicates,

$$G_H = G_{OH} = 100/35 \simeq 3.5.$$

Thus, the high yield of the radicals indicated by the scavenger studies points to the necessity of postulating alternative modes of formation of free radicals besides by ionic recombination (h, i, j). The earlier view of the direct formation of radicals from excited water molecule

$$H_2O \;\rightsquigarrow\; H_2O^* \rightarrow \cdot H + \cdot OH \qquad (v)$$

may also be operative to some extent.

9.8.2 CONSTITUTION OF RADICALS $\cdot$H AND $\cdot$OH

Studies of absorption spectra of the radicals to assess their concentration in intensely irradiated water have not been quantitative due to several side reactions specially in polar media, where the $\cdot$H and $\cdot$OH radicals have an acidic and a basic form, thus:

Radical	Acidic form (by adding H^+)	Basic form (by removing H^+)
$\cdot$H	H_2^+	e_{aq}^-
$\cdot$OH	H_2O^+	O^-

9.8.3 STEADY STATE CONCENTRATION OF RADICALS

The equilibrium or steady state concentration of free radicals in the bulk of the medium *outside the spurs* can be computed to a fair degree of approximation by making following reasonable assumptions.

(a)   The radicals are homogeneously distributed in the bulk.

(b)   The $G(R)$, *i.e.* the G value for formation of radicals is ~ 10 for a dose rate of 10^3 Gy/s ($= 10^5$ rads/s),

(c)   Each radical + radical encounter results in a molecular product (reactions l to p) with a bimolecular rate constant of the order of 10^9 M^{-1} s^{-1}.

The rate of energy absorption for a dose rate of 10^3 Gy/s

$$= 6.24 \times 10^{18} \text{ eV g}^{-1} \text{ s}^{-1}$$

$$= 6.24 \times 10^{21} \text{ eV } l^{-1} \text{ s}^{-1},$$

(assuming the mass of a litre of water $= 1000$ g).

The rate of formation of free radicals, assuming $G(R) = 10$ per 100 eV,

$$= 6.24 \times 10^{20} \ l^{-1} \text{ s}^{-1}$$

$$= \frac{6.2 \times 10^{20}}{6.022 \times 10^{23}} \text{ moles free radical } l^{-1} \text{ s}^{-1}$$

$$\simeq 10^{-3} \text{ M s}^{-1}.$$

The rate of removal of free radicals by bimolecular recomoination

$$= k_2 \, [R]^2$$

where $[R]$ is the molar concentration of radicals and k_2 is the bimolecular rate constant, assumed to be 10^9 M^{-1} s^{-1}.

Equating the rates of formation and removal:

$$10^{-3} = 10^9 \, [R]^2$$

$$\therefore \quad [R]_{bulk} = 10^{-6} \text{ moles/l.}$$

This is the steady state concentration of radicals in the bulk; the value in the spurs is, however, much higher. The latter can be estimated assuming around 10 radicals in a spherical spur of radius of about 1 nm:

$$[R]_{spur} = \frac{10 \times 10^3}{4/3 \times 3.14 \times (10^{-7})^3 \times 6.022 \times 10^{23}} \text{ moles}/l$$

$$\simeq 4 \text{ moles}/l.$$

Such a high concentration of radicals in the spurs results in radical-radical reactions (l to p) while their low concentration in bulk can cause only radical-molecular reactions (q, r).

9.9 Radiolysis of Some Aqueous Solutions

The radiolysis of a large number of aqueous solutions of acids, bases, salts, redox mixtures, and other complex systems, of organic and biomolecules have been studied, and the yields of radiolytic products measured. In most cases, appropriate mechanisms of the radiolytic processes have been proposed. In all cases, the radiation effects on the solutes are indirect, being brought about by the *prp* of water and little by the direct interaction of radiation with the solute, except at high concentrations of the latter. We shall consider here only a few simple systems; for others literature cited in the bibliography may be consulted.

9.9.1 RADIOLYSIS OF FRICKE DOSIMETER SOLUTION

Because of its wide use as a chemical dosimeter, the radiolysis of the Fricke solution (10^{-3} M ferrous sulphate in 0.4 M sulphuric acid in the presence of dissolved air) assumes importance. (The use of the Fricke dosimeter is described in Sec. 9.6.2.)

The quantitatively reproducible oxidation of Fe^{2+} to Fe^{3+} on radiolysis is explained on the following mechanism:

$$Fe^{2+} + \cdot OH \rightarrow Fe^{3+} + OH^- \qquad (1)$$

$$Fe^{2+} + H_2O_2 \rightarrow Fe^{3+} + \cdot OH + OH^- \qquad (2)$$

$$Fe^{2+} + \cdot HO_2 \rightarrow Fe^{3+} + \cdot HO_2^- \qquad (3)$$

$$\cdot HO_2^- + H^+ \rightarrow H_2O_2 \qquad (4)$$

The $\cdot HO_2$ needed in (3) is obtained by the reaction

$$\cdot H + O_2 \rightarrow \cdot HO_2 \qquad (k)$$

The yield of the final product Fe^{3+} is related to the radical and molecular yields by the expression

$$G\ (Fe^{3+})_{air} = 2G_{H_2O_2} + 3G_H + G_{OH} \qquad (9.31)$$

$$= (2 \times 0.8) + 3(3.7) + 2.9^*$$

$$= 15.6.$$

*The relevant G values are taken from Sec. 9.7.7.

The accepted value of $G(Fe^{3+})$ in Fricke dosimetry for 1.25 MeV γ from ^{60}Co, 2 MeV electrons and for 0.7 MeV β from ^{32}P is 15.5.

9.9.2 REDOX REACTIONS DUE TO TRANSFER OF ENERGY FROM IRRADIATED ALKALI HALIDES

Another way of effecting redox reactions, which are thermodynamically possible but inhibited at room temperature, consists in exposing the reaction mixture to γ radiation[18-21]. As an extension of this, it was further observed by us that instead of direct exposure to γ radiation, the energy stored in a γ irradiated alkali halide (by itself a non-reactant), may be utilized to effect the reaction. The procedure consists in adding to a solution of the reactants, γ irradiated sodium chloride and the reaction is found to proceed to a measurable extent at *room temperature*, as if the reactants had been directly exposed to radiation. This indicates a transfer of energy stored in the crystal in the form of F and hole centres to effect the reaction. As an example is cited the redox reaction between BrO_3^- and I^- ions effected at room temperature by the transfer of energy stored in NaCl irradiated to a dose of the order of 10 kGy $(= 1$ Mrad$)$[22-23]

$$(1) \qquad BrO_3^- + I^- \xrightarrow{NaCl^*} Br^- + I_2 + IO_3^-$$
$$\qquad\quad 1M \qquad 1mM \qquad\qquad\quad 17\% \quad 10\%$$

The yields of I_2 and IO_3^- are with reference to the initial amount of the iodide taken. During the dissolution of irradiated NaCl in water the F and hole centres yield e_{aq}^-, $\cdot H$ and $\cdot Cl$: or $\cdot Cl_2^-$ species. These react with the I^- and BrO_3^- species resulting in

$$\cdot Cl + I^- \rightarrow Cl^- + 0.5 I_2 \qquad\qquad (i)$$

$$\cdot Cl_2^- + I^- \rightarrow 2Cl^- + 0.5 I_2 \qquad\qquad (ii)$$

$$e_{aq}^- + BrO_3^- \rightarrow BrO_3^{2-} \qquad\qquad (iii)$$

$$\cdot H + BrO_3^- \rightarrow BrO_3^{2-} + H^+ \qquad\qquad (iv)$$

A part of the free iodine liberated in (i) and (ii) is oxidized by the Br(IV) species produced in (iii) and (iv) to IO_3^- as in (v)

$$BrO_3^{2-} + 0.5 I_2 \rightarrow IO_3^- + Br^- \qquad\qquad (v)$$

Other reactions involving energy transfer studied by us are:

$$(2) \quad Fe^{2+} \text{ (Fricke solution)} \xrightarrow{NaCl^*} Fe^{3+}$$

$$(3) \quad BrO_3^- + NO_2^- \xrightarrow{NaCl^*} Br^- + NO_3^-$$

$$(4) \quad BrO_3^- + As\text{ (III)} \xrightarrow{NaCl^*} Br^- + As(V)$$

(5)   Rhodomine-B sol $\xrightarrow{\text{NaCl*}}$ Reduced species of the dye which is ether soluble and which fluoresces at 570 nm.

(6)   Xylenol orange $\xrightarrow{\text{NaCl*}}$ Reduced species (peak at 450 nm). (peak at 568 nm)

9.10   A Time Scale of Radiolytic Events

We close this study by listing a time scale of events in the radiolysis of water. It should be noted that the times indicated are approximate and may cover a range $\times 10^{\pm 1}$.

Stage 1   Primary interaction of radiation with matter

10^{-18}s   High energy γ photon traverses an atom/molecule.

10^{-17}s   Fast electron traverses an atom/molecule.

10^{-16}s   Thermal neutron traverses an atom/molecule.

10^{-15}s   Electronic excitation by Franck-Condon principle.

Reactions in stage 1

$$H_2O \rightsquigarrow H_2O^+ + e^-$$
$$H_2O \rightsquigarrow H_2O^* \rightarrow H_2O^+ + e^-.$$

Stage 2   Secondary reactions: energy transfer

10^{-14}s   Period for an atomic vibration in a molecule, Ion+molecule reactions.

10^{-13}s   Excited atom loses vibrational energy, Dissociation of an excited molecule: Products: H_3O^+, e^-, $\cdot H$, $\cdot OH$, $\cdot HO_2$.

10^{-12}s   Thermalization of the secondary electron, Electron capture, Period for radical jump.

10^{-11}s   Relaxation of water dipoles, Product: e_{aq}^-.

Stage 3   Chemical reactions

10^{-10}s   Radical+radical reactions, Products: H_2O, H_2O_2, H_2, O_2.

10^{-9} s   Diffusion-controlled reactions, Reactions of $e_{aq}^- +$ dissolved solutes.

10^{-8} s   Fluorescence: singlet state deexcitation.

10^{-5} s   Radicals diffuse out of spurs, Radical + solute reactions (redox reactions).

10^{-3} s   Phosphorescence: triplet state deexcitation, Most reactions are complete: final products.

References
(where marked *, see Bibliography)

1.   A.H. Samuel and J.L. Magee. *J. Chem. Phys.*, 1953, **21**, 1080.
2.   H.A. Bethe and J. Ashkin*.
3.   J.W.T. Spinks and R.J. Woods*.
4.   G.W. Grodstein, *National Bureau of Standards* (U.S.), 1957, *Circular No. 583.*
5.   H.F. Fricke and E.J. Hart, *J. Chem. Phys.*, 1935, **3**, 60.
6.   J.W. Boyle, *Radiation Research*, 1962, **17**, 427.
7.   E.J. Hart, W.J. Ramler and S.R. Rocklin, *Radiation Research*, 1956, **4**, 378.
8.   T.J. Hardwick, W.S. Guentner, *J. Phys. Chem.*, 1953, **63**, 896.
9.   W.A. Armstrong and D.W. Grant, *Nature*, 1958, **182**, 747.
10. N.F. Barr and M.B. Stark. *Radiation Research*, 1960, **12**, 1
11. G.V. Taplin*.
12. M. Cottin, *J. Chim. Phys.*, 1959, **56**, 1024.
13. R.L. Platzman*.
14. A.O. Allen and H.A. Schwarz, *Proc. II Intern. Conf. Peaceful Uses of Atomic Energy, U.N.*, Geneva, 1958, **29**, 30.
15. C.J. Hochanadel and S.C. Lind, *Ann. Rev. Phys. Chem.*, 1956, **7**, 83.
16. A.O. Allen*.
     (a) A.O. Allen, *Radiation Research*, 1954, **1**, 85.
17. R.F. Firestone, *J. Amer. Chem. Soc.*, 1957, **79**, 5593.
18. H.J. Arnikar, S.F. Patil, A.A. Bodhe and R.D Pokharkar, *Radiochem. Radioanal. Letters*, 1975, **23**, 307.
19. H.J. Arnikar, S.F. Patil, B.S.M. Rao, A.A. Bodhe and R.D. Pokharkar, *Radiochim. Acta*, 1976, **23**, 109.
20. H.J. Arnikar, S.F. Patil, B.S.M. Rao and M.J. Bedekar, *Radiochem. Radioanal. Letters*, 1977, **28**, 337.
21. H.J. Arnikar and S.K. Patnaik, *Current Science*, 1977, **46**, 638.
22. H.J. Arnikar, B.S.M. Rao and M.J. Bedekar, *Radiochem. Radioanal. Letters*. 1978, **36**, 73.
23. H.J. Arnikar, 11th International Hot Atom Chemisty Symposium, Univ. of California, Davis (CA) 1982.

Problems

9.1   Given the electron absorption coefficient to be 0.211 b per electron for 1 MeV γ-radiation, calculated the molecular, mass and linear coefficients for (a) water, (b) ethanol and (c) methanol, given the densities of (a), (b) and (c) to be 1.000, 0.789 and 0.793 respectively.

[		b/molecule	cm^2/g	cm^{-1}
(a)	water	2.11	0.0706	0.07 6
(b)	ethanol	5.486	0.0718	0.0567
(c)	methanol	3.738	0.0715	0.0567]

9.2   Find the molecular and mass absorption coefficients of (a) benzene and (b) cyclohexane, given the following data:

	density	linear abs. coef.
benzene	0.879 g/cm^3	0.06014 cm^{-1}
cyclohexane	0.779 ,,	0.05656 ,,

	b/molecule	cm²/g
(a) benzene	8.862	0.0684
(b) cyclohexane	10.128	0.0726]

9.3 Calculate the mass absorption coefficient for 1 MeV γ-radiation for (a) NaI, (b) $NaIO_3$, (e) $Ca(PO_3)_2$ and (d) $Ca_3(PO_4)_2$.

[(a) 0.0576, (b) 0.0591, (c) 0.0630, (d) 0.0632 cm² g⁻¹]

9.4 Find the biologically effective dose in sieverts and in rem for a radiation dose of 0.6 Gy due to (a) α particles, (b) thermal neutrons and (c) γ-radiation, given RBE value for (a), (b) and (c) to be 10, 2.5 and 1, respectivaly

[(a) 6 Sv or 600 rem, (b) 1.5 Sv or 150 rem, (c) 0.6 Sv or 60 rem]

9.6 Calculate the $\overline{Z/A}$ values for (a) carbon tetrachloride, (b) acetic acid and (c) cyclohexane.

[(a) 0.5211, (b) 0.5333 and (c) 0.5714]

9.6 Find the thickness of lead required to reduce the level of radiation due to ^{60}Co source at a point (a) from 0.1 Gy/min to 3.1 mGy/h, (b) from 100 Gy/min to 0.1 mGy/h, (c) What is the half-thickness of lead for this radiation?

[(a) 16.82 cm (b) 27.39 cm (c) 1.059 6 cm.]

9.7 Assuming γ-radiation from ^{60}Co interacts mainly by Compton scattering, calculate the dose absorbed in 6 h by (a) chloroform, (b) bromoform and (c) iodoform at a position at which the radiation dose measured by a Fricke dosimeter is 4.06 Gy/min, given Z/A for the Fricke solutions is 0.553.

[(a) 1.284, (b) 1.170 and (c) 1.114 kGy in 6 h],

9.8 A mixture of equal weights of ethanol and acetic acid is irradiated by γ-radiation from a ^{60}Co source. What fraction of the energy is absorbed by ethanol (take Z/A for this mixture to be the mean of Z/A values of the components).

[D ethanol/D mixture = 0.5145]

9.9 A 10 cm³ sample of $CHCl_3$ (density 1.48) is irradiated by γ from a ^{60}Co source for 10 min. The water extract at the end of irradiation contained 30×10^{-6} mole of HCl. The Fricke dosimeter at the same position for 100 min of irradiation gave at 304 nm an O.D. for Fe^{3+} of 0.5633 in a cell of 1 cm path length. The extinction coefficient at this wavelengtn is 2174 litre mole⁻¹ cm⁻¹ and density of the Fricke solution is 1.024. Assuming $G(Fe^{3+}) = 15.5$, find G(HCl) in the radiolysis of $CHCl_3$. [1412]

Appendix I

Disintegration series of naturally occurring and artificially made radioactive elements

The radioactive disintegration series, three naturally occurring $4n + 0$; $4n + 2$; and $4n + 3$, and one artificially made, the $4n + 1$ series are described here. Since the only changes involved are α and β decays, the mass numbers of the nuclides change only by 4 units or not at all. Hence, all the nuclides of a given series must belong to one or the other of the terms, $4n$, $4n + 2$, $4n + 3$, or $4n + 1$, where n is an integer. These are also named after the longest lived member of the series, *viz.* the Thorium, Uranium, Actinium and Neptunium series, respectively. The α and β decays are represented by the vertical and horizontal arrows ($\downarrow$ and $\rightarrow$), respectively. The old names, where they existed, are shown below the nuclides in paranthesis. Below that follows the half-life in years (y), days (d), hours (h), minutes (m) and seconds (s). Also, these may be preceded by the usual prefixes, *viz.* $G = 10^9$, $M = 10^6$, $m = 10^{-3}$ and $\mu = 10^{-6}$. In the case of branched decay (α and β), the figure shown is the total half-life period. To avoid crowding of figures, the energies of the α and β rays emitted are omitted.

(i)   The disintegration of the 4n + 0 or the Thorium series
(naturally occurring)

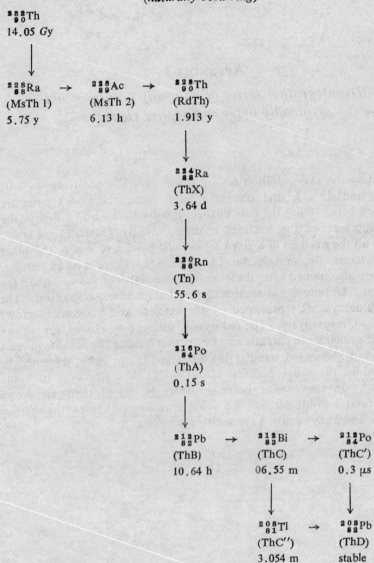

$^{232}_{90}$Th
14.05 Gy

$^{228}_{88}$Ra → $^{228}_{89}$Ac → $^{228}_{90}$Th
(MsTh 1)   (MsTh 2)   (RdTh)
5.75 y   6.13 h   1.913 y

$^{224}_{88}$Ra
(ThX)
3.64 d

$^{220}_{86}$Rn
(Tn)
55.6 s

$^{216}_{84}$Po
(ThA)
0.15 s

$^{212}_{82}$Pb → $^{212}_{83}$Bi → $^{212}_{84}$Po
(ThB)   (ThC)   (ThC′)
10.64 h   06.55 m   0.3 μs

$^{208}_{81}$Tl → $^{208}_{82}$Pb
(ThC″)   (ThD)
3.054 m   stable

(ii)   *The disintegration of the 4n + 2 or the Uranium series (naturally occurring)*

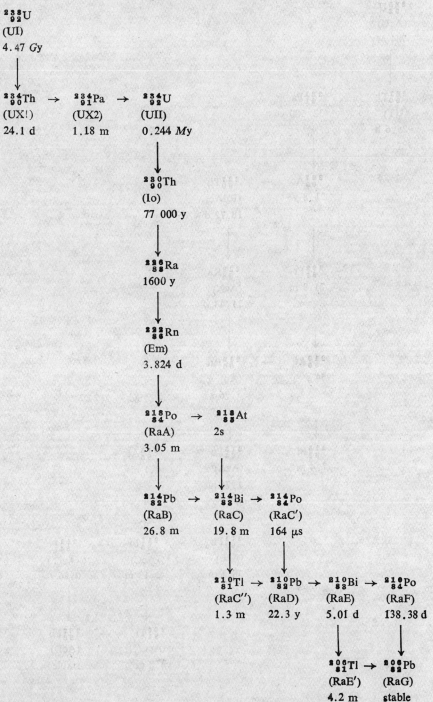

$^{238}_{92}U$
(UI)
4.47 *Gy*

$^{234}_{90}Th$ → $^{234}_{91}Pa$ → $^{234}_{92}U$
(UX1)   (UX2)   (UII)
24.1 d   1.18 m   0.244 *My*

$^{230}_{90}Th$
(Io)
77 000 y

$^{226}_{88}Ra$
1600 y

$^{222}_{86}Rn$
(Em)
3.824 d

$^{218}_{84}Po$ → $^{218}_{85}At$
(RaA)   2s
3.05 m

$^{214}_{82}Pb$ → $^{214}_{83}Bi$ → $^{214}_{84}Po$
(RaB)   (RaC)   (RaC')
26.8 m   19.8 m   164 μs

$^{210}_{81}Tl$ → $^{210}_{82}Pb$ → $^{210}_{83}Bi$ → $^{210}_{84}Po$
(RaC'')   (RaD)   (RaE)   (RaF)
1.3 m   22.3 y   5.01 d   138.38 d

$^{206}_{81}Tl$ → $^{206}_{82}Pb$
(RaE')   (RaG)
4.2 m   stable

(iii) *The disintegration of 4n + 3 or the Actinium series*
(naturally occurring)

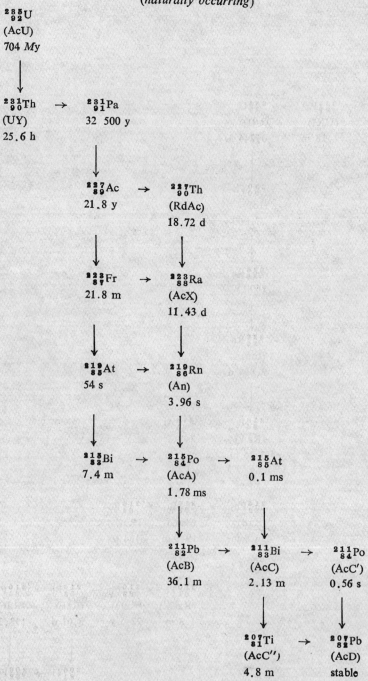

$^{235}_{92}$U
(AcU)
704 *My*

$^{231}_{90}$Th → $^{231}_{91}$Pa
(UY)   32 500 y
25.6 h

$^{227}_{89}$Ac → $^{227}_{90}$Th
21.8 y   (RdAc)
     18.72 d

$^{223}_{87}$Fr → $^{223}_{88}$Ra
21.8 m   (AcX)
     11.43 d

$^{219}_{85}$At → $^{219}_{86}$Rn
54 s   (An)
     3.96 s

$^{215}_{83}$Bi → $^{215}_{84}$Po → $^{215}_{85}$At
7.4 m   (AcA)   0.1 ms
     1.78 ms

$^{211}_{82}$Pb → $^{211}_{83}$Bi → $^{211}_{84}$Po
(AcB)   (AcC)   (AcC′)
36.1 m   2.13 m   0.56 s

$^{207}_{81}$Ti → $^{207}_{82}$Pb
(AcC″)   (AcD)
4.8 m   stable

(iv) *The disintegration of the 4n + 1 or the Neptunium series
(artificially prepared)*

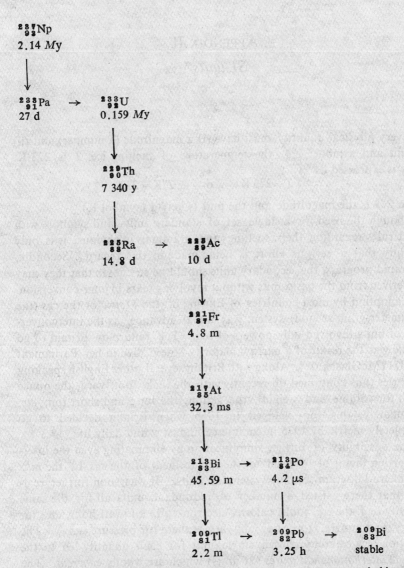

$^{237}_{93}$Np
2.14 *My*

$^{233}_{91}$Pa $\rightarrow$ $^{233}_{92}$U
27 d   0.159 *My*

$^{229}_{90}$Th
7 340 y

$^{225}_{88}$Ra $\rightarrow$ $^{225}_{89}$Ac
14.8 d   10 d

$^{221}_{87}$Fr
4.8 m

$^{217}_{85}$At
32.3 ms

$^{213}_{83}$Bi $\rightarrow$ $^{213}_{84}$Po
45.59 m   4.2 µs

$^{209}_{81}$Tl $\rightarrow$ $^{209}_{82}$Pb $\rightarrow$ $^{209}_{83}$Bi
2.2 m   3.25 h   stable

It may be noted that in this artificial series the end stable product is bismuth, unlike in the three naturally occurring series where the end product is lead.

APPENDIX II
*SI units**

Every physical quantity must have (i) a magnitude (a number) and (ii) a unit and symbol: *e.g.* the temperature of melting ice T is 273 K. This is expressed as

$$T = 273 \, K \qquad \text{or} \qquad T/K = 273.$$

Here 273 is the magnitude and the unit is kelvin (symbol K).

Though the need for a single set of standard units and symbols with strict rules regarding their spelling and grammar is obvious, it is only recently that a serious effort is being made in this regard. Secondly, for rapid progress, the secondary units should be so chosen that they may be derived from the basic units without involving tears in inter-conversion. The adoption by most countries of Europe of the *Metric* or the *cgs* (the centimeter-gram-second) system was a real advance, as the interconversion of units involved only powers of ten. The failure by Britain to go metric was the result of a narrow majority vote of five in her Parliament in 1871 (McGlashan)**. Along with Britain several other English speaking countries thus continued till recently with the inch, foot, yard, the ounce (both for volume and weight), the gallon, the long and short ton, *etc.* Fortunately, this too changed in 1965 when Britain decided to go completely metric by 1975 in commerce, industry and daily life.***

The possibility of further simplification by eliminating even the inter-conversion factor of $10^{\pm n}$ led to the replacement of the *cgs* by the *mks* (the metre-kilogram-second) system of units. It was soon further realized that there existed a number of redundant units all for the same quantity (*e.g.* the erg, joule, calorie, electron-volt, kilowatt-hour, etc. for energy, and mmHg, torr, bar and atmosphere for pressure, *etc.*). The retention of a carefully chosen single unit for each quantity led to the *systéme internationale d'unitès* (SI units) which are wholly *coherent*. The derived SI units result merely by multiplying and/or dividing by the relevant basic units, *involving no numerical factor, not even powers of ten e.g.*,

*A part of this material is taken with permission from *A Course in Physical Chemistry*, by H.J. Arnikar and R.A. Kulkarni, © 1977, authors and Orient Longman Ltd.

**M.L. McGlashan: see Bibliography.

***India went metric in 1957.

The SI unit of force is newton (N) = mass × acceleration

$$= kg\,m\,s^{-2}$$

The SI unit of energy is joule (J) = force × length

$$= N\,m$$

$$= kg\,m^2\,s^{-2}$$

The SI unit of pressure is pascal (Pa)

$$= force/area$$

$$= N\,m^{-2}$$

$$= kg\,m^{-1}\,s^{-2}$$

'Spelling and grammar' of symbols

Scientific culture requires a strict observance of rules regarding symbols commonly agreed upon. The more important of these constituting the 'spelling and grammar' of symbols are listed below.

(i) *Writing of large numbers*: (a) The digits should be grouped in threes on either side of the decimal, with no commas between groups, however a space is to be left between the groups, *e g.* 12 845 687.987. The mass of neutron = 1.008 665 u where u is the unified atomic mass unit = 1.660 530 × 10^{-27} kg. The Rydberg constant R_H = 1.096 775 8 × 10^7 m^{-1}.

(ii) *The decimal point:* (a) this is a full point (·) to be written in line with the digits *e.g.* 7.4.* (b) If the number is a pure decimal, a zero must precede the decimal point, *e.g.* 0.562 not .562.

(iii) *Writing symbols and prefixes:* (a) No full point is to be used either between or after the prefix or the symbol except when it happens to end a sentence *e.g.* The thickness of this book = 24 mm not 24 m.m. (b) There is no plural for symbols. The half-life of ^{128}I = 25 min not 25 mins.

(c) There should be no space between the prefix and the symbol. The wavelength of sodium D line = 589.6 nm not 589.6 n m.

(d) Between two symbols meant to multiply, space must be left. The Planck constant = 6.626 196 × 10^{-34} J s not Js. The gas constant R = 8.31 J K^{-1} mol^{-1} not JK^{-1} mol^{-1}.

(e) A single prefix alone should be used, *i.e.* double prefixes should *not* be used. *e.g.* 589.6 × 10^{-9} m may be written as 589.6 nm and not as 589.6 m μm; a capacity of 6.4 × 10^{-12} F must be written as 6.4 pF and not as 6.4 μμF.

---

*In French and German the comma stands for the decimal point: thus 7, 4.

(f) Note one exception: Though the SI unit for mass is kg, all prefixes must be used with gram and not with kg, *e.g.* 10^6 g may be written as Mg and not as kkg, 10^{-3} g may be written only as mg and not μ kg nor as 10^{-6} kg.

(iv) *A symbol with a prefix must be regarded as a single symbol,* hence, no parenthesis need be used, *e.g.* $cm^2 = (0.01 \text{ m})^2 \equiv 10^{-4}\,m^2$ and not 0.01 m^2; $dm^3 \equiv (0.1 \text{ m})^3 = 10^{-3}\,m^3 = 1000\;cm^3 =$ litre; $\mu s^{-1} \equiv (10^{-6}\,s)^{-1} = 10^6\;s^{-1}$ and not $10^{-6}\;s^{-1}$.

(v) *Areas and volumes* are to be quoted in same units and written as follows.

e.g. A foil of size 25×10 mm

A crystal of size $12 \times 12 \times 2$ mm

(vi) *Combination of units* should be written in one line avoiding more than one solidus or the dividing line. *e.g.* ionic mobility of the $(H_3O)^+$ ion at 25 °C is 36.2×10^{-4} cm per sec and under a field of 1 volt per cm. The correct way of writing this is:

ionic mibility of $(H_3O)^+$ ion at 25 °C

$$= 36.2 \times 10^{-4}\;cm^2\;s^{-1}\;V^{-1}$$

$$= 36.2 \times 10^{-8}\;m^2\;s^{-1}\;V^{-1}\text{ (in SI units)}$$

Writing the above as 36.2×10^{-4} cm/s/V/cm is wrong.
The acceleration due to gravity $= 981$ cm $s^{-2} = 9.81$ m s^{-2}. This is not to be written as 981 cm/s/s.

However, when only one unit is implied in the denominator the use of a solidus is permissible. *e.g.* velocity of light 3×10^8 m/s or 3×10^8 m s^{-1}.

(vii) *If a unit is named after a person*, the symbol must be written with a capital letter. *e.g.* Potential difference of 220 V, a current of 16 A, a solution of 4.5 μCi strength, *etc.* However, if the unit is written in full, no capital letter is to be used; thus: A potential difference of 220 volts, a current of 16 amperes, a solution of 4 5 microcurie strength, etc.

(viii) *Temperature*

(a) For thermodynamic temperature the unit is kelvin, symbol K and not °K *e.g.* the freezing point of water $= 273.15$ K not $=$ 273.15 °K.

(b) The common temperature unit is °C, read as degree celsius, not degree centigrade, (for centigrade is a unit of angle). The normal human body temperature is 37.00 °C $= 310.15$ K. Note the spacing in writting °C not 37.00°C.

(ix) *Heading of columns of tables*
This is illustrated by the following example:

Table: Melting points of metals

Metal	Melting point T_m/K	
Magnesium	923	(not T_m (K): for it implies $T_m \times K$)
Copper	1356	
Iron	1812	

(x)   *The labelling of axes of graphs* is shown by the following example for the plot of log polarization (P_m) in cm³, (Y-axis) *versus* the reciprocal of temperature in kelvin, (X-axis).   Let the range of variation of P_m be from 0 to 50 cm³ and that of $1/T$ from 0 to 6 × 10⁻³ K⁻¹. The correct labels for the axes would be:

   Y-axis: P_m/cm^3 with the scale running from 0 to 50

   X-axis: 10^3 K/T with the scale running from 0 to 6.0.

For a list of basic and derived SI Units, prefixes for multiples and submultiples, their dimensions and equivalents, any book on the subject listed in the Bibliography may be consulted.

APPENDIX III

Values of Constants

(1) Some Fundamental Constants

(Based on the data of B.N. Taylor, W.H. Parker and D.N. Langenberg, *Reviews of Modern Physics*, 1969, Vol, 41, p. 375)

(a) General Quantities

Quantity	Symbol	Value
Avogadro constant	L (earlier N)	$6.022\ 17 \times 10^{23}\ \text{mol}^{-1}$
Electron charge	e	$1.602\ 19 \times 10^{-19}\ \text{C}$
		$1.602\ 19 \times 10^{-20}\ \text{emu}$
		$4.803\ 25 \times 10^{-10}\ \text{esu}$
Faraday constant	$F = L.e$	$9.648\ 67 \times 10^{4}\ \text{C mol}^{-1}$
Gas constant	R	$8.314\ 34\ \text{J mol}^{-1}\ \text{K}^{-1}$
Boltzmann constant	$k = R/L$	$1.380\ 62 \times 10^{-23}\ \text{J K}^{-1}$
Planck's constant	h	$6.626\ 20 \times 10^{-34}\ \text{J s}$
Unit angular momentum	$\hbar = h/2\pi$	$1.054\ 60 \times 10^{-34}\ \text{J s}$
Velocity of light (in vacuum)	c	$2.997\ 93 \times 10^{8}\ \text{m s}^{-1}$
Bohr magneton	μ_B	$9.274\ 1 \times 10^{-24}\ \text{J T}^{-1}$ (or A m^2)
Nuclear magneton	μ_N	$5.050\ 95 \times 10^{-27}\ \text{J T}^{-1}$ (or A m^2)

(b) Rest Masses ($^{12}\text{C} = 12.000\ 000$)

Unified atomic mass unit u		$1.660\ 53 \times 10^{-27}\ \text{kg}$
		931.481 MeV
Electron	m_e	$9.109\ 56 \times 10^{-31}\ \text{kg}$
		$5.485\ 93 \times 10^{-4}\ \text{u}$
		$0.511\ 004$ MeV

Neutron	m_n	1.674 92 $\times$ 10^{-27} kg
		1.008 665 u
		939.55 MeV

Proton	m_p	1.672 61 $\times$ 10^{-27} kg
		1.007 277 u
		938.259 MeV

Hydrogen atom	M_H	1.673 52 $\times$ 10^{-27} kg
		1.007 825 u
		938.77 MeV

(c) *Some Special Units and their Equivalents*

Length	fermi	1 F	10^{-15} m
Area	barn	1 b	10^{-28} m^2
Time	day	1 d	8.64 $\times$ 10^4 s
	year	1 y	3.16 $\times$ 10^7 s
Energy	electron-volt	1 eV	1.602 19 $\times$ 10^{-19} J
	1 eV/atom (or molecule)		
	= L.eV/mol		9.65 $\times$ 10^4 J mol^{-1}
Radioactivity	curie	1 Ci	3.7 $\times$ 10^{10} disintegra-tion/s
SI unit	becquerel	1 Bq	1 disintegration/s
			2.7 $\times$ 10^{-11} Ci
		1 Ci	37 GBq
Radiation dose	rad	1 r	10^{-5} J g^{-1}
			6.24 $\times$ 10^7 MeV g^{-1}
SI unit	gray	1 Gy	1 J kg^{-1} = 100 r
		1 r	10^{-2} Gy

Bibliography

1. Nuclear Properties, Radioactivity and Nuclear Reactions: Theories and Models

Bhatki, K.S., *Radiochemistry of Bismuth*, Energy, R and D Administration, NAS-NS 3061, Springfield (Virginia), 1977.

Blatt, J.M. and Weisskopf, V.F., *Theoretical Nuclear Physics*, Wiley, New York, 1952.

Burcham, W.E., *Nuclear Physics/An Introduction*, 2nd ed., Longman, London, 1973.

Cohen, B.L., *Concepts of Nuclear Physics*, McGraw-Hill, New York, 1971 (Tata McGraw-Hill ed., New Delhi, 1975).

Elton, L.R.B., *Nuclear Sizes*, Oxford Univ. Pr. 1961.

Enge, H.A., *Introduction to Nuclear Physics*, Addison-Wesley, Reading (Mass) 1966.

Evans, R.D., *The Atomic Nucleus*, McGraw-Hill, New York, 1955 (Tata McGraw-Hill ed., New Delhi, 1976).

Friedlander, G., Kennedy, J.W. and Miller, J.M., *Nuclear and Radiochemistry*, Wiley-Interscience, New York, 1964.

Haissinsky, M., *Nuclear Chemistry and Its Applications*, Addison-Wesley, Reading (Mass), 1964.

Haissinsky, M. (Ed.), *Actions Chimiques et Biochimiques des Radiations*, Masson et cie, Paris, 1965.

Halliday, D., *Introductory Nuclear Physics*, Wiley, New York, 1955.

Harvey, B.G., *Introduction to Nuclear Physics and Chemistry*, Prentice-Hall, Englewood Cliffs, (N.J.), 1963 (Prentice-Hall, India, EEE ed., 1965).

Kaplan, I., *Nuclear Physics*, Addison-Wesley, Reading (Mass), 1963, (India Book House, Bombay, 1978).

Kikuchi, K. and Kawai, M., *Nuclear Matter and Nuclear Reactions*, North-Holland, Amsterdam, 1968.

Lefort, M., *Nuclear Chemistry*, D. Van Nostrand, London, 1968.

Littlefield, T.A. and Thorley, N., *Atomic and Nuclear Physics: An Introduction*, 3rd ed. Van Nostrand Reinhold, London, 1979 (English Language Book Society, London, 1979).

Mayer, G.M. and Jensen, J.H.D., *Elementary Theory of Nuclear Shell Structure*, Wiley, New York, 1955.

Overman, R.T., *Basic Concepts of Nuclear Chemistry*, Chapman and Hall, London, 1965.

Seaborg, G.T., *Man-made Transuranium Elements*, Prentice-Hall, Englewood Cliffs (N.J.). 1963.

Segrè, B., *Experimental Nuclear Physics*, Wiley, New York, 1953.

Segrè, E., *Nuclei and Particles*, W.A. Benjamin, Reading (Mass.) 1977.

White, H.E., *Introduction to Atomic and Nuclear Physics*, Van Nostrand Reinhold, New York, 1970 (Affiliated East-West Press, New Delhi, 1970).

Wilets, L., *Theories of Nuclear Fission*, Clarendon Press, Oxford, 1964.

2. Reactors: Nuclear Power

Amphlett, C.B., *Treatment and Disposal of Radioactive Wastes*, Pergamon Press, Oxford, 1961.

Bishop, A.S., *Project Sherwood,*: *The US Program in Controlled Fusion*, Addison-
    Wesley, Reading (Mass), 1958.
Flagg, J.J., *Chemical Processing of Reactor Fuels*, Academic Press, New York, 1961.
Glasstone, S., *Sourcebook on Atomic Energy*, D. Van Nostrand, New York, 1967,
    (Affiliated East-West Press, New Delhi, 1969).
Glasstone, S. and Edlund, M.C., *The Elements of Nuclear Reactor Theory*, Van
    Nostrand, New York, 1952.
Goodman, C. (Ed.), *The Science and Engineering of Nuclear Power*, Addison-
    Wesley, Cambridge (Mass), 1947.
Littler, D.J. and Raffle, J.F., *An Introduction to Nuclear Reactor Physics*, Pergamon
    Press, London, 1957.
Liverhant, S.E., *Elementary Introduction to Reactor Physics*, Wiley, New York, 1960.
Martin, F.S. and Miles, G.L., *Chemical Processing of Nuclear Fuels*, Butterworths
    London, 1958.
Salmon, A., *The Nuclear Reactor*, Wiley, New York, 1964.
Simon, A.I., *An Introduction to Thermonuclear Research*, Pergamon Press, New
    York, 1959.
Smyth, H.D., *Atomic Energy for Military Purposes*, Princeton Univ. Princeton
    (N.J.), 1945.

3. Radiochemistry: Applications of Radioactivity and Isotopes

Bowen, H.J.M., *Chemical Applications of Radioisotopes*, Metheun, London, 1969.
Daudel, P., *Radioactive Tracers in Chemistry and Industry*, Charles Griffin, London,
    1960.
Duncan, J.F. and Cook, G.B., *Isotopes in Chemistry*, Clarendon Press, Oxford,
    1968.
Extermann, R.C. (Ed), *Radioisotopes in Scientific Research* (4 *volumes*), *Proceedings
    of the UNESCO International Conference, Paris*, Pergamon Press, London,
    1958.
Habermann, E.R. (Ed), *Radioimmunoassey and Related Procedures in Medicine*,
    IAEA, Vienna Volumes 1974 and 1977.
IAEA, *Tracers in Industry and Geophysics*, IAEA, Vienna, 1967.
Kamen, M.D. *Isotopic Tracers in Biology*, Academic Press, New York, 1957.
McKay, H.A.C., *Principles of Radiochemistry*, Butterworths, 1971.
Nesmeyanov, An.N , *Radiochemistry*, Mir Publishers, Moscow, 1974.
Overman, R.T. and Clark, H.M., *Radioisotope Techniques*, McGraw-Hill, New York,
    1960.
Piraux, H., *Radioisotopes and Their Industrial Applications*, N.V. Philips' Gloeilamp-
    enfabrieken, Eindhoven, 1964.
Rankama, K., *Isotope Geology*, McGraw-Hill, New York, 1954.
Silver, S., *Radioisotopes in Medicine and Biology*, Henry Kimpton, London, 1962.
Wahl, A.C. and Bonner, N.A. (Ed.), *Radioactivity Applied to Chemistry*, Wiley, New
    York, 1951.
Wolf, G., *Isotopes in Biology*, Academic Press, New York. 1964.

4. Radiation Chemistry

Allen, A.O., *The Radiation Chemistry of Water and Aqueous Solutions*, Van Nos-
    trand, Princeton, N.J., 1961.
Johns, A.C., *Radiation Dosimetry*, (Ed. G.J. Hine and G.L. Brownell), Academic
    Press, 1956.
Lea, D.E., *Actions of Radiations on Living Cells*, Cambridge University Press, 1946.

Platzman, R.L., *Basic Mechanisms in Radiobiology*, National Research Council Publication, 305, ashington, D.C., 1953.

Spinks, J.W.T. and Woods, R.J., *An Introduction to Radiation Chemistry*, Wiley, New York, 1964.

Swallow, A.J., *Radiation Chemistry of Organic Compounds*, Pergamon Press, Oxford, 1960.

Taplin, G.V., *Radiation Dosimetry* (Eds. G.J. Hine and G.L. Brownell), Academic Press, New York, 1956.

Whyte, G.N., *Principles of Radiation Dosimetry*, Wiley, New York, 1959.

5. *Constants*: *Units and Data*

Arnikar, H.J. and Kulkarni, R.K., *A Course in Physical Chemistry*, (Ch. 1, SI Units), Orient Longman, Bombay, 1977.

Harrison, R.D. (Ed.), *Book of Data, Chemistry, Physical Science, Physics*, Penguin Books for Nuffield Foundation, Harmondsworth, 1973.

Lederer, C.M. and Shirley, V.M., *Tables of Isotopes*, Wiley Interscience, New York, 1978.

McGlashan, M.L., *Physico-Chemical Quantities and Units*, 2nd ed., Royal Institute of Chemistry, London, 1971.

Nuclear Data, Academic Press, 1969.

Stark, J.G. and Wallace, H.G., *Chemistry Data Book: SI Edition*, John Murray, London, 1973.

Author Index

AUTHOR INDEX   329

Lefort, M., 183, 323
Libby, W.F., 261, 281
Lind, S.C., 308
Link, W.T., 183
Littlefield, T.A., 282, 323
Littler, D.J., 324
Liverhant, S.E., 225, 324
Low, W., 43, 50
Lynen, F., 281

Magat, M., 244, 281
Magee, J.L., 301, 308
Majorana, E., 16
Marquez, L., 206, 207
Martin, F.S., 225, 281, 324
Mattuch, J.H.E., 18
Mayer, M.G., (see Goeppert-Mayer)
McGlashan, M.L., 18, 325
McGuire, 145
McKay, H.A.C., 243, 281, 324
McMillan, E.M., 86
Meeker, C.L., 158, 183
Meersche, M. van, 281
Mehta, O.P., 282
Meitner, L., 197, 205, 207
Miles, G.L., 225, 324
Miles, L.E.M., 269, 282
Miller, J.M., 158, 183, 184, 323
Mooring, F.P., 169, 183
Moseley, H.G.J., 279
Mottelson, B.R., 52, 81
Mourewx, H., 244, 281
Mozer, F.S., 73, 86
Muxart, R., 144

Nesmeyanov, An. N., 281, 324
Newton, G.W.A., 175, 183
Nordheim, L.W., 35, 50
Nuttal, J.M., 111, 145

Ohmart, 279
Oppenheimer, J.R., 172
Overman, R.T., 104, 145, 281, 323, 324

Paneth, F., 235, 281
Parker, W.H., 320
Patil, S.F., 281, 308
Patnaik, S.K., 308
Pauli, W., 49, 57, 121, 125
Pauly, J., 281
Penfold, A.S., 119, 145
Perlman, I., 23, 49
Peterson, J.M., 86
Petrjak, K., 202, 207
Phillips, M., 172

Piraux, H., 270, 282, 324
Platzman, R.L., 301, 302, 308, 325
Pleasonton, F., 142, 145
Pokharkar, R.D., 308
Pontecorvo, B., 183, 281
Porter, C.E., 85, 86
Porter, F.T., 130, 145
Prasad, S.D., 281

Raffle, J.F. 324
Rainwater, J., 81, 86, 158, 183
Ramler, W.J., 308
Ramsay, W., 88
Rangan, L.K., 281
Rankama, K., 18, 86, 324
Rao, B.S.M., 308
Rasetti, F., 183, 281
Rasmussen, J.O., 141, 145
Ravenhall, D.G., 21, 49
Reines, F., 125, 145
Rocklin, S.R., 308
Röntgen, W.K., 284
Ruben, S., 238, 281
Rutherford, E., 88, 112, 173

Saha, N., 236, 281
Sakharov, A., 6
Salmon, A., 225, 324
Samuel, A.H., 301, 308
Sargent, B.W., 126, 127, 145
Savel, P. 282
Savitch, P., 186, 187
Saxon, D.S., 59
Schmidt, T., 35, 50, 88
Schrödinger, E., 45, 48, 113
Schwarz, H.A., 308
Seaborg, G.T., 90, 108, 135, 144, 183, 252
   253, 282, 323
Segrè, E., 8, 9, 18, 49, 73, 86, 145,   183,
   281, 323
Serber, R., 85, 86
Shirley, V.M., 281, 325
Silver, S., 282, 324
Simon, A.I., 18, 184, 324
Simonoff, G.N., 161, 166, 183
Singh, L.M., 268, 282
Sklodowska, M. (see Curie, M.)
Smyth, H.D., 18, 206, 225, 324
Snell, A.H., 142, 145
Soddy, F., 88
Spinks, J.W. T., 288, 292, 302, 308, 325
Stark, J. G., 18, 325
Stark, M.B., 308
Stein, W.E., 193, 206
Stephens, K.G., 183

Subject Index

ERRATA

Page	For	Read
3, line 9 from bottom	$2.5\bar{\nu} +$ MeV	$\bar{\nu} + 2.5$ MeV
22, line 7	$/F^*$	$/F^{3*}$
49, last para, line 4	having even integral	having integral
50, Problem 2.8, line 2	$g = .5854$ and 1	5.5854 and 2.002
line 3	$(b) = 2.22 \times 10^{10}$ Hz	4.20×10^{10} Hz
58, para (b), line 6	(Fig. 1.3)	(Fig. 1.4)
59, Equation 3.6	$e^{\cdot \mu^2 r^2}$	$e^{-\mu^2 r^2}$
92, para 2, last line	Sec. 8.17	Sec. 8.7
134, line 1	$I_i = I_f = 0$	$I_i = I_f$
163, line 2 from bottom, ADD after 'is given by'		$\bar{\tau} = \dfrac{\hbar}{\Gamma} = \dfrac{6.6 \times 10^{-16}}{\Gamma}$ s
180, line 6	Ninety percent	Ninetynine percent
182, para (iii), line 2	high energy flux	high energy high flux
205, 6.11.1, line 1	Meitner	Meitner[15]
line 8 matter under 'Symmetric fission' to be replaced by		$^{99}_{42}\text{Mo} + ^{100}_{42}\text{Mo}$ (stable) $\Big\downarrow 2\beta^-$ $^{99}_{44}\text{Ru}$ (stable)
line 12	$^{99}\text{Nb}_{58}$ and $^{100}\text{Nb}_{59}$ have 8 and 9	$^{99}\text{Mo}_{57}$ and $^{100}\text{Mo}_{58}$ have 7 and 8
208, Problem 6.7	$^{87}\text{Br} = 86.022$ u	$^{87}\text{Br} = 86.922$ u
last line	1040 MeV	201.9 MeV
291, line 1 after Equation 9.11	$\theta \, 2p$ to	θ upto

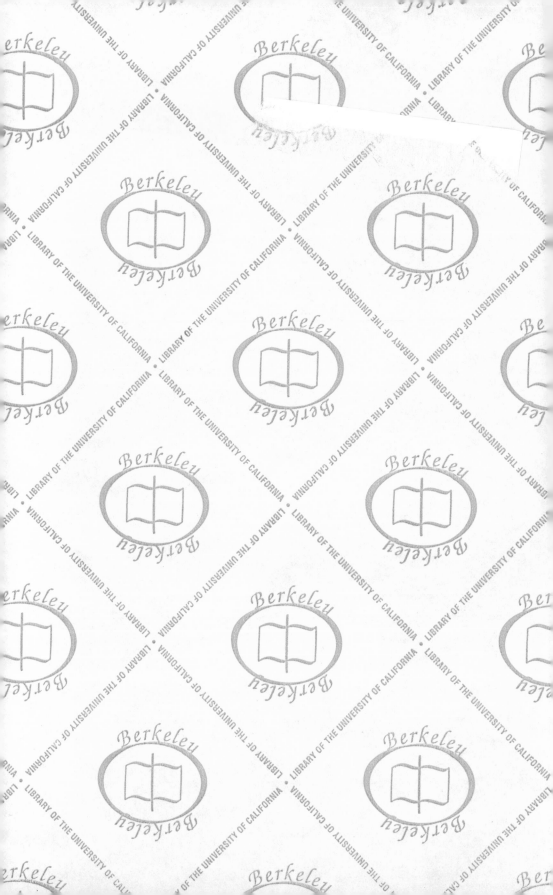

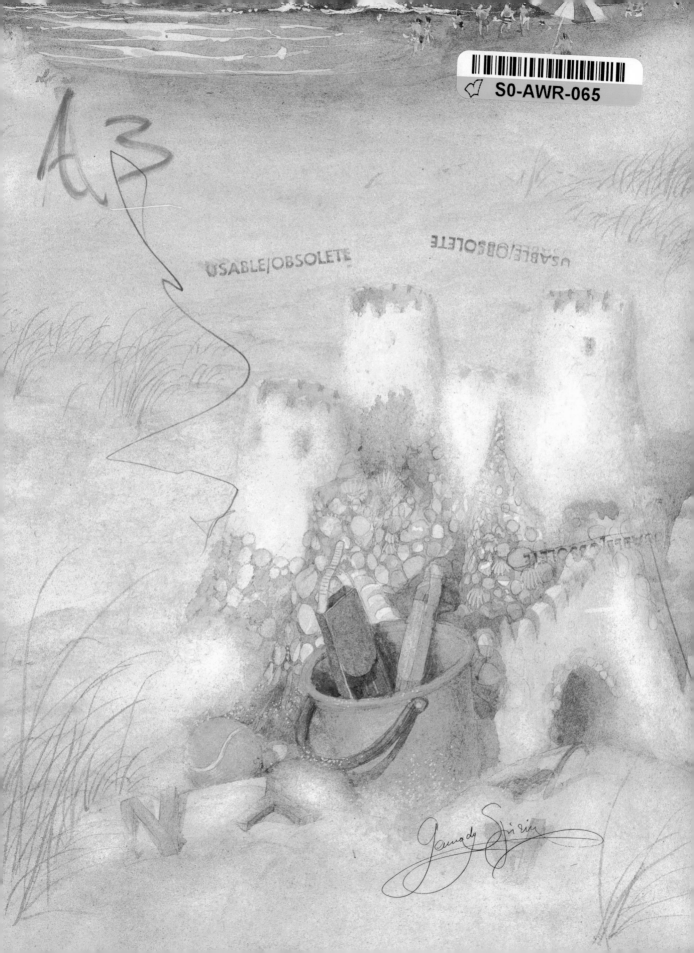

DIAMOND COVE

Harcourt Brace & Company

DIAMOND COVE

Senior Authors

Roger C. Farr

Dorothy S. Strickland

Authors

Richard F. Abrahamson ♦ Alma Flor Ada ♦ Barbara Bowen Coulter
Bernice E. Cullinan ♦ Margaret A. Gallego
W. Dorsey Hammond
Nancy Roser ♦ Junko Yokota ♦ Hallie Kay Yopp

Senior Consultant

Asa G. Hilliard III

Consultants

V. Kanani Choy ♦ Lee Bennett Hopkins ♦ Stephen Krashen ♦ Rosalia Salinas

Harcourt Brace & Company

Orlando Atlanta Austin Boston San Francisco Chicago Dallas New York Toronto London

ISBN 0-15-309117-7

2 3 4 5 6 7 8 9 10   048   99 98 97

Dear Reader,

Imagine that you have discovered a special place, like the castle on the cover of this book. It is a place to explore, a place to build, and a place to enjoy the natural world.

This book, **Diamond Cove**, is like a special place. In these pages, you can meet new people and learn about how nature stays in balance. You can travel to new communities, such as Ayutla in Mexico, Harlem in New York City, and Henson Creek in the Blue Ridge Mountains. In **Diamond Cove**, you can build new friendships and new understandings. You can do all of this while enjoying wonderful stories, poems, and articles.

Welcome to **Diamond Cove**! Perhaps you will make some discoveries here that nobody else has made.

Sincerely,

The Authors

The Authors

THE
RANDOM HOUSE
Book of
POETRY
for Children

A Treasury of 572 Poems for Today's Child

Nature's Great
Balancing Act
IN OUR OWN BACKYARD

ALL
EYES
ON THE
POND

Wolf
Island

Celia Godkin

WOLVES

BY GAIL GIBBONS

Borreguita and the Coyote

illustrated by Petra Mathers

THE BALANCE OF NATURE

CONTENTS

MY GREAT-AUNT ARIZONA

BY GLORIA HOUSTON
ILLUSTRATED BY SUSAN CONDIE LAMB

Grandfather's Journey

ALLEN SAY

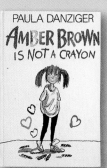

PAULA DANZIGER

AMBER BROWN IS NOT A CRAYON

SHERRY GARLAND

THE LOTUS SEED

TATSURO KIUCHI

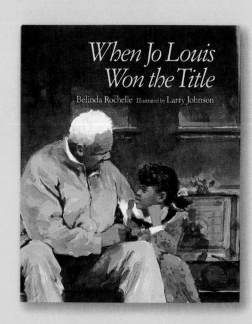

When Jo Louis Won the Title

Belinda Rochelle   Illustrated by Larry Johnson

Traveling to New Communities

CONTENTS

 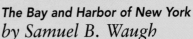

Exploring Challenges

CONTENTS

11

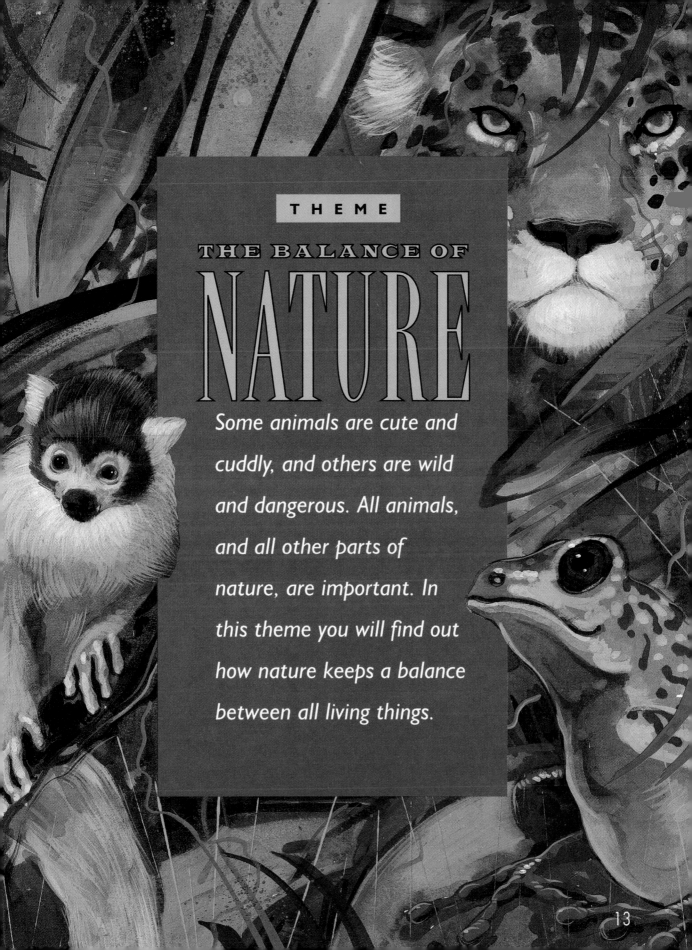

THE BALANCE OF
NATURE

Some animals are cute and cuddly, and others are wild and dangerous. All animals, and all other parts of nature, are important. In this theme you will find out how nature keeps a balance between all living things.

THE BALANCE OF NATURE

CONTENTS

All About Alligators

*written and illustrated
by Jim Arnosky*

Learn what alligators look
like, where they live, how
they move, what they eat,
and how dangerous
they are.

SLJ Best Books;
Outstanding Science Trade Book

Signatures Library

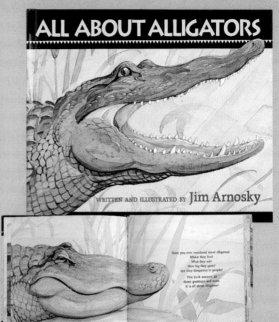

Dolphin Adventure: A True Story

by Wayne Grover

A dolphin family turns to
a human diver for help in
this exciting true story.

Outstanding Science Trade Book

Signatures Library

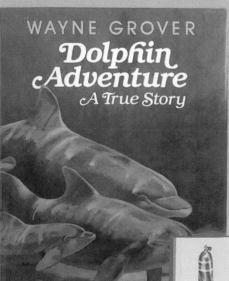

When Hunger Calls
by Bert Kitchen

Each different kind of animal has its own special skills for catching its dinner.

A Journey of Hope/Una Jornada de Esperanza
by Bob Harvey and Diane Kelsay Harvey

A baby sea turtle makes her way from the nest to the sea, in a journey filled with danger.

Outstanding Science Trade Book

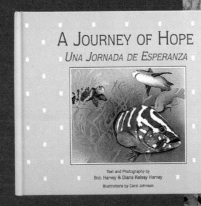

The Year of the Panda
by Miriam Schlein

Lu Yi helps to rescue a panda, and in the process he discovers a possible career for the future.

Outstanding Science Trade Book

Borreguita

Borreguita and the Coyote

SLJ Best Books

Notable Trade Book
in Social Studies

and the Coyote

A Tale from Ayutla, Mexico

retold by Verna Aardema
illustrated by Petra Mathers

On a farm at the foot of a mountain, there once lived a little ewe lamb. Her master called her simply *Borreguita*, which means "little lamb."

One day Borreguita's master tied her to a stake in a field of red clover. The lamb was eating the lush plants when a coyote came along.

The coyote growled, "*Grrr*! Borreguita, I'm going to eat you!"

Borreguita bleated, "*Baa-a-a-a, baa-a-a-a*! Oh, Señor Coyote, I would not fill you up. I am as thin as a bean pod. When I have eaten all this clover, I shall be fat. You may eat me *then*."

Coyote looked at the skinny little lamb and the wide clover field. "*Está bien*. That is good," he said. "When you are fat, I shall come back."

After many days the coyote returned. He found the lamb grazing in a meadow. He growled, "*Grrr*! Borreguita, you are as plump as a tumbleweed. I'm going to eat you *now*!"

Borreguita bleated, *"Baa-a-a-a, baa-a-a-a!* Señor Coyote, I know something that tastes ever so much better than lamb!"

"What?" asked Coyote.

"Cheese!" cried Borreguita. "My master keeps a round of cheese on his table. He eats it on his tacos."

The coyote had never heard of cheese, and he was curious about it. "How can I get some of this cheese?" he asked.

Borreguita said, "There is a pond at the end of the pasture. Tonight, when the moon is high, meet me there. And I will show you how to get a cheese."

"Está bien," said Coyote. "I will be there."

That night, when the full moon was straight up in the sky, Borreguita and Coyote met at the edge of the pond.

There, glowing in the black water, was something that looked like a big, round cheese.

"Do you see it?" cried Borreguita. "Swim out and get it."

Coyote slipped into the water and paddled toward the cheese. He swam and swam, *shuh, shuh, shuh, shuh.* But the cheese stayed just so far ahead. Finally, he opened his mouth and lunged—WHOOOSH!

The image shattered in the splash!

Pond water rushed into Coyote's mouth. Coughing and spluttering, he turned and headed for the shore.

When he reached it, the little lamb was gone. She had tricked him! Coyote shook the water off his fur, *freh, freh, freh.*

Then he looked up at the big cheese in the sky and howled, "OWOOOOOAH!"

At dawn the next day Borreguita went to graze near a small overhanging ledge of rock on the side of the mountain. She knew that the coyote would be coming after her, and she had a plan.

As the sun rose over the mountain, Borreguita saw the coyote coming. He was sniffing along, with his nose on some trail. She crawled under the ledge and lay on her back, bracing her feet against the top.

When the coyote found her, he growled, "*Grrr!* Borreguita, I see you under there. I'm going to pull you out and eat you!"

Borreguita bleated, "*Baa-a-a-a, baa-a-a-a!* Señor Coyote, you can't eat me *now*! I have to hold up this mountain. If I let go, it will come tumbling down."

The coyote looked at the mountain. He saw that the lamb was holding it up.

"You are strong," said Borreguita. "Will you hold it while I go for help?"

The coyote did not want the mountain to fall, so he crept under the ledge and put up his feet.

"Push hard," said Borreguita. "Do you have it now?"

"I have it," said Coyote. "But hurry back. This mountain is heavy."

Borreguita rolled out of the shallow cave and went leaping and running all the way back to the barnyard.

Coyote held up that rock until his legs ached and he was hungry and thirsty. At last he said, "Even if the mountain falls, I'm going to let go! I can't hold it any longer."

The coyote dragged himself out and covered his head with his paws. The mountain did not fall. Then he knew—the little lamb had fooled him again.

Coyote sat on his haunches and howled, "OWOOOOOAH!"

Early the next morning the coyote hid himself in a thicket in the lamb's pasture. When she drew near, he sprang out with a WOOF! And he said, "Borreguita, you will not escape this time! I'm going to eat you *now!*"

Borreguita bleated, "*Baa-a-a-a, baa-a-a-a!* Señor Coyote, I know I deserve to die. But grant me one kindness. Swallow me whole so that I won't have to suffer the biting and the chewing."

"Why should I make you comfortable while I eat you?" demanded the coyote. "Anyway, I couldn't swallow you all in one piece even if I wanted to."

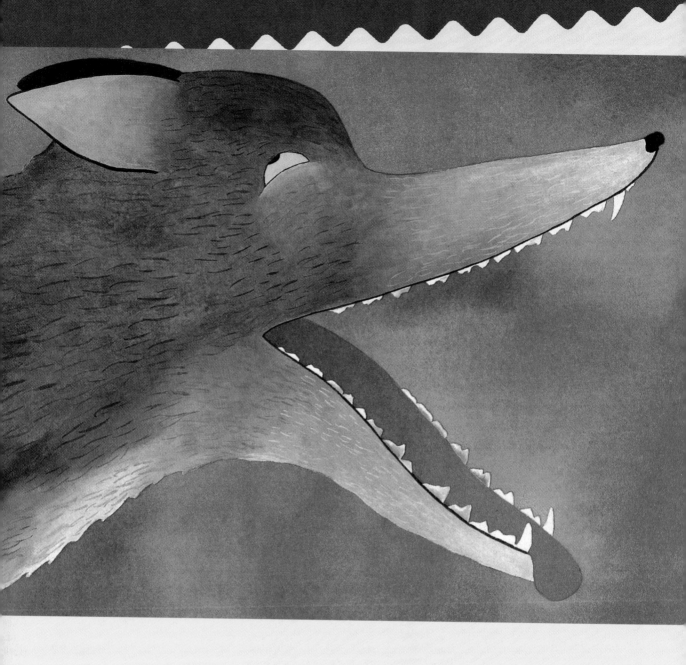

"Oh, yes, you could!" cried Borreguita. "Your mouth is so big, you could swallow a cougar. Open it wide, and I will run and dive right in."

Coyote opened his mouth wide and braced his feet.
Borreguita backed away. Then she put her head down and
charged. BAM! She struck the inside of Coyote's mouth so
hard she sent him rolling.

"OW, OW, OW!" howled the coyote as he picked himself up and ran away—his mouth feeling like one big toothache!

And from that day on, Borreguita frisked about on the farm at the foot of the mountain. And Coyote never bothered her again.

THE END
FIN

As a child, Verna Aardema loved to read. Her family often had a hard time tearing her away from the book she was reading at the time—even when she had to help out around the house!

When Verna was in the sixth grade, she wrote a poem that she was very proud of. As soon as Verna's mother read it, she knew her daughter would be a writer. From then on, Verna's mother encouraged her daughter whenever she could. Verna would run out the door right after dinner and go to a nearby swamp to think about the things she wanted to write. Soon, she was making up stories and telling them to the kids in her neighborhood.

Verna Aardema has now written more than twenty books for children, retelling popular folktales. Like most authors, she spends time revising her work. See the next page, which shows an early draft of "Borreguita and the Coyote."

> "Writing is not easy but the rewards are great! When starry-eyed boys and girls tell me they want to be authors, I hug them for success."

Borreguita and the Coyote
A Tale from Ayutla
Mexico

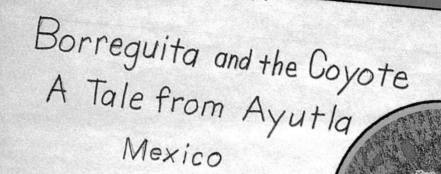

On a farm at the foot of a mountain in Mexico, there once lived a little ewe lamb. Her master called her simply *Borreguita*, which means "little lamb."

One day Borreguita's master tied her to a stake in an alfalfa field. The lamb was eating the lush green plants when a coyote came along.

The coyote said, "Borreguita, I'm going to eat you!"

Borreguita bleated, "BA-A-A, BA-A-A! Señor Coyote, I would not fill you up. I am thin as a bean pod. When I have eaten all this alfalfa, I shall be fat. You may eat me then."

Coyote looked at the skinny little lamb and the wide alfalfa field. "*Está bien*. That is good," he said. "When you are fat, I shall come back."

After many days the coyote returned. He found the lamb grazing in a meadow. He said, "Borreguita, you are as plump as a tumbleweed. I'm going to eat you now!"

"Señor Coyote," cried Borreguita, "I know something that tastes ever so much better than lamb!"

"What?" asked Coyote.

"Cheese!" cried Borreguita. "My master keeps a round of cheese on his table. He eats it on his tacos."

The coyote had never heard of cheese, and he was curious about it. "How can I get some of this cheese?" he asked.

Borreguita said, "There is a pond at the end of the pasture. Tonight, when the moon is high, meet me there. And I will show you how to get a cheese."

"*Está bien*," said Coyote. "I will be there."

That night, when the full moon was straight up in the sky, Borreguita and Coyote met at the edge of the pond.

There, glowing in the black water, was something that looked like a big, round cheese.

"Do you see it?" cried Borreguita. "Swim out and get it."

Coyote slipped into the water and paddled toward the cheese. He swam and swam, but the cheese stayed just so far ahead. Finally, he opened his mouth and lunged—WHOOSH!

Response Corner

WRITE A POSTCARD

Postcards from Ayutla

Look in an atlas for a map of Mexico. Use the index to help you locate the city of Ayutla. Notice the landforms and bodies of water nearby. What would you see if you visited Ayutla? Write a postcard describing the area to your friends back home. On the front of your postcard, draw a scene that you might see in Ayutla.

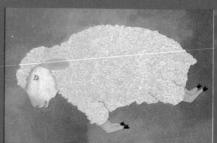

Brains or Brawn?

Like "Borreguita and the Coyote," many other stories have one character who is weak but successful. With a classmate, make a list of story characters like Borreguita, who were more successful than a stronger character. For each character, write a sentence telling what qualities helped him or her to succeed.

The Moral of the Story...

Coyote finally learned his lesson after many troubles. Think about a lesson you learned the hard way. Then write a one-page short story with a moral, or lesson, at the end. Draw pictures to go with your story. You and your classmates may want to make a book of your stories.

What Do You Think?

▼ How does Borreguita outsmart Coyote?

▼ What is your favorite illustration in this story? Describe what it shows, and tell why you like it.

▼ Coyote is a character in many Native American and Mexican stories. What is he like in this story?

Wolves

Award-Winning
Author and
Illustrator

BY GAIL GIBBONS

GRAY WOLF OR
TIMBER WOLF

It is a snowy moonlit night in the northern woods. An animal shakes the snow from its thick fur, throws its head back and joins its companions in a long howl. The animal is a wolf.

There are two different types of wolves. One is the gray wolf, or timber wolf. A gray wolf can have black, white, brown or gray fur depending on where it lives. Thirty-two different kinds of gray wolves have been identified. Some of them don't exist anymore.

RED WOLF

The other type of wolf is the red wolf. Red wolves aren't really red. Instead, they are the combination of black, gray and reddish brown. They are smaller and more slender than gray wolves. Only one of the three original different kinds of red wolves exists today. Very few of them live in the wild.

The first ancestors of wolves lived more than 50 million years ago. Over time, these creatures developed into wolves.

Wolves are members of the dog family, called Canidae. All dogs are related to wolves.

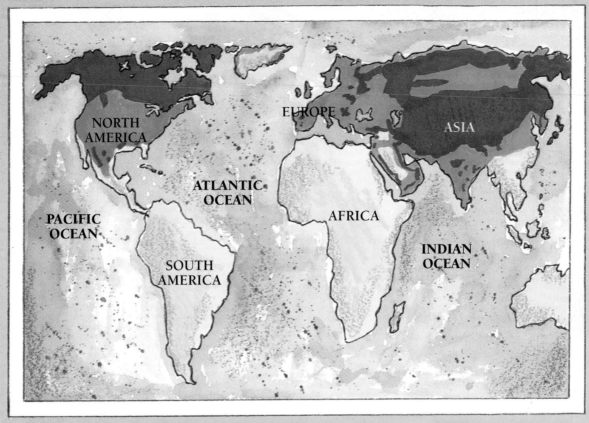

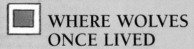 **WHERE WOLVES ONCE LIVED**

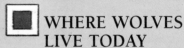 **WHERE WOLVES LIVE TODAY**

A few hundred years ago, wolves lived all around the world. People hunted them and also took over much of their territory. There were fewer wolves and they moved away. Today most wolves are found in the northern parts of the world.

Most male wolves weigh more than 100 pounds. The females weigh less. Wolves are very strong and have long legs, a long tail, and are covered with fur.

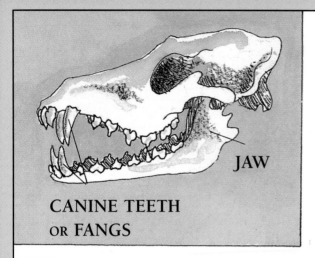

CANINE TEETH
OR **FANGS**

JAW

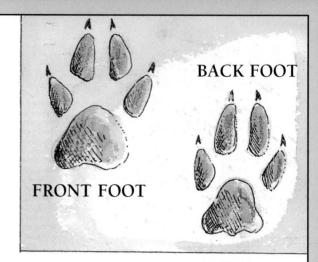

BACK FOOT

FRONT FOOT

Wolves are hunters. They are carnivores, which means they eat meat. They have strong jaws and forty-two teeth for tearing, chewing and grinding. Four of the teeth are called canine teeth, or fangs. Wolves use their canine teeth to grip an animal when they catch it.

Wolves have a keen sense of smell for sniffing out their prey. They can hear sounds from far away, too. When wolves roam, they leave big paw prints behind. Some tracks can be as large as a grownup's hand.

Gray wolves live in groups called packs. These packs can be made up of three to more than twenty wolves. It is believed that red wolves don't form packs. Wolf packs live and hunt in territories which can cover an area as big as 500 square miles. They mark the boundaries with their urine, which leaves a scent that warns other wolf packs to stay away. Each pack has adult males and females, and their pups.

The leader of a pack is called an alpha wolf. An alpha wolf is smart and strong. He will fight any wolf that tries to take over his pack. The alpha wolf is the tallest in the pack. When he looks the other wolves in the eye, they crouch down and tuck their tails between their hind legs. Sometimes they roll over and lick the alpha wolf's face, letting him know he's boss.

The members of a pack care for each other. They protect each other when other wolf packs try to invade their territory. They hunt and share their food together, too. The alpha wolf decides where and when to hunt. It would be difficult for a wolf to catch a big animal alone. Hunting in packs helps them survive.

Once they spot their prey, the chase begins. Wolves' legs are built for speed and running long distances. Often, an animal outruns them. Other times the prey tires and slows down.

The pack fans out in a circle around the animal. Then one wolf charges and attacks the animal. It hangs on tightly. Others attack.

Soon the fight is over. The hungry wolves can eat. Wolves hunt many different kinds of animals like moose, deer and caribou. They also hunt smaller animals such as rabbits, beavers and small rodents.

WHIMPER

SNARL

WOOF

BARK

Wolves make different sounds to "talk" to each other. They whimper when they are excited or restless. A snarl means the wolf is being threatened. A short woof is a warning, and a bark means danger is near.

Wolves howl, too. The sound is eerie and sometimes seems sad. They howl to tell other packs to stay out of their territory. Often, it is the way they stay in touch with the others in their pack when they are separated. Sometimes they howl before a hunt.

Wolves communicate in other ways, too. They show their teeth
when they are angry. When a wolf is scared, its ears go flat against
its head. A wagging tail means the wolf is happy. If just the tip of
the tail wags, it could be ready to attack.

Wolves often mate for life. Wolf pups are born in the spring.
The alpha female is the only one of the females in a pack to give
birth to a litter of pups. There can be three to fourteen pups. They
only weigh about one pound at birth and cannot see or hear. They
nuzzle up against their mother to drink her milk in the den where
they live.

When the pups are about three weeks old, they are allowed out of their den to romp and play. The mother and some of the other wolves take turns babysitting while the rest of the pack is hunting. When the hunters return, the pups greet them. When they lick the wolves' jaws, the wolves bring up some of the food they have eaten and feed it to the pups. The pups are now old enough to eat meat.

At six months old the pups are almost as big as the adult wolves. They are strong enough and old enough to begin learning how to hunt. They join the pack as it roams in search of food.

For centuries people have been afraid of wolves. They thought wolves were their enemies. Scientists who study wolves are learning that wolves have been misunderstood. Wolves tend to live peacefully among themselves. They are shy and rarely attack people. When this happens, they have probably been threatened.

When wolves hunt, often the animals they kill are weak and sickly. The healthy and stronger animals survive. Wolves are not cruel. They are just very efficient hunters.

Occasionally wolves attack farm or ranch animals. This can make the farmers or ranchers want to kill them. Wolves are hunted for their fur, too.

Because wolves are in danger of extinction, some people realize they must be protected. Some scientists and people who work at zoos help wolves by raising them so they can be released into the wild. In many parts of the world laws have been passed making it illegal to hunt wolves.

By studying wolves in their natural surroundings and watching them for long periods of time, scientists have learned that wolves play an important part in the balance of our natural world. The old fears and myths about wolves are dying. Wolves deserve to live undisturbed.

If enough people care, there will be wild wolves for years to come, and the howling sounds these beautiful creatures make will still be heard.

MORE WAYS OF THE WOLVES

Wolves are the largest of the wild dogs, which include coyotes, foxes, and others.

Wolves have very few enemies. These enemies can be other packs of wolves, bears, and people.

Wolves usually trot or run in a way called loping. They are very fast runners. Some can run up to forty miles per hour.

A pack of howling wolves can be heard from as far away as ten miles.

When wolves hunt in snow, they walk in single file. They take turns making tracks for the others to walk in.

Wolves vary in size. The smallest kind in the world is the Arabian wolf. It is only about 32 inches long.

In North America there is no record of a healthy wolf ever attacking a person.

Some experts believe ancient people learned how to hunt by watching packs of wolves hunt.

Wolves are good swimmers but rarely follow prey into water during a chase.

In captivity, wolves have been known to live up to seventeen years. In the wild, life is much harder. Wolves usually live to be only nine to ten years old.

GAIL GIBBONS
Talks About Wolves

Our family lives out in the country in Vermont. When my daughter was about twelve, she saw a wolf as she was coming home from school. It startled her, and then it ran away. Actually, they both ran. My daughter ran into the house while the wolf ran into the woods.

Around the same time, I noticed several articles in the newspaper about wolves. One was about wolves in Alaska, and the other was about putting wolves back into the national forests. There are so many myths about wolves that I decided to write a book about them and find out the truth for myself.

When I write, I do the research for the book first. Also, it's very important for me to actually see what I'm writing about. For this book, I spent time at the Bronx Zoo, where I observed wolves.

After I've done my research and written the book, I find an expert who can help me check my work. For me, a book takes about a year from the time I get an idea to the time I send it off to my editor. Usually, I'm working on several books at once.

Response

THE REAL STORY

You read in the selection that there are many myths about wolves that are not true. Write a short story that helps show the truth about wolves. You might make the main character a wolf who is in danger. Help your reader see some good things about wolves.

A WOLF'S FRIEND

Lawmakers and scientists are just some of the people who are trying to protect wolves. Study advertisements in a newspaper. Then write your own ad, asking for volunteers to help save wolves. Try to make people see that this project is important.

Corner

SAFETY IN THE WILD

Many people want to save wolves. Others, such as hikers and campers, may fear them. People in forest areas need to be very careful because wild animals can be dangerous. Make a poster of safety tips to help people be safe around wild animals.

WHAT DO YOU THINK?

- How does Gail Gibbons feel about wolves? How do you know?

- What else would you like to know about wolves? Where could you find that information?

- Should animals always be allowed to roam wherever they want? Why or why not?

ART &
LITERATURE

In this theme, you have been reading about how animals survive in nature. How is this Chinese painting like the selections you have read?

Why do you think the frog is watching the dragonflies?

The Detroit Institute of Arts; Founders Society Purchase.

EARLY AUTUMN

by Qian Xuan

Qian Xuan painted this picture about seven hundred years ago.
Artists at that time used brushes dipped in different ink colors to
make their paintings. They spoke of "writing" a painting.

Wolf Island

by Celia Godkin

Outstanding Science Trade Book

Once there was an island. It was an island with trees and meadows, and many kinds of animals. There were mice, rabbits and deer, squirrels, foxes and several kinds of birds.

All the animals on the island depended on the plants and the other animals for their food and well-being. Some animals ate grass or other plants; some ate insects; some ate other animals. The island animals were healthy. There was plenty of food for all.

A family of wolves lived on the island, too, a male wolf, a female, and their five cubs.

One day the wolf cubs were playing on the beach while their mother and father slept. The cubs found a strange object at the edge of the water.

It was a log raft, nailed together with boards. The cubs had never seen anything like this before. They were very curious. They climbed onto it and sniffed about. Everything smelled different.

While the cubs were poking around, the raft began to drift slowly out into the lake. At first the cubs didn't notice anything wrong. Then, suddenly, there was nothing but water all around the raft.

The cubs were scared. They howled. The mother and father wolf heard the howling and came running down to the water's edge.

They couldn't turn the raft back, and the cubs were too scared to swim, so the adult wolves swam out to the raft and climbed aboard. The raft drifted slowly and steadily over to the mainland. Finally it came to rest on the shore and the wolf family scrambled onto dry land.

There were no longer wolves on the island.

Time passed. Spring grew into summer on the island, and summer into fall. The leaves turned red. Geese flew south, and squirrels stored up nuts for the winter.

Winter was mild that year, with little snow. The green plants were buried under a thin white layer. Deer dug through the snow to find food. They had enough to eat.

Next spring, many fawns were born.

There were now many deer on the island. They were eating large amounts of grass and leaves. The wolf family had kept the deer population down, because wolves eat deer for food. Without wolves to hunt the deer, there were now too many deer on the island for the amount of food available.

Spring grew into summer and summer into fall. More and more deer ate more and more grass and more and more leaves.

Rabbits had less to eat, because the deer were eating their food. There were not many baby bunnies born that year.

Foxes had less to eat, because there were fewer rabbits for them to hunt.

Mice had less to eat, because the deer had eaten the grass and grass seed. There were not many baby mice born that year.

Owls had less to eat, because there were fewer mice for them to hunt. Many animals on the island were hungry.

The first snow fell. Squirrels curled up in their holes, wrapped their tails around them for warmth, and went to sleep. The squirrels were lucky. They had collected a store of nuts for winter.

Other animals did not have winter stores. They had to find food in the snow. Winter is a hard time for animals, but this winter was harder than most. The snow was deep and the weather cold. Most of the plants had already been eaten during the summer and fall. Those few that remained were hard to find, buried deep under the snow.

Rabbits were hungry. Foxes were hungry. Mice were hungry. Owls were hungry. Even the deer were hungry. The whole island was hungry.

The owls flew over to the mainland, looking for mice. They flew over the wolf family walking along the mainland shore. The wolves were thin and hungry, too. They had not found a home, because there were other wolf families on the mainland. The other wolves did not want to share with them.

Snow fell for many weeks. The drifts became deeper and deeper. It was harder and harder for animals to find food. Animals grew weaker, and some began to die. The deer were so hungry they gnawed bark from the trees. Trees began to die.

Snow covered the island. The weather grew colder and colder. Ice began to form in the water around the island, and along the mainland coast. It grew thicker and thicker, spreading farther and farther out into the open water. One day there was ice all the way from the mainland to the island.

The wolf family crossed the ice and returned to their old home.

The wolves were hungry when they reached the island, and there were many weak and sick deer for them to eat. The wolves left the healthy deer alone.

Finally, spring came. The snow melted, and grass and leaves began to grow. The wolves remained in their island home, hunting deer. No longer would there be too many deer on the island. Grass and trees would grow again. Rabbits would find enough food. The mice would find enough food. There would be food for the foxes and owls. And there would be food for the deer. The island would have food enough for all.

Life on the island was back in balance.

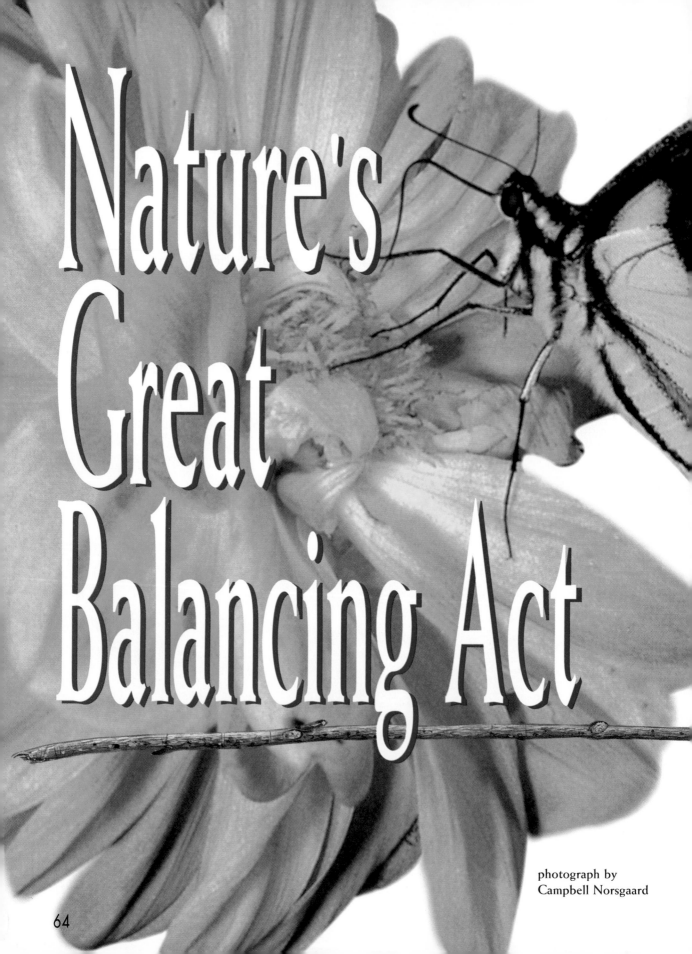

Nature's Great Balancing Act

photograph by
Campbell Norsgaard

Outstanding
Science
Trade Book

IN OUR OWN BACKYARD

BY E. JAEDIKER NORSGAARD

Welcome to our backyard!

ou won't find a tame grass carpet, but a large semi-wild wonderland that stretches from our house to the bordering woods. Some years ago we decided to let everything grow as it pleases. Now it's a community where many of our fellow creatures are at home. On a summer day, grasshoppers will jump away from your footsteps. You'll see bees buzzing around raspberry bushes, butterflies landing on wildflowers, birds feeding insects to their young. There are chipmunks and a family of bold raccoons. Deer venture out of the woods to nibble hedges and shrubs.

photograph by Campbell Norsgaard

All creatures in the animal kingdom depend on plants and on each other for survival, one feeding on another. They are all parts of a gigantic puzzle in which the pieces fit together but, like a kaleidoscope, are forever changing. You are a mammal, and you are a part of that puzzle too, though you are quite different from other mammals and from birds, reptiles, amphibians, and insects. All living things are members of nature's great balancing act. You can see how this works right here in our own backyard.

Nature's great balancing act depends on food chains. All food chains begin with plants. Plants are able to make their own food, using energy from the sun, and they pass that energy on to animals that eat them. Plants are the basis of all the food and energy that you and other animals use.

When an animal eats a plant or eats another animal, it becomes part of a food chain. In our backyard, as well as everywhere else, all food chains begin with plant-eaters (herbivores) and usually end with a meat-eater (carnivore). Food chains can be short or as long as five or six links. If you eat

Like many mammals, this red fox eats plants and animals.

an apple, that is a two-link food chain. If you eat meat from a sheep or cow that has eaten plants, that is a three-link food chain. You are at the top of those food chains.

Here in the backyard, one food chain might begin with a moth sipping nectar from a flower. The moth is caught by a sparrow and fed to its young in the nest in our hedge. The young bird might be taken from its nest and eaten by a raccoon. The raccoon is at the top of this food chain. There are no predators[1] in the backyard to eat the raccoon.

---

[1] **predators**: animals that live by eating other animals

ENERGY
comes from the sun.

RACCOON
eats sparrows.

PLANT
uses the
sun's energy.

SPARROWS
eat moth.

MOTH
sips nectar
from plant.

Another food chain might start with a fly feeding on decaying vegetation[2] in the backyard. The fly is caught and eaten by a spider. The spider is eaten by a toad, which is eaten by a fox.

First links in any food chain are usually the smallest but most abundant plants and animals. Microscopic green algae and other plant plankton[3] float in the ponds, lakes, and seas. They are eaten in great quantities by water insects and small crustaceans,[4] which are eaten by small fishes, which are, in turn, eaten by larger fishes that may end up on your dinner table.

Each time an animal eats a plant or one animal eats another, a tiny bit of the sun's energy is passed along the food chain. Each animal uses some of that energy and passes along what is left. Amazingly, the used energy is not destroyed, only changed into other forms or passed into the atmosphere.[5]

BALANCING POPULATIONS

Animal populations are kept in balance by the amount of food available and by predators in the food chain. Take mice, for instance. You can't really catch sight of them scurrying through the tall grass in the backyard, eating seeds. They move quickly to avoid enemies. During a summer of heavy rainfall and lush vegetation, the mouse population

---

[2] **decaying vegetation**: rotting plants
[3] **algae and plant plankton**: simple plants that float or drift in the water

[4] **crustaceans**: animals with a tough shell that live in water, like lobsters and crabs
[5] **atmosphere**: the air around the earth

This long-eared owl helps keep the mouse population in balance.

increases, providing more food for hawks and owls and other mouse-eaters. When less food is available, mice tend to raise fewer young. This affects the numbers of hawks and owls also. If the insect and rodent populations decrease,[6] owls and hawks raise fewer young or find better territory or else starve. A balance of numbers is maintained.

[6] **decrease**: to go down in size or number

Some farmers shoot hawks and owls, believing that they kill a few chickens. But without these predators, rabbits and mice overpopulate and spread into cultivated fields to eat corn, wheat, oats, rye, barley, rice, and sugar cane—the grasses which are first links in human food chains. This is what happens when we upset a balanced community.

FEATHERED HELPERS

Birds are a great help in keeping the numbers of insects in balance.

The friendly chickadees are greeting us from the lilac bushes, with their cheerful call . . . dee-dee-dee . . . between dashes to the feeder for sunflower seeds, or excursions into the brush for caterpillars and other insects and spiders.

A couple of barn swallows are catching winged insects to feed their babies in a mud-and-straw nest on a high beam in our garden tool shed.

These newly hatched barn swallows rely on their parents for food.

A pair of cardinals is swooping down on grasshoppers. I can't help hoping that no snake or owl raids their nest in the hedge, but that's a possibility.

The tiny house wren parents are tireless hunters, making continuous trips from dawn until dark to satisfy the high-pitched hunger cries of their babies in the nest box near our kitchen window. A young bird may eat its weight in insects every day!

In the spring, we watch the birds compete for inchworms, hopping from twig to twig, picking the leaves clean.

We saw the female Baltimore oriole peel dried fibers off last year's tall dogbane plant with her beak and fly high up in the oak tree to weave them into her nest. She and the male who courted and won her fed their nestlings with soft parts of insects, and themselves ate caterpillars, beetles, wasps,

This young blue jay is not yet ready to hunt for its own food.

grasshoppers, and ants.

Young blue jays with innocent faces and fresh white and blue feathers follow their parents around, fluttering their wings to be fed, although they've grown as large as the adults.

Birds are a joy to watch as they go about their business, protecting the plants in our backyards and gardens from an oversupply of leaf-eating insects.

Too many grasshoppers can be harmful to a garden.

73

A family of deer often comes out of the small woods bordering our backyard and browses among the plants. When we go outside, they stop and stare at us with wide eyes, then turn and leap gracefully away, wiggling their white tails.

In winter, they walk through the snow up to the house itself to nibble hedges and shrubs. Deer can double their numbers in a single year. Long ago, their populations were kept in check mainly by cougars (mountain lions) that leaped on them from low tree limbs. And by packs of wolves, and by native American Indians who hunted them for food, buckskins, and doeskins. Today, without predators except man in many places, deer sometimes eat every leaf and bud in their range, and some starve in winter.

Without predators, these deer can upset the balance of nature.

The lively little chipmunks have found an easy way to make a living. Besides collecting wild plant seeds, one is sitting near the bird feeder, stuffing so many fallen sunflower seeds into his mouth that the pouches in his cheeks puff up like small balloons. He races to his underground nest to store them away and is soon back for more, running quickly to avoid hawks and other predators.

Chipmunks store nuts and seeds for the cold winter months ahead.

A red fox sometimes walks stealthily into our backyard at sunset, hunting mice and birds. The chipmunks dart into their burrows where they're safe from the fox, but not from weasels.

As we wait for more furry visitors, the evening air is filled with scraping sounds of katydids calling their own names, and the high jingle bell chorus of snowy tree crickets. They feed on the foliage[7] in which they hide, daring to advertise for mates at night when the birds that prey on them are asleep.

---

[7] **foliage**: the leaves on trees and plants

Katydids hide from their enemies by blending in with leaves and branches.

A family of raccoons and an opossum make trails through the backyard, stopping to munch berries. This is part of their regular rounds as they seek out mice, lizards, grasshoppers, and crickets, and grub in the mud for frogs.

Opossums eat many different kinds of animals.

Frogs live in the mud and can catch flying insects with their long tongues.

In case they're still hungry, the raccoons are bold enough to look in our kitchen window or tap on the door and invite themselves in for a snack. The opossum, who eats almost anything, gets in on the act. After all, humans have taken over much of their territory.

This bold raccoon is looking for a snack in an unusual place!

A Bug Sat in a Silver Flower

by Karla Kuskin

illustrated by Daniel Moreton

Award-Winning Poet

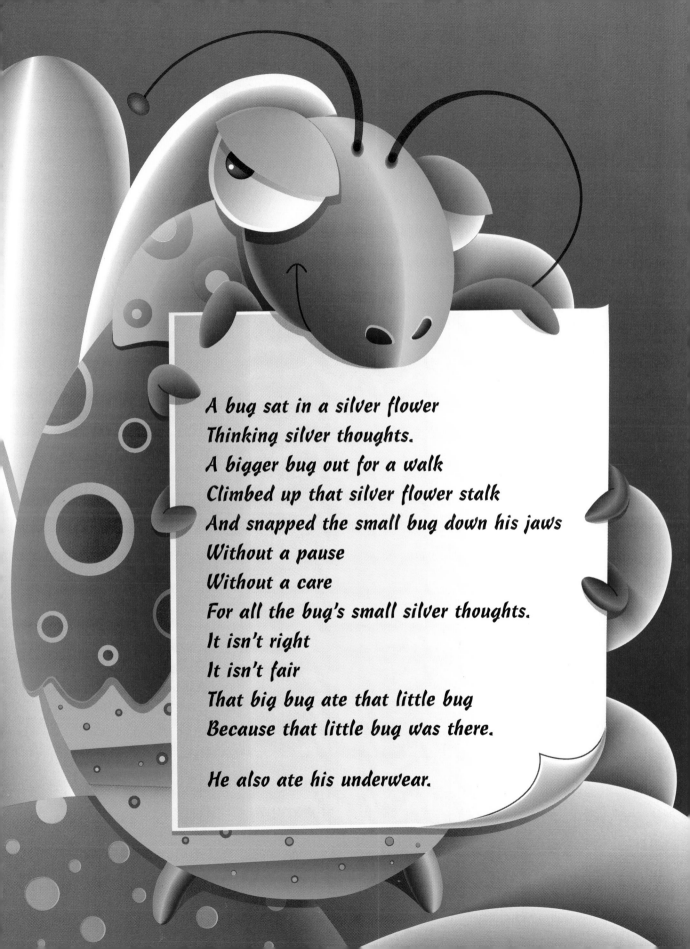

A bug sat in a silver flower
Thinking silver thoughts.
A bigger bug out for a walk
Climbed up that silver flower stalk
And snapped the small bug down his jaws
Without a pause
Without a care
For all the bug's small silver thoughts.
It isn't right
It isn't fair
That big bug ate that little bug
Because that little bug was there.

He also ate his underwear.

THIS JUST IN...

Write a television news story for the Backyard News Network (BNN). Give the latest facts on the crime described in "A Bug Sat in a Silver Flower." Has the big bug been caught? Where was he last seen? Read your bulletin to your classmates.

RESPONSE

PYRAMIDS ARE NOT JUST IN EGYPT

Do you know where to find a food pyramid? It's not a place you visit. It's a healthful eating plan. Study the food pyramid shown on a food label. Then use the pyramid to help you write healthful menus for breakfast, lunch, and dinner for one week. Share your menus with your family or classmates.

IN YOUR OWN SCHOOLYARD

Take a walk outside around your school with your teacher and classmates. Take notes on the different plants and animals you see. With classmates, create a mural showing the food chain in your area. Display the mural in class.

CORNER

WHAT DO YOU THINK?

- How do different kinds of animals "balance" each other?

- Would you like to have a backyard like the one you read about? Why or why not?

- What would happen if there were no birds in the backyard? How do you know?

ALL EYES ON

by
Michael J. Rosen

illustrated by
Tom Leonard

THE POND

Here and there around this pond, countless eyes watch what goes on. Listen. They're all calling you: *Come closer, look! Come see my view.*

A world of water multiplies
within the eyes of dragonflies,
whose gazes are kaleidoscopes
that spy atop the cattail slopes.

The snapping turtle sometimes sees
the muddy deep, sometimes the trees,
and sometimes nothing but inside
the painted shell where it can hide.

87

From where the spider always clings
the view is largely tangled things
dangling in the crisscrossed strands
that weave the windows where it stands.

What they can lift and what they can't
directs the life of every ant,
toting picnic crumbs they've found
to store in tunnels underground.

89

The snail sees simply what it's on
as it glides up a stalk or frond.
Where next? The snail can still decide
as it glides down the other side.

The water strider walks the shine
where air and water form a line.
What's up above? What's down below?
It never has the chance to know.

With echoes bouncing through the night,
the bat can see without its sight.
Soundless shadows, hidden prey—
a bat may swoop and snatch away.

To what's ahead, the crawdad's blind.
It only sees what's left behind.
Whooshing backward by its tail,
the crawdad leaves a cloudy trail.

Peering toward the breezy air
where clouds are what the branches bear,
the bluegill watches at the brink
the flitting things it hopes will sink.

There . . . beside the fallen log,
the yellow peepers of a frog
who waits beside an old tree trunk,
nabs a fly, and jumps, *kerplunk*.

Paddling through the cattail shoots,
lily pads and toppled roots,
a mallard dips and dives and dunks
to munch upon the duckweed clumps.

Chittering swallows skitter so fast
and skim the waves as they soar past,
keeping an eye on all that's afloat—
a branch, a beetle, an anchored boat.

frog
water strider
swallow
crawdad
spider
mallard
snail
ant
bat
snail
swallow
dragonfly
bluegill
mallard

snapping turtle
water strider
ant
crawdad
snail
bluegill
mallard

The pond itself, seen from the sky,
appears to be a giant's eye.
What's it watching, staring back?
A storm? The clouds? The zodiac?

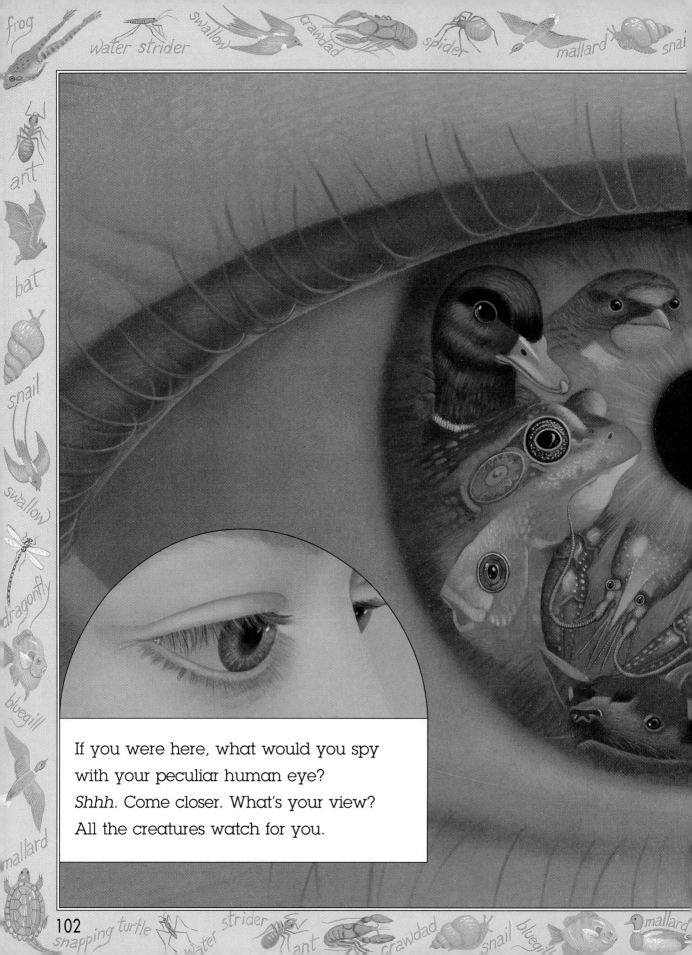

If you were here, what would you spy
with your peculiar human eye?
Shhh. Come closer. What's your view?
All the creatures watch for you.

frog · water strider · swallow · crawdad · spider · mallard · snail

ant · bat · snail · swallow · dragonfly · bluegill · mallard

102 · snapping turtle · water strider · ant · crawdad · snail · bluegill · mallard

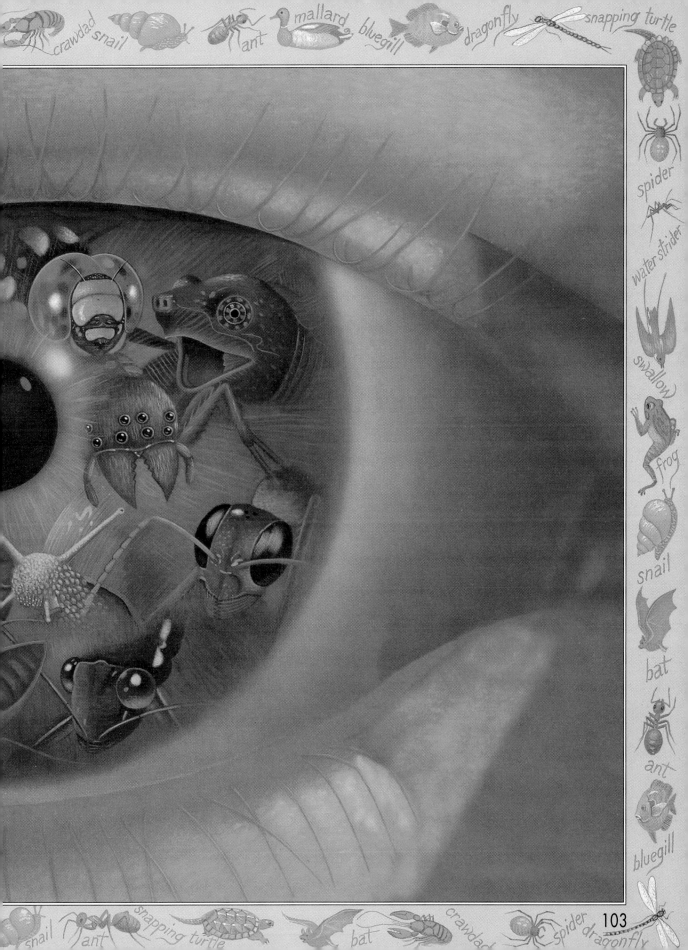

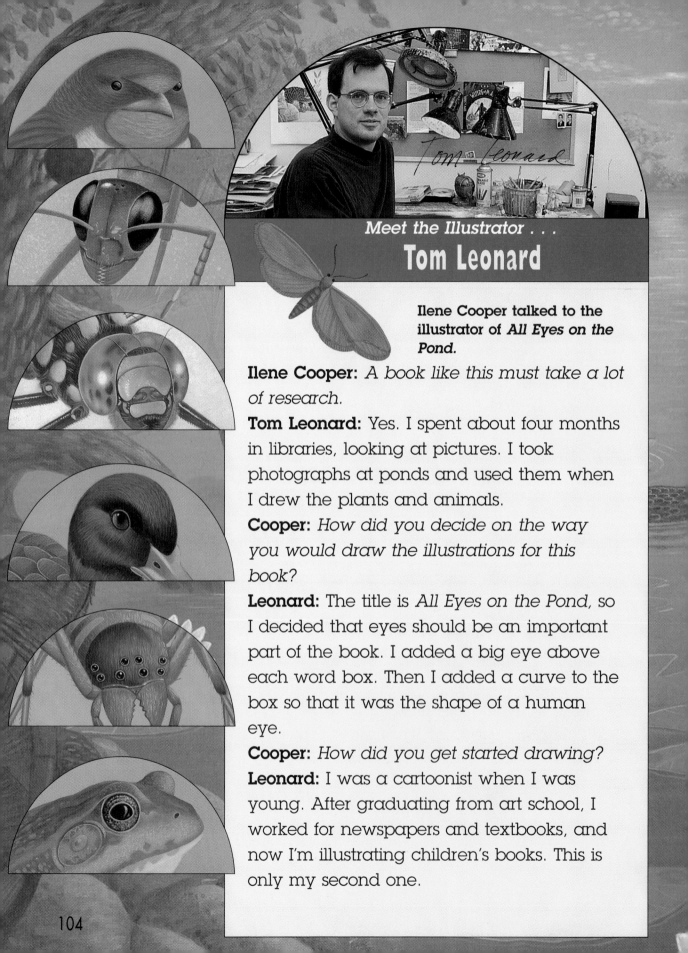

Meet the Illustrator . . .
Tom Leonard

Ilene Cooper talked to the illustrator of *All Eyes on the Pond*.

Ilene Cooper: *A book like this must take a lot of research.*

Tom Leonard: Yes. I spent about four months in libraries, looking at pictures. I took photographs at ponds and used them when I drew the plants and animals.

Cooper: *How did you decide on the way you would draw the illustrations for this book?*

Leonard: The title is *All Eyes on the Pond,* so I decided that eyes should be an important part of the book. I added a big eye above each word box. Then I added a curve to the box so that it was the shape of a human eye.

Cooper: *How did you get started drawing?*

Leonard: I was a cartoonist when I was young. After graduating from art school, I worked for newspapers and textbooks, and now I'm illustrating children's books. This is only my second one.

Ilene Cooper, an author herself, talked to the author of *All Eyes on the Pond.*

Ilene Cooper: *This book is about a different way of seeing, isn't it?*

Michael Rosen: Yes. Some people think it's about pond life, but it is really about how different creatures see the same thing. When I visit schools, I often ask children, "What does your pet see that you don't see?" I like changing places, thinking as some other person or creature.

Cooper: *Although you didn't illustrate this book, you are also an illustrator. Did you do a lot of writing and drawing as a child?*

Rosen: I remember I drew monsters. I didn't draw from real life—I didn't even know you could do that. All of my drawings came from my imagination.

Cooper: *Did you know that writing and illustrating were going to be your career?*

Rosen: No, I was going to be a doctor. But I met another writer, and I learned that writing could be more than a hobby—it could be a world that you both invent and live within.

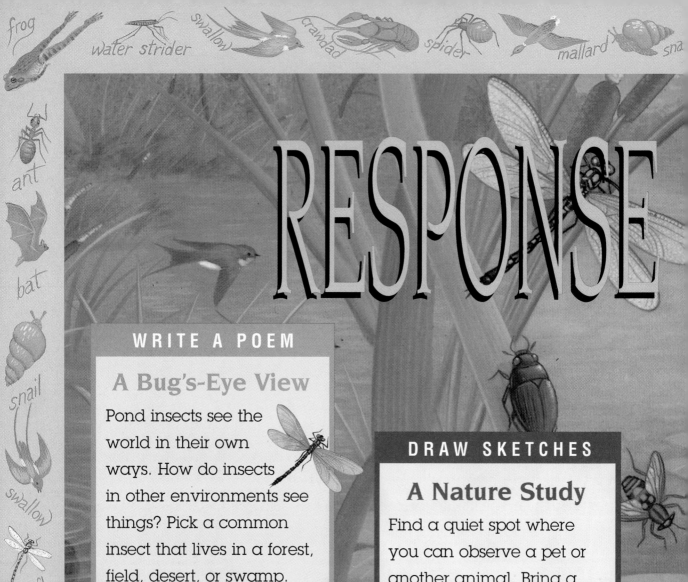

RESPONSE

WRITE A POEM

A Bug's-Eye View

Pond insects see the world in their own ways. How do insects in other environments see things? Pick a common insect that lives in a forest, field, desert, or swamp. Write a poem about how it sees its environment.

DRAW SKETCHES

A Nature Study

Find a quiet spot where you can observe a pet or another animal. Bring a sketch pad and a pencil or charcoal and draw several sketches of the animal. Choose your favorite sketch, and add color with paint or markers to create the finished picture. Then write one or two sentences telling what you learned about the animal.

CORNER

PREPARE A REPORT

All About Eyesight

Animals see differently because their eyes are built differently. How are human eyes built? Work with a partner to prepare a short oral report about human eyes. Use pictures, charts, and other aids to make your report more interesting.

What Do You Think?

Why do the different animals who live near the pond see different things?

Which pond animal is your favorite? Why?

What would you *hear* if you visited a pond? Describe the sounds some of the animals might make.

spider
water strider
swallow
frog
snail
bat
ant
bluegill

THEME WRAP-UP

All living things—wild and tame, predators and prey—are part of the balance of nature. How is this fact shown in the selection "Wolves"? How is it shown in "Nature's Great Balancing Act"?

Understanding how animals live is important. What did you think of wolves before you read these stories, and what do you think of them now? Have you changed your mind about wolves? Explain your answer.

ACTIVITY CORNER

Choose an animal that must eat other animals to live. Read about the animal in an encyclopedia or a nonfiction book. Then write a short report about the animal's habits. Tell where it lives, what it eats, how it sleeps, and any other facts you find interesting.

Traveling to New Communities

Have you or members of your family ever lived in a different place? It's not always easy to move to a new community. But, as you will learn from the stories in this theme, new places can be exciting and interesting, too.

Traveling to New Communities

·CONTENTS·

111

Bookshelf

Dandelions
by Eve Bunting

When Zoe realizes that her mother misses the city she grew up in, she does something to make her mother feel more at home on the prairie.

Teachers' Choice

Signatures Library

DANDELIONS

Written by
EVE BUNTING

Illustrated by
GREG SHED

The Statue of Liberty
America's Proud Lady

Jim Haskins

The Statue of Liberty
by Jim Haskins

America's "proud lady" has greeted countless immigrants with the promise of freedom.

Award-Winning Author

Signatures Library

Halmoni and the Picnic
by Sook Nyul Choi

Yunmi's third–grade class helps her grandmother feel comfortable in the United States.

Back Home
by Gloria Jean Pinkney

A city girl from the North learns about farm life in the South when she visits her mother's relatives.

ALA Notable Book; Notable Trade Book in Social Studies; Award-Winning Illustrator

Amber Brown Goes Fourth
by Paula Danziger

Amber's best friend has moved. Who will help her face fourth grade?

Award-Winning Author

My Great-Aunt
ARIZO

MY GREAT-AUNT
ARIZONA

BY
GLORIA HOUSTON

ILLUSTRATED BY
SUSAN CONDIE LAMB

ALA
Notable Book

Teachers' Choice

Notable
Trade Book in
Social Studies

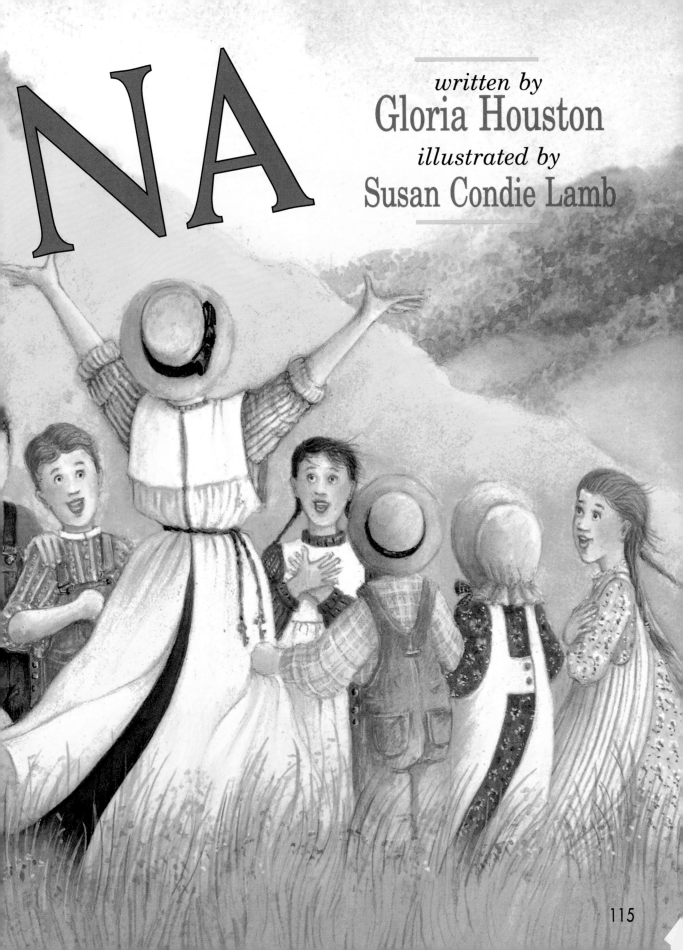

NA

written by
Gloria Houston

illustrated by
Susan Condie Lamb

My great-aunt Arizona was born in a log cabin her papa built in the meadow on Henson Creek in the Blue Ridge Mountains. When she was born, the mailman rode across the bridge on his big bay horse with a letter.

The letter was from her brother, Galen, who was in the cavalry, far away in the West. The letter said, "If the baby is a girl, please name her Arizona, and she will be beautiful, like this land."

Arizona was a very tall little girl. She wore her long brown hair in braids. She wore long full dresses, and a pretty white apron. She wore high-button shoes, and many petticoats, too. Arizona liked to grow flowers.

She liked to read,
and sing, and square
dance to the music
of the fiddler on
Saturday night.

Arizona had
a little brother,
Jim. They played
together on the
farm. In summer
they went barefoot
and caught tadpoles
in the creek.

In the fall
they climbed the
mountains searching
for galax and
ginseng roots.

In the winter they made snow cream with sugar, snow, and sweet cream from Mama's cows. When spring came, they helped Papa tap the maple trees and catch the sap in buckets. Then they made maple syrup and maple-sugar candy.

Arizona and her brother Jim walked up the road that wound by the creek to the one-room school. All the students in all the grades were there, together in one room. All the students read their lessons aloud at the same time. They made a great deal of noise, so the room was called a blab school.

The students carried their lunches in lard buckets made of tin. They brought ham and biscuits. Sometimes they had fried apple pie. They drank cool water from the spring at the bottom of the hill. At recess they played games like tag and William Matrimmatoe.

When Arizona had read all the books at the one-room school, she crossed the mountains to the school in another village, a village called Wing. It was so far away that she rode her papa's mule. Sometimes she rode the mule through the snow.

When Arizona's mother died, Arizona had to leave school and stay home to care for Papa and her brother Jim. But she still loved to read—and dream about the faraway places she would visit one day. So she read and she dreamed, and she took care of Papa and Jim.

Then one day Papa brought home a new wife. Arizona could go away to school, where she could learn to be a teacher. Aunt Suzie invited Arizona to live at her house and help with the chores. Aunt Suzie made her work very hard. But at night Arizona could study—and dream of all the faraway places she would visit one day.

Finally, Arizona returned to her home on Henson Creek. She was a teacher at last.

She taught in the one-room school where she and Jim had sat. She made new chalkboards out of lumber from Papa's sawmill, and covered them with polish made for shoes. She still wore long full dresses and a pretty white apron. She wore high-button shoes and many petticoats, too. She grew flowers in every window. She taught students about words and numbers and the faraway places they would visit someday.

"Have you been there?" the students asked.

"Only in my mind," she answered. "But someday you will go."

Arizona married the carpenter who helped build the new Riverside School down where Henson Creek joins the river. So Miss Arizona became Mrs. Hughes, and for the rest of her days she taught fourth-grade students who called her "Miz Shoes."

And when her daughter was born, Miz Shoes brought the baby to school, to the sunny room where flowers grew in every window.

122

Every year Arizona had a Christmas tree growing in a pot. The girls and boys made paper decorations to brighten up the tree. Then they planted their tree at the edge of the school yard, year after year, until the entire playground was lined with living Christmas trees, like soldiers guarding the room where Arizona taught, with her long gray braids wound 'round her head, with her long full dress, and pretty white apron, with her high-button shoes, and many petticoats, too.

The boys and girls who were students in her class had boys and girls who were students in her class. And they had boys and girls who were students in her class.

For fifty-seven years my great-aunt Arizona hugged her students. She hugged them when their work was good, and she hugged them when it was not. She taught them words and numbers, and about the faraway places they would visit someday.

"Have you been there?" the students asked.

"Only in my mind," she answered. "But someday you will go."

My great-aunt Arizona taught my dad, Jim's only son. And she taught my brother and me in the fourth grade. With her soft white braids wound 'round her head, she taught us about faraway places we would visit someday.

My great-aunt Arizona died on her ninety-third birthday. But she goes with me in my mind—A very tall lady, in a long full dress, and a pretty white apron, with her high-button shoes, and her many petticoats, too. She's always there, in a sunny room with many flowers in every window, and a hug for me every day.

She never did go to the faraway places she taught us about. But my great-aunt Arizona travels with me and with those of us whose lives she touched. . . .

She goes with us in our minds.

Gloria Houston

Gloria Houston, like her great-aunt Arizona, loves teaching. For fifteen years, she taught students in elementary school through high school. She now teaches writing and children's literature to college students in Tampa, Florida.

Gloria Houston says about her great-aunt, "She truly lives on in what she gave to her students, including me. I have traveled because she made the places in my geography book seem so real. Most important, she made each student feel special. Years later, each member of her class still thinks he or she was Aunt Arizona's pet."

Susan Condie Lamb

Susan Condie Lamb is a full-time artist who has illustrated many children's books. She has also designed sets and costumes for plays. She found that experience a big help as she drew pictures for *My Great-Aunt Arizona*.

Susan Condie Lamb grew up in Connecticut. Although she lived in New York City for a while, today she's back in Connecticut. She lives with her husband and her son, Charlie.

RESPONSE CORNER

A Note of Thanks

Arizona Hughes was an important adult in many children's lives. Choose an important adult in your life. Write a thank-you note telling that person why he or she is special to you.

The Little Red Schoolhouse

Work with a group to turn a corner of your classroom into a model of a one-room school. Use boxes and other materials to make the desks, the stove, and other furniture. Give a tour to your classmates. Explain how this school is different from your own school.

Wish You Were Here

Suppose Great-Aunt Arizona really had traveled to faraway places. Write one or two postcards that she might have sent to her students. Share the postcards with a partner.

What Do You Think?

- What kind of person was Arizona? How do you know?

- If you could go back to Arizona's time, what would you like to see and do?

- How might Arizona's life be different if she were living today? Explain your answer.

Grandfather's Journey

written and illustrated
by *Allen Say*

My grandfather was a young man when he left his home in Japan and went to see the world.

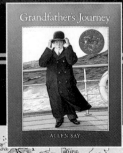

He wore European clothes for the first time and began his
journey on a steamship. The Pacific Ocean astonished him.

For three weeks he did not see land. When land finally
appeared it was the New World.

He explored North America by train and riverboat, and often
walked for days on end.

Deserts with rocks like enormous sculptures amazed him.

The endless farm fields reminded him of the ocean he had crossed.

Huge cities of factories and tall buildings bewildered and yet excited him.

He marveled at the towering mountains and rivers as clear as the sky.

He met many people along the way. He shook hands with
black men and white men, with yellow men and red men.

The more he traveled, the more he longed to see new places,
and never thought of returning home.

Of all the places he visited, he liked California best. He loved the strong sunlight there, the Sierra Mountains, the lonely seacoast.

After a time, he returned to his village in Japan to marry his childhood sweetheart. Then he brought his bride to the new country.

They made their home by the San Francisco Bay and had a
baby girl.

As his daughter grew, my grandfather began to think about his own childhood. He thought about his old friends.

He remembered the mountains and rivers of his home. He surrounded himself with songbirds, but he could not forget.

Finally, when his daughter was nearly grown, he could wait no
more. He took his family and returned to his homeland.

Once again he saw the mountains and rivers of his childhood.
They were just as he had remembered them.

Once again he exchanged stories and laughed with his old friends.

But the village was not a place for a daughter from San Francisco.
So my grandfather bought a house in a large city nearby.

There, the young woman fell in love, married, and sometime later I was born.

When I was a small boy, my favorite weekend was a visit to my grandfather's house. He told me many stories about California.

He raised warblers and silvereyes, but he could not forget the mountains and rivers of California. So he planned a trip.

But a war began. Bombs fell from the sky and scattered our lives like leaves in a storm.

When the war ended, there was nothing left of the city and of the house where my grandparents had lived.

So they returned to the village where they had been children.
But my grandfather never kept another songbird.

The last time I saw him, my grandfather said that he longed to see California one more time. He never did.

And when I was nearly grown, I left home and went to see California for myself.

After a time, I came to love the land my grandfather had loved, and I stayed on and on until I had a daughter of my own.

But I also miss the mountains and rivers of my childhood. I miss my old friends. So I return now and then, when I can not still the longing in my heart.

The funny thing is, the moment I am in one country, I am homesick for the other.

I think I know my grandfather now.
I miss him very much.

Meet the Author and Illustrator

ALLEN SAY

Allen Say is one of America's most successful writers and illustrators of children's books. He spent two years creating *Grandfather's Journey*. After it was published in 1993, it won many of the highest honors in children's literature, including the Caldecott Medal. Allen Say's earlier books, including *El Chino, Tree of Cranes,* and *A River Dream,* have also won important awards.

Grandfather's Journey is fiction, but it is based on real life. Allen's grandfather truly was a world traveler, and he especially loved steamships. After traveling around the world, he lived in California for many years and then returned to Japan.

Allen was born in Yokohama, Japan. He began to draw even before he could walk. As a small child, Allen drew on walls, doors, and anything else he could reach. When he was twelve years old, he was thrilled to study art with a famous cartoonist in Japan.

160

At age sixteen, Allen Say moved to the United States. He found himself suddenly alone in a country he knew little about. He did not speak a word of English, and he felt out of place in his new school. It was a difficult time in Allen's life. He shows how he felt at that time in the painting on page 157. He says, "My favorite painting in *Grandfather's Journey* is the picture of myself, standing in the sun-drenched, empty parking lot. I love that painting."

Before Allen Say began making his living by painting, he worked as a photographer. If you look closely at the paintings in *Grandfather's Journey*, you might think they are a little like old-fashioned photographs. The people seem to be looking right at you, as if they are posing for a camera.

Allen Say has learned how to capture the feelings of his characters in his art. By sharing *Grandfather's Journey* with us, he is sharing the feelings of many immigrants to America. The next time you meet someone who has just moved to the United States, remember *Grandfather's Journey*. Remember how Allen Say must have felt as he stood in that empty parking lot.

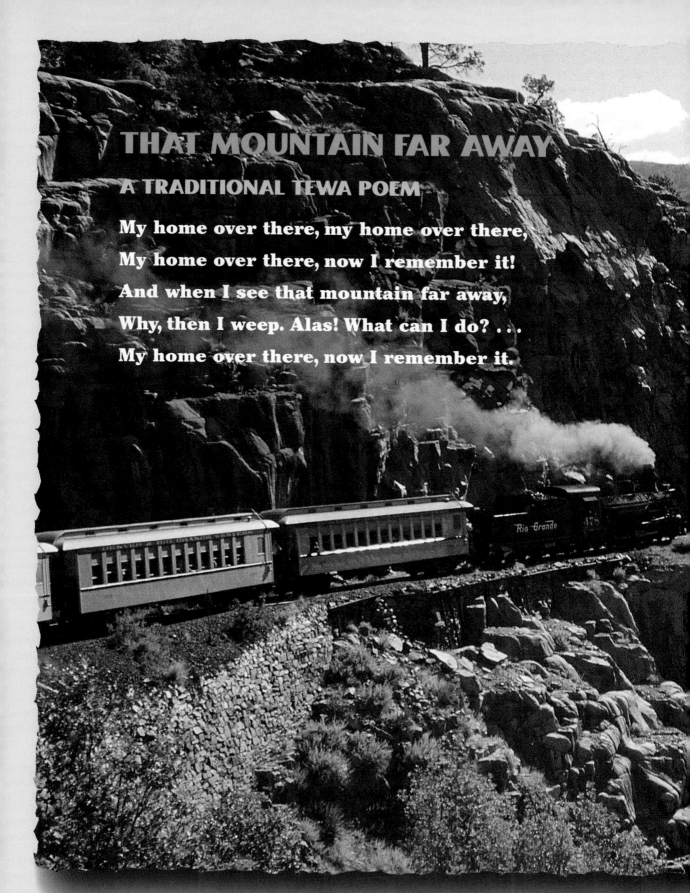

THAT MOUNTAIN FAR AWAY

A TRADITIONAL TEWA POEM

My home over there, my home over there,

My home over there, now I remember it!

And when I see that mountain far away,

Why, then I weep. Alas! What can I do? . . .

My home over there, now I remember it.

TRAVEL

EDNA ST. VINCENT MILLAY

The railroad track is miles away,
    And the day is loud with voices speaking,
Yet there isn't a train goes by all day
    But I hear its whistles shrieking.

All night there isn't a train goes by,
    Though the night is still for sleep and dreaming
But I see its cinders red on the sky
    And hear its engine steaming.

My heart is warm with the friends I make,
    And better friends I'll not be knowing,
Yet there isn't a train I wouldn't take,
    No matter where it's going.

Train from Durango to Silverton, Colorado   *Photograph by David Herman*

Response

DRAW A MAP

The Peaceful Pacific

Grandfather crossed the Pacific Ocean when he traveled from Japan to California. Look up the Pacific Ocean in an encyclopedia. Draw a map that shows the larger islands between Japan and the United States. On your map, write five interesting facts about the Pacific Ocean.

MODEL CLOTHING

What's in Style?

When he lived in America, Grandfather wore Western-style clothing. In Japan, he wore a traditional kimono. Did your ancestors wear a special kind of clothing? If you can, bring that clothing to class and model it. Or bring in a photograph that shows it. How is the special clothing different from the clothing you wear today?

Corner

MAKE A TRAVEL BROCHURE

Far, Far Away

Allen Say's grandfather and the poet who wrote "Travel" liked to visit new places. Have you seen pictures in a magazine of a place that you would like to visit? Make a travel brochure of that place. Include photographs or magazine pictures.

What Do You Think?

- How is the grandson in the story like his grandfather?

- Which of the paintings from this story is your favorite? Explain why you like it.

- Think about somewhere far away that you would like to visit someday. How would you get there? What might you see?

The Lotus Seed

by Sherry Garland
illustrated by Tatsuro Kiuchi

SHERRY GARLAND

THE LOTUS SEED

TATSURO KI...

ALA
Notable
Book

HOA SEN

Trong đầm gì đẹp bằng sen.
Lá xanh, bông trắng lại chen nhị vàng.
Nhị vàng, bông trắng, lá xanh,
Gần bùn mà chẳng hôi tanh mùi bùn.

—Vô danh

THE LOTUS FLOWER

Nothing that grows in a pond
Surpasses the beauty of the lotus flower,
With its green leaves and silky yellow styles
Amidst milky white petals.
Though mired in mud, its silky yellow styles,
Its milky white petals and green leaves
Do not smell of mud.

— Anonymous
(translation of poem by Dinh D. Vu)

*M*y grandmother saw
the emperor cry
the day he lost
his golden dragon throne.

She wanted something
to remember him by,
so she snuck down
to the silent palace,
near the River of Perfumes,
and plucked a seed
from a lotus pod
that rattled
in the Imperial garden.

She hid the seed
in a special place
under the family altar,
wrapped in a piece of silk
from the *ao dai*
she wore that day.
Whenever she felt sad
or lonely,
she took out the seed
and thought of the
brave young emperor.

And when she married
a young man
chosen by her parents,
she carried the seed
inside her pocket
for good luck, long life,
and many children.
When her husband
marched off to war,
she raised her
children alone.

One day bombs fell
all around,
and soldiers
clamored door to door.
She took the time
to grab the seed,
but left her mother-of-pearl
hair combs lying
on the floor.

One terrible day
her family scrambled
into a crowded boat
and set out
on a stormy sea.
Bà watched the mountains
and the waving palms
slowly fade away.
She held the seed
in her shaking fingers
and silently said good-bye.

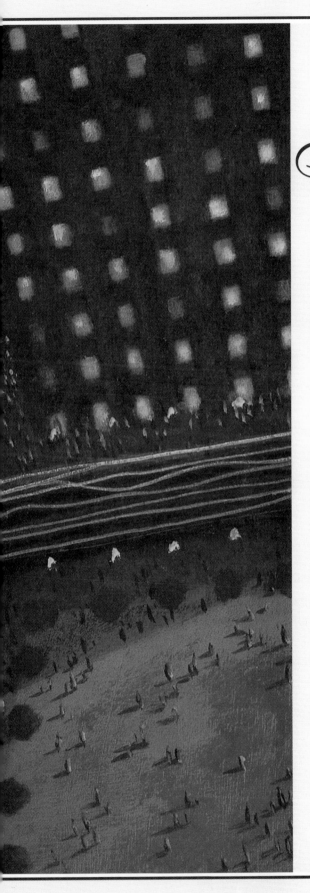

$\mathcal{S}$he arrived in a
strange new land
with blinking lights
and speeding cars
and towering buildings
that scraped the sky
and a language
she didn't understand.

She worked many years,
day and night,
and so did her children
and her sisters
and her cousins, too,
living together
in one big house.

Last summer
my little brother
found the special seed
and asked questions
again and again.
He'd never seen a lotus bloom
or an emperor
on a golden dragon throne.

So one night
he stole the seed
from beneath the family altar
and planted it
in a pool of mud
somewhere near Bà's
onion patch.

$\mathcal{B}$à cried and cried
when she found out
the seed was gone.
She didn't eat,
she didn't sleep,
and my silly brother
forgot what spot of earth
held the seed.

hen one day in spring
my grandmother shouted,
and we all ran
to the garden
and saw
a beautiful pink lotus
unfurling its petals,
so creamy and soft.

"It is the flower
of life and hope,"
my grandmother said.
"No matter how
ugly the mud
or how long the seed
lies dormant,
the bloom will
be beautiful.
It is the flower
of my country."

When the lotus blossom
faded and turned
into a pod,
Bà gave each of
her grandchildren
a seed
to remember her by,
and she kept one
for herself
to remember the emperor by.

I wrapped my seed
in a piece of silk
and hid it
in a secret place.
Someday I will plant it
and give the seeds
to my own children
and tell them about the day
my grandmother saw
the emperor cry.

Sherry Garland
Talks About The Lotus Seed

Writer Ilene Cooper interviewed Sherry Garland.

Ilene Cooper: *The Lotus Seed is about people from Vietnam. Have you ever visited that country?*

Sherry Garland: No, although I would like to very much. But I have come to know many Vietnamese people.

Cooper: *Where did the idea for* The Lotus Seed *come from?*

Garland: I had written a novel for adults in which a Vietnamese woman carries a lotus seed. That novel was never published. One day, the idea of the woman and her lotus seed came back to me. In one sitting, I wrote the children's book.

Cooper: *The illustrator of this book, Tatsuro Kiuchi, is Japanese. How did he do his work?*

Garland: I sent him photos of Vietnamese clothing and other things, and he worked from those. The publisher even sent him a lotus flower because he had never seen one.

Cooper: *What do Vietnamese people think of your book?*

Garland: I don't know how the people in Vietnam would feel about it. But Vietnamese Americans I have shown it to like it very much. Older people, especially those who actually came from Vietnam, remember their growing-up years fondly and talk about their country all the time.

Response Corner

PRESENT A REPORT

SYMBOLS OF AMERICA

A bald eagle, the Statue of Liberty, and the American flag are all symbols that have special meanings to Americans. Research one of these symbols. Write a short report about your choice, and present it to your classmates.

WRITE A DIARY ENTRY

TREASURES

In "The Lotus Seed," the grandmother has to leave her homeland in a hurry. She has to leave many things behind. If you had to leave your home quickly, what three things would you take with you? Write a diary entry explaining your choice.

OUR ROOTS

Sometimes young people have a hard time understanding the past. Imagine that the grandmother in the story wants to explain to her grandson what the lotus seed means to the family. Write a letter in which she tells how she felt on the day she thought the seed was lost forever. Then have her tell how she felt when the lotus flower bloomed.

What Do You Think?

- Why does the person telling this story hide her own lotus seed at the end?

- How do you think the grandmother feels when she first moves to this country? Why do you think as you do?

- People come to America from all over the world. What kinds of things do they keep to remind them of their old homes or of how their families used to live?

Art & Literature

Museum of the City of New York,
Gift of Mrs. Robert M. Littlejohn; 8'1" x 16'6"

In the 1800s, most immigrants to the United States arrived in New York by ship. Traveling across the ocean took much longer then, and the ships were not as clean and dry as modern ships. How do you think the people in this painting felt when they reached America?

188

The Bay and Harbor of New York
by Samuel B. Waugh

Samuel B. Waugh was born in Mercer, Pennsylvania. He spent many years in Italy, but he did most of his work in Philadelphia. No one knows exactly when *The Bay and Harbor of New York* was painted, but it was probably close to 1855.

AMBER BROWN
IS NOT A CRAYON

by Paula Danziger
illustrated by Tony Ross

Award-Winning Author

Amber Brown and Justin Daniels have been best friends since preschool. They even sit together on the imaginary trips Mr. Cohen's class takes to different parts of the world. Amber thinks her year is going great until she learns that Justin is moving to Alabama. One day while Justin is packing a box of important items, the two friends get into an argument about keeping a chewing gum ball that they have been adding to for a year and a half. Will they make up?

Today, Mr. Cohen's class is going to have a pizza party.

That's the good news.

The bad news is that it's a going-away party for my ex-best friend, Justin Daniels, and we still haven't spoken to each other.

I've been waiting for him to say "I'm sorry."

I don't know what he's been waiting for.

So we've been sitting in class right next to each other without saying a word.

Well, hardly a word.

I confess. Once I did say, "Hey, dirt bag. Would you please pass the eraser?"

And he said, "Crayon brain, get your own eraser."

It hurts a lot but I'm not going to give in on this one.

Justin is just so stubborn.

Today, the class "returned" from our trip to China.
Next we'll be "going" to Australia.

I can't wait.

Justin, however, won't be "going." He'll be going to Alabama for real.

I wish Al Abama was a real person so I could tell him how much I hate him.

As Brandi Colwin walks by our desks, I call out, "Hey, Brandi. Don't forget. We're going to sit next to each other when we go to Australia."

Then Justin turns to Hannah and says, "I'll be sure to send you some postcards from Alabama."

I yawn, a big yawn, right in his face, to show I don't care, and then I pretend to scrunch up over my worksheet so that he can't see that I'm very close to crying.

Mr. Cohen flicks the lights off and on.

"The pizza will be here in five minutes. Extra cheese, mushrooms, the works."

I pick up my head and look over at Justin. He doesn't look any happier than I feel.

I make a decision and call out, "Tell the guy to hold the anchovies," and then look right at Justin, pretending to be holding wiggly anchovies.

He starts to laugh. I pretend to flip an anchovy over to him.

He pretends to grab it.

"Let's go stand in the hall for a minute," Justin says, picking up his knapsack.

We both walk over to Mr. Cohen and ask to
go out in the hall for a few minutes.

"Sure." He motions to the door.

As we walk out, I think I hear Mr. Cohen say,
"Finally."

Once we get out there, we just stand quietly
for a few minutes.

Then we both say "I'm sorry" at the same time and link pinkies.

"I don't want you to go." I start to cry, just a little.

Justin takes a deep breath and says, "I don't want to go either. You think this is easy? My new school is so big. I don't know anyone there. What if I forget my locker combination? All the kids there already know each other. My parents say I have to be brave, to be a good example for Danny. That it will be fun. But I know my mom is nervous about moving, too. I heard her talking to your mom. And it's too late to join a little league team, and everyone there thinks I talk funny and I have to learn to say 'Y'all' and 'Ma'am,' and . . . and . . ."

I say, "And?"

Justin turns red. "And I'm going to miss you."

I smile for what seems like the first time in years.

We stand for a few minutes and then I say, "Why didn't you tell me that sooner?"

"Because you stopped talking to me," he says.

"You wouldn't talk to me." I defend myself. "Not about the important stuff."

"It's hard." He looks down at his untied shoelaces.

I say, "I want you to stay."

Justin looks up. "Me, too. But I can't. My parents are making me go. But they said you and your mom could visit this summer."

This summer. I better start practicing "Y'all" and "Ma'am."

Justin pulls something out of his knapsack.

It's a badly wrapped present.

I open the package.

It's a tissue box.

Inside the tissue box is the chewing gum ball.

"Thanks. It's the best present ever," I say, knowing that I will save it for the rest of my life.

The pizza guy arrives with ten pizzas. My stomach smells the extra cheese. Mr. Cohen comes out.

"You two better get inside before everyone eats up all of this pizza. It's your party, Justin."

As we walk inside, I think about how it will be when Justin and I grow up and he doesn't have to move just because his parents move.

Maybe someday we can open our own company. I'll be president one week and he'll be president the next. We'll sell jars of icing and boxes of cookies.

Maybe someday we'll travel around the world trying out new flavors of chewing gum, and the chewing gum ball will get so big that we'll build a house for it.

Until then, maybe, I can save some of my allowance each week and call Justin once in a while. He can do the same.

I think I'm going to learn his new phone number by heart.

Whenever I think about third grade, I'm going to think about Justin, and I bet he's always going to think about me.

SAY HELLO TO
Paula Danziger

Paula Danziger knew in the second grade that she wanted to be a writer. That's when she began noticing and remembering things that happened to her so she could write about them later.

During Paula's childhood, her family moved a lot. She lived in Washington, D.C., in New Jersey, and in a rented farmhouse in Pennsylvania. Paula read books all the time. "Thank goodness for the local librarian. She gave me lots of wonderful books to read, and she let me know she cared."

Paula Danziger was once a teacher, and she uses her teaching experiences in her writing. Some of the events in her books come from real things that happened in her classroom. "What matters to me is that kids like my books, and that my books touch their lives and make them feel less alone."

READ A MAP

Map It Out

Amber will have a friend in another part of the country. On a map, find the places where your family and friends live. In what direction would you travel to get to their homes? About how far would you have to travel? Use the distance scale and the compass rose to help you. Share your findings with your family and classmates.

Response Corner

WRITE AN ADVICE COLUMN

Make Up and Be Friends

Friends sometimes have disagreements. With a partner, talk about why friends might disagree and how they can make up. Write an advice column about disagreements. Take turns writing and answering the questions. Share your "column" with your class.

Joking Around

A sense of humor can help you make and keep friends. It worked for Amber! Look through some joke books to find jokes that you think others might enjoy. Read a few of them to your class.

What Do You Think?

■ What problem must Amber Brown face?

■ Would you like to read more about Amber Brown? Why or why not?

■ Justin is nervous about moving. How do you think he will feel about his new home a year from now? Why do you think so?

201

When Jo Louis

by Belinda Rochelle

illustrated by Larry Johnson

Award-Winning
Author

Won the Title

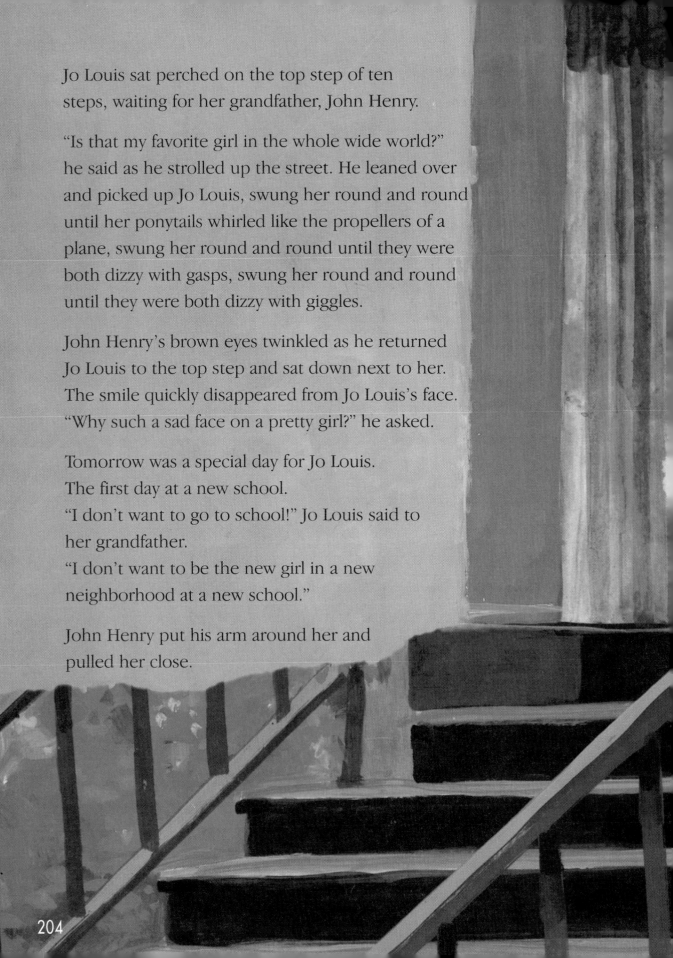

Jo Louis sat perched on the top step of ten
steps, waiting for her grandfather, John Henry.

"Is that my favorite girl in the whole wide world?"
he said as he strolled up the street. He leaned over
and picked up Jo Louis, swung her round and round
until her ponytails whirled like the propellers of a
plane, swung her round and round until they were
both dizzy with gasps, swung her round and round
until they were both dizzy with giggles.

John Henry's brown eyes twinkled as he returned
Jo Louis to the top step and sat down next to her.
The smile quickly disappeared from Jo Louis's face.
"Why such a sad face on a pretty girl?" he asked.

Tomorrow was a special day for Jo Louis.
The first day at a new school.
"I don't want to go to school!" Jo Louis said to
her grandfather.
"I don't want to be the new girl in a new
neighborhood at a new school."

John Henry put his arm around her and
pulled her close.

"Why don't you want to go to school?" he asked.

"I'll probably be the shortest kid in class, or I'll be the one who can't run as fast as the other kids. I finish every race last."

"It's just a matter of time before a new school is an old school. Just a matter of time before you'll be able to run really fast, and you won't always finish last," he said, patting her hand. "What's the real reason you don't want to go to school?" John Henry asked.

Jo Louis shook her head. It was hard to explain. She just knew it would happen. Someone would ask THE question. IT was THE question, the same question each and every time she met someone new: *"What's your name?"*

It was that moment, that question, that made Jo Louis want to disappear. And it really wouldn't make a difference if she were taller, and it wouldn't make a difference that she was the new kid in school, and it wouldn't make a difference if she could run really fast. She just wished that she didn't have to tell anyone her name.

Her grandfather picked her up and placed her on his knee. "Let me tell you a story," he said.

206

"When I was just a young boy living in
Mississippi," he began, "I used to dream about
moving north. To me it was the promised land.
I wanted to find a good job in the big city.
Cities like Chicago, St. Louis. But everybody,
I mean everybody, talked about Harlem in
New York City. Going north, it was all anybody
ever talked about. I would sit on the front porch
and just daydream about those big-city places.
The way some folks told it everything was perfect.
Even the streets in the big city were paved with
gold, and it was all there just waiting for me."
John Henry's eyes sparkled as his voice quickened.
"When I saved enough money, I crowded onto
the train with other small-town folks headed north.
Everything I owned fit into a torn, tattered suitcase
and a brown box wrapped in string.

"I rode the train all day and all night.
Like a snake winding its way across the Mississippi
River, that train moved slowly through farmlands
and flatland, over mountains and valleys, until it
reached its final destination."

Jo Louis closed her eyes.
She loved her grandfather's stories—his
words were like wings and other things. She
listened closely until she felt she was right
there with him.

209

"'New York City! New York! New York!'
the conductor bellowed as the train pulled
into the station.

"I headed straight to Harlem. I had never
seen buildings so tall. They almost seemed
to touch the sky. Even the moon looked
different in the big city. The moonlight
was bright and shining, the stars
skipped across the sky.

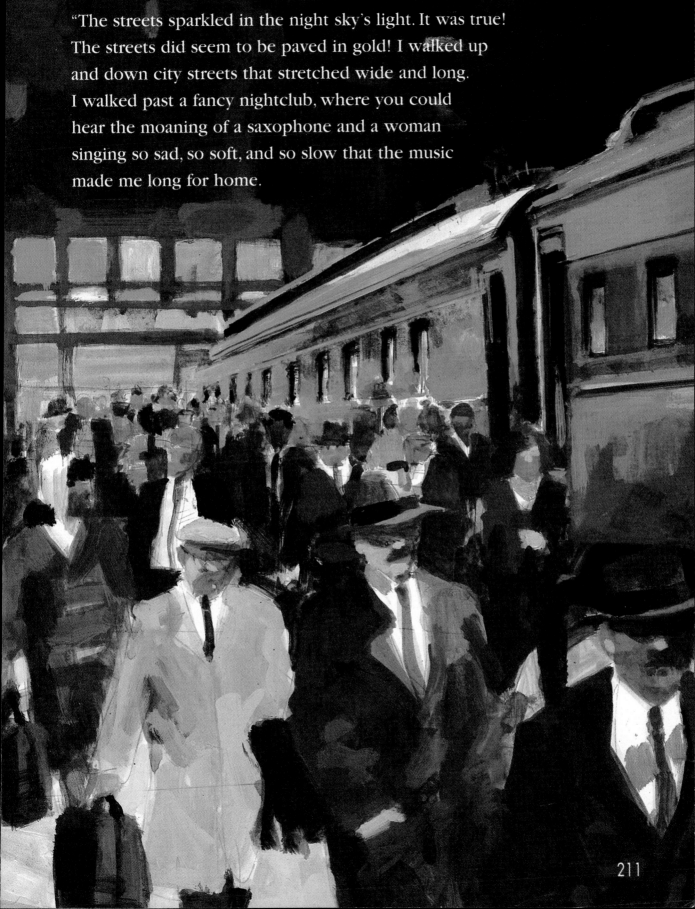

"The streets sparkled in the night sky's light. It was true!
The streets did seem to be paved in gold! I walked up
and down city streets that stretched wide and long.
I walked past a fancy nightclub, where you could
hear the moaning of a saxophone and a woman
singing so sad, so soft, and so slow that the music
made me long for home.

211

"And then, all of a sudden the sad
music changed to happy music.
That saxophone and singing started to swing.
Hundreds of people spilled out into the
sidewalks, waving flags, scarves,
waving handkerchiefs and tablecloths.
Hundreds of people filled the streets
with noise and laughter, waving hats and
anything and everything, filling the sky with
bright colors of red, white, green, yellow,
blue, purple, and orange.

"Everybody was clapping,
hands were raised high to the sky.
Up and down the street,
people were shouting and singing.
Cars were beeping their horns;
bells were ringing.

212

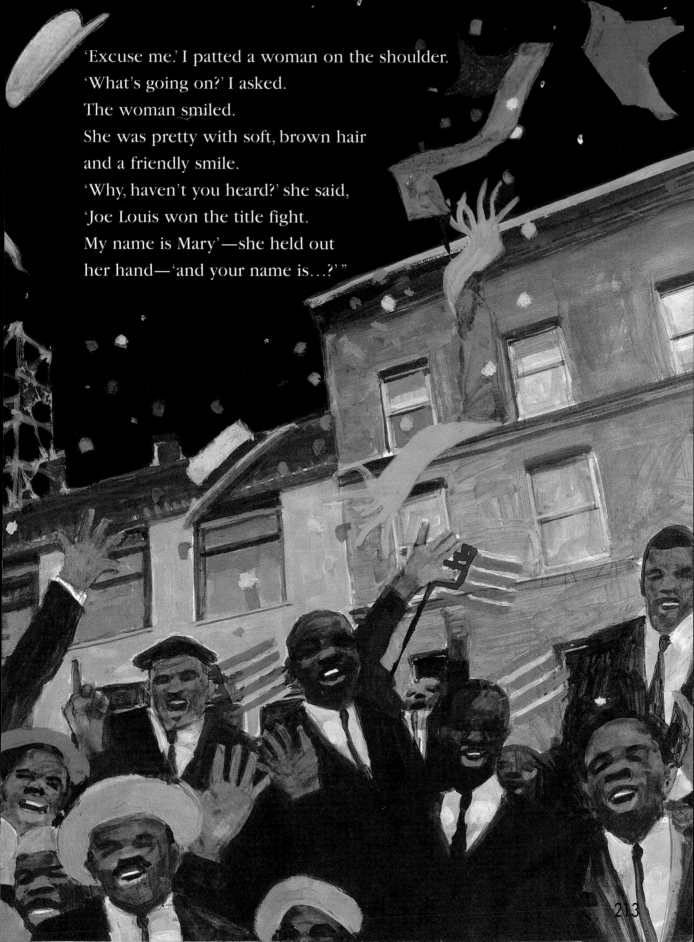

'Excuse me.' I patted a woman on the shoulder.
'What's going on?' I asked.
The woman smiled.
She was pretty with soft, brown hair
and a friendly smile.
'Why, haven't you heard?' she said,
'Joe Louis won the title fight.
My name is Mary'—she held out
her hand—'and your name is…?'"

John Henry smiled and hugged Jo Louis close.
"It was a special night for me. It was a special
night for black people everywhere.
Joe Louis was the greatest boxer in the world.
He was a hero. That night he won the fight
of his life. A fight that a lot of people thought
he would lose. Some folks said he was too slow,
others said he wasn't strong enough.
But he worked hard and won. It was a special
night, my first night in the big city, and
Joe Louis won the fight. But the night
was special for another reason."

"It was the night you met Grandma,"
Jo Louis said, and she started to smile.

"It was a special night that I'll never forget.
I named your father Joe Louis, and he
named you, his first child, Jo Louis, too."
Her grandfather tickled her nose.
"That was the night you won the title.
You should be very proud of your name.
Every name has a special story."

214

The next day Jo Louis took a deep breath as she walked into
her new school classroom and slipped into a seat.
The boy sitting next to Jo Louis tapped her on the shoulder.
"My name is Lester. What's your name?"

Jo answered slowly, "My name is Jo . . . Jo Louis."
She balled her fist and closed her eyes and braced herself.
She waited, waited for the laughter, waited for the jokes.
She peeked out of one eye, then she peeked out the other eye.

"Wow, what a great name!" he said, and smiled.

Author
Belinda Rochelle

Belinda Rochelle

Belinda Rochelle loves sports. "I remember my grandmother telling me stories about Joe Louis," she says, "and about what his fights meant to African Americans." Years later, Belinda Rochelle used her grandmother's stories to help her write *When Jo Louis Won the Title*.

Belinda Rochelle's first writing project was about another famous American—Abraham Lincoln. When she was in sixth grade, she wrote a play for her class about President Lincoln. That's when Belinda knew that she wanted to become a writer.

Illustrator Larry Johnson

When Larry Johnson was in third grade, he learned two important things about himself. The first was that he loved sports. The second was that he had a talent for art. So he began making drawings about sports and sports figures.

When Jo Louis Won the Title isn't really a sports story, but Larry Johnson's love of sports made him a "natural" to illustrate it. The fact that he is a grandfather made the job even more fun for him!

Response Corner

Being the New Kid

How would you feel if you were Jo Louis, in a new neighborhood and a new school? Work with a group to make a poster for new students like Jo Louis. Write ten tips that could help a new student feel at home in your school.

Legends of the Past

Jo Louis's grandfather was named for John Henry, an African American folk hero. Read the folktale about John Henry, and find a copy of the song about him. Retell the tale to your classmates. If you like to sing, perform the song as well.

Harlem Heroes

Jo's grandfather was raised in Mississippi, but he traveled to Harlem in New York City. Many other African Americans traveled to Harlem at the same time. Look up Harlem in an encyclopedia. Start a picture gallery of famous African Americans who have lived in this community. Draw their faces, and add information about why they are important.

What Do You Think?

• How does her grandfather's story make Jo Louis feel?

• Jo Louis was worried that she would be teased about her name. Why is it wrong for children to tease each other about their names?

• How did the people in New York City feel about the fighter Joe Louis? Is there a sports star who is important to your community? Why is that person important?

Theme Wrap-Up

Why do you think some people want to travel to new places? Why do some people prefer to stay home? Think about the characters in this theme to help you answer.

If Great-Aunt Arizona met Jo Louis, what do you think they would say to each other? Why do you think so?

ACTIVITY CORNER

Find out about newcomers in your town or city, or in a city nearby. First, call or write to the Chamber of Commerce. Ask how many people have moved to the area in the past five years. Then, find out where most of the newcomers came from. Share your results with your classmates.

THEME

Exploring Challenges

We can explore space because creative inventors and scientists have thought of new ways to make rockets, cameras, and other tools. Creative people also think about new ways to solve problems here on Earth. As you read the selections in this theme, think about creative ways to solve problems and meet challenges in your everyday life.

THEME
Exploring
Challenges

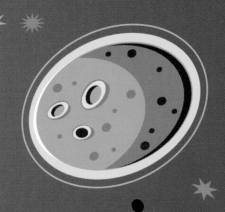

Contents

Bookshelf

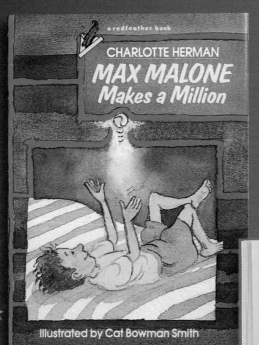

Illustrated by Cat Bowman Smith

Max Malone Makes a Million
by Charlotte Herman

Max and his friend Gordy are determined to earn a million dollars.
Signatures Library

Julian's Glorious Summer
by Ann Cameron

Julian's friend Gloria gets a new bike. It seems that Julian is downright unhappy when his father also buys him a new bike.
Award-Winning Author
Signatures Library

By Ann Cameron
Illustrated by Dora Leder

What's Out There?
A Book About Space
by Lynn Wilson

Explore the Sun, the Moon, and the planets, and learn about how they move.

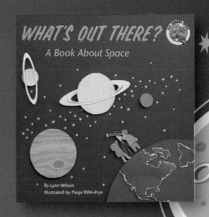

Cam Jansen and the Mystery of the Television Dog
by David A. Adler

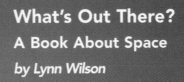

Cam and her friends meet a famous pooch—who then disappears.

Award-Winning Illustrator

Sam and the Lucky Money
by Karen Chinn

Sam has trouble deciding how to spend his special holiday money— until he finds a truly good use for it.

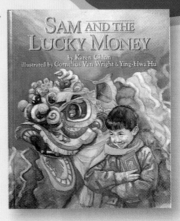

Russell Stannard is Professor of Physics at the Open University in Britain. In his spare time, he builds large sculptures in his backyard.

JOURNEY THROUGH THE

BY RUSSELL STANNARD

SOLAR SYSTEM

Leaving Home

●●●●●●●●●●●●●●●●●●●●●●●●

Come with me on a journey to the far depths of space. I shall show you the solar system.

There are so many strange and wonderful things to understand, so many mysteries to unravel—not only about the universe, but also about ourselves and our place in the world.

What do we need for the trip? Imagination. There's no other way to make this journey. No spaceship ever built (or ever likely to be built) can take us where we wish to go. But even though the trip has to be an imaginary one, scientists are fairly sure this is what such a journey would be like . . .

Just a Minute!

Before we blast off into space, let's think for a moment. The Earth we live on is part of the universe we wish to explore. Except for the Moon, and possibly the nearby planets, it is the only part of the universe we can actually get our hands on. The laws of nature that rule everything going on here might be the same laws that apply everywhere else. So why not take a quick look around here on Earth, before we launch out into the unknown?

Round or Flat?

First of all, there is the shape of the Earth. Long ago, everyone thought the Earth was flat—apart from the odd hill or valley, of course. There's no doubt it looks flat. At the seaside the water seems to stretch on forever, as far as the eye can see.

But suppose on a clear day we look through a pair of binoculars at a distant ship. As it travels away from us, it seems to sink as it disappears over the horizon.

This is because the Earth is actually round. It is a ball 7,926 miles (12,756 km) across.

Going Down

Right under our feet, nearly 8,000 miles (13,000 km) down, is the other side of the Earth. What keeps the people who live there from falling off?

First we have to stop thinking that there is some special direction in space called "down," such that everything is pulled in that direction. All directions in space are similar to one another. The important thing is that when something falls, it falls toward the Earth—it is the Earth that does the pulling.

To do this, our planet uses a force, an invisible one, called gravity. The strength of this force depends on how far away you are from the Earth. The bigger the distance, the weaker the force. If you go twice the distance away from the Earth's center, the force drops to a quarter; three times the distance, a ninth; ten times the distance, a hundredth; and so on. But although it gets weaker and weaker, it never completely disappears; it stretches out into space, to infinity.

The force is strongest on the surface of the Earth. Gravity is what holds you down in your seat at this very moment. If you get up and jump, gravity will pull you back again.

Although the Earth is round, it's not a perfect sphere—it bulges slightly at the equator. The diameter through the center of the Earth is 7,900 miles from pole to pole, but 7,926 miles across the equator.

Now, if you and I are pulled toward the center of the Earth, the same will be true of everyone else, wherever they are on the surface of the Earth. They will all talk about being pulled "down." But all their "downs" are different.

The Force That Shapes the Universe

It is not just the things outside the Earth that feel the pull of gravity; the stuff that makes up the Earth itself feels it too. Every part of the Earth is pulling on every other part of it. That's why the Earth ends up round; it's the best way of packing things together so that

"How come people on the other side of the world don't fall off?"

"How come people on the other side of the world don't fall off?"

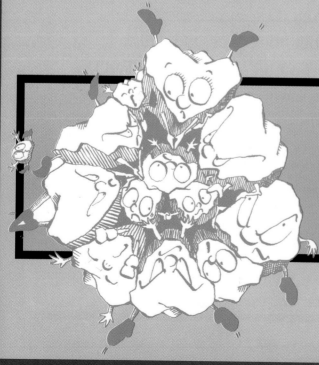

Gravity makes every part of the Earth pull on every other part and tries to drag them all to the center. That's why our planet is round.

they can all get as close as possible to one another. All the bits of rock and dirt try to get to the center of the Earth, but they are stopped by others that got there first.

Why am I telling you this? The point is, even before we get in our rocket and leave the Earth, we already have some idea of what we are likely to find out on our travels. If the Earth attracts everything with gravity, then perhaps everything we'll come across in space attracts everything else with gravity. In fact, we shall find *it is the force of gravity that shapes the entire universe*. Not only that, but if being round is the most practical shape for the Earth, then most things out there are likely to be round too.

Looking Up

When we look up at the sky, to where we shall soon be heading, what do we see? The Sun, the Moon, and the stars. They are all moving slowly across the sky and around our planet. Or are they? They certainly appear to be. But people have been fooled by appearances before. Learning things often involves unlearning things first. (Remember the "down" that wasn't everyone's "down.")

For example, people used to think the sky was a great hollow dome, with twinkly lights (the stars) stuck to it. They were amazed to learn that it wasn't so. Not only that, but the stars, the Sun, and the Moon were not going around the Earth once every 24 hours. It was the Earth that was spinning. The Earth completes one of its turns every 24-hour day.

When people still believed everything went around the Earth, we thought we were at the center of the universe. That meant we human beings must be very important. We *are* important (at least, I think so), but not for that reason. This is an example of the way discoveries about the universe can raise interesting questions about ourselves.

The fact that the Earth spins like a top leads us to expect that most other things we shall discover in our travels will also be spinning.

Where To?

The largest objects in the sky are, of course, the Sun and Moon. They appear to be roughly the same size. But again we must be careful. The apparent size of something depends on how far away it is.

The Moon is almost 400 times closer to the Earth than the Sun is, and 100 times closer than the nearest planet.

In fact, the Moon is much closer. It is our nearest neighbor in space. So it sounds like a good place, at long last, to start our space journey.

FIRST STOP
THE MOON

Three... two... one...
blast off!

● ● ● ● ● ● ● ● ● ● ● ● ● ● ● ● ●

As we approach the Moon, the first thing we notice is that it is a round ball; it is not a flat disk, which is what it looks like from Earth. (But a round ball is the shape we expect from gravity, right?)

Secondly, the Man in the Moon has disappeared! His face, with those staring eyes and the open mouth which always seems to be saying "Oooh," has broken up into mountains and valleys pitted with deep holes and craters. These were made by meteoroids, thousands of rocks that fly through space and crash into anything that gets in their way.

Unlike the meteoroids, we land our craft gently.

The Moon's diameter is 2,160 mi. (3,476 km). That is roughly equal to the distance across Australia. It would take 81 Moons to weigh the same as Earth.

Twelve astronauts walked on the Moon between 1969 and 1972. Their footprints are still there, in the moon-dust that covers the surface. This is because there is no wind and rain to wear them away.

Going for a Stroll

Walking on the Moon is fun. You feel very light. You can take big, big steps. And boy how you can jump! Six times as high as on the Earth.

This is because the Moon's gravity force is not as strong as the Earth's—only one-sixth. Your weight depends on the gravity force. If gravity is only one-sixth as strong, your weight on the Moon will be only one-sixth of your weight on the Earth.

Why is the Moon's gravity so much less than the Earth's? The Moon does not have as much mass as the Earth; it is not as heavy. In the first place, it is smaller. In the second, the material from which it is made has a lower density; it is not packed together as tightly as the Earth's material.

But although the Moon's gravity is weak, notice that *it does have a gravity force.* (Don't be fooled by those pictures of astronauts floating around weightless inside their spacecraft.) Remember, *everything* has a gravity force.

Give Me Air!

Because the Moon's gravity is so weak, there is no atmosphere here; the Moon can't hold on to one. The atmosphere, if there ever was one, just floated away. There is no air, no water, no life—all very different from the Earth.

This is why astronauts must wear space suits on the Moon; they have to carry their own supply of air to breathe.

The Far Side

● ●

Just as the Earth spins around like a top as it orbits the Sun, so the Moon spins too. It takes 27.3 days, roughly one month, to spin around once, which is the same time it takes to orbit the Earth. And that means we always see the same side of the Moon on Earth. We call this side the near side. Until a spacecraft sent back photographs in 1959, no one had ever seen the far side. What did the photos show? Oddly, many many more craters than on the near side.

   And now we must leave the Moon. "Already?" you ask. I'm afraid so. Quite frankly, our travels have much more exciting things in store!

THE SUN: A BOMB THAT GOES OFF SLOWLY

As seen from the Earth, the Moon and the Sun may look similar. In fact, they are very different. The Moon is a round dusty rock; the Sun is a huge ball of flaming hot gas. And I do mean huge; the distance from one side of the Sun to the other, its diameter, is 865,000 miles (1.4 million km). That is 109 times the diameter of the Earth. The reason it doesn't look a lot bigger than the Moon is that the Sun is much farther away.

Because the Sun's gas is so hot, it swirls and rushes and jiggles around a lot. You might think that all this movement

More than one million Earths could fit inside the Sun.

would throw the gas off into space. But no. The Sun has 333,000 times the mass of the Earth, and it has an enormous gravity force. It is this force that keeps the

Next Stop, the Sun?

take-off...

Just as the Moon orbits the Earth, so the Earth orbits the Sun. It does this once every 365 days—in other words, once a year. And it stays at a distance of roughly 93 million miles (150 million km) from the Sun. That is a long way. A spacecraft traveling at the speed of a jumbo jet would take about 20 years to get to the Sun. (That's a lot of inflight movies!) If, like an airplane flight, the fare was based on a rate of about 18 cents per mile, a one-way ticket would cost nearly $17 million!

As you approach the Sun (but not too closely!), you'll see that its surface is anything but smooth and regular. The flaming hot gas is always seething and swirling about. Some of the gas leaps up high; these are called solar prominences. The surface is also marked by darker patches known as sunspots; these are regions of somewhat cooler gas.

...arrival

Spring, Summer, Fall, Winter

The Earth's orbit around the Sun is almost a circle, but not quite. It is slightly squashed. We call its oval shape an ellipse. So our distance from the Sun varies slightly during the year it takes us to complete the orbit. Is this why we have hot weather in summer and cold in winter?

No. The effect of this varying distance is very tiny. The real reason for the different seasons has to do with the way the Earth spins while it is orbiting the Sun. As we have already learned, the Earth spins like a top. It does this around an imaginary line that joins the North and South poles and is called the axis.

Looking at the diagram, you can see how this North-South axis is tilted to one side. Suppose it was *not* like this. Suppose it was bolt upright. Then there would be no seasons; the weather would stay the same all year round. The only effect of spinning would be to give us night and day—night when we were facing away from the Sun, day when we faced toward it.

But that is not how the axis is arranged. It is tilted. So, if we live in the North, at one stage of the orbit the axis tends to tip us slightly toward the Sun—the Sun beats down on us and we get long, hot summer days. Meanwhile, those living in the South are pointed away from the Sun; its rays hit them at only a glancing angle, and that's when they get their winter. On the opposite side of the orbit, six months later, we change places; it is then our turn to have winter, and theirs to have summer.

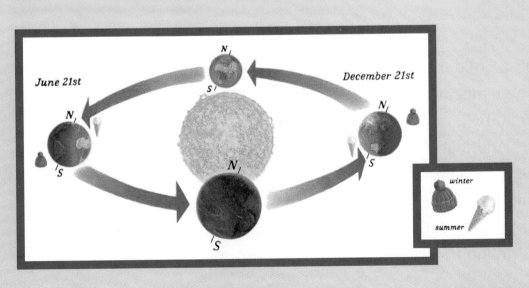

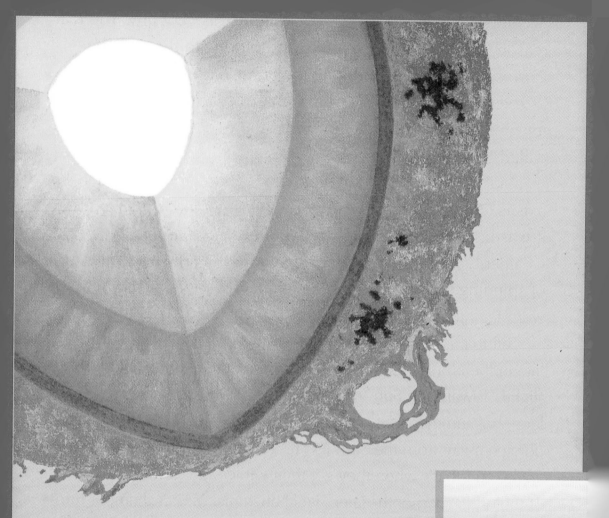

Phew! It's Hot!

It's a good thing we stay a long way from the Sun. The temperature of its surface is about 10,000°F (5,500°C).

And that is just the temperature of the surface. Deep down inside the Sun, the temperature increases. It becomes hotter and hotter, until right at the very center of the Sun the temperature is 27 million°F (15 million°C).

The temperature of ice is 32°F (0°C) and boiling water is 212°F (100°C). Think about how hot 10,000°F (5,500°C) must be!

The Sun's Central Heating System

● ● ● ● ● ● ● ● ● ● ● ● ● ● ● ● ● ● ●

The Sun pours out heat and light all the time. How does it manage to do this and still stay hot? What kind of fuel does it use to keep its fires burning? The answer is nuclear fuel—which stores the same kind of energy you get in a hydrogen bomb.

The heart of the fire is deep down in the central core of the Sun. It has been burning for 4.6 billion years. When you stop to think about it, that is really quite amazing. A hydrogen bomb going off *slowly*!

There are times when it appears as if the Sun's great fire has gone out. This is when the Moon passes between us and the Sun and blocks our view of the Sun. We call this an eclipse. When will the Sun's fire *really* go out? The Sun has enough fuel to last another 5 billion years.

Sunlight takes 8.3 minutes to reach Earth. That means the Sun you see now is actually how the

Sun looked 8.3 minutes ago. (But you should never look directly at the Sun—it could blind you!)

VISITING THE NEIGHBORS

The Earth is not the only planet going around the Sun. There are eight others. And what a mixed bunch they are!

NEPTUNE

EARTH

VENUS

SUN

MERCURY

MARS

JUPITER

The Planets Next Door

We start with Mercury, the planet closest to the Sun. It races around the Sun at 30 miles (48 km) per second, completing its orbit in only 88 days instead of the Earth's sluggardly 365. Like all the planets, Mercury is also spinning on its axis. It spins more slowly than the Earth, taking 59 days for a full turn instead of one. This makes it look as if the Sun is passing across the sky incredibly slowly. So much so that Mercury's "day" (from noon one day to noon the next) is twice as long as its "year" (one orbit around the Sun). That means you would get two birthdays every day!

SATURN

Mercury

Diameter: 3,032 mi.
Average distance from Sun:
36 million mi.
Speed:
30 mi./second.

But before you rush to set up house on Mercury, think about this: because Mercury is so much closer to the Sun than the Earth is, the Sun looks almost three times as big from this planet. During the day, the temperature is 662°F (350°C); at night it drops to minus 365°F (−221°C). Mercury looks a bit like the Moon, with lots of craters, and like the Moon, it has no atmosphere. It is definitely not the sort of place where I would want to live.

The next planet out from the Sun is Venus. It spins very slowly, in the opposite direction to the Earth's spin.

Venus is about the same size as the Earth and does have an atmosphere. But it is not the type of atmosphere we humans need for breathing. It is mostly a gas called carbon dioxide. One of the interesting things about this gas is the way it prevents heat escaping from the planet; it acts like a thick blanket. The result? The Sun's rays get trapped, and the surface of Venus becomes extremely hot:

860°F (460°C). That is hot enough to melt lead. No other planet is that hot, not even Mercury, the closest to the Sun. But it gets worse. High above this blanket of gas, clouds full of acid rain swirl around the planet, blown along by winds of up to 224 miles (360 km) per hour.

Venus

Diameter: 7,521 mi.
Average distance from Sun:
67 million mi.
Speed:
22 mi./second.

As we continue our journey out from the Sun, we come next to the Earth. I don't have to tell you about that one!

Earth

Diameter: 7,926 mi.
Average distance from Sun:
93 million mi.
Speed: 18.6 mi./second.

Just beyond the Earth's orbit we get to Mars. People used to think that Mars might be a good place to search for life. But space probes have found none. It just seems to be a world of dead volcanoes, craters, very little atmosphere, and raging dust storms. Mars may look red-hot; in fact it's very cold, with an average temperature of minus 58°F (−50°C).

Mars has a couple of very small moons called Phobos and Deimos. These two are so small that they've never had enough gravity to pull all their matter into a tight round ball—that's why they've ended up lumpy and misshapen, like potatoes.

So much for the four rocky planets close to the Sun. Farther out we get four very different planets, all of them HUGE.

A Giant Among Giants

The first is Jupiter—the largest planet of all, with a diameter 11 times that of the Earth. Like the other giant planets, it is mostly a ball of hydrogen and helium. This is in the form of gas at the surface, but deeper down the gas gets packed

Mars

Diameter:
4,217 mi.
Average distance from Sun:
142 million mi.
Speed: 15 mi./second.

Jupiter

Diameter: 88,734 mi.
Average distance from Sun: 484 million mi.
Speed: 8 mi./second.

together so thickly it becomes more like a liquid than a gas. At the center is a core of hot, molten rock, somewhat like the molten lava that comes out of volcanoes on Earth. In other words, there is probably nothing solid about Jupiter, or the other big planets. There's no ground where you can stand and say, "I'm standing on the planet, and what is above me is the planet's atmosphere." In a sense, it is all atmosphere, much like the Sun itself.

When it comes to moons, Jupiter has plenty—16! Ganymede is more than 3,100 miles (5,000 km) across; it's the biggest moon of all.

Icy Rings, Frozen Moons

Next comes Saturn, second in size only to Jupiter. It is famous for being surrounded by many beautiful, wide, flat rings. These are not solid as you might think; they are made up of a vast number of pieces of ice. Some are the size of snowflakes, others are as big as snowballs, and the largest are several yards across. They all move around Saturn in orbit like tiny, tiny moons.

Saturn is not alone in having rings—the other three giant planets also have them. But compared to those of Saturn, they are fewer and much harder to see.

Saturn

Diameter: 74,600 mi.
Average distance from Sun: 870 million mi.
Speed: 6 mi./second.

Saturn also holds the record for moons—18 of them at the last count—though some are very small. One of them, Titan, is large, larger even than planet Mercury. And it has an atmosphere twice as dense as that of Earth. So scientists wonder whether there might be some form of life on this moon. It would be a very simple form because Titan is a long way from the Sun and is very, very cold. It is like an Earth that has been kept in cold storage. We'll have to wait for some future space probe to pay it a visit before we find out whether there's any early form of life there.

Two Blue Giants

As we go deeper still into space, away from the Sun, Uranus is next. Unlike the Earth, which spins on a slightly tilted axis, Uranus spins on its side. It has several narrow rings and 15 moons. Uranus has an atmosphere that is mainly hydrogen, with some helium and methane. Its clouds of methane are what make this planet a lovely shade of blue. Below the

Uranus

Diameter: 32,000 mi.
Average distance from Sun: 1.8 billion mi.
Speed: 4.2 mi./second.

Neptune

Diameter: 30,200 mi.
Average distance from Sun: 2.8 billion mi.
Speed: 3.4 mi./second.

atmosphere there is a rocky core, but whether this is molten or solid is not yet known.

Then comes Neptune, the second blue planet. Savage winds tear across this planet at 1,400 miles (2,200 km) per hour. Far above the storms, eight moons and a few rings orbit more peacefully. One of the moons, Triton, is almost as big as our own Moon. Triton is the coldest place we know—it's minus 390°F (−235°C) there.

P.S. Pluto

Lastly, beyond the giant planets there is Pluto, the smallest planet of all. A ball of rock and ice covered with nitrogen, Pluto has only one-fifth the diameter of Earth. It is so far away that it takes 248 years to complete one huge orbit around the Sun. Pluto has an elliptical orbit, long and squashed and tilted at a different angle from those of the other planets. For 20 years of its orbit Pluto actually comes closer to the Sun than Neptune; for those 20 years Neptune is the most distant planet of all. Another thing about Pluto is that, like Uranus, it spins on its side.

Pluto

Diameter: 1,470 mi.
Average distance from Sun: 3.7 billion mi.
Speed: 2.9 mi./second.

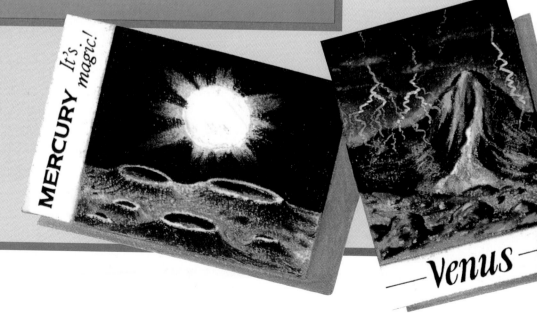

MERCURY It's magic!

Venus

Pluto's moon, Charon, is large for a moon; it is half the diameter of its "parent" planet. Not only that, but it is 20 times closer to Pluto than our Moon is to Earth. Which means that Charon must look huge in the sky over Pluto— seven times bigger than our Moon does over Earth.

The Sun's Family

So there we have it, the nine planets. As I said, a very mixed bunch, varying greatly in size and the stuff from which they are made. They vary in temperature, too—from the 860°F (460°C) heat of Venus to the minus 455°F (−271°C) chill on the surface of distant Neptune.

Note that only one planet has the right kind of temperature and materials to be a home for advanced forms of life: the Earth!

Mars

Wish you were here!

Moonwalk '69

EARTH

I AM FLYING

BY **JACK PRELUTSKY**

ILLUSTRATED BY TOM LEONARD

I am flying! I am flying!
I am riding on the breeze,
I am soaring over meadows,
I am sailing over seas,
I ascend above the cities
where the people, small as ants,
cannot sense the keen precision
of my aerobatic dance.

I am flying! I am flying!
I am climbing unconfined,
I am swifter than the falcon,
and I leave the wind behind,
I am swooping, I am swirling
in a jubilant display,
I am brilliant as a comet
blazing through the Milky Way.

I am flying! I am flying!
I am higher than the moon,
still, I think I'd best be landing,
and it cannot be too soon,
for some nasty information
has lit up my little brain—
I am flying! I am flying!
but I fly without a plane.

THE INVENTOR THINKS UP HELICOPTERS

by Patricia Hubbell
illustrated by Ju-Hong Chen

"Why not
a
vertical
whirling
winding
bug,
that hops like a cricket
crossing a rug,
that swerves like a dragonfly
testing his steering,
twisting and veering?
Fleet as a beetle.
Up
down
left
right,
jounce, bounce, day and night.
It could land in a pasture
    the size of a dot . . .
Why not?"

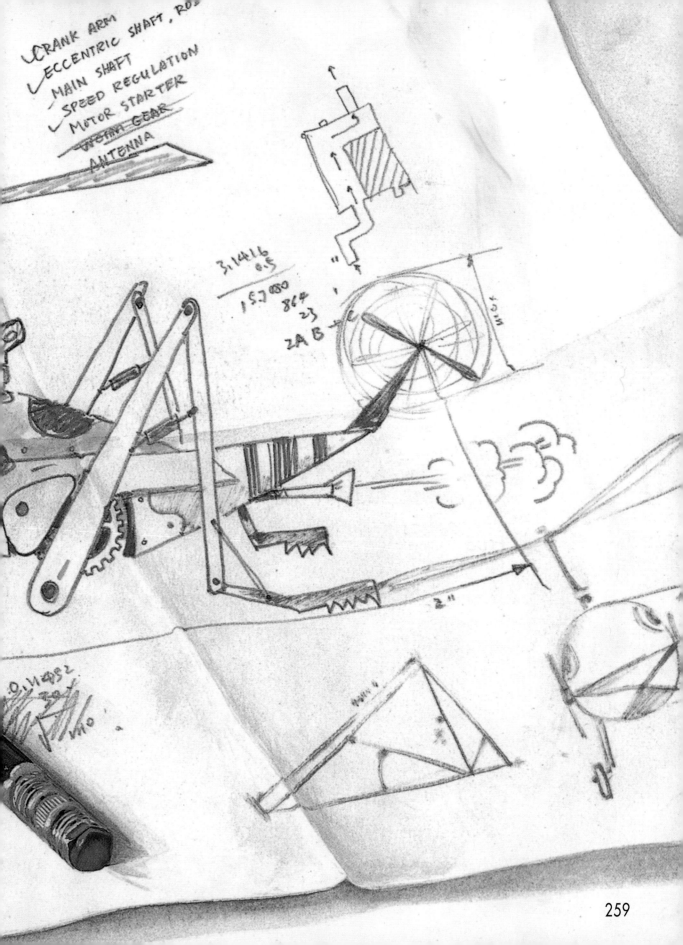

CRANK ARM
ECCENTRIC SHAFT, ROD
MAIN SHAFT
SPEED REGULATION
MOTOR STARTER
WORM GEAR
ANTENNA

3.14416
0.5

151000
864
23
∠A B

C

0.14452
30

259

RESPONSE

MAKE A CHART

Do You Have the Time?

When it's morning in San Francisco, it's afternoon in New York and evening in London. Find out how many time zones there are in the world. Make a chart that shows the time in each time zone when it is noon where you live. Display your chart in your classroom.

COMPARE AND CONTRAST

Look! Up in the Sky...

Earth is the only planet known to have life. But the other planets, too, have things that are special about them. With a partner, research any two of the other planets and compare them. Find out how they are the same and how they are different. Report your findings to the class.

CORNER

Fly Me to the Moon

There have been many songs written about the Moon. With a partner, make up your own Moon song. Include one fact about the Moon. You might want to make your words fit a tune you know. Sing your song for your classmates.

What Do You Think?

• What do you think the Earth would be like if it were a lot farther away from the Sun?

• What are the most interesting facts you learned in "Journey Through the Solar System"?

• Earth seems to be the only planet in the solar system that has life. Why do you think this is so?

Patently

Which patents did we invent?

Are these inventions for real? Well, eight of them received patents! (The U.S. Patent Office gives patents to inventions that it decides are new and useful. Then, only the inventor can produce that invention.) But a couple of the devices on these pages are fake—we made them up! Can you tell which inventions are real, and which two are phony?

The answers are on page 265.

1. Hats, Caps and Other Head Wear

Patent No. 273,074 (1883)
Want a beautiful headpiece that'll shine in the dark? Dip a hat or cap in special glow-in-the-dark powder. Now your hat will stand out at night. As a bonus, your cap will be easy to spot in dark closets.

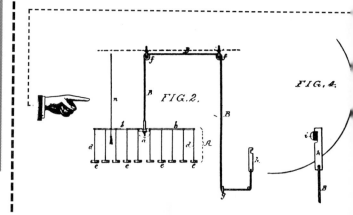

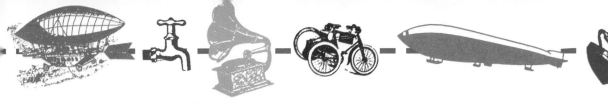

Ridiculous

by Saul T. Prince from *3-2-1 Contact* magazine

2. Device for Waking Persons from Sleep

Patent No. 256,265 (1882)

This is a dream of an alarm clock. Say you set the alarm for 8:00 A.M. At that time, the device lowers towards you. Soon, the corks dangling from its frame bump into your face, gently waking you up.

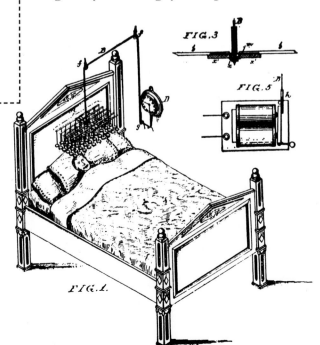

3. Device for Producing Dimples

Patent No. 560,351 (1896)

Dimples are popular. But if you don't have them, you can make them, said the designer of this machine. Just place the knob on your chin or cheek and push the roller around it to form a dimple.

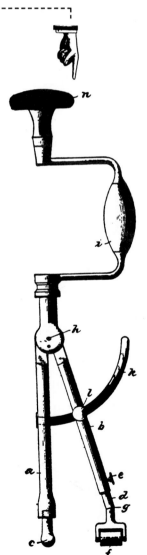

4. Motor Vehicle Attachment

Patent No. 777,369 (1904)

At the turn of the century, cars scared horses on the road. How to keep horses from being spooked was a serious problem. Here's one solution: Attach a fake horse to the front of a car! Then you've turned a scary horseless carriage into a friendly horse-drawn carriage!

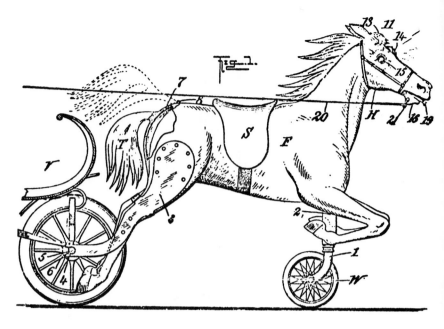

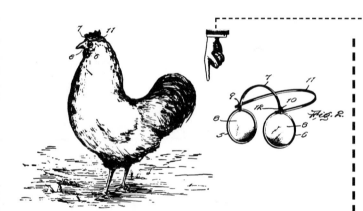

5. Eye Protector for Chickens

Patent No. 730,918 (1903)

These glasses aren't for nearsighted chickens. They're protectors for fighting fowls. They were designed to keep chickens from pecking each other's eyes.

6. Pneumatic Parade Shoes

Patent No. 1,785,406 (1935)

Pressing a button on the shoe fills the heel and sole with air. They stretch out, adding five inches to the wearer's height. This device allows the wearer to see over people's heads at parades and other events.

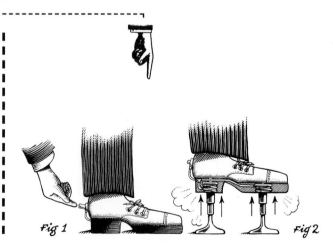

Fig 1   Fig 2

7. Velocipede

Patent No. 190,644 (1870)

This carriage doesn't have horse power—it's got dog power. It operates like a gerbil wheel. Put two dogs inside the vehicle's front wheel. When they run, so does the car.

8. Mouth Opening Alarm

Patent No. 2,999,232 (1961)

This device makes sure you sleep with your mouth closed. When the sleeper's jaw drops, a battery-powered alarm goes off, and the device vibrates. This wakes up the sleeper. After this happens over and over, the person learns to sleep with his or her mouth closed.

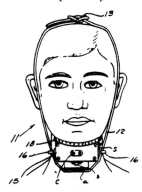

9. Gum Blowing Mouthpiece

Patent No. 2,438,946 (1975)

To blow perfect bubbles, chew some bubble gum and then remove it. Place the plastic device in your mouth. Stretch the bubble gum over the plastic mouthpiece and blow. It can also be worn as a sports mouthpiece—allowing you to blow bubbles while playing basketball, football and other contact sports.

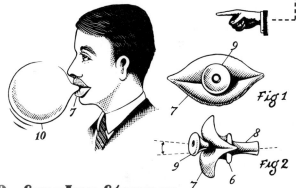

Fig 1

Fig 2

10. Smoker Stopper

Patent No. 3,655,325 (1972)

Want to stop someone from smoking? This machine was designed to snuff out the habit: When you pick up the cigarette package, it starts coughing.

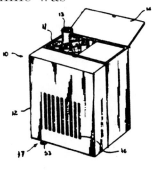

Creative Minds AT WORK

BY JEAN MARZOLLO

Whether we are exploring space or just making life simpler, new inventions can help solve problems. Meet two men who changed the way we live today.

Thomas Alva Edison

(1847-1931)

He invented the electric light bulb, the record player, and many more amazing things.

Thomas Alva Edison was born in Milan, Ohio. The youngest of seven children, he was called Alva. Alva was a curious child, always asking his mother why things worked the way they did. He liked to experiment, too. Once he sat on some goose eggs to see if he could hatch them.

When Alva was seven, his family moved to Michigan. At school, he was whipped by the teacher for asking too many questions. When his mother found this out, she took Alva out of school. From then on, she taught him at home. She had been a teacher and tried to make learning fun for Alva.

As Thomas Alva Edison grew up, he began to invent things. At the age of 23, he figured out a better way to make a telegraph machine. He sold his plan for $40,000. With the money, he opened a workshop, or laboratory, in West Orange, New Jersey. There, he invented a better typewriter. He then moved to Menlo Park,

"WIZARD OF MENLO PARK"

Thomas Alva Edison in his laboratory.

New Jersey, and invented an improved telephone. Thomas Edison invented the record player (called a phonograph) in 1877. Two years later, he invented the electric light bulb. People called him the "Wizard of Menlo Park."

Edison's ears had been injured when he was a young man. As a result, his hearing was poor. As he grew older, his hearing grew worse, but Edison said his deafness helped him concentrate. He was happiest when he was inventing things in his laboratory.

Scientists work in different ways. George Washington Carver mostly worked alone. Marie and Pierre Curie worked together. Thomas Edison liked to work with a team of people. He said that genius was "1 percent inspiration and 99 percent perspiration." With a team of people, the perspiration part of the work could be shared and thus go faster. Edison received many awards for his work.

George Washington Carver

(c. 1864–1943)

He discovered hundreds of new uses for plants.

George Washington Carver was born a slave in Diamond, Missouri. A slave is a person who is owned by someone else. The owner can make the slave work for no pay. In the early history of the United States, white people brought black people from Africa and forced them to work on their farms. When these slaves had children, their birth dates were not always written down. That is why there is a *c* before the date above. It stands for *circa* (SER-ka), which means "about." George Washington Carver was born about 1864.

Shortly after he was born, his father was killed in an accident and his mother was kidnapped. George was raised by his owners. In 1865, when George was one year old and Abraham Lincoln was president, slavery was abolished, or ended. The people who had owned George continued to raise him. They taught him to read and write.

As a child, George loved plants. When he grew up, he went to college and studied agriculture, the science of farming. It was very hard for African Americans to go to college then because many colleges did not accept black people. George Washington Carver worked at different jobs to pay for his education. When he was 32, he was asked to teach at the Tuskegee Institute, a college for African Americans. He taught agricultural students how to grow more plants on their land.

Although he liked teaching, George Washington Carver liked scientific research more. He liked to look at plants and ask, "What would happen if . . . ?" George Washington Carver experimented with peanuts, sweet potatoes, and soybeans in his laboratory. He discovered more than 300 different products, including ink, soap, and a milk substitute that could be made from peanuts alone.

George Washington Carver was given many prizes for his research. Toward the end of his life, Carver gave much of the money he had earned to the Tuskegee Institute, so that other scientists

George Washington Carver works with students in his laboratory at Tuskegee Institute.

Art and Literature

Sometimes we say that people who have big dreams are "reaching for the stars." The scientists and inventors you have read about in this theme had big dreams. What do you think they might have said to the women in this painting? Why?

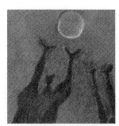

Women Reaching for the Moon (1946)
by Rufino Tamayo

Rufino Tamayo was born in Oaxaca, Mexico, in 1911. He created his own style of painting by combining traditional Mexican art with bold shapes and bright colors.

A Class

from KID CITY Magazine
photos by Les Morsillo

YAY!
The kids at Microsociety
think their school is the
greatest!

272

It's a living:
these kids go to school, to work, to the bank, and to court!

Act

Mic Society Bank

It's 2 PM at the Microsociety School in Yonkers, New York. It's a very important time of the day. Why? That's when the bank opens! Kids quickly finish their lunch and rush to their jobs as bank tellers. Other kids are getting in line to put their "savings" into their bank accounts. Still others are taking money out of the bank to go shopping, or pay their fines at the Treasury Department.

What's Going On?

Kids at the Microsociety School get taught in a very special way. Half the school day is probably very much like yours—with regular classes like math or reading or gym. But the other half is spent the way many grownups spend their days—working and trying to save money.

Can You Lend Me Five Batistas Until Friday?

The kids use fake money instead of real cash. Their money is named after the Superintendent of Schools. For example, it was called "Batistas" when Donald Batista was Superintendent.

Some kids work in the bank, some work in the courtroom, some work in the market on "Market Days." Recycled materials, such as tin cans and paper are used to make stuff that the kids sell to each other. *Kid City* watched as one sales kid said to a customer, "I have a nice change purse here, only ten Batistas!"

Safely in the bank:
Here kids are putting their money in the bank. That's called a deposit. When they take money out, it's called a withdrawal.

Table 5
15 Batistas
All Items
This Table Only!

What's on sale?

At the Department of Economic Development, kids buy raw materials to make products. Then they sell their stuff to other kids on market day. They sell things like wallets, pencil holders, even jewelry.

Pay Up!

Sometimes there are long lines at the "Department of the Treasury." That's where kids go to pay fines for bad behavior. The kids made up the rules and fines themselves. If you're late for class, you have to pay twenty Batistas. If you run in the hallways, that's fifty Batistas. And don't fight or make noise in the library—that'll cost you *one hundred* Batistas!

School Is Fun!

The school principal, Fred Hernandez, thinks the Microsociety School is a lot of fun for kids. "Teachers usually tell kids to sit down. Be quiet. Don't play," said Mr. Hernandez. "Our school is different because kids get to play every day!" All the kids love their special school, too. "I love going to the bank and going to court," said one kid. "It makes me feel like a grownup!"

Don't break the law!
Kids go to the Department of the Treasury to pay their fines. They also must pay a monthly tax of forty Batistas.

May I help you?
The kids who work in the bank are happy to help their friends open accounts and fill out their bank books.

If You Made a Million

by David M. Schwartz
pictures by Steven Kellogg

ALA
Notable Book
Children's Choice
Teachers' Choice

IF YOU MADE
A MILLION
by David M. Schwartz
pictures by Steven Kellogg

CHEERFUL AND WILLING
HELPERS
WANTED
by MARVELOSISSIMO
THE MATHEMATICAL MAGICIAN

CONGRATULATIONS! YOU'VE EARNED A PENNY.

ONE PENNY

It will buy anything that costs one cent.

WELL DONE! YOU'VE MADE A NICKEL.

ONE NICKEL

is worth the same as

FIVE PENNIES

HOORAY! NOW YOU HAVE A DIME.

ONE DIME

has the same value as TWO NICKELS

or TEN PENNIES

280

EXCELLENT! FOR YOUR HARD WORK YOU'VE EARNED A QUARTER.

ONE QUARTER

is the same amount of money as FIVE NICKELS

or TWO DIMES AND ONE NICKEL

or THREE NICKELS AND ONE DIME

or TWENTY-FIVE PENNIES

BLOW UP this BOA Earn 25¢

WONDERFUL! YOU ARE NOW A DOLLAR RICHER.

ONE DOLLAR

**is worth as much
as FOUR QUARTERS**

FIX THIS
FOUNTAIN'S FLOW

Earn $1.

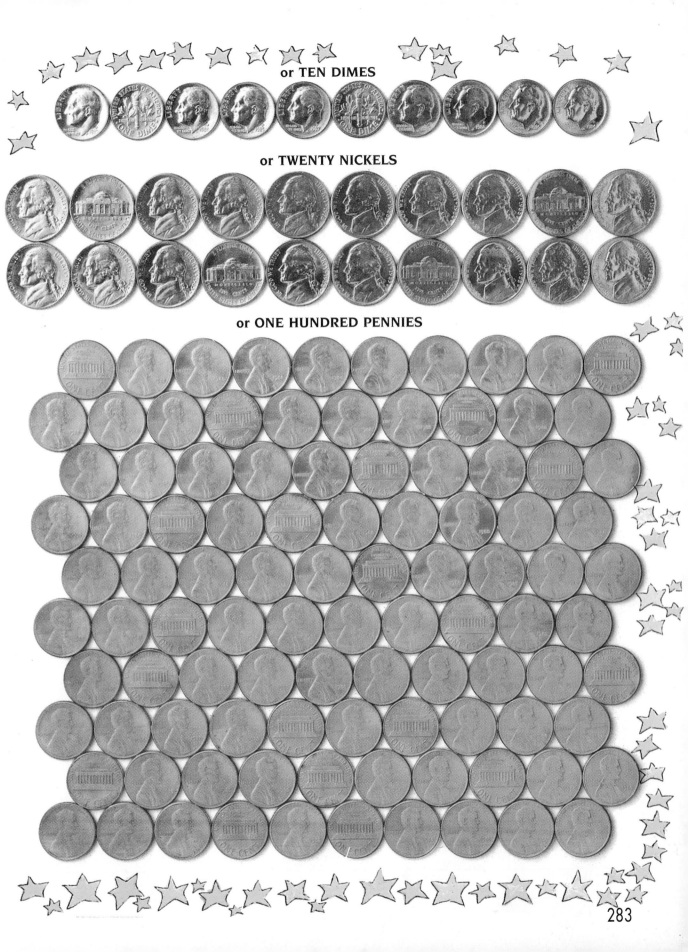

or TEN DIMES

or TWENTY NICKELS

or ONE HUNDRED PENNIES

283

You could use your dollar to buy
one hundred pieces of penny candy,

or twenty five-cent balloons,

or ten stickers for ten cents each,
or four rubber balls that cost
twenty-five cents apiece.

Or perhaps you'd like to save your dollar.
You could put it in the bank,
and a year from now it will be worth $1.05.

The bank wants to use your money,
and it will pay you five cents
to leave your dollar there for a year.
The extra five cents is called interest.

If you waited ten years, your dollar would earn
sixty-four cents in interest just from sitting in the bank.

Are you interested in earning lots of interest? Wait
twenty years, and one dollar will grow to $2.70.

DELICIOUS! YOU'VE BAKED A CAKE AND EARNED FIVE DOLLARS.

You could be paid with one five-dollar bill

or five one-dollar bills. It doesn't matter.
They have the same value.

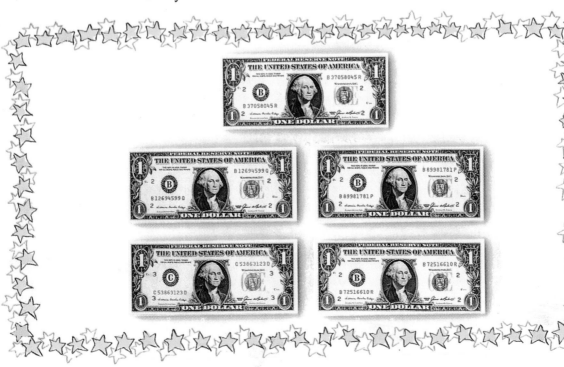

STUPENDOUS! YOU'VE MADE TEN DOLLARS.

How would you like to be paid?

One ten-dollar bill? Two five-dollar bills?

Ten one-dollar bills?

Or perhaps one five and five ones?

Take your pick—they're all worth ten dollars.

If you prefer coins, you can have
a five-foot stack of pennies
(that's one thousand of them) or
a fifteen-inch stack of two hundred nickels.
You could also be paid with one hundred dimes,
which would stack up to just over five inches.
Or you can receive your ten dollars
as a $3\frac{1}{4}$-inch pile of forty quarters.

You could spend your ten dollars on ten kittens
or one thousand kitty snacks.

Or you could take your mom to the movies.

But maybe you'd rather save your money.
If you leave your ten dollars in the bank
for ten years, it will earn $6.40 in interest,
and you will have $16.40.

If you leave it there for fifty years,
your ten dollars will grow to $138.02.

YOU'VE WORKED HARD TO EARN
ONE HUNDRED DOLLARS.
You've decided to spend it on a plane ticket
to the beach. You could pay with
a hundred-dollar bill, or two fifty-dollar bills,
or five twenty-dollar bills, or many other
combinations—
six fives, three tens, and two twenties, for instance.

Paying with pennies?
You'll need ten thousand of them,
and they'll make a fifty-foot stack.

YOU'VE WORKED LONG AND HARD,
AND YOU'VE EARNED A THOUSAND DOLLARS!
You're going to buy a pet.

You could pay with coins or bills.

If you don't like the idea of carrying
a thousand dollars around with you,
you can put it in the bank
and pay for the hippo with a check.

The check tells your bank to give $1,000
to the person who sold you the hippo.

Here's how it works: You give the check
to the person who sold you the hippo,
and he gives it to his bank,
and his bank sends it to a very busy
clearinghouse in the city,
and the clearinghouse tells your bank
to take $1,000 out of your money.

After your bank does that,
the clearinghouse tells the hippo salesman's bank
to add $1,000 to his money, so he can take it
and use it whenever, and however, he likes.
Maybe he'll use it to raise more hippos.

If you used pennies to purchase
a $10,000 Ferris wheel,
someone might not be too happy about it.
Even if you used ten thousand one-dollar bills,
they would be mighty hard to handle.

Probably a check would be best.

MAGNIFICENT! YOU'VE EARNED $50,000.
And you've just read about
a well-worn, unloved, but perfectly fixable
castle for sale. The price: $100,000.

The castle costs $100,000 and you have only $50,000.
You're $50,000 short, but you can still buy the castle.
You could use the money you earned as a down payment
and ask a bank to lend you the rest.

Then you would pay the bank back,
a little at a time, month after month . . .

for many years.

But the amount you must pay the bank
will be *more* than what you borrowed.
That's because the bank charges
for lending you money. The extra money
is called interest, just like the interest
the bank pays to you when it uses your money.
Now you are using the bank's money, so you must
pay interest to the bank.

If you have some very expensive plans,
you may have to take on a tough job
that pays well.

If you think ogre-taming would be
an exciting challenge, you can have fun
and make a great deal of money, too.
Of course, you may not enjoy
taming obstreperous ogres or building bulky bridges
or painting purple pots. Enjoying your work
is more important than money, so you should look
for another job or make less expensive plans.

CONGRATULATIONS! YOU'VE MADE A MILLION.

A MILLION DOLLARS!
That's a stack of pennies ninety-five miles high,
or enough nickels to fill a school bus,
or a whale's weight in quarters.

Would you prefer your million in paper money?
Even a paper million is a hefty load:
A million one-dollar bills would weigh 2,500 pounds
and stack up to 360 feet.

What's the smallest your million could be?
One-hundred-dollar bills are the largest made today,
and it would take ten thousand of them
to pay you for your feat of ogre-taming.
But a check for $1,000,000
would easily fit in your pocket or purse.
And it's worth the same as the towering stacks
of pennies or bills.

Now you can afford to buy tickets to the moon.

Or you can purchase some real estate
for the endangered rhinoceroses.

But if you'd rather save your million
than spend it, you could put it
in the bank, where it would earn interest.
The interest on a million is about $1,000 a week,
or $143 a day, or $6 an hour, or 10 cents a minute.
Just from sitting in the bank!

If you keep your million, you can probably
live on the interest without doing any more work
for the rest of your life. You might like that,
or you could find it rather dull.

Making money means making choices.

SO WHAT WOULD
YOU DO IF YOU
MADE A MILLION?

David M. Schwartz

Talking to
David Schwartz

Ilene Cooper interviewed author David Schwartz.

Ilene Cooper: *Where did the idea for this book come from?*

David Schwartz: *If You Made a Million* grew from my earlier book about big numbers, *How Much Is a Million?* We see these big numbers in the newspaper every day, but very few of us understand them. So I wrote *How Much Is a Million?* After that book came out, people said, "We liked it, but you didn't talk about the kinds of millions we like best—millions of dollars!"

Cooper: *You've said you were always interested in big numbers. What did you mean by that?*

Schwartz: Let me give you an example. I've always liked the stars. I would look up at night and wonder how long it would take me to count them all. I also liked to take long bike rides. I would say, "Wow, this is a really long ride, but I wonder what it would be like to ride to Alpha Centauri, the nearest star." Alpha Centauri is more than four light years away. Light travels 186,000 miles per second. That's like going around the world seven times in one second. . . . Well, you see what I mean. I was always dealing with big numbers.

Cooper: *Do you plan to write more books about big numbers?*

Schwartz: Yes. I'm already working on a book about numbers beyond a million. It's going to combine math with one of my other great interests—nature.

Talking to
Steven Kellogg

Ilene Cooper interviewed illustrator Steven Kellogg.

Ilene Cooper: *Did you ever earn money from your art when you were a child?*

Steven Kellogg: As a matter of fact, I did. I would knock on people's doors and say, "I just drew a picture of your pet. Maybe you'd like to buy it." Some people did!

Cooper: *How did you feel about money when you were young?*

Kellogg: I found out pretty early on that it was good to have money in your pocket, so I was always getting jobs around the neighborhood. When I was old enough to ride my bike out of the neighborhood, I got a job with a woman who raised dogs. That was great because I love animals.

Cooper: *If You Made a Million is different from the other books you've done, isn't it?*

Kellogg: Yes! The book presented an interesting challenge—how do you illustrate a book that's mostly numbers? I thought the book needed a main character so I invented Marvelosissimo, the Mathematical Magician.

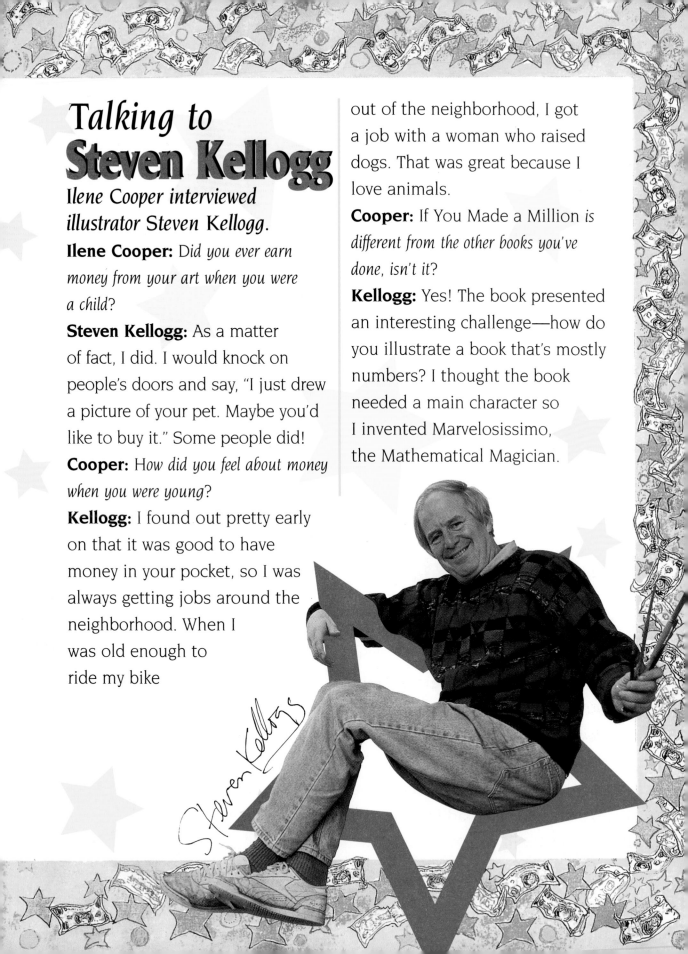

Response Corner

Spending and Saving

Saving is an important habit to learn. Plan a weekly budget. First, decide how much money you will start with. Next, figure out how much you need to spend and how much you can save. Then follow your plan!

Wanted: Baby-sitter

Want ads in newspapers list jobs. Study the want ads in your newspaper. Now think of a job you would like someone to do, such as baby-sit your little brother or sister. Write an ad for the job, and post it in your classroom.

Career Interview

As you read in "If You Made a Million," how much money you earn depends on what kind of job you have. But money isn't the only thing to think about when choosing a job. Interview a family member about his or her work. Ask that person why he or she chose to do that kind of work.

★ What Do You Think? ★

- If you earned a lot of money, why might you want to save some of it in a bank rather than spend it all?

- What would be the best way to pay for something that cost a lot of money? Would you use coins, dollars, or a check? Explain your answer.

- How would you explain to someone from another planet what money is and what it is used for?

The King and the Poor Boy

*A Cambodian folktale
retold by
Muriel Paskin Carrison
from a translation by the Venerable Kong Chhean*

In a small village near the edge of the forest, there once lived a buffalo boy who had no mother or father. His uncle, who was the chief cook for the king, pitied the poor boy. So he invited the boy to stay with him in the palace. The grateful boy worked hard to help his uncle. He washed the plates, polished the cups, cleaned the dining room tables, and mopped the floors. At the end of each month, his uncle gave him six *sen*[1] as his wages.

Now the king frequently inspected the palace quarters. He often noticed the hardworking boy mopping the floors or polishing the cups, cheerfully and in good humor. One day the king asked the boy, "Do you receive wages for your hard work?"

---

[1] six *sen*: Cambodian money, worth about six cents

The boy bowed and said, "Yes, I do, Your Majesty. I earn six *sen* every month."

Then the king asked, "Do you think you are rich or do you think you are poor?"

"Your Majesty," the boy replied, "I think that I am as rich as a king."

The king was taken by surprise. "Why is this poor boy talking such nonsense?" he mused to himself.

Once more, the king spoke to the boy, "I am a king and I have all the power and riches of this country. You earn only six *sen* a month. Why do you say you are as rich as I am?"

The boy laid down his broom and slowly replied to the king, "Your Majesty, I may receive only six *sen* each month, but I eat from one plate and you also eat from one plate. I sleep for one night and you also sleep for one night. We eat and sleep the same. There is no difference. Now, Your Majesty, do you understand why I say that I am as rich as a king?"

The king understood and was satisfied.

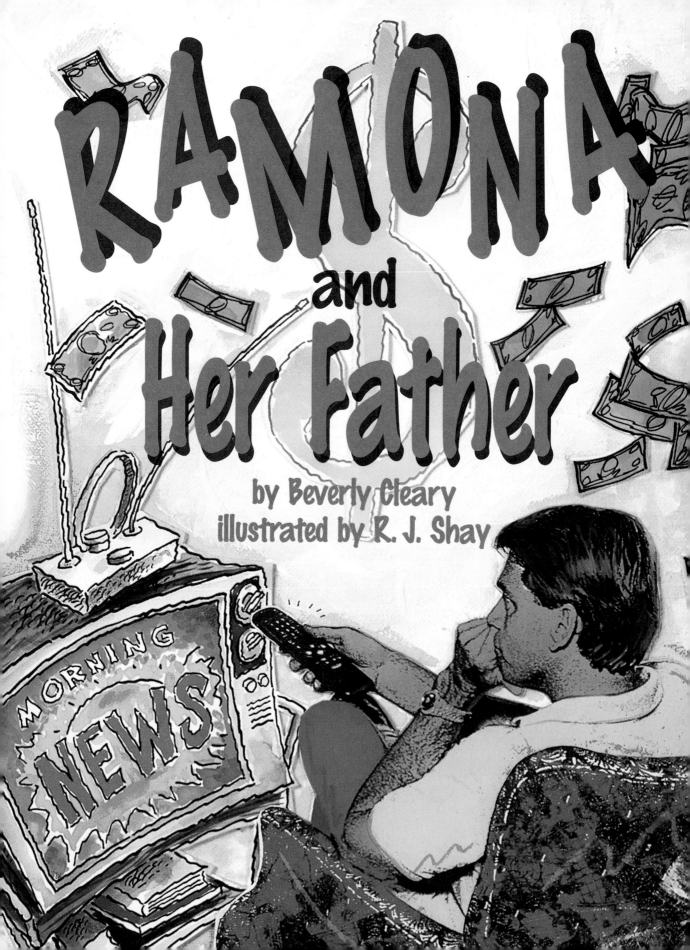

Ever since Mr. Quimby lost his job, Ramona has been wondering if he is too worried to love her anymore. He certainly isn't any fun these days. Ramona decides to solve the family's problems by earning a million dollars. She figures she can do this by starring in a television commercial. She has seen kids on TV do things like eat margarine and wear silly crowns. One girl even told her mom that her pantyhose looked like elephant legs, and she didn't get into trouble. Ramona is sure she can do these things and more. So she starts practicing. . . .

Ramona continued to practice until she began to feel as if a television camera was watching her wherever she went. She smiled a lot and skipped, feeling that she was cute and lovable. She felt as if she had fluffy blond curls, even though in real life her hair was brown and straight.

One morning, smiling prettily, she thought, and swinging her lunch box, Ramona skipped to school. Today someone might notice her because she was wearing her red tights. She was happy because this was a special day, the day of Ramona's parent-teacher conference. Since Mrs. Quimby was at work, Mr. Quimby was going to meet with Mrs. Rogers, her second-grade teacher. Ramona was proud to have a father who would come to school.

Feeling dainty, curly-haired, and adorable, Ramona skipped into her classroom, and what did she see but Mrs. Rogers with wrinkles around her ankles. Ramona did not hesitate. She skipped right over to her teacher and, since there did not happen to be an elephant in Room 2, turned the words around and said, "Mrs. Rogers, your pantyhose are wrinkled like an elephant's legs."

Mrs. Rogers looked surprised, and the boys and girls who had already taken their seats giggled. All the teacher said was, "Thank you, Ramona, for telling me. And remember, we do not skip inside the school building."

Ramona had an uneasy feeling she had displeased her teacher.

She was sure of it when Howie said, "Ramona, you sure weren't very polite to Mrs. Rogers." Howie, a serious thinker, was usually right.

Suddenly Ramona was no longer an adorable little fluffy-haired girl on television. She was plain old Ramona, a second-grader whose own red tights bagged at the knee and wrinkled at the ankle. This wasn't the way things turned out on television. On television grown-ups always smiled at everything children said.

During recess Ramona went to the girls' bathroom and rolled her tights up at the waist to stretch them up at the knee and ankle. Mrs. Rogers must have done the same thing to her pantyhose, because after recess her ankles were smooth. Ramona felt better.

That afternoon, when the lower grades had been dismissed from their classrooms, Ramona found her father, along with Davy's mother, waiting outside the door of Room 2 for their conferences with Mrs. Rogers. Davy's mother's appointment was first, so Mr. Quimby sat down on a chair outside the door with a folder of Ramona's schoolwork to look over. Davy stood close to the door, hoping to hear what his teacher was saying about him. Everybody in Room 2 was anxious to learn what the teacher said.

Mr. Quimby opened Ramona's folder. "Run along and play on the playground until I'm through," he told his daughter.

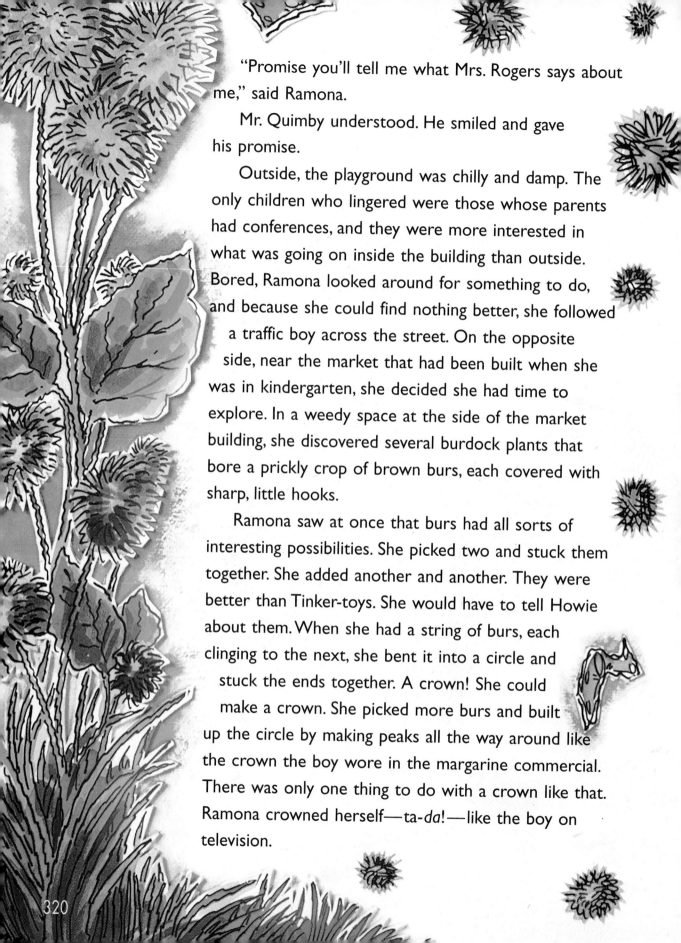

"Promise you'll tell me what Mrs. Rogers says about me," said Ramona.

Mr. Quimby understood. He smiled and gave his promise.

Outside, the playground was chilly and damp. The only children who lingered were those whose parents had conferences, and they were more interested in what was going on inside the building than outside. Bored, Ramona looked around for something to do, and because she could find nothing better, she followed a traffic boy across the street. On the opposite side, near the market that had been built when she was in kindergarten, she decided she had time to explore. In a weedy space at the side of the market building, she discovered several burdock plants that bore a prickly crop of brown burs, each covered with sharp, little hooks.

Ramona saw at once that burs had all sorts of interesting possibilities. She picked two and stuck them together. She added another and another. They were better than Tinker-toys. She would have to tell Howie about them. When she had a string of burs, each clinging to the next, she bent it into a circle and stuck the ends together. A crown! She could make a crown. She picked more burs and built up the circle by making peaks all the way around like the crown the boy wore in the margarine commercial. There was only one thing to do with a crown like that. Ramona crowned herself—ta-*da!*—like the boy on television.

Prickly though it was, Ramona enjoyed wearing the crown. She practiced looking surprised, like the boy who ate the margarine, and pretended she was rich and famous and about to meet her father, who would be driving a big shiny car bought with the million dollars she had earned.

The traffic boys had gone off duty. Ramona remembered to look both ways before she crossed the street, and as she crossed she pretended people were saying, "There goes that rich girl. She earned a million dollars eating margarine on TV."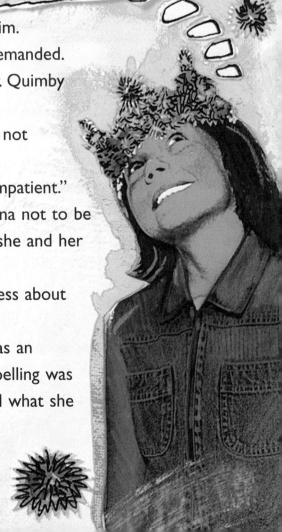

Mr. Quimby was standing on the playground, looking for Ramona. Forgetting all she had been pretending, Ramona ran to him. "What did Mrs. Rogers say about me?" she demanded.

"That's some crown you've got there," Mr. Quimby remarked.

"Daddy, what did she *say*?" Ramona could not contain her impatience.

Mr. Quimby grinned. "She said you were impatient."

Oh, that. People were always telling Ramona not to be so impatient. "What else?" asked Ramona, as she and her father walked toward home.

"You are a good reader, but you are careless about spelling."

Ramona knew this. Unlike Beezus, who was an excellent speller, Ramona could not believe spelling was important as long as people could understand what she meant. "What else?"

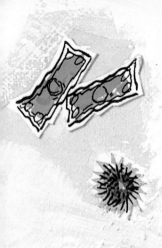
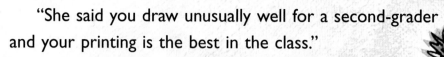

"She said you draw unusually well for a second-grader and your printing is the best in the class."

"What else?"

Mr. Quimby raised one eyebrow as he looked down at Ramona. "She said you were inclined to show off and you sometimes forget your manners."

Ramona was indignant at this criticism. "I do not! She's just making that up." Then she remembered what she had said about her teacher's pantyhose and felt subdued. She hoped her teacher had not repeated her remark to her father.

"I remember my manners most of the time," said Ramona, wondering what her teacher had meant by showing off. Being first to raise her hand when she knew the answer?

"Of course you do," agreed Mr. Quimby. "After all, you are my daughter. Now tell me, how are you going to get that crown off?"

Using both hands, Ramona tried to lift her crown but only succeeded in pulling her hair. The tiny hooks clung fast. Ramona tugged. Ow! That hurt. She looked helplessly up at her father.

Mr. Quimby appeared amused. "Who do you think you are? A Rose Festival Queen?"

Ramona pretended to ignore her father's question. How silly to act like someone on television when she was a plain old second-grader whose tights bagged at the knees again. She hoped her father would not guess. He might. He was good at guessing.

By then Ramona and her father were home. As Mr. Quimby unlocked the front door, he said, "We'll have to see what we can do about getting you uncrowned before your mother gets home. Any ideas?"

Ramona had no answer, although she was eager to part with the crown before her father guessed what she had been doing. In the kitchen, Mr. Quimby picked off the top of the crown, the part that did not touch Ramona's hair. That was easy. Now came the hard part.

"Yow!" said Ramona, when her father tried to lift the crown.

"That won't work," said her father. "Let's try one
bur at a time." He went to work on one bur, carefully
trying to untangle it from Ramona's hair, one strand at
a time. To Ramona, who did not like to stand still, this
process took forever. Each bur was snarled in a
hundred hairs, and each hair had to be pulled before
the bur was loosened. After a very long time, Mr.
Quimby handed a hair-entangled bur to Ramona.

"Yow! Yipe! Leave me some hair," said Ramona,
picturing a bald circle around her head.

"I'm trying," said Mr. Quimby and
began on the next bur.

Ramona sighed. Standing still doing nothing was
tiresome.

After what seemed like a long time, Beezus came
home from school. She took one look at Ramona
and began to laugh.

"I don't suppose you ever did anything
dumb," said Ramona, short of patience and anxious lest
her sister guess why she was wearing the remains of a
crown. "What about the time you—"

"No arguments," said Mr. Quimby. "We have a
problem to solve, and it might be a good idea if we
solved it before your mother comes home from work."

Much to Ramona's annoyance, her sister sat down
to watch. "How about soaking?" suggested Beezus. "It
might soften all those millions of little hooks."

"Yow! Yipe!" said Ramona. "You're pulling too hard."

Mr. Quimby laid another hair-filled bur on the table.
"Maybe we should try. This isn't working."

"It's about time she washed her hair anyway," said Beezus, a remark Ramona felt was entirely unnecessary. Nobody could shampoo hair full of burs.

Ramona knelt on a chair with her head in a sinkful of warm water for what seemed like hours until her knees ached and she had a crick in her neck. "Now, Daddy?" she asked at least once a minute.

"Not yet," Mr. Quimby answered, feeling a bur. "Nope," he said at last. "This isn't going to work."

Ramona lifted her dripping head from the sink. When her father tried to dry her hair, the bur hooks clung to the towel. He jerked the towel loose and draped it around Ramona's shoulders.

"Well, live and learn," said Mr. Quimby. "Beezus, scrub some potatoes and throw them in the oven. We can't have your mother come home and find we haven't started supper."

When Mrs. Quimby arrived, she took one look at her husband trying to untangle Ramona's wet hair from the burs, groaned, sank limply onto a kitchen chair, and began to laugh.

By now Ramona was tired, cross, and hungry. "I don't see anything funny," she said sullenly.

Mrs. Quimby managed to stop laughing. "What on earth got into you?" she asked.

Ramona considered. Was this a question grown-ups asked just to be asking a question, or did her mother expect an answer? "Nothing," was a safe reply. She would never tell her family how she happened to be wearing a crown of burs. Never, not even if they threw her into a dungeon.

"Beezus, bring me the scissors," said Mrs. Quimby.

Ramona clapped her hands over the burs. "No!" she shrieked and stamped her foot. "I won't let you cut off my hair! I won't! I won't! I won't!"

Beezus handed her mother the scissors and gave her sister some advice. "Stop yelling. If you go to bed with burs in your hair, you'll really get messed up."

Ramona had to face the wisdom of Beezus's words. She stopped yelling to consider the problem once more. "All right," she said, as if she were granting a favor, "but I want Daddy to do it." Her father would work with care while her mother, always in a hurry since she was working full time, would go *snip-snip-snip* and be done with it. Besides, supper would be prepared faster and would taste better if her mother did the cooking.

"I am honored," said Mr. Quimby. "Deeply honored."

Mrs. Quimby did not seem sorry to hand over the scissors. "Why don't you go someplace else to work while Beezus and I get supper on the table?"

Mr. Quimby led Ramona into the living room, where he turned on the television set. "This may take time," he exclaimed, as he went to work. "We might as well watch the news."

Ramona was still anxious. "Don't cut any more than you have to, Daddy," she begged, praying the margarine boy would not appear on the screen. "I don't want everyone at school to make fun of me." The newscaster was talking about strikes and a lot of things Ramona did not understand.

"The merest smidgin," promised her father. *Snip. Snip. Snip.* He laid a hair-ensnarled bur in an ashtray. *Snip. Snip. Snip.* He laid another bur beside the first.

"Does it look awful?" asked Ramona.

"As my grandmother would say, 'It will never be noticed from a trotting horse.'"

Ramona let out a long, shuddery sigh, the closest thing to crying without really crying. *Snip. Snip. Snip.* Ramona touched the side of her head. She still had hair there. More hair than she expected. She felt a little better.

The newscaster disappeared from the television screen, and there was that boy again singing:

FORGET YOUR POTS.
FORGET YOUR PANS.
IT'S NOT TOO LATE
TO CHANGE YOUR
PLANS.

Ramona thought longingly of the days before her father lost his job, when they could forget their pots and pans and change their plans. She watched the boy open his mouth wide and sink his teeth into that fat hamburger with lettuce, tomato, and cheese hanging out of the bun. She swallowed and said, "I bet that boy has a lot of fun with his million dollars." She felt so sad. The Quimbys really needed a million dollars. Even one dollar would help.

327

Snip. Snip. Snip. "Oh, I don't know," said Mr. Quimby. "Money is handy, but it isn't everything."

"I wish I could earn a million dollars like that boy," said Ramona. This was the closest she would ever come to telling how she happened to set a crown of burs on her head.

"You know something?" said Mr. Quimby. "I don't care how much that kid or any other kid earns. I wouldn't trade you for a million dollars."

"Really, Daddy?" That remark about any other kid—Ramona wondered if her father had guessed her reason for the crown, but she would never ask. Never. "Really? Do you mean it?"

"Really." Mr. Quimby continued his careful snipping. "I'll bet that boy's father wishes he had a little girl who finger-painted and wiped her hands on the cat when she was little and who once cut her own hair so she would be bald like her uncle and who then grew up to be seven years old and crowned herself with burs. Not every father is lucky enough to have a daughter like that."

Ramona giggled. "Daddy, you're being silly!" She was happier than she had been in a long time.

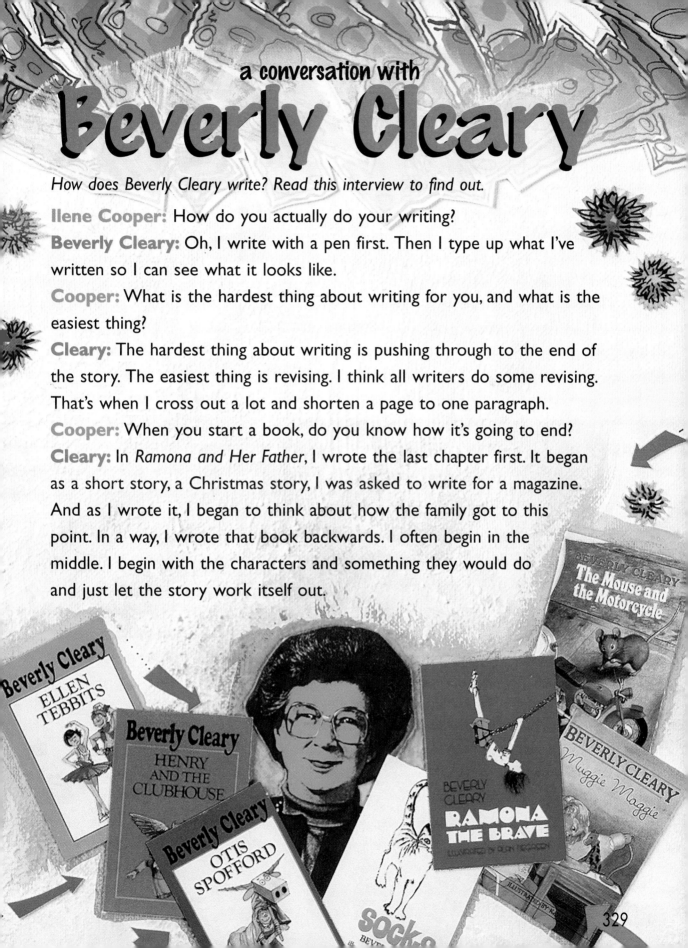

a conversation with
Beverly Cleary

How does Beverly Cleary write? Read this interview to find out.

Ilene Cooper: How do you actually do your writing?

Beverly Cleary: Oh, I write with a pen first. Then I type up what I've written so I can see what it looks like.

Cooper: What is the hardest thing about writing for you, and what is the easiest thing?

Cleary: The hardest thing about writing is pushing through to the end of the story. The easiest thing is revising. I think all writers do some revising. That's when I cross out a lot and shorten a page to one paragraph.

Cooper: When you start a book, do you know how it's going to end?

Cleary: In *Ramona and Her Father*, I wrote the last chapter first. It began as a short story, a Christmas story, I was asked to write for a magazine. And as I wrote it, I began to think about how the family got to this point. In a way, I wrote that book backwards. I often begin in the middle. I begin with the characters and something they would do and just let the story work itself out.

The Travelin' Burs

The burs that Ramona used for her crown became a thorny problem. Many seeds have unusual ways of traveling from a flower to a place where they can grow. In a science book or an encyclopedia, find out about some of these seeds. On a chart, name the seeds, explain how they travel, and draw a picture of each one.

RESPONSE

Odd Jobs Needed

Ramona wanted to help her family by working in a television commercial. What jobs could a young person like Ramona really do? List your ideas. Include ways that Ramona could help in her own home, without being paid.

TAKE NOTES

I'll Buy That!

Television commercials are a type of advertisement. Advertisements try to get people to buy things. For one or two days, pay special attention to all the advertisements you see and hear, and take notes. What are the people in each advertisement like? Does the ad use many words or just a few? How many times is the name of the product used? Compare your notes with a classmate.

CORNER

What Do You Think?

• At the end of the story, Ramona is happier than she's been in a long time. Why has her mood changed?

• What do you like most about Ramona? What do you like least?

• Ramona learns a lesson about what is really important in life. How important is money in your life? Are there other things that are more important to you? Explain.

Theme Wrap-Up

Creating a new invention is a challenge. Doing a job that helps someone is another kind of challenge. Which of the challenges in this theme do you think would be the most exciting? Why?

If Ramona ever does make a million dollars, what do you think she should do with it? Think about the selection "If You Made a Million" to help you answer.

Activity Corner

Hold a classroom science fair. Ask several students to work on projects, inventions, and experiments to show at the fair. Invite people from other classes to visit the fair.

Glossary

WHAT IS A GLOSSARY?

A glossary is like a small dictionary at the back of a book. It lists some of the words used in the book, along with their pronunciations, their meanings, and other useful information. If you come across a word you don't know as you are reading, you can look up the word in this glossary.

Using the

Like a dictionary, this glossary lists words in alphabetical order. To find a word, look it up by its first letter or letters.

To save time, use the **guide words** at the top of each page. These show you the first and last words on the page. Look at the guide words to see if your word falls between them alphabetically.

Here is an example of a glossary entry:

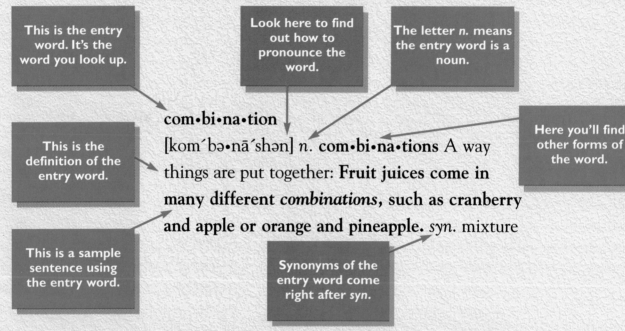

This is the entry word. It's the word you look up.

Look here to find out how to pronounce the word.

The letter *n.* means the entry word is a noun.

This is the definition of the entry word.

Here you'll find other forms of the word.

com•bi•na•tion
[kom´bə•nā´shən] *n.* **com•bi•na•tions** A way things are put together: **Fruit juices come in many different *combinations*, such as cranberry and apple or orange and pineapple.** *syn.* mixture

This is a sample sentence using the entry word.

Synonyms of the entry word come right after *syn.*

ETYMOLOGY

Etymology is the study or history of how words are developed. Words often have interesting backgrounds that can help you remember what they mean. Look in the margins of the glossary to find the etymologies of certain words.

Here is an example of an etymology:

value   The Latin word *valēre* means "to be strong." The Old French language used this word to make the word *value*, changing the meaning to "worth."

Glossary

PRONUNCIATION

The pronunciation in brackets is a respelling that shows how the word is pronounced.

The **pronunciation key** explains what the symbols in a respelling mean. A shortened pronunciation key appears on every other page of the glossary.

PRONUNCIATION KEY*

a	add, map	m	move, seem	u	up, done
ā	ace, rate	n	nice, tin	û(r)	burn, term
â(r)	care, air	ng	ring, song	yoo	fuse, few
ä	palm, father	o	odd, hot	v	vain, eve
b	bat, rub	ō	open, so	w	win, away
ch	check, catch	ô	order, jaw	y	yet, yearn
d	dog, rod	oi	oil, boy	z	zest, muse
e	end, pet	ou	pout, now	zh	vision, pleasure
ē	equal, tree	oo	took, full	ə	the schwa, an
f	fit, half	oo	pool, food		unstressed vowel
g	go, log	p	pit, stop		representing the
h	hope, hate	r	run, poor		sound spelled
i	it, give	s	see, pass		*a* in *above*
ī	ice, write	sh	sure, rush		*e* in *sicken*
j	joy, ledge	t	talk, sit		*i* in *possible*
k	cool, take	th	thin, both		*o* in *melon*
l	look, rule	th	this, bathe		*u* in *circus*

Other symbols:
- separates words into syllables
- ´ indicates heavier stress on a syllable
- ´ indicates light stress on a syllable

Abbreviations: *adj.* adjective, *adv.* adverb, *conj.* conjunction, *interj.* interjection, *n.* noun, *prep.* preposition, *pron.* pronoun, *syn.* synonym, *v.* verb.

*The Pronunciation Key, adapted entries, and the Short Key that appear on the following pages are reprinted from *HBJ School Dictionary* Copyright © 1990 by Harcourt Brace & Company. Reprinted by permission of Harcourt Brace & Company.

af•fect
[ə•fekt´] *v.* **af•fects**
To change; to cause something else to happen: **This experiment shows how sunlight** *affects* **the growth of plants.** *syn.* influence

al•low•ance
[ə•lou´əns] *n.* A set sum of money a person gets regularly, such as each week: **Gordon gets an** *allowance* **of five dollars every week.**

a•mount
[ə•mount´] *n.* A certain number of something; a sum: **The** *amount* **of money I had was not enough to buy the poster.** *syn.* quantity

anx•ious
[angk´shəs] *adj.* Worried; uneasy: **Valerie was** *anxious* **about oversleeping because she thought she might miss the school bus.**

ar•rive
[ə•rīv´] *v.* **ar•rived** To get to a place: **Ivan** *arrived* **at the game at four o'clock.** *syn.* reach

as•ton•ish
[ə•ston´ish] *v.*
as•ton•ished To surprise; to fill with wonder: **It was a clear night, and the number of stars in the sky** *astonished* **him.** *syn.* amaze

blind
[blīnd] *adj.* Unable to see: **Most fish that live in dark caves are** *blind.*

brace

[brās] *v.* **braced** To prepare for something that might be bad; to hold oneself tightly in place: **Ryan held onto a pole on the bus as he *braced* himself for a sudden stop.**

buck•et

[buk´it] *n.* **buck•ets** A round container with a flat bottom and a curved handle, used to carry things: **Shelly filled two *buckets* with water, got some soap and a mop, and was ready to wash the floor.** *syn.* pail

C

cab•in

[kab´in] *n.* A small wooden house, sometimes made of big logs: **Our family stays in a *cabin* by a lake every summer.** *syn.* hut

car•pen•ter

[kär´pən•tər] *n.* A person who makes things out of wood: **The *carpenter* made a bookcase for our room.**

child•hood

[chīld´hŏod´] *n.* The time when someone is young: **Tara had a very happy *childhood* and always played with her friends.** *syn.* youth

choice

[chois] *n.* **choic•es** The act of picking which one: **There were many *choices* to make at the bakery, but we decided to get muffins and apple tarts.** *syns.* decision, selection

bucket The Old English word *buc* also means "belly." A *bucket* is a container that holds things, just as a belly is a container that holds food.

cabin

a	add	o͝o	took
ā	ace	o͞o	pool
â	care	u	up
ä	palm	û	burn
e	end	yo͞o	fuse
ē	equal	oi	oil
i	it	ou	pout
ī	ice	ng	ring
o	odd	th	thin
ō	open	th	this
ô	order	zh	vision

ə = { a in *above*
e in *sicken*
i in *possible*
o in *melon*
u in *circus* }

comfortable
This word comes from *comfort,* which used to mean "strong." In the 1800s, its meaning changed and became "at ease."

creek

com·bi·na·tion
[kom´bə·nā´shən] *n.*
com·bi·na·tions A way things are put together: **Fruit juices come in many different** *combinations,* **such as cranberry and apple or orange and pineapple.** *syn.* mixture

com·fort·a·ble
[kum´fər·tə·bəl] *adj.*
Restful; at ease: **In the summer, José feels** *comfortable* **in his air-conditioned house.**

com·mer·cial
[kə·mûr´shəl] *n.* An advertisement on television or radio, used for selling something: **The** *commercial* **for the new cereal made Kelly feel hungry.**

con·grat·u·la·tions
[kən·grach´ə·lā´shənz] *n.* Good wishes letting someone know you are happy for him or her: *Congratulations* **on your team's great game!**

crea·ture
[krē´chər] *n.* **crea·tures** An animal: **Many different** *creatures* **live in the rain forest.**

creek
[krēk or krik] *n.* A small, narrow river that may not be very deep: **The cowboy got fresh water for his horse from the** *creek.* *syn.* stream

cu·ri·ous
[kyŏŏr´ē·əs] *adj.* Wanting to know or find out more: **Elena was** *curious* **and wanted to learn how rainbows are formed.** *syn.* questioning

D

depth

[depth] *n.* **depths** A far distance into something; the part deep down: **The sunken ship was lost in the *depths* of the sea.**

des·ti·na·tion

[des′tə·nā′shən] *n.* The place someone is going to; a goal: **The *destination* of our trip was New York City, and we were eager to get there.**

de·stroy

[di·stroi′] *v.* **de·stroyed** To put an end to; to break something apart so badly that it cannot be fixed: **After the storm, our garden was *destroyed* and we had to replant everything.** *syns.* ruin, wreck

dor·mant

[dôr′mənt] *adj.* Not moving or growing for a period of time; at rest: **The plants under the snow are *dormant*, but they will grow again in the spring.** *syn.* asleep

E

earn

[ûrn] *v.* **earned** To get as payment for hard work: **Han *earned* some money by washing cars.** *syn.* gain

ech·o

[ek′ō] *n.* **ech·oes** A sound that comes back again: **Tommy shouted into the cave and heard the *echoes* of his voice come back softer and softer, again and again.** *syn.* repetition

echo

depths *Depth* comes from the word *deep*. *Deep* comes from a word that means "diving duck." Many words have come from *deep*, such as *dimple*, *dip*, and *dive*.

earn

a	add	o͝o	took
ā	ace	o͞o	pool
â	care	u	up
ä	palm	û	burn
e	end	yo͞o	fuse
ē	equal	oi	oil
i	it	ou	pout
ī	ice	ng	ring
o	odd	th	thin
ō	open	t͟h	this
ô	order	zh	vision

ə = {
a in *above*
e in *sicken*
i in *possible*
o in *melon*
u in *circus*
}

graze

hesitate
Hesitate once meant "to become stuck." It now means "to pause or wait."

em•per•or
[em´pər•ər] *n.* A person who rules a land: **The *emperor* lived in a beautiful palace, and he made all the laws himself.** *syn.* king

en•er•gy
[en´ər•jē] *n.* The force or power to make things work; the ability to make things go: **Eating breakfast in the morning gives me *energy* to work during the day.**

ex•ist
[ig•zist´] *v.* To be; to live: **Dinosaurs do not *exist* anymore, but we can learn about them in books.**

ex•tinc•tion
[ik•stingk´shən] *n.* When there is no more of a kind of animal or plant: **The white tigers in India are faced with *extinction* because people have hunted them too much.**

graze
[grāz] *v.* **graz•ing** To feed on grass: **The cows were *grazing* on the hillside where the grass was thick.**

hes•i•tate
[hez´ə•tāt´] *v.* To stop and think whether to do or say something: **Carol saw her father *hesitate* before he bought the purple lamp.** *syns.* pause, delay

home•sick
[hōm´sik´] *adj.* Sad because you miss your family and the place you live: **Aretha was very *homesick* while she was at overnight camp.** *syn.* lonely

I

L

i·den·ti·fy

[ī·den´tə·fī´] *v.*
i·den·ti·fied To see and know by name; to point out: **Julian *identified* three butterflies while on a field trip to the park.** *syn.* recognize

im·age

[im´ij] *n.* A picture or likeness of, as seen in a mirror: **Katy saw her *image* reflected in the store window.** *syn.* appearance

im·pa·tience

[im·pā´shəns] *n.*
A feeling of not wanting to wait; not wanting things to slow down: **Sam made a mistake on the test because of his *impatience* to be the first one done.** *syn.* eagerness

ledge

[lej] *n.* A narrow, flat shelf that sticks out from a steep rock or wall: **Carlos put some flower-pots on the *ledge* outside the window.**

M

man·ners

[man´ərz] *n.* Polite ways to do things; ways to do things that show good behavior: **My mother taught me the good *manners* to always say "Please" and "Thank you."** *syn.* etiquette

mol·ten

[mōl´tən] *adj.* Made into a hot liquid by heat: **When a volcano becomes active, *molten* rock, or lava, flows out of it.**

molten *Molten* is from the word *melt.* The first meaning of *melt* was "soft." When something *melts,* it usually becomes a liquid or a "soft" substance.

a	add	ŏŏ	took
ā	ace	ōō	pool
â	care	u	up
ä	palm	û	burn
e	end	yōō	fuse
ē	equal	oi	oil
i	it	ou	pout
ī	ice	ng	ring
o	odd	th	thin
ō	open	ŧħ	this
ô	order	zh	vision

$$\mathrm{ə} = \begin{cases} a \text{ in } above \\ e \text{ in } sicken \\ i \text{ in } possible \\ o \text{ in } melon \\ u \text{ in } circus \end{cases}$$

341

peculiar
Peculiar comes from a Latin word meaning "private property." *Pecu* meant "cattle," and years ago cattle were very important property. The meaning then changed to "belonging only to oneself." In English, it came to mean "being the only one of its kind."

N

ner•vous

[nûr´vəs] *adj.* Worried and somewhat fearful: **I felt *nervous* about singing in front of the class, but I did it anyway.** *syn.* uneasy

O

or•bit

[ôr´bit] *v.* **orbits** To move around another object, usually in space: **The Earth *orbits* the sun once a year.** *syn.* circle

P

pave

[pāv] *v.* **paved** To cover an area of ground with something hard, such as concrete: **The street in front of my house was once dirt, but it was *paved* last week.**

pe•cul•iar

[pi•kyōol´yər] *adj.* Belonging to only one person or thing; strange or unusual: **Jennifer had a *peculiar* dog that ate carrots.** *syns.* unique, odd

peer

[pir] *v.* **peer•ing** To look closer to see more clearly: **Billy was *peering* under the bed, looking for his shoes.**

pop·u·la·tion
[pop´yə·lā´shən] *n.*
pop·u·la·tions A group or kind; a certain group of people or animals living in one place: **Some owl *populations* are in danger because people are cutting down too many of the trees that they live in.** *syn.* inhabitants

post·card
[pōst´kärd] *n.*
post·cards A stiff, rectangular piece of paper with a picture on one side and writing space on the other side, made to be sent through the mail: **While Carmen was traveling with her parents, she kept in touch with her friends by sending them *postcards*.**

R

re·ceive
[ri·sēv´] *v.* To get something, as in a gift: **I will *receive* 5 cents for every soda can I turn in.** *syns.* acquire, obtain

re·mind
[ri·mīnd´] *v.* **re·mind·ed** To cause to remember; to make someone think of something again: **The tacos *reminded* Jane of her trip to Mexico and of the wonderful food she ate there.**

S

sax·o·phone
[sak´sə·fōn´] *n.* A musical instrument in the shape of a curved brass tube: **Mike plays a *saxophone* in the band.**

saxophone

saxophone

a	add	o͝o	took
ā	ace	o͞o	pool
â	care	u	up
ä	palm	û	burn
e	end	yo͞o	fuse
ē	equal	oi	oil
i	it	ou	pout
ī	ice	ng	ring
o	odd	th	thin
ō	open	th	this
ô	order	zh	vision

ə = {
 a in *above*
 e in *sicken*
 i in *possible*
 o in *melon*
 u in *circus*

soldier The Latin word *solidus* means "military pay." French changed it to *solde*, and the person getting the military pay was called a *soldior*. English changed it to *soldier*.

soldier

sea•coast

[sē´kōst´] *n.* The area where the land meets the ocean: **When walking along the seacoast,** it is fun to watch the waves. *syns.* shore, beach

silk

[silk] *n.* A kind of cloth made from a strong, shiny, threadlike material: **Suki likes scarves made of silk because they feel so smooth.**

sol•dier

[sōl´jər] *n.* **sol•diers** A person in the army; someone who watches over others and keeps them from harm: **The soldiers guard the queen when she is outside the palace.** *syns.* protector, fighter

spy

[spī] *v.* To watch closely without being seen: **The little kids always spy on us because they want to find our secret clubhouse.**

sur•face

[sûr´fis] *n.* The outer part of something; the outer layer that covers something: **The surface of the moon is rocky and dry.**

sur•vive

[sər•vīv´] *v.* To live through; to stay alive: **Dolphins need to come up for air in order to survive in the ocean.** *syn.* remain

swal•low

[swol´ō] *v.* To make something go down the throat and into the stomach: **I try to chew my food well, so it will be easy to swallow.**

T

tame

[tām] *adj.* Under control, not wild: **The *tame* animals in the petting zoo will not bite.** *syn.* gentle

throne

[thrōn] *n.* A chair for a ruler: **The king sat on his *throne* as the crown was placed on his head.**

U

un•der•ground

[un´dər•ground´] *adj.* Below the earth: **We went into the tunnel and rode the *underground* train.**

uni•verse

[yōō´nə•vûrs´] *n.* Everything in the world; the sun, stars, and planets: **Astronauts see parts of the *universe* that cannot be seen from Earth.**

V

val•ue

[val´yōō] *n.* The worth; the price: **This painting has great *value* because the painter is famous.** *syn.* cost

view

[vyōō] *n.* What can be seen from a place: **I have a *view* of the street from my window.**

Y

yawn

[yôn] *v.* To open the mouth wide when one is sleepy: **Tyrone was sleepy and he soon began to *yawn*.**

throne

value The Latin word *valēre* means "to be strong." The Old French language used this word to make the word *value*, changing the meaning to "worth."

a	add	ŏŏ	took
ā	ace	ōō	pool
â	care	u	up
ä	palm	û	burn
e	end	yōō	fuse
ē	equal	oi	oil
i	it	ou	pout
ī	ice	ng	ring
o	odd	th	thin
ō	open	th̶	this
ô	order	zh	vision

$$ə = \begin{cases} a \text{ in } above \\ e \text{ in } sicken \\ i \text{ in } possible \\ o \text{ in } melon \\ u \text{ in } circus \end{cases}$$

INDEX OF
Titles and Authors

Page numbers in color refer to biographical information.

Acknowledgments

For permission to reprint copyrighted material, grateful acknowledgment is made to the following sources:

Beautiful America Publishing Company: Cover illustration by Carol Johnson from *A Journey of Hope/Una Jornada de Esperanza* by Bob Harvey and Diane Kelsay Harvey. Copyright 1991 by Little America Publishing Co.

Curtis Brown Ltd.: Corrected galley from *Borreguita and the Coyote* by Verna Aardema. Originally published in *A Bookworm Who Hatched,* Richard C. Owen Publishers, Inc., 1993.

Children's Television Workshop: "Patently Ridiculous" by Saul T. Prince, illustrated by John Lawrence/Bernstein & Associates from *3-2-1 Contact Magazine,* May 1994. Copyright 1994 by Children's Television Workshop. "A Class Act" from *Kid City Magazine,* March 1993. Text copyright 1993 by Children's Television Workshop.

Dial Books for Young Readers, a division of Penguin Books USA Inc.: Cover illustration by Jerry Pinkney from *Back Home* by Gloria Jean Pinkney. Illustration copyright © 1992 by Jerry Pinkney.

Dutton Signet, a division of Penguin Books USA Inc.: From *Nature's Great Balancing Act in Our Own Backyard* by E. Jaediker Norsgaard, photographs by Campbell Norsgaard. Text copyright © 1990 by E. Jaediker Norsgaard; photographs copyright © 1990 by Campbell Norsgaard.

Fitzhenry & Whiteside, Limited, Markham, Ontario: *Wolf Island* by Celia Godkin. Copyright © 1989 by Celia Godkin.

Greenwillow Books, a division of William Morrow & Company, Inc.: Cover illustration by Jim Fowler from *Dolphin Adventure: A True Story* by Wayne Grover. Illustration copyright © 1990 by Jim Fowler. "I Am Flying" from *The New Kid on the Block* by Jack Prelutsky, cover illustration by James Stevenson. Text copyright © 1984 by Jack Prelutsky; cover illustration copyright © 1984 by James Stevenson.

Grosset & Dunlap, Inc., a division of The Putnam & Grosset Group: Cover illustration by Paige Billin-Frye from *What's Out There? A Book About Space* by Lynn Wilson. Illustration copyright © 1993 by Paige Billin-Frye.

Harcourt Brace & Company: Cover illustration by Greg Shed from *Dandelions* by Eve Bunting. Illustration copyright © 1995 by Greg Shed. *The Lotus Seed* by Sherry Garland, illustrated by Tatsuro Kiuchi. Text copyright © 1993 by Sherry Garland; illustrations copyright © 1993 by Tatsuro Kiuchi.

HarperCollins Publishers: *My Great-Aunt Arizona* by Gloria Houston, illustrated by Susan Condie Lamb. Text copyright © 1992 by Gloria Houston; illustrations copyright © 1992 by Susan Condie Lamb. "A Bug Sat in a Silver Flower" from *Dogs & Dragons, Trees & Dreams* by Karla Kuskin. Text copyright © 1980 by Karla Kuskin. Cover illustration by Kam Mak from *The Year of the Panda* by Miriam Schlein. Illustration copyright © 1990 by Kam Mak.

Holiday House, Inc.: *Wolves* by Gail Gibbons. Copyright © 1994 by Gail Gibbons.

Henry Holt and Company: Cover illustration by Cat Bowman Smith from *Max Malone Makes a Million* by Charlotte Herman. Illustration copyright © 1991 by Catherine Bowman Smith.

Houghton Mifflin Company: Cover illustration by Karen M. Dugan from *Halmoni and the Picnic* by Sook Nyul Choi. Illustration copyright © 1993 by Karen Milone Dugan. *When Jo Louis Won the Title* by Belinda Rochelle, illustrated by Larry Johnson. Text copyright © 1994 by Belinda Rochelle; illustrations copyright © 1994 by Larry Johnson. *Grandfather's Journey* by Allen Say. Copyright © 1993 by Allen Say.

Hyperion Books For Children: *All Eyes on the Pond* by Michael J. Rosen, illustrated by Tom Leonard. Text copyright © 1994 by Michael J. Rosen; illustrations © 1994 by Tom Leonard.

Alfred A. Knopf, Inc.: *Borreguita and the Coyote* by Verna Aardema, illustrated by Petra Mathers. Text copyright © 1991 by Verna Aardema; illustrations copyright © 1991 by Petra Mathers.

Larousse Kingfisher Chambers Inc., New York: From *Our Universe: A Guide To What's Out There* (Retitled: "Journey Through the Solar System") by Russell Stannard, illustrated by Michael Bennallack-Hart, Helen Floate, and Diana Mayo. Text copyright © 1995 by Russell Stannard; illustrations copyright © 1995 by Larousse plc.

Lee & Low Books, Inc.: Cover illustration by Cornelius Van Wright and Ying-Hwa Hu from *Sam and the Lucky Money* by Karen Chinn. Illustration copyright © 1995 by Cornelius Van Wright and Ying-Hwa Hu.

Lerner Publications Company, Minneapolis, MN: Cover photograph by Jake Rajs from *The Statue of Liberty: America's Proud Lady* by Jim Haskins. Copyright © 1986 by Jim Haskins.

Lothrop, Lee & Shepard Books, a division of William Morrow & Company, Inc.: *If You Made a Million* by David M. Schwartz, illustrated by Steven Kellogg. Text copyright © 1989 by David M. Schwartz; illustrations copyright © 1989 by Steven Kellogg; photographs of money copyright © 1989 by George Ancona.

Morrow Junior Books, a division of William Morrow & Company, Inc.: From *Ramona and Her Father* by Beverly Cleary. Text copyright © 1975, 1977 by Beverly Cleary. Cover illustration by Louis Darling from *Ellen Tebbits* by Beverly Cleary. Copyright 1951 by Beverly Cleary. Cover illustration by Alan Tiegreen from *Ramona the Brave* by Beverly Cleary. Copyright © 1975 by Beverly Cleary. Cover illustration by Louis Darling from *The Mouse and the Motorcycle* by Beverly Cleary. Copyright © 1965 by Beverly Cleary. Cover illustration by Beatrice Darwin from *Socks* by Beverly Cleary. Copyright © 1973 by Beverly Cleary. Cover illustration by Louis Darling from *Henry and the Clubhouse* by Beverly Cleary. Copyright © 1962 by Beverly Cleary. Cover illustration by Louis Darling from *Otis Spofford* by Beverly Cleary. Copyright 1953 by Beverly Cleary. Cover illustration by Kay Life from *Muggie Maggie* by Beverly Cleary. Illustration copyright © 1990 by William Morrow and Company, Inc.

G. P. Putnam's Sons: From *Amber Brown Is Not a Crayon* by Paula Danziger, illustrated by Tony Ross. Text copyright © 1994 by Paula Danziger; illustrations copyright © 1994 by Tony Ross. Cover illustration by Tony Ross from *Amber Brown Goes Fourth* by Paula Danziger. Illustration copyright © 1995 by Tony Ross.

Random House, Inc.: Cover illustration by Dora Leder from *Julian's Glorious Summer* by Ann Cameron. Illustration copyright © 1987 by Dora Leder. Cover illustration by Arnold Lobel from *The Random House Book of Poetry for Children,* selected by Jack Prelutsky. Copyright © 1983 by Random House, Inc.

Marian Reiner, on behalf of Patricia Hubbell and Ju-Hong Chen: "The Inventor Thinks Up Helicopters" from *The Tigers Brought Pink Lemonade* by Patricia Hubbell, illustrated by Ju-Hong Chen. Text copyright © 1988 by Patricia Hubbell; illustrations copyright © 1988 by Ju-Hong Chen.

Scholastic Inc.: Cover illustration from *All About Alligators* by Jim Arnosky. Copyright © 1994 by Jim Arnosky. From *My First Book of Biographies* (Retitled: "Creative Minds at Work") by Jean Marzollo. Text copyright © 1994 by Jean Marzollo.

Charles E. Tuttle Company, Inc.: "The King and the Poor Boy" from *Cambodian Folk Stories from the Gatiloke,* retold by Muriel Paskin Carrison, from a translation by The Venerable Kong Chhean. Text © 1987 by Charles E. Tuttle Publishing Co., Inc.

Viking Penguin, a division of Penguin Books USA Inc.: Cover illustration by Susanna Natti from *Cam Jansen and the Mystery of the Television Dog* by David A. Adler. Illustration copyright © 1981 by Susanna Natti.

Dinh D. Vu: "Nothing that grows..."/"Hoa Sen" from *The Lotus Seed* by Sherry Garland.

Walker Books Limited, London: Cover illustration from *When Hunger Calls* by Bert Kitchen. Copyright © 1994 by Bert Kitchen. Originally published in the United States by Candlewick Press, Cambridge, MA.

Every effort has been made to locate the copyright holders for the selections in this work. The publishers would be pleased to receive information that would allow the corrections of any omissions in future printings.

Photo Credits

Key: (t) top, (b) bottom, (c) center, (l) left, (r) right, (bg) background, (i) inset

John Lei/OPC, 18, 55, 199(bg), 200-201; Melody Norsgaard/Newcombe Productions, 64-65; Herb Segars/Animals Animals. 68; Stephen Dalton/Photo Researchers, 70; Art Wolfe/Tony Stone Images, 71; Dwight Kuhn/Bruce Coleman, Inc., 72; Laura Riley/Bruce Coleman, Inc. 73(t), 77(b); E. R. Degginger/Animals Animals, 73(b); W. Bayer/Bruce Coleman, Inc. 74-75; S. Nielsen/Bruce Coleman, Inc, 76; Joe McDonald/Animals Animals, 77(t); Phil Degginger/Bruce Coleman, Inc., 78; Keith Gunnar/Bruce Coleman, Inc, 78-79; Robert P. Carr/Bruce Coleman, Inc., 79; Sal DiMarco/Black Star/Harcourt Brace & Company, 104; Wes Bobbitt/Black Star/Harcourt Brace & Company, 127; Culver Pictures, 130-131(bg), 160-161(bg), 164-165(bg); Dale Higgins/Harcourt Brace & Company, 160; Bob Newey, 199; Dennis Brack/Black Star/Harcourt Brace & Company, 217(t); Rick Friedman/Black Star/Harcourt Brace & Company, 217(b) Richard B. Levine, 218(t); Debra P. Hershkowitz, 218(b); Jeff Greenberg/Photo Researchers, 219(t), 219(b); Superstock, 226-227, 229(i), 230, 236-237, 239(i), 246-247(b), 260(bg); Earl Young/FPG International, 228-229; Telegraph Colour Library/FPG International, 233, 234-235, 260(i); NASA, 235(i), 238-239, 243-245, 246, 247(b), 248-253, 261(t), 261(c), 261(b); David Hardy/Photo researchers, 254; the Bettmann Archive, 269, 271; Les Morsillo, 274-279

Illustration Credits

Gennady Spirin, Cover Art; Lori Lohstoeder, 6-7, 13-17, 108; Margaret Kasahara, 8-9, 109-110, 113, 220; Wayne Vincent, 10-11, 221-225, 332; Tyrone Geter, title page; Lehner & White, misc. icons; Petra Mathers, 18-37; Gail Gibbons, 38-51; Celia Godkin, 54-63; Tom Leonard, 64-69, 86-87, 92-93, 258-259; Kristin Goeters, 69; Daniel Moreton, 80-81; Tom Leonard, 84-107; Susan Condie Lamb, 114-129; Allen Say, 130-161, 164-165; Arvis Stewart, 161; Tatsuro Kiuchi, 166-187; Paula Danziger, 190-198, 200-201; Larry Johnson, 202-217; Tyrone Geter, 217; Tom Leonard, 256-257; Ju-Hong Chen, 258-295; Hugh Whyte, 268-271; Steven Kellogg, 278-313; R.J. Shay, 316-331